A NATURAL APPROACH TO CHEMISTRY

SECOND EDITION

HSU
CHANIOTAKIS
CARLISLE
DAMELIN

LAB-AIDS®
Experiencing Science

The preferred citation format for this book is:
Chaniotakis and Hsu, (2016).
A Natural Approach to Chemistry, Second Edition
Ronkonkoma, NY: LAB-AIDS, Inc.

ISBN: 978-1-63093-281-7
Q4 5 6 7 8 9 10 11   22 21 20 19 18

Published by:

17 Colt Court
Ronkonkoma, NY 11779
Website: www.lab-aids.com

This book was written, illustrated, published and printed in the United States of America.

From the authors

We hope you find *A Natural Approach to Chemistry* to be an engaging and effective program for your students. As we developed the program, we strove for clarity and completeness within the context of a practical and useful chemistry course for all students. We drew inspiration and examples from the human body and from the environment to connect chemistry to students' lives, today and in their future. We pruned and trimmed to make room to cover key ideas in greater depth and in various contexts. For example, you will find fundamental ideas such as valence and molarity explained repeatedly over several chapters. In our experience, students need to see abstract but important ideas several times, in different contexts, before they truly learn them. After all, how many times did *you* parallel park before trying your driver's test?

As teachers ourselves, we place a lot of emphasis on effective, hands-on activities that bring students to the core of important concepts, such as the chemical formula. We also know that students have many strongly held misconceptions, such as the difference between heat and temperature. We asked ourselves: What are the few most important concepts we want students to understand and use? We then took the most direct experimental path to get them there. You will see some novel, and maybe unfamiliar, techniques in this program, such as using molecular models to learn the chemical formula, or using $0^{\circ}C$ as a thermal energy reference. However, these techniques really work! Many traditional procedures, some of which date from Lavoisier, we found to be too abstract for learning at the level of an average high school student. We designed the unique lab equipment to ensure that it will do what the curriculum needs it to do, reliably, and in a way that maximizes student engagement and learning. In many ways the labs are the heart and soul of this course, and we hope you make them a core part of your instruction as well.

Chemistry is a fascinating, beautiful, and extraordinarily important subject. Given the challenges of alternative energy, modified foods, new medicines, and environmental issues, we believe it is crucial that all thinking people have a basic understanding of chemistry. You will find a balance of deep conceptual treatment as well as rigorous but grade-appropriate quantitative problems and techniques.

We are writing this program for everyone who wants to know how this world of ours works.

Tom Hsu
Manos Chaniotakis
Debbie Carlisle
Dan Damelin
2015

A NATURAL APPROACH TO CHEMISTRY

Principal Authors

Dr. Tom Hsu is nationally known as an innovator in integrated science curricula. He has developed a model for effectively integrating inquiry into science curricula. He is the author of six published middle and high school science programs in physics, physical science, and chemistry. Dr. Hsu did chemical engineering for Eastman Kodak, Xerox, and Dupont and also has taught grade 4 through graduate school. Dr. Hsu is cofounder of Ergopedia corporation. He holds a Ph.D. in applied plasma physics from MIT.

Dr. Manos Chaniotakis, a professor at MIT for 18 years, is recognized for teaching innovative, hands-on courses. He is cofounder of Ergopedia corporation, which develops inquiry-based science curricula, including books, equipment, and electronic media. He enjoys teaching high school science, which he does at every opportunity. Dr. Chaniotakis consults and develops instruments for the analytical chemistry industry, including meters for pH, conductivity, and ion concentration. Dr. Chaniotakis holds a Ph.D. in plasma physics and fusion engineering from MIT.

Debbie Carlisle taught high school chemistry, biochemistry, and biology for 20 years at Phillips Academy and other schools. She has worked with students at all levels of ability from introductory to AP. Debbie enhanced many important aspects of the laboratory program at Phillips that made it more exciting and accessible to students. Debbie has a master's degree in biological science, biochemistry, and technology.

Dan Damelin has taught high school chemistry since 1993. He is also the Principal Investigator on the National Science Foundation funded Molecular Workbench project, which has created extensive molecular modeling and computer simulations for teaching physics, chemistry, and biology. Dan has a Master of Science degree in chemistry, environmental science, and computer science from Tufts University.

Consultants

Dr. Nikos Chaniotakis
Professor of Chemistry
University of Crete, Greece

Technical

Dr. Michael Short
Engineering and software

Jared Sartee
Mechanical engineering

Graphic Arts

James A. Travers
Lead graphic artist & illustrator

Linda L. Taylor
Taylor Graphics, Ashfield, MA

Reviewers

David M. Axelson
Chemistry Teacher
East Providence High School
Providence, RI

David Bain
Science Department Chair
Lakes Community High School
Lake Villa, IL

Kathleen M. Beebe
Chemistry Teacher
Portsmouth High School
Portsmouth, RI

Amy L. Biagioni, M.Ed.
Chemistry Teacher
Cranston High School West
Cranston, RI

Timothy J. Brown
Chemistry Teacher
Woonsocket High School
Woonsocket, RI

Jennifer P. Cameron
Chemistry Teacher
Lincoln High School
Lincoln, RI

Peggy Carnahan, PhD
Education Specialist
Our Lady of the Lakes University
San Antonio, TX

Britany W. Coleman, M.A.
Chemistry Teacher
Lincoln High School
Lincoln, RI

Kiara Cui
Massachusetts Institute of Technology
Department of Chemical Engineering
Cambridge, MA

Marina Dang, Ph.D.
Chemistry Teacher
Curriculum Developer
Cambridge, MA

Ron DeFronzo
Science Education Specialist
East Bay Education Collaborative
Warren, RI

Reviewers

Janet Dickinson
Chemistry Lead Teacher
Kingwood High School
Kingwood, TX

Suzanne Doucette
Chemistry Teacher
Woonsocket High School
Woonsocket, RI

Brian Fortney, Ph.D.
Assistant Instructor
The University of Texas at Austin
Austin, TX

Judy Grubbs
K–12 Science Specialist
Region 7 Education Service Center
Kilgore, TX

Helaine Hager
Chemistry Teacher
E Cubed Academy
Lincoln, RI

Thomas J. Holstein, Jr., M.S.
Chemistry Teacher
Portsmouth High School
Portsmouth, RI

Pamela R. Kahn
Chemistry Teacher
Cranston High School West
Cranston, RI

Ronald Kahn
Science Education Specialist
East Bay Education Collaborative
Warren, RI

Janet R. Kasparian, M.S.
Biology and Chemistry Teacher
Portsmouth High School
Portsmouth, RI

Kimberly A. Laliberte, M.S., P.M.P.
Chemistry Teacher
East Providence High School
Providence, RI

Christine M. Lawrence
Special Education Teacher
Portsmouth High School
Portsmouth, RI

Deirdre D. London, M.Ed.
Chemistry Teacher
Cranston High School West
Cranston, RI

Donald Lurgio
Chemistry Teacher
East Providence High School
Providence, RI

Peter Madeiros
Chemistry Teacher
Woonsocket High School
Woonsocket, RI

Judy H. McGowan
Chemistry Teacher
Mount Pleasant High School
Providence, RI

Elaine Megyar, Ph.D.
Professor of Chemistry
Rhode Island College
Providence, RI

James Megyar, Ph.D.
Professor of Chemistry
Rhode Island College
Providence, RI

Janet M. Miele
Chemistry Teacher
Woonsocket High School
Woonsocket, RI

Roxanne Minix-Wilkins, M.S.
Science Program Coordinator
Region 5 Education Service Center
Silsbee, TX

Thomas S. Morra
Chemistry Teacher
Mount Pleasant High School
Providence, RI

Alana J. Nelson, M.A.
Chemistry Teacher
East Providence High School
Providence, RI

Dennis A. Nobrega, M.Ed. CAGS
Chemistry Teacher
East Providence High School
Providence, RI

Amanda Nycole Noble
Chemistry Teacher
Portsmouth High School
Portsmouth, RI

Leanne M. Gordon Perry, M.S.
Biology and Chemistry Teacher
Portsmouth High School
Portsmouth, RI

Kathleen Siok
Chemistry Specialist
East Bay Education Collaborative
Warren, RI

Loraine Snead
Science Coordinator
YSC Academy
Wayne, PA

Jeffrey Soares
Science Education Specialist
East Bay Education Collaborative
Warren, RI

Elizabeth Joy Toller
Massachusetts Institute of Technology
Department of Physics
Cambridge, MA 02137

Kristian Fischer Trampus, M.Ed.
Director, East Texas STEM Center
University of Texas at Tyler
Tyler, TX

Keith D. Ward
Chemistry Teacher
Cranston High School West
Cranston, RI

Brenda G. Weiser, Ed.D.
Clinical Associate Professor Science
Education, University of Houston
Clear Lake, TX

Ellen Will
Chemistry Teacher
East Providence High School
Providence, RI

Donna M. Wise, M.Ed.
Science Specialist
Region 7 Education Service Center
Kilgore, TX

Judy York, M.S.
Education Specialist
Region 12 Education Service Center
Waco, TX

Angela Q. Zhang
Massachusetts Institute of Technology
Department of Biology
Cambridge, MA

David Ziegler
Chemistry Teacher
Rifle High School
Rifle, CO

A NATURAL APPROACH TO CHEMISTRY

Using the text

One idea per page, and it is always at the top of the page

Side headings for a quick outline of the reading

More than 3,000 illustrations that teach, with valuable content

Vocabulary words right at the bottom of the page where they appear

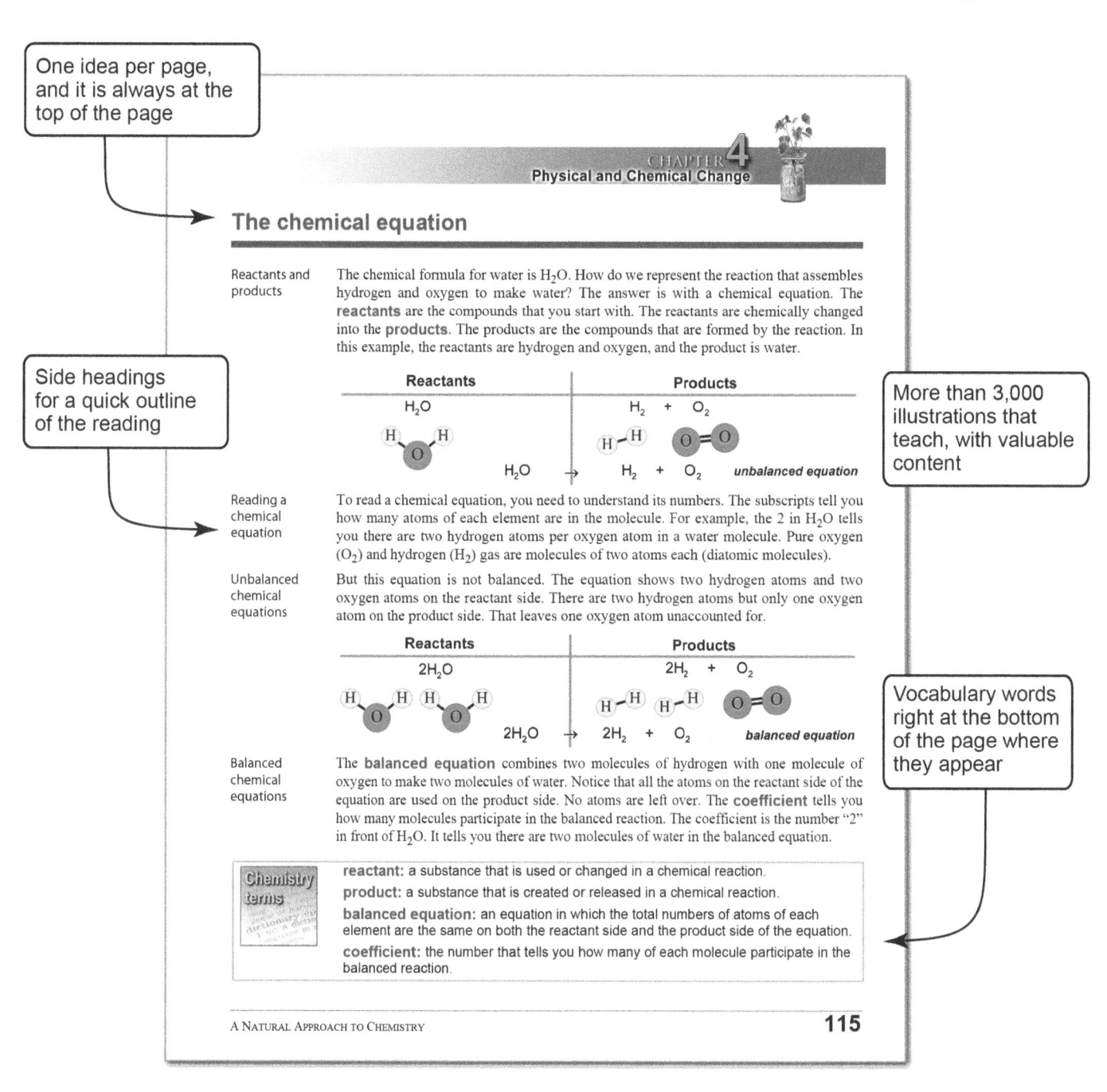

CHAPTER 4
Physical and Chemical Change

The chemical equation

Reactants and products

The chemical formula for water is H_2O. How do we represent the reaction that assembles hydrogen and oxygen to make water? The answer is with a chemical equation. The **reactants** are the compounds that you start with. The reactants are chemically changed into the **products**. The products are the compounds that are formed by the reaction. In this example, the reactants are hydrogen and oxygen, and the product is water.

Reactants	Products
H_2O	H_2 + O_2

$H_2O \rightarrow H_2 + O_2$ *unbalanced equation*

Reading a chemical equation

To read a chemical equation, you need to understand its numbers. The subscripts tell you how many atoms of each element are in the molecule. For example, the 2 in H_2O tells you there are two hydrogen atoms per oxygen atom in a water molecule. Pure oxygen (O_2) and hydrogen (H_2) gas are molecules of two atoms each (diatomic molecules).

Unbalanced chemical equations

But this equation is not balanced. The equation shows two hydrogen atoms and two oxygen atoms on the reactant side. There are two hydrogen atoms but only one oxygen atom on the product side. That leaves one oxygen atom unaccounted for.

Reactants	Products
$2H_2O$	$2H_2$ + O_2

$2H_2O \rightarrow 2H_2 + O_2$ *balanced equation*

Balanced chemical equations

The **balanced equation** combines two molecules of hydrogen with one molecule of oxygen to make two molecules of water. Notice that all the atoms on the reactant side of the equation are used on the product side. No atoms are left over. The **coefficient** tells you how many molecules participate in the balanced reaction. The coefficient is the number "2" in front of H_2O. It tells you there are two molecules of water in the balanced equation.

Chemistry terms

reactant: a substance that is used or changed in a chemical reaction.

product: a substance that is created or released in a chemical reaction.

balanced equation: an equation in which the total numbers of atoms of each element are the same on both the reactant side and the product side of the equation.

coefficient: the number that tells you how many of each molecule participate in the balanced reaction.

A NATURAL APPROACH TO CHEMISTRY

Problem solving

A NATURAL APPROACH TO
CHEMISTRY

Organization of the book

Themes

Energy is a unifying theme that explains why chemistry occurs
The atomic model of matter is consistently woven through every chapter
Understanding of "why" chemistry occurs is emphasized
Principles are illustrated with examples from the human body and the environment

Chemistry is important, relevant, and learnable by all students.

Chapters 1–4: Fundamentals

Present a comprehensive overview of all the main ideas in chemistry such as the atomic nature of matter, systems, temperature, and energy. Students don't get bogged down in the details but see the conceptual "big picture."

Chapters 5–14: Core Concepts

Present in-depth coverage of all major topic areas. They develop *usable* understanding of the big ideas laid out in the first four chapters. The treatment includes strong conceptual development as well as algebra-based quantitative problem solving. *All academic content and instruction standards for chemistry have been met by the end of Chapter 14.*

Each chapter begins with a real-lab example as a point of engagement for the content of the chapter. One to three additional labs per chapter develop more aspects of chemistry.

Chapters 15–21: Applications

Provide deeper exploration of significant areas of interest in chemistry. For example, Chapter 15 addresses the chemistry of rechargeable batteries. Chapter 16 addresses materials science, such as metal alloys. Chapter 21 looks at recent evidence for oceans of liquid water on Europa and Enceladus and the sulfuric atmosphere of Venus.

Table of Contents

A NATURAL APPROACH TO CHEMISTRY

SECOND EDITION

CHAPTER 1

The Science of Chemistry

What is chemistry?

Why is chemistry important to know?

What does *chemistry* mean to you? What do you think of when you read the word *chemical*? Do you think of smelly concoctions in test tubes, mixed by a scientist in a white lab coat?

Would it surprise you to know that *you* are a mixture of chemicals? So is a tree, the ocean, and even the cleanest, purest air. A glass of orange juice contains more than 100 chemicals. In fact, the word *chemical* describes any pure material around you, from the chlorophyll in a plant to the vitamins in your food. Water (H_2O) is a chemical. Sodium chloride, or table salt (NaCl), is another chemical. In being "alive," your body is constantly changing chemicals into different chemicals, both using and releasing energy in the process.

Chemistry is the science of matter and its changes. The process that creates rain from evaporating water is part of chemistry. Digestion of food is part of chemistry. In short, chemistry describes the material world around you and the myriad ways in which the material world changes. As you will see, not all chemicals are hazardous to your health! Our world is chemicals, as are we. Some chemicals are necessary for growth and survival, while others are poisons. A wise person knows enough about chemistry to tell the difference!

Is this chemistry?

Is this chemistry?

Study Skills

Studying chemistry like any other science subject requires us to concentrate and take notes. Whether sitting in class listening, conducting an investigation, or reading the text at home, taking notes is an important part of the learning process. Written notes should summarize the key points, not capture every word spoken by your teacher. Ask yourself: What is the most important concept? What words or techniques are new to me?

Many students find it useful to outline the important concepts in the book or a verbal class presentation. Natural Approach to Chemistry has been written with "one idea per page," so the page titles can easily be used as main headings in an outline. Every paragraph on a page of this chemistry book has its own, short title that can form the sub-headings in an outline. Vocabulary words, key illustrations, and equations can form additional sub-headings for your outline.

A picture is worth a thousand words, right? Science class is full of illustrations: diagrams, graphs, images, and even animations! What is the message a particular illustration is trying to convey? Try writing down a one sentence summary of the main point conveyed by each illustration you encounter—preferably using science words!

Outlining a chemistry lesson

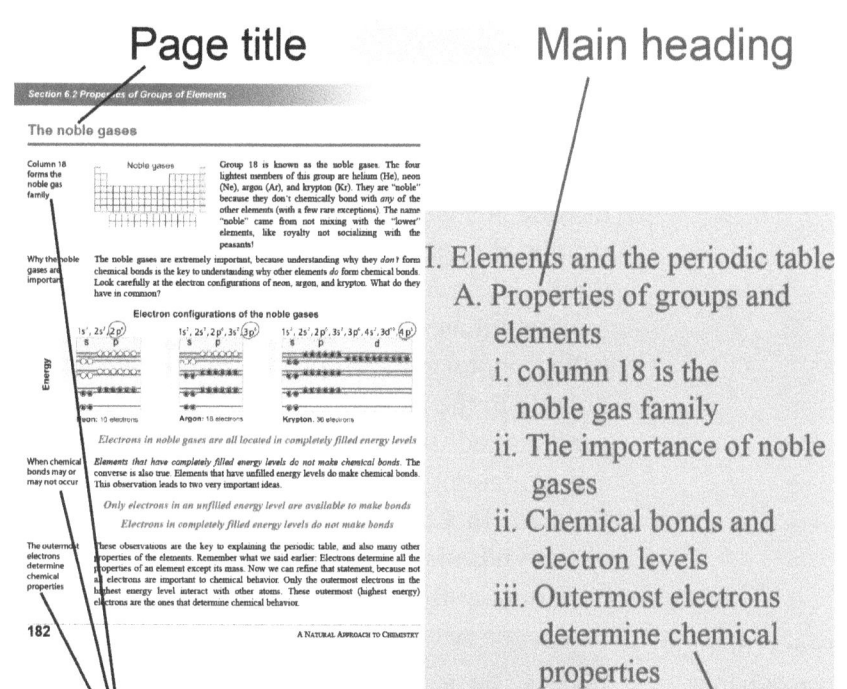

Page title

Main heading

I. Elements and the periodic table
  A. Properties of groups and elements
    i. column 18 is the noble gas family
    ii. The importance of noble gases
    ii. Chemical bonds and electron levels
    iii. Outermost electrons determine chemical properties

Paragraph titles

Sub-headings

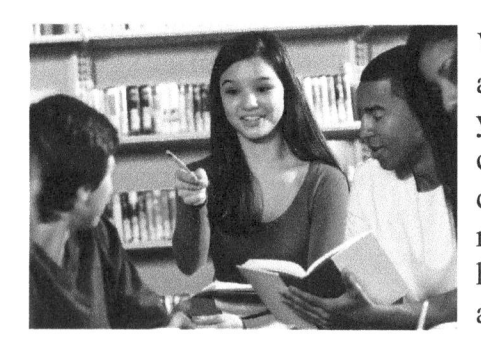

What should you do if you need more information or don't understand a concept? Some of the most important resources are right around you: your classmates and teachers. When you formulate your question about chemistry, try to use appropriate science vocabulary. If you have a question while studying after school, write it down to ask in class the next day, or to ask a friend. Preparing a question to ask in class can help you—and other classmates—to grasp difficult concepts. It is even a good idea to write down one or two questions every time you study!

1.1 What Chemistry Is About

Where does the mass of a tree come from?

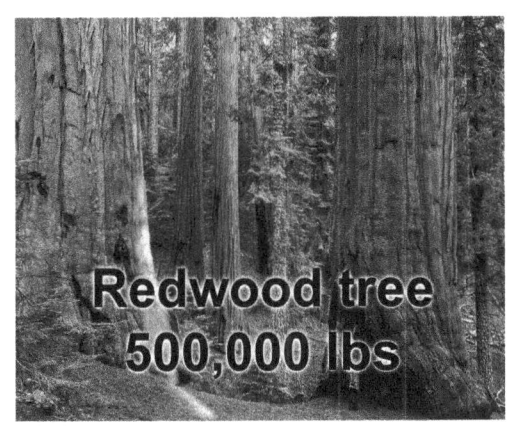

Redwood tree 500,000 lbs

When a tree grows, where does the matter come from? How does the tree get bigger? We know that matter cannot come from *nothing*. A big redwood tree might weigh 500,000 pounds. If all this weight came from the soil, we would see big holes in the ground around large trees. But, we do not! Experiments reveal that only a tiny fraction of mass is lost from the soil around a tree. If the matter in a tree does not come from the soil, then where does all this matter come from?

Most of the solid matter in a tree comes from air

The answer is mostly *from the air*! A tree takes in carbon dioxide from the air and water from the ground. Carbon dioxide is a gas, but it is still matter. You don't "feel" the weight of a gas like air because the matter is spread very thinly. However, there is a *lot* of air—more than enough to create majestic trees! An incredible chemical reaction called photosynthesis plucks carbon atoms from carbon dioxide in the air and compacts them into molecules of a sugar called glucose. The glucose along with water and a tiny amount of minerals from the soil is used to build the tree. In Chapter 10 we will learn a lot more about photosynthesis and other chemical reactions that are important to life on Earth.

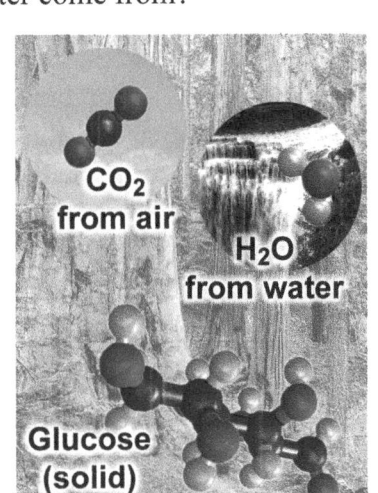

CO_2 from air

H_2O from water

Glucose (solid)

Fire: a chemical reaction that changes matter from one form to another

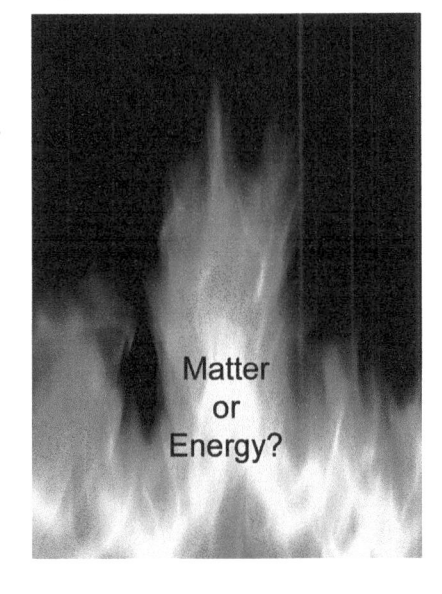

Matter or Energy?

Discussion topic

What is fire? Is it a chemical? Is it matter? Is it energy? In early times it was believed that air, earth, water, and fire were the major elements of the universe. You can feel fire, see it, and smell it, so our senses tell us it is present. Water, air, and earth are all made up of many atoms connected together, so they do represent types of matter! Fire is a form of heat and light energy, not matter. Chemical reactions transform one kind of matter, such as wood, into other kinds of matter, such as ashes, smoke, and water. Fire is produced when matter changes its form. For example, when wood burns, the carbon reacts with oxygen, producing energy and carbon dioxide. This energy is the heat and the light that we feel from a fire.

Chemistry in your body

Why should you eat foods high in antioxidants?

Berries are a good source of antioxidants

We are told to eat foods that are high in antioxidants, such as blueberries, cranberries, artichokes and beans. How does this help us? The answer has to do with the chemistry of life. When energy in food is used by our cells, chemicals called *free radicals* are produced as a by-product. Free radicals are very *reactive*. Think of a pinball game where the ball is the "free radical." Anything the pinball hits may become damaged. The ball continues to bounce around and damage useful chemicals until it is absorbed by something. In the pinball machine, an "absorbed" ball falls to the bottom and is no longer "in play" where it can cause more damage.

What do antioxidants do?

In your body, antioxidants absorb free radicals before they can do much damage. Once neutralized by an antioxidant, free radicals are harmless. That is why it is important to have high levels of antioxidants in your body. Antioxidants become even more important with age because your metabolism becomes less efficient. This causes the number of free radicals to increase. Antioxidants have been shown to help prevent age-related diseases such as cancer.

What is the purpose of vitamins?

Vitamins are chemicals that the body needs but does not produce itself from the raw materials in food. For example, vitamin C is used by the body to make *collagen*. Collagen is found in joints and tendons that connect muscles and bones. If you don't get enough vitamin C from fresh fruits and vegetables, you may develop *scurvy*. Scurvy is a disease that used to sicken or even kill sailors on long ocean voyages.

Different kinds of vitamins

Some vitamins dissolve in fat (vitamins A, D, E, and K) and others dissolve in water (vitamin C and B complexes). Water-soluble vitamins need to be consumed each day since they are excreted in urine. Fat-soluble vitamins are stored in your liver, so they do not need to be replaced in your body every day.

Too much of certain vitamins can be as harmful as too little. All vitamin supplements list the Recommended Daily Allowance (RDA) for each vitamin.

Discussion topic

Humans require vitamins in very small amounts; you can get sick from either too much (overdose) or too little (deficiency). That's why scientists came up with nutritional guidelines that give approximate daily recommended amounts of each one. Read the label on a vitamin bottle. Do you find terms that you recognize? Discuss with your classmates and your teacher.

Water: a very important chemical

Most of your body is water

A physically fit human body is about 60% water by weight. Take away the water and the rest is mostly different proteins and fats, with about 6% other chemicals and minerals such as calcium, phosphorus and iron. During one hour of exercise, you may lose as much as two liters of water by sweating and breathing! You also lose small amounts of dissolved salts. If the lost water and dissolved salts are not replaced, your body stops working. Hydration is very important for athletes. Look at the back of hydration drink. What elements do you find listed on it?

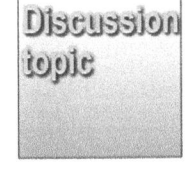

Discussion topic

Human body
(physically fit)

60% water
17% proteins
17% fats
6%
   calcium
   phosphorus
   glycogen
   sodium
   potassion
   iron
   zinc
   sulfur +
   others

Water is critical to life

The process of living requires your body to change the chemicals in food into other chemicals needed by your blood, muscles, nerves, and the rest of your body. Solids like sugar cannot easily move around in your body. This is why most of the chemistry of life happens only in water. There are two main reasons for this:

1. Many substances dissolve in water, including sugars, salts, and proteins.

2. Once dissolved, chemicals can circulate and interact with other chemicals.

Sugar is a chemical that dissolves in water

A good example of a chemical that dissolves in water is sugar. Sugar is made of tiny particles (molecules) that are so small that more than a million would fit on the head of a pin. Water is also made of tiny particles! A tablespoon of sugar is solid. The sugar molecules are stuck to each other. When sugar is mixed with water, the tiny molecules separate from each other. Each sugar molecule disperses among many water molecules. In fact, the sugar seems to visibly "disappear" once it has been dissolved. One taste will tell you the sugar is still there, even though it has been dissolved.

Solute
(solid sugar)

Solution
(sugar dissolved in water)

Solid sugar
molecules fixed in place

Dissolved sugar
molecules free to move

Measurements and units

Why units are necessary

In science, it is often not enough to say "it's hot." Scientists want to communicate precisely how hot. To describe how hot it is you might say 82 degrees Fahrenheit (82°F). The value 82°F has two parts: a number (82) and a unit (°F). The number tells you how much and the unit tells you what the number means. One without the other can lead to big mistakes. If you say 82 degrees without specifying the unit, a person from Canada might think you mean 82 Celsius (82°C), which is a fatally hot 180°F, while 82°F is comfortable for the beach!

Units

To understand chemistry, you need to speak the language of units. Just about everything that can be measured has its own unit. Below are some of the ones that are most useful.

TABLE 1.1. Some units in chemistry

Kinds of units you use in chemistry

Unit	Used for	Unit	Used for
Celsius degree (°C)	temperature	second (s)	time
Fahrenheit degree (°F)	temperature	meter (m)	length
kelvin (K)	temperature	centimeter (cm)	length
kilogram (kg)	mass	joule (J)	energy
gram (g)	mass	watt (W)	power
liter (L)	volume	pascal (P)	pressure
milliliter (mL)	volume	ampere (A)	electric current
mole (mole)	counting atoms	candela (cd)	luminous (light) intensity

Quantities have more than one unit

SI units

Notice that there can be more than one unit for the same quantity. Many soda bottles measure liquid in liters. A graduated cylinder measures volume in milliliters. The seven units highlighted in green on Table 1.1 are the base units of the international system (SI), the system of units used in this book.

Definition of measurement

When you put a substance on a balance, you are making a **measurement** of its mass. A measurement is a specific kind of information that describes a physical quantity with both a number and a unit. The value 105.4 grams is a measurement because it has a number (105.4) and a unit (grams) that describe a physical quantity.

Chemistry terms

measurement: information that describes a physical quantity with both a number and a unit.

Mass and weight

Mass

Mass is a measure of how much matter there is. A grain of salt has very little mass and a planet has a great amount of mass. Note that size (or volume) does not by itself tell you how much matter there is. A block of foam and a brick can be the same size, but one contains much more matter than the other. Don't be fooled by size. The definitive, reliable way to communicate a quantity of matter is by giving its mass.

Weight

A digital balance uses **weight** to measure mass. Weight is the *force* of gravity. The balance senses the weight of whatever you place on it. Then it calculates the mass by dividing by the number 9.8, which is the acceleration due to gravity. Pounds or ounces are units of weight, not mass, in the English system of units.

The kilogram

Mass is measured in **kilograms (kg)** and **grams (g)**. One kilogram is about the mass of a one liter bottle of water you buy at the grocery store. One gram is about the mass of a single peanut. There are 1,000 grams in 1 kilogram and 0.001 kilograms in 1 gram.

1 kg
mass of a 1 liter bottle of water

1 g
mass of a single peanut

Equal masses means equal amounts of matter

When we say an object has a mass of one kilogram, we are saying that the object has the same amount of matter as one kilogram of water. Even if we do not know what the object is made of, we can measure how much matter it has. Air is very light, but a cubic meter of air at sea level has a mass of about 1 kg. Put your hand out of the window in a moving car and you can feel the effect of the mass of the air against your hand.

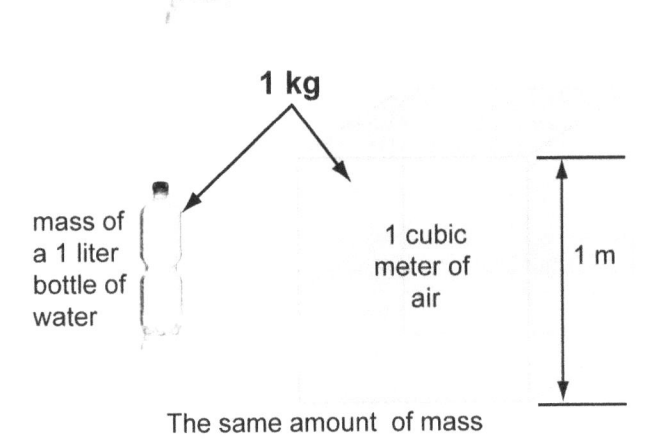

mass of a 1 liter bottle of water

1 kg

1 cubic meter of air

1 m

The same amount of mass

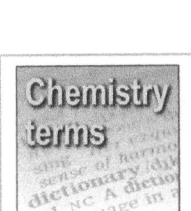

mass: the amount of matter, measured in units of grams or kilograms (SI).

weight: a force (push or a pull) that results from gravity acting on mass, measured in newtons in the SI system of units and pounds or ounces in the English system of units.

kilogram: SI unit of mass.

gram: unit of mass equal to 1/1,000 kg.

Volume

The definition of volume	**Volume** is an amount of space having length, width, and height. A large object, like a box truck, takes up a lot of space and has a large volume. A tiny object, like a mouse, has a relatively tiny volume.
The units of volume	In your chemistry lab, most of your measurements of volume will be in **liters** (L) or **milliliters** (mL). One liter is the volume of a cube 10 centimeters on a side. One milliliter is the volume of a cube one centimeter on a side. A milliliter is a fairly small volume; there are 5 mL in a standard teaspoon. The chart below shows several volume units and their equivalent in liters and milliliters.

1 teaspoon	1 cup	1 gallon
5 mL	237 mL	3,785 mL

Volume units are derived from length units	Fundamentally, the unit for volume comes from the unit for length. A centimeter (cm) is a unit of length. The volume of a cubic centimeter is $1 \text{ cm} \times 1 \text{ cm} \times 1 \text{ cm} = 1 \text{ cm}^3$. A milliliter has the same volume as a cubic centimeter. One liter, the volume of a soda bottle, is the same as $10 \text{ cm} \times 10 \text{ cm} \times 10 \text{ cm} = 1,000 \text{ cm}^3$. Empty a one liter bottle and it just fills a 10 centimeter cube. Cubic meters (m³) are used for larger volumes. There are 1,000 liters in a cubic meter.

1 mL

1 cubic centimeter (cm³)

1 cm

The graduated cylinder	The **graduated cylinder** is a tool for measuring the volume of liquids. Most graduated cylinders have markings that read in milliliters. The example shows a volume of 75 mL. Notice that you read the graduated cylinder at the flat (lowest) part of the surface. Water adheres slightly to glass and plastic, so the surface creeps up around the edges. This shape is called a *meniscus*. To read a graduated cylinder, you read the lowest point of the meniscus, not the highest point.

This cylinder reads 75 mL

Graduated cylinder

Chemistry terms

volume: an amount of space having length, width, and height.

liter: an SI unit of volume equal to a cube 10 centimeters on a side, or 1,000 cm³.

milliliter: a unit of volume equal to a cube 1 cm on a side, or 1 cm³.

graduated cylinder: an instrument used to measure volume.

Density

Equal size does not mean equal mass

You come into contact with many kinds of matter every day. Some matter is solid and hard, such as iron and plastic. Some matter is liquid, such as water, and some is a gas, such as air. Even within the category of solid matter, there are big differences. Think about the differences among plastic, iron, and glass. Imagine you had a solid cube of each substance, and all the cubes were the same size and painted black. Does each contain the same amount of matter? Could you tell which was plastic, iron, or glass?

Equal size does not mean equal mass

Polethylene plastic   Glass   Iron

Density describes the mass per unit volume

A block of plastic and a block of steel may be the same size, but one has much more *mass* than the other. Because of the difference, plastic floats in water and iron sinks. Whether an object floats or sinks in water is related to its *density*. **Density** describes how much mass is in a given volume of a material. The units of density are mass divided by volume, often grams per cubic centimeter (g/cm³).

$$density = \frac{mass}{volume}$$

$$d = \frac{m}{V}$$

Density

Iron has a high density; it contains 7.8 grams of mass per cubic centimeter (7.8 g/cm³). A one centimeter cube of plastic contains only 0.94 grams of matter (0.94 g/cm³).

1. Density is a property of matter that is independent of size or shape.

2. Density is mass per unit volume.

The density of water and air

Solids range in density from cork (0.12 g/cm³) to platinum, a precious metal with a density of 21.5 g/cm³. The density of water is about one gram per cubic centimeter. The density of air is much lower, about 0.001 grams per cubic centimeter.

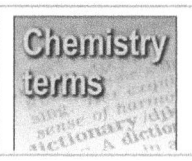

Chemistry terms

density: a property of a substance that describes how much matter the substance contains per unit volume; typical units are grams per cubic centimeter (g/cm³).

Doing calculations with density

Measuring density

To find the density of a material, you need to know the mass and volume of a solid sample of the material. Mass is measured with a balance or a scale. For simple shapes you can calculate the volume. For irregular objects, the *displacement method* is used to find the volume. Suppose you want to know the volume of five steel nuts. First you record the volume of water in the graduated cylinder before inserting the nuts. Then you gently drop the five nuts in and record the volume again. The volume of the nuts is the measured change in volume.

Densities of common substances

TABLE 1.2. Densities of common substances

Material	Density (g/cm³)		Material	Density (g/cm³)
Platinum	21.5		Nylon plastic	2.3
Lead	11.3		Rubber	1.2
Iron	7.8		Liquid water	1.0
Titanium	4.5		Polyethylene plastic	0.94
Aluminum	2.7		Ice	0.92
Glass	2.7		Oak (wood)	0.60
Granite	2.6		Pine (wood)	0.44
Concrete	2.3		Cork	0.12

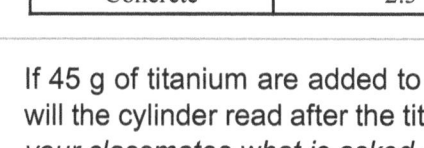

If 45 g of titanium are added to a graduated cylinder containing 50 mL of water, what will the cylinder read after the titanium has been added? *Before going on, discuss with your classmates what is asked and what is given.*

Asked: *Volume reading after adding 45 g of titanium*

Given: *45 g of titanium, density of titanium d = 4.5 g/cm³, 50 mL of water*

Relationships: *d = m/V*

Solve: *d = m ÷ V; therefore V = m ÷ d*
V = 45 g ÷ 4.5 g/cm³ × 1.0 mL / cm³ = 10 mL.
The titanium adds 10 mL to the cylinder, which now reads 60 mL.

Answer: *60 mL*

Discussion: *This is an example of measurement using the displacement method.*

Pressure

Force and fluids

Think about what happens when you pump a bicycle tire. As you push down on the pump, you squeeze air into the tire. The tire expands and gets firm. The firmness of the inflated tire is an example of *pressure*. **Pressure** is a force per unit area exerted by matter, often when it is restrained from moving or expanding. For example, suppose the bicycle tire is inflated to a pressure of 60 pounds per square inch (60 psi). Each square inch of the inside of the tire feels a force of 60 pounds from the trapped air in the tire.

Pressure inside the tire pushes out equally in all directions with more force than pressure outside the tire.

Force

A **force** is an action, like a push or a pull, that has the ability to make things move (or stop them). In the SI system, force is measured in newtons. However, not many people use newtons in ordinary life. One pound is equivalent to about 4 and a half newtons. (4.4 N = 1.0 lbs). In chemistry, we are not so interested in forces; we are more interested in the ratio of force per unit area, which is pressure.

Pressure is most important in the understanding of gases (such as air) or liquids (such as water). For example, consider the water in a hose. If there is pressure in the water, the pressure exerts forces in all directions on any surface touching the water. You can prove this is true by poking a hole in the hose. The water squirts out no matter whether you poke the hole in the top, bottom, or side of the hose.

Pressure acts equally in all directions.

Pressure in a liquid or gas pushes equally in all directions

You know that liquids flow to take the shape of a container. This happens because liquids have weight. Weight pulls down, but in a liquid or gas, the downward force of gravity adds to the pressure, which pushes equally in all directions. Pressure pushes the boundary of a liquid outward until it fills its container in the precise shape that gets the most liquid closest to the ground.

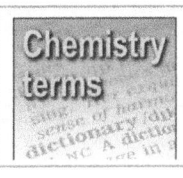

Chemistry terms

pressure: force per unit area with units of Pa (N/m^2) or psi (lb/in^2) or atm; acts equally in all directions within a liquid or a gas.

force: an action, such as a push or a pull, that has the ability to change the motion of an object, such as to start it moving, stop it, or turn it.

A NATURAL APPROACH TO CHEMISTRY

Air pressure

Is an empty bottle really empty?

Hold up an empty plastic water bottle and think about what is inside. What comes to mind? Nothing? Is an empty bottle really full of nothing? To answer the question, consider what happens when you put the cap tightly on the empty bottle and try to squeeze it flat. You can't do it—something in the "empty" bottle prevents you from squeezing it flat. If you open the cap, you can squeeze the bottle easily. Whatever is inside an empty bottle comes out if the cap is off, but it is trapped inside if the cap is on.

Air is matter

Air is matter! Air is transparent, and its mass is spread so thin that you move through it easily. Put your hand out a moving car window and you can instantly feel that air has mass because it takes force to push it out of the way. In fact, a cubic meter of air has a mass of about one kilogram, or about the same as a one-liter bottle of water.

Feeling the mass of air in a moving car

The weight of air creates air pressure

Air has weight. The weight of the atmosphere creates pressure that acts equally in all directions. A board with an area of one square meter feels a force from air pressure of 101,325 newtons on one side. That is an incredible 22,780 pounds! The board doesn't move because air pressure acts equally in all directions, so the other side of the board feels an equal force in the opposite direction. The board doesn't move, but it's not because air is nothing! The board doesn't move because the air pressure is equal on all sides.

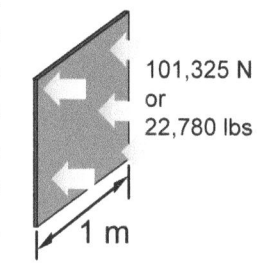

101,325 N or 22,780 lbs

1 m

Demonstrating air pressure

To demonstrate air pressure, watch what happens when you suck the air out of a bottle. Why does the bottle collapse? You did not apply any force to it. The bottle collapses because removing some air from the inside makes the pressure inside lower than the pressure outside. The pressure of the *outside* air is what crushes the bottle.

Units of pressure

If you have a force of 1 newton distributed over an area of 1 square meter, you have a pressure of 1 **pascal** (Pa). The pascal is the SI unit of pressure, but it is very small. Many chemistry applications use *atmospheres* as a unit of pressure. One **atmosphere** (1 atm) is 101,235 Pa, and that is the average pressure of the air at sea level.

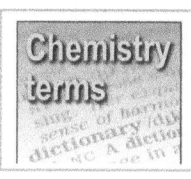

Chemistry terms

pascal (Pa): SI unit of pressure, equal to one newton of force per square meter of area (Pa = 1 N/m²).

atmosphere (atm): a large unit of pressure equal to 101,325 Pa; the average pressure of air at sea level; also equal to 14.7 pounds per square inch (14.7 psi).

Accuracy and precision

Precision

When we take a number of measurements, **precision** tells us how close the measured values are to each other. A balance that can read to 0.1 grams has a precision of 0.1 g. Many of your lab experiments will be done with balances that have this precision.

Accuracy

The word **accuracy** tells us how close a measurement is to the true value. For example, a meter stick that has been stretched can make a measurement of length that is precise to one millimeter. However, measurement will not be accurate because the meter stick is no longer one meter long.

Measurements are never "perfect"

Measurements of real quantities in experiments are never exact. For example, you cannot determine that something has a mass of *exactly* 10 g. Why not? Because measurements of mass are made with instruments, such as balances. All real instruments have a limit to how small a quantity they can measure.

Is the mass exactly 10.0 g?

Suppose you have an accurate balance that can measure mass to a precision of 0.1 g. You claim the mass is exactly 10.0 g because your balance shows 10.0. However, suppose the real mass was 10.02 g. Your balance *rounded the measurement off to 10.0*. One way to show this is to write your measurement as 10.0 ± 0.1 g. This tells a reader that the actual mass could have been anything between 9.9 and 10.1 g.

We don't know since any mass between 9.9 and 10.1 would round off to 10.0

Why accuracy and precision are important

For many of your lab experiments, two masses of 10.01 g and 10.03 g can be considered the same because they differ by only 0.02 g. This is smaller than the balance can measure. When analyzing the observations you make in the lab, you must consider both the accuracy and the precision of your measurements before making a conclusion. A measurement that is not *accurate* may lead you to the wrong conclusion. With a measurement that is not *precise* you may not be able to tell the difference between agreement and disagreement.

Accurate

Accurate and precise

Precise, but not accurate

Not accurate and not precise

Chemistry terms

accuracy: a term that describes how close a measurement is to the true value.

precision: a term that describes how close measured values are to each other.

Significant figures

How many decimal places do you record?

Suppose you measure 10.0 g of sugar on a balance. The balance has a precision of 0.1 g. In your data table do you write down 10 or 10.0 g? Does it make a difference? The answer is yes, it does!

Do you record 10 or 10.0 g?

Significant figures tell the precision of a measurement

Scientists use the rule of **significant figures** as a way of recording data that tells the precision of a measurement without writing ± after each value. The rule is that *the last written digit is uncertain by plus or minus the value of the uncertainty*. For example, suppose you write the measurement as 10 g. According to the rule of significant figures, you can trust the first digit (1) and assume the second digit (0) is plus or minus one, or ± 1 g. The actual mass of sugar could have been anything between 9 and 11 g. The uncertainty is of 1 out of 10, or 10% in the measurement! If you write it as 10.0 g, it now has three significant figures. You can "trust" the first two digits (10) and the uncertainty is only plus or minus one tenth, or ± 0.1. The uncertainty is now 1 out of 100, or 1%.

Certain rules must be followed when calculating with significant figures

- *In numbers that do not contain zeros, all digits are significant.*
- *When zeros are contained in a number, it is significant if it is between other digits or at the end to the right of a decimal point. Leading zeros are not significant.*
- *When rounding, if the first digit to the right of the last significant figure is less than 5, that digit and all others following are dropped. If that digit is greater than 5, the last signficant figure is increased by one and the rest of the digits dropped.*
- *When adding or subtracting, the answer should have the same number of decimal places as the quantity with the smallest number of decimal places.*
- *When multiplying or dividing, the answer should have the same number of significant figures as the quantity with the smallest number of significant figures.*

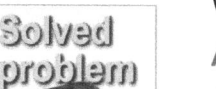
Solved problem

What value should be recorded for the volume measurement in the picture?

Asked:	*The value with the correct number of significant figures*
Given:	*You can estimate to a tenth of the graduation of a cylinder or ruler.*
Relationships:	*The last digit on the right is assumed to be ± 0.1.*
Solve:	*The meniscus is right on 18, so estimate 18.0 mL.*
Answer:	*18.0 mL*
Discussion:	*The real value is confidently known to be between 17.9 and 18.1 mL.*

Chemistry terms

significant figures: a way of writing data that tells the reader how precise a measurement is.

Very large numbers

Describing large and small quantities

Atoms are so small that describing them requires extreme numbers. A single grain of sand contains 200,000 *million million* atoms. This number written out the usual way is

$$200,000 \text{ million million} = 200,000,000,000,000,000,000$$

Don't worry if you cannot get your mind around this huge number—no one can without a reference. Fortunately, there is a shorthand method for writing and calculating with extremely large or small numbers. The method is called **scientific notation**.

Scientific notation for large numbers

Scientific notation works by expressing very small or very large numbers as the product of two smaller numbers. The first number is called the **mantissa**. The second number is a *power of 10*. Any number can be represented as a mantissa times a power of 10. As an example consider the number 1,500:

- 1,500 = 15 × 100. The number 15 is the mantissa. The number 100 is the power of 10.

- 100 = 10 squared and is usually written as 10^2.

- So 1,500 = 15 × 10^2. The small superscript number 2 in 10^2 is called the **exponent**.

Numbers larger than 1

$10^1 = 10$
$10^2 = 100$
$10^3 = 1,000$
$10^4 = 10,000$
$10^5 = 100,000$
$10^6 = 1,000,000$
$10^7 = 10,000,000$
$10^8 = 100,000,000$
$10^9 = 1,000,000,000$

Writing the base

The mantissa is usually written with only one digit in front of the decimal point. For example, 1,500 would be written 1.5×10^3 because 10^3 is 1,000. To make 1,500 into 1.5, you have to move the decimal point by three places so the correct power of 10 is 10^3.

For the number 1,500, scientific notation does not seem to be very beneficial. However, 200,000 million million in scientific notation is 2×10^{17}. This number is much easier to write and calculate with when expressed in scientific notation. The number 6.02×10^{23} is very important in chemistry and it is very nicely presented in scientific notation.

Solved problem

Convert 34,500 to scientific notation.

Asked: *The number in scientific notation*

Given: *34,500 as a decimal number*

Relationships: *10,000 = 10^4*

Answer: *3.45×10^4*

Chemistry terms

scientific notation: a method of writing numbers as a base times a power of 10.

mantissa: a decimal number that multiplies the power of 10 in scientific notation.

exponent: the power of 10 for a number written in scientific notation, such as the 2 in the number $5 \times 10^2 = 500$.

Very small numbers

Chemistry may use very small numbers

Many of the important ideas in chemistry involve what happens on the size of individual atoms, the particles of matter. Atoms are extraordinarily small. A grain of sand is only 0.01 centimeters across. A single atom is a million times smaller, or 0.00000001 centimeters across. Fortunately, scientific notation allows us to work with extremely small numbers as easily as with large numbers.

Scientific notation for small numbers

Powers of 10 that are negative mean numbers smaller than one. Consider the number 0.0015. Let's write it in scientific notation:

- 0.0015 = 1.5 × 0.001

- The number 0.001 is $1 \div 1{,}000 = 1 \div 10^3 = 10^{-3}$

- $0.0015 = 1.5 \times 10^{-3}$ in scientific notation

It is important to remember that a negative sign on the exponent of 10 *does not mean the whole number is negative*! Negative exponents just mean that the value is less than one.

Numbers smaller than 1

$10^{-9} = 0.000\ 000\ 001$
$10^{-8} = 0.000\ 000\ 01$
$10^{-7} = 0.000\ 000\ 1$
$10^{-6} = 0.000\ 001$
$10^{-5} = 0.000\ 01$
$10^{-4} = 0.000\ 1$
$10^{-3} = 0.001$
$10^{-2} = 0.01$
$10^{-1} = 0.1$

Solved problem

Convert 0.00065 to scientific notation.

Asked:	*The number in scientific notation*
Given:	*0.00065 as a decimal number*
Relationships:	*$0.0001 = 10^{-4}$*
Answer:	*6.5×10^{-4}*

Using a calculator

Scientific calculators can work with numbers in scientific notation, *if* you know how to enter them! On the specific calculator in the diagram, you use the following keystrokes to enter the number 1.5×10^{-3}. The keystrokes may be different on other calculators; however, the key labeled "EE" is usually the one that allows you to enter the exponent.

For this calculator (others may differ)

To enter the number 5.5×10^{-3} you press

The calculator display reads

5.5 E-3

Converting between units

Two measurements can only be compared if both are in the same units

Suppose you drive to Mexico and gas at one filling station costs $1.25 per *liter*. Across the border in Texas, gas is $4.05 per *gallon*. Which is less expensive?

The answer is not obvious. Think of the different systems of units as different languages. To compare two measurements, both need to be in the same units. That means you must translate between the language of dollars per liter and that of dollars per gallon. To translate Spanish to English you need a Spanish/English dictionary. To translate between units you need **conversion factors**. Conversion factors are ratios of two units. An example is that one gallon = 3.785 L. To convert the gas prices, we use the conversion factor.

Solved problem

Convert $1.25 / L to dollars per gallon.

Asked: *A value in dollars per gallon*

Given: *$1.25/L*

Relationships: *1 gallon = 3.785 L*

Solve: $\left(\dfrac{\$1.25}{\cancel{L}}\right)\left(\dfrac{3.785\ \cancel{L}}{1\ \text{gallon}}\right) = \left(\dfrac{\$4.73}{\text{gallon}}\right)$

Answer: *$4.73/gallon*

Discussion: *$1.25/L is more expensive than $4.05/gallon.*

Converting from one unit to another

To do a conversion, arrange the conversion factors as ratios and multiply them so that unwanted units cancel out. You should be left with only the units you want. There are many conversion factors on the inside back cover of this book.

Another word for units is *dimensions*. The process of converting between units with conversion factors is also called **dimensional analysis**. Dimensional analysis is a very powerful tool and it is used extensively by scientists and engineers. It is also a very useful tool in our daily lives.

Some useful conversion factors

$\dfrac{1\ \text{m}}{39.37\ \text{in}}$	$\dfrac{1\ \text{L}}{1000\ \text{mL}}$	$\dfrac{1\ \text{kg}}{1000\ \text{g}}$
$\dfrac{1\ \text{inch}}{2.54\ \text{cm}}$	$\dfrac{1\ \text{gallon}}{3.785\ \text{L}}$	$\dfrac{1\ \text{min}}{60\ \text{s}}$
$\dfrac{1\ \text{m}}{100\ \text{cm}}$	$\dfrac{1\ \text{teaspoon}}{5\ \text{mL}}$	$\dfrac{1\ \text{hour}}{3600\ \text{s}}$
$\dfrac{1\ \text{cm}}{10\ \text{mm}}$	$\dfrac{1\ \text{cm}^3}{1\ \text{mL}}$	$\dfrac{1\ \text{g}/_{\text{mL}}}{1000\ \text{kg}/_{\text{m}^3}}$

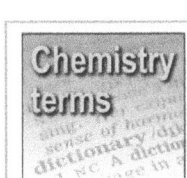

Chemistry terms

conversion factor: a ratio of two different units that has a value of 1.

dimensional analysis: technique of using conversion factors to convert between units.

1.2 Scientific Inquiry

The search for explanations

The Greek scientist Aristotle thought that smoke rose because smoke was a form of fire, and fire's natural place was in the Sun. Rocks fell because rocks were made of earth and earth's natural place was on the ground. Aristotle was not stupid. His eyes told him the correct behavior of things. Smoke rises and rocks fall. However, today the explanation for *why* has changed. Today we explain the same observations using the ideas of gravity, density, and buoyancy. Why do we think today's explanation is correct? If Aristotle was so smart (and he was), then why did he have the wrong explanation?

Why does smoke rise?

Why do rocks fall?

Natural laws

We believe that everything that happens in the universe obeys the same set of rules that we call **natural laws**. Unfortunately, the natural laws are not written down, nor are we born knowing them. *The primary goal of science is to discover what the natural laws are.* Humans learned science by asking harder and harder questions. Aristotle's questions were among the earliest, and they reflected a much smaller body of understanding than we have today.

Inquiry is learning by questioning

Learning through questions is called **inquiry**. An inquiry is like a crime investigation in that there is a mystery to solve. In a criminal inquiry, something illegal happened and the detective must figure out what it was. In a scientific inquiry, the mystery is how and why things happen the exact way they do.

Deduction and theories

Of course, the criminal detective did not see what happened. The detective must *deduce* what happened in the past from information collected in the present. In the process of inquiry, the detective asks questions. The best questions lead to *evidence*. Eventually, the detective comes up with a **theory** about what happened.

When is a theory correct?

At first, the detective's theory is only one explanation among several of what *might have happened*. The detective must have proof that a theory describes what actually *did happen*. To be proven, a theory must pass three demanding tests:

1. It must be supported by significant evidence.
2. There can't be a *single piece* of evidence that disagrees with the theory.
3. The theory must be unique.

If two theories both fit the facts equally well, you cannot tell which is correct. Only when a theory passes all three tests does it become a potential solution to the mystery.

Chemistry terms

natural laws: the unwritten rules that govern everything in the universe.

inquiry: the process of learning through asking questions.

theory: an explanation that is supported by evidence.

Experiments and hypotheses

In science, a hypothesis is a tentative explanation for something

Science is largely learned by trial and error over a long period of time and by many people. New scientific knowledge begins when you observe something interesting and wonder why or how it happens. For example, it takes sugar a long time to dissolve when you stir it into cold water. This leads to a question: Does temperature affect how quickly sugar dissolves in water? You may make a guess, "I think sugar dissolves faster in hot water." This tentative answer, or educated guess, is called a **hypothesis**. A good hypothesis has outcomes you can test to see whether they really happen the way you think they will.

Does sugar dissolve faster in hot water?

Hypotheses are tested by experiments

25°C   35°C

Experiment

An **experiment** is a situation you set up specifically to see what happens, often to test a hypothesis. You might try several different temperatures of water to see if the dissolving time is different. The results of your experiment help you change your hypothesis. You might even discard your first hypothesis altogether in favor of a new one that better fits the results of the experiment.

The truth is what actually happens, not the hypothesis!

The results of real experiments and observations are the test of what is true in science. It does not matter what anyone thinks, says, or even writes in a book. We believe the scientific ideas in this book only because they have been tested over and over with actual experiments, some for over a hundred years. You gain the benefit of that experience so you don't have to test every idea yourself. However, what is between these covers is just the beginning. Our knowledge of science is always growing. Someday we hope you will add your own pages to a book of science! To scientifically unravel the mysteries of nature, your thinking must always be guided by what nature actually does, either through experiments or direct observations.

Chemistry terms

science: the process of using evidence to create predictions that can be tested, as well as the knowledge resulting from this process.

hypothesis: a tentative explanation for something, or a tentative answer to a question.

experiment: a situation specially set up to observe how something happens or to test a hypothesis.

Experimental and control variables

Designing good experiments

A student is asked to experimentally test the hypothesis that dissolving time is inversely proportional to temperature. The student adds different amounts of sugar to different cups of water at different temperatures. The data below show that the sugar in cup B dissolves the fastest. Do the results of the experiment support the hypothesis?

Trial A
25°C
5 g sugar
100 mL water
53 s to
dissolve

Trial B
45°C
2 g sugar
60 mL water
35 s to
dissolve

Trial C
35°C
8 g sugar
150 mL water
47 s to
dissolve

Evaluate and critique scientific evidence

Scientific evidence must be *critiqued* and *evaluated*, for accuracy and for experimental design. The student's evidence is inconclusive because *three variables* were changed. A **variable** is a quantity, such as temperature, that is measured or changed. The data shows that the dissolving rate changed, but it is not clear *which variable* caused the change.

- Dissolving could be affected by the amount of water.

- Dissolving could be affected by temperature.

- Dissolving could be affected by the amount of sugar.

The experimental variable

A better design for the experiment would be to add the same amount of sugar to the same amount of water in each cup with *only* the temperature changed. With this experimental design any change in dissolving rate could clearly be linked to temperature. The single variable that is changed in an experiment is called the **experimental variable**. For this experiment, temperature should be the experimental variable.

Trial A
25°C
5 g sugar
100 mL water
53 s to
dissolve

Trial B
45°C
5 g sugar
100 mL water
32 s to
dissolve

Trial C
35°C
5 g sugar
100 mL water
44 s to
dissolve

Control variables

In good experimental design, all variables except the experimental variable are kept constant. The variables kept constant are called **control variables**. The volume of water and the amount of sugar should be control variables.

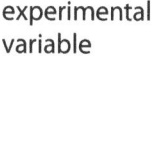

Chemistry terms

variable: a quantity that is measured or changed in an experiment or observation.
experimental variable: the single variable that is changed to test its effect. **control variables:** variables that are kept constant during an experiment.

Uncertainty and error

All measurements have error and error is not a mistake

Suppose you use a stopwatch to measure the dissolving time in the experiment with sugar and water. It is hard to tell the exact moment when all the sugar has been completely dissolved. If you repeat the experiment three times, each time you will obtain a slightly different result *even if you do the exact same thing*. This is because any measurement always contains some uncertainty, or **error**. In the context of measurement, *error is not a mistake*. Error is the unavoidable difference between a measurement and the true value of what you are measuring. Errors can be small if the experiment is accurate and precise, but there is *always* error in any measurement, no matter how careful you are.

25°C
5 g sugar
100 mL water

Data from sugar-dissolving experiment

Trial	Sugar	Water	Temp.	Time
1	5.0 g	100 mL	25.4°C	53 s
2	5.0 g	100 mL	25.1°C	45 s
3	5.0 g	100 mL	26.1°C	48 s
avg.	5.0 g	100 mL	25.5°C	48.7 s

The average

When you make many measurements of the same thing you should notice that they cluster around an **average** value. Some measurements are more than the average and some are less. To calculate the average (or mean), you add up all the measurements and divide by the number of measurements you have. For example, the average of the dissolving times is 48.7 s. Notice that the average has one more significant figure than any individual data point.

Taking the average

1 add up the values
$$53 + 45 + 48 = 146$$

2 divide by the number of measurements
$$146 \div 3 = 48.7$$

Why finding an average is useful

There are two important reasons why you should always make several measurements and find an average:

1. The average of several measurements is usually more accurate than a single measurement. The average is more accurate because errors in the negative direction partially cancel errors in the positive direction. That's why there is one more significant figure.

2. The differences between the average and the actual measurements gives you an estimate of the amount of error in your measurements.

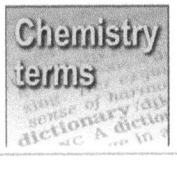
Chemistry terms

error: the unavoidable difference between a real measurement and the unknown true value of the quantity being measured.

average (or mean): value obtained from a set of measurements by adding up all measurement values and dividing by the total number of measurements.

Comparing data: when are two results the same?

What does it mean for results to be the same?

Earlier in this chapter we said that one criterion for scientific evidence was that it must be *reproducible*. Reproducibility means *two* things that we can now discuss more carefully:

1. Others who repeat the same experiment get the same result.

2. If you repeat the experiment the same way, you get the same result.

When different numbers are "the same"

According to Rule 2, the experiment with dissolving fails the test for scientific evidence. Three repetitions gave three different measurements (53, 45, and 48 s). How can you tell whether results are the *same* when all results have errors in them? The word "same" when applied to experimental measurements does not mean what it does in ordinary conversation. Two measurements are considered the same if their difference is less than or equal to the amount of error. *This is an important concept to remember*.

Two measurements are considered the same if their difference is less than or equal to the amount of error

How to estimate the error

How can we know the error if we do not know the true value of a measurement? The way scientists estimate the error is to *assume the average is the true value*.

1. Find the difference between each measurement and the average.

2. The error is roughly the largest difference between the average and a measured value.

Estimating the error

Time	Average	Difference
53 s	48.7 s	+4.3 s
45 s	48.7 s	−3.7 s
48 s	48.7 s	−0.7 s

The largest difference between the data and the average is 4.3 s so the estimated error is about ± 4 s

Later you may learn a more sophisticated way to estimate the error in a measurement, called the *standard deviation*. For now, the largest difference is 4.3 s so, by rounding, the error is ±4 s. If the largest value of the error was 4.6 then we would have rounded up to 5.

Significant figures in the result

The result of our experiment is the average value plus or minus the error. What is the correct number of significant figures? We know that we can't have more significant figures in our result than the number of significant figures that our measurements have. In other words the calculations performed on the data, such as the average in this case, cannot increase the number of significant figures. Our data have two significant figures and so the average should also have two significant figures. The calculated average of 48.7 is rounded up to 49. The error is ±4 s and the result is 49 ± 4 s.

Drawing conclusions from data

We do experiments to reach conclusions

The point of experiments is to produce data that allow a scientist (like you) to come to a **conclusion**. A conclusion is a stated decision whether the results of experiments or observations confirm your idea, the hypothesis, or not. *You need to know about errors before you can make a conclusion.*

Are these results different?

Here is an example. Suppose another group measures the dissolving time at 27°C and finds it to be *slower* than you did at 25°C. They use the same 5 g of sugar and 100 mL of water, so the two experiments should be comparable. Do the experiments prove that sugar dissolves *slower* in warmer water? At first glance, that is what the results suggest. In fact, that conclusion is *not* supported once you consider the error.

Group A

25°C
5 g sugar
100 mL water

Data from sugar-dissolving experiment

Trial	Sugar	Water	Temp.	Time
1	5.0 g	100 mL	25.4°C	53 s
2	5.0 g	100 mL	25.1°C	45 s
3	5.0 g	100 mL	26.1°C	48 s
avg.	5.0 g	100 mL	25.5°C	48.7 s

Group B

27°C
5 g sugar
100 mL water

Data from sugar dissolving experiment

Trial	Sugar	Water	Temp.	Time
1	5.0 g	100 mL	27.4°C	52 s
2	5.0 g	100 mL	28.1°C	47 s
3	5.0 g	100 mL	27.1°C	49 s
avg.	5.0 g	100 mL	27.5°C	49.3 s

When differences are significant

In both experiments the error is about plus or minus 4 s. The difference between the two groups is 0.6 s, which is *smaller than the estimated error in the results*. The conclusion is that there is no **significant difference** between the results. Both groups have the same time: 49 ± 4 s. A difference between data is only *significant* if the difference is substantially greater than the error. This is an important consideration because experiments rarely produce exactly the same numbers twice in a row. Numbers that are different in a mathematical sense may not be *significantly* different in a scientific sense.

To evaluate any experimental result one must critique the evidence by asking: Is the observed "effect" significantly bigger than the uncertainty in the measurement?

Chemistry terms

conclusion: a stated decision whether or not the results of experiments or observations confirm an idea or hypothesis.

significant difference: situation in which the difference between two results is substantially greater than the error in either result.

Scientific evidence

Qualities of scientific evidence

Good experiments produce scientific evidence for the scientific theory under investigation. This may be measurements, data tables, graphs, observations, or other information that describes what actually happens. Science has limitations and can only explain something if the evidence is **objective** and **repeatable**. "Objective" means the evidence should describe only what actually happened as exactly as possible. The personal opinions of the person doing the experiment do not count as scientific evidence. "Repeatable" means that others who repeat the same experiment observe the same results.

Evidence may come from observations

Scientific evidence may come from observing natural phenomena without doing an experiment. The resulting scientific theories are based on these phenomena. For example, Galileo used his telescope to observe the Moon and recorded his observations by sketching. The sketches are *objective* because they represent what he actually saw. Others who looked through his telescope saw the same thing; therefore the sketches are also *repeatable*. The scientific evidence of Galileo's sketches convinced people that the Moon was actually a world like Earth with mountains and valleys. This was not what people believed prior to Galileo's time.

Galileo's sketches

Scientific evidence must be **objective** and **repeatable**

The scientific meaning of words

It is important that scientific evidence be communicated clearly, with no room for misunderstanding. Scientists attach careful meanings to words such as "weight" and "mass." Many "everyday" words are defined more precisely in science. For example, "heat" in chemistry means a certain type of *energy* that depends on temperature. This definition allows a quantity of heat to be defined with a precise measurement that tells someone else exactly how much energy is involved.

Procedures describe how scientific evidence is collected

The way scientific evidence is gathered is usually important to understanding what the evidence means. Any presentation of scientific evidence always includes a description of how the evidence was collected. For example, an experiment includes a **procedure**, which describes how the experiment was done. The procedure includes important details, such as what instruments were used to make any measurements. The procedure must include enough detail so that someone else familiar with chemistry can repeat the same experiment to verify the repeatability of the evidence.

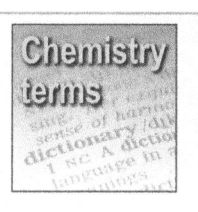
Chemistry terms

objective: term that describes only what actually occurred without opinion or bias.

repeatable: term used to describe an experiment or observation made in the same way for which the same results or observations can be duplicated.

procedure: detailed instructions on how to do an experiment or make an observation.

The scientific method

Learning by the scientific method

It takes a long time to learn by trying everything. Furthermore, you can never be sure you tried *everything*. The **scientific method** is a much more dependable way to learn.

The scientific method

1. Scientists observe nature, then invent or revise hypotheses about how things work.

2. The hypotheses are tested against evidence collected from observations and experiments.

3. Any hypothesis that correctly accounts for all of the evidence from the experiments is a potentially correct theory.

4. A theory is continually tested by collecting new and different evidence. Even a single piece of evidence that does not agree with a theory causes scientists to return to step 1.

observe and think

make a hypothesis

revise and improve a theory

compare to experiments & observations

Why the scientific method works

The scientific method is the underlying logic of science. It is basically a cautious way to build a supportable, evidence-based understanding of our natural world. Each theory is continually tested against the results of observations and experiments, possibly from a variety of sources and by many different scientists. The development of more advanced technology or even new fields of science allows us to further test theories. Such testing leads to continued refinement of theories, and we end up with reliable explanations to more and more different things. The way people have learned about things great and small, to the Solar System and beyond, can be traced through many hypotheses.

1.3 Matter and Energy

Chemistry describes the different forms of matter

Look at a bicycle and describe what the bicycle is made of. To a scientist, a bicycle is made of **matter**. Matter is everything that has mass and takes up space. This book is matter. You are matter. Even the air is matter. At the next level of detail, a bicycle contains many different kinds of matter, such as steel, aluminum, plastic, and rubber. Chemistry is about the different kinds of matter and how they are created. Chemistry also tells us how matter can be changed from one kind to another.

The phases of matter: solid, liquid, and gas

The matter in a bicycle comes in three **phases** we call *solid*, *liquid*, and *gas*. Solid matter, like the steel frame or rubber tires, is stiff, holds its shape, and may be strong. Liquid matter, like the oil in the wheel bearings, flows and does not hold its shape. The air in the tires is a gas. Gaseous matter flows like liquid, but it also expands to fill any container. You may not believe air has mass and is matter, but consider letting the air out of the bicycle tires. What happens? The air in the tires can easily support both bicycle and rider because air *does* have mass and under sufficient pressure can exert large forces.

The thermal energy in matter determines its phase

Whether matter is solid, liquid, or gas depends on how much internal thermal energy is associated with its constituent molecules and atoms. The lowest thermal energy form of matter is solid. Matter that contains a moderate amount of thermal energy is liquid. Matter that contains a relatively high internal energy can be a gas. If you heat steel hot enough it can become a gas. There is a fourth state of matter, plasma, that appears at even higher energies. Lightning is a plasma.

Chemistry terms

matter: material that has mass and takes up space.

phases: the physical forms of matter: solid, liquid, and gas (and plasma).

Energy

Energy

Energy is a measure of a system's ability to change or create change in other systems. A hot cup of coffee has more energy than a cold cup with the same volume. As the coffee cools, its energy warms the air around it.

Forms of energy

Energy appears in many forms and is transformed during changes. **Potential energy**, or stored energy, is transformed into **kinetic energy** when we race down from the top of a roller coaster. **Chemical energy** stored in the bonds of fuel molecules is transformed into heat or thermal energy when the fuel is burned.

$$CH_4 + 2O_2 \rightarrow 2H_2O + CO_2 + energy$$

Chemical energy

Thermal energy

Hot steam

Mechanical energy

Things tend to flow from higher energy to lower energy

When left alone, systems in nature tend to go from higher energy to lower energy. Warm objects have more energy than cold ones. The energy flows from warm to cold until there is no longer a temperature difference. The same is true of chemical energy. We will see that many chemical reactions occur because the energy of the matter involved is lower after the reaction than it was before.

Conservation of energy

What happens to the energy in hot coffee as it cools? The energy lost by the coffee is *exactly* balanced by the energy gained by the room. The idea that energy is converted from one form into another without a change in the total amount is called the **law of conservation of energy**. This very important natural law says that *energy can never be created or destroyed, just converted from one form into another.* The law of conservation of energy is one of the most important laws in all of science. It applies to all forms of energy, not just heat.

± 120 volts ± 120 volts ± 120 volts

0 volts 0 volts 0 volts

Safety ground (0 volts)

Electrical energy

Chemistry terms

energy: a measure of a system's ability to change or create change in other systems, typically measured in joules.

potential energy: stored energy due to the position of an object

kinetic energy: the energy of motion

chemical energy: energy stored in chemical bonds of molecules

law of conservation of energy: law of nature that states that energy can never be created or destroyed, just converted from one form into another.

"Using" and "conserving" energy

"Conserving" energy

Almost everyone has heard that it is good to "conserve energy" and not to waste it. This is sound advice because energy from gasoline or electricity costs money and uses resources. What does it mean to "use energy" in the everyday sense? If energy can never be created or destroyed, how can it be "used up"? Why do people worry about "running out" of energy?

4 times less electrical energy for the same light output

"Using" energy

When you "use" energy by turning on a light, you are really converting energy from one form (electricity) to other forms (light and heat). What gets "used up" is the amount of energy *in the form of electricity*. Electricity is a valuable form of energy because it is easy to move over long distances (through wires). In the "chemical" sense, the energy is not "used up" but converted into other forms. The total amount of energy stays constant.

Power plants

Electric power plants don't *make* electrical energy. Energy cannot be created. What power plants do is convert other forms of energy (chemical, solar, or nuclear) into electrical energy. When someone advises you to turn out the lights to conserve energy, he or she is asking you to use less electrical energy. If people used less electrical energy, power plants would burn less oil, gas, or other fuels in "producing" the electrical energy they sell.

"Running out" of energy

Many people are concerned about "running out" of energy. What they worry about is running out of certain *forms* of energy that are easy to use, such as oil and gas. When you use gas in a car, the chemical energy in the gasoline mostly becomes heat energy. It is not practically possible to put the energy back into the form of gasoline, so we say the energy has been "used up" even though the energy itself is still there, only in a different form.

Coal
chemical energy

Power plant

Light and thermal energy

Measurement and analysis

Learning how to measure and use units is an important part of chemistry, and also an important part of your life! Scientists use measurements to gather data and test theories. You use measurements for health and medicine, to purchase things you need, to build, and even to travel. For example, when you add gasoline to a car at the gas station, the pump measures the amount so that you know how much has been transferred into your car. The next time you are near a gas pump, look for the inspection sticker. Every state checks gas pumps to ensure they are measuring accurately. This is important since when you pay for a gallon of gas you should be getting a gallon in your car, not less.

Gas pumps are inspected regularly to ensure that they accurately measure in full gallons

Health is a field that requires numerous measurements. Besides height and weight, almost everything doctors use to monitor your health is based on measurements, referred to as "lab" work or radiology (x rays or ultrasound). When young children go to the doctor for a checkup, a lead test is often performed. A blood sample is taken and the amount of lead in their blood is measured. Lead levels are measured in micrograms per deciliter (µg/dL). A microgram is one millionth of a gram. A deciliter is 0.1 L or 100 mL. One µg in 100 mL is a *very* small amount and yet it can be measured reliably.

Lead in children's blood
10 µg/dL: danger level
15 µg/dL: required action
70 µg/dL: injury or death

Recently there have been many advances in measuring devices. Scientists have had to come up with new ways to measure. Airport security has become very important and a unique measuring device was designed to help with the screening process.

Major airports now use an instrument that bombards cargo with high-energy particles (gamma rays). These particles are able to detect high levels of nitrogen. Nitrogen is the element most commonly found in explosives. This method of screening is effective and saves a great deal of time searching through large amounts of cargo and luggage.

Gamma ray scanners measure airport cargo for excess nitrogen

Air quality is another important area requiring measurement. Environmental scientists use units of parts per million (ppm) to describe the concentration of compounds such as carbon monoxide (CO). A CO level of 1 ppm means there is 1 gram of carbon monoxide per million grams of air. Units of ppm are used to monitor harmful chemicals such as nitrous oxides, and also harmless substances such as fragrances from perfumes! New sensor technology is capable of detecting very low levels of gases and pollutants, even less than one part per million. These new sensors allow us to warn people if unhealthy pollutants at high levels are in the air. When pollutant levels are high, people with breathing problems may choose to stay indoors.

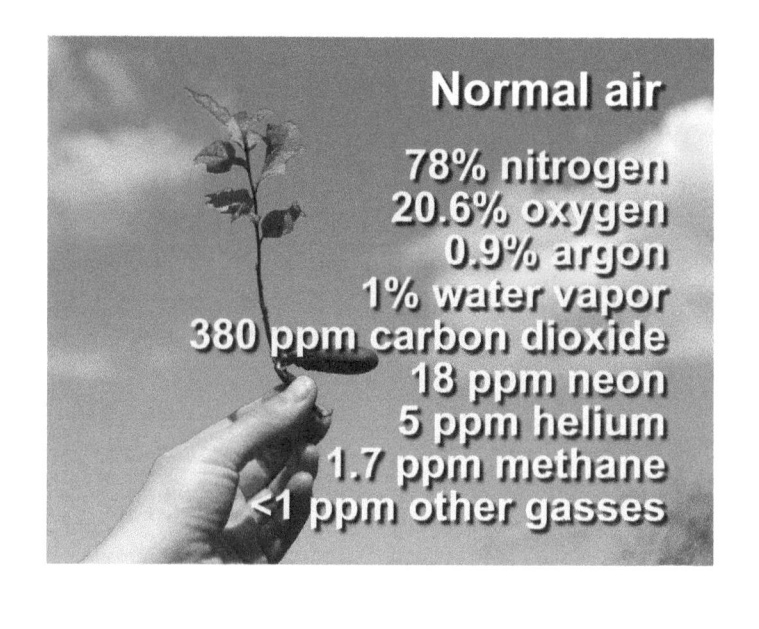

Normal air

78% nitrogen
20.6% oxygen
0.9% argon
1% water vapor
380 ppm carbon dioxide
18 ppm neon
5 ppm helium
1.7 ppm methane
<1 ppm other gasses

Sometimes new knowledge can be scary without knowing how to interpret it. Now that we can measure small amounts of chemicals more accurately, we are more aware of what is in our air, food, and water. Sometimes we should worry, such as when lead or arsenic is found in drinking water; other times, there is no problem at all, such as finding a few ppm of dissolved iron in drinking water, since iron is a necessary mineral nutrient. Knowing what is present allows us to better understand our environment. Just keep in mind that many chemicals, such as ascorbic acid (vitamin C) and potassium, are necessary for health!

Learning to think like a scientist means that we learn to ask questions, perform experiments, and gather information. When we perform experiments, our observations help us to collect information and make sense of it. Sometimes our "interpretation" of the information leads us to a new idea. This is the exciting part of science. Forensic scientists work together to try to solve mysteries and to provide useful information that may help people.

A forensic chemist has several ways to identify what type of molecules are present in materials. For example, during a criminal investigation samples of clothing fibers, medications, and perhaps blood stains are collected and sent to the forensic laboratory for analysis. The investigating detective knows that one suspect takes a certain medication. The forensic chemist uses a sophisticated measuring instrument called a *mass spectrometer* to identify the chemicals in the lab samples. If there is a match with the suspect's medication, that is a useful piece of evidence. As you might imagine, experience in the laboratory helps a chemist to decide what tests to run and how to interpret what the results mean.

A forensic chemist does serious detective work in the lab

Chapter 1 Review

Vocabulary

Match each word to the sentence where it best fits.

Section 1.1

pressure	measurement
force	mass
Pascal	weight
milliliter	gram
graduated cylinder	volume
accuracy	air
precise	density
significant figures	atmosphere
conversion factor	mantissa
scientific notation	exponent
kilogram	elements
	atom

1. As a tree grows, its mass comes primarily from _____.

2. A bicycle tire expands because the _____ inside is greater than it is outside.

3. The _____ are pure forms of matter that cannot be broken down into simpler substances.

4. The _____ is the smallest particle of matter that retains the identity of an element.

5. The amount of matter in an object is most accurately given by the object's _____.

6. A/An _____ could be a push or a pull.

7. The _____ is the SI unit of mass.

8. _____ is a measure of the amount of space something occupies.

9. The _____ is a small unit of pressure equal to one newton per square meter.

10. Chemists use a/an _____ to measure the volume of a liquid accurately.

11. The _____ of a measurement tells you how close it is to the actual known value.

12. A volume measured to be 12 mL is less _____ than one measured to be 12.0 mL.

13. When changing the units of a measured value, a student must use a/an _____ so that the units cancel properly.

14. The _____ tells you how much mass of a substance there is per unit volume.

15. One _____ is the average pressure at sea level on Earth.

16. The _____ is the number that corresponds to N when a value is written as $N \times 10^6$.

17. Scientists use _____ to express very large or very small numbers.

Section 1.2

science	experiments
hypothesis	inquiry
objective	repeated
average	procedure
theory	error
natural laws	uncertainty
significant	control variable
variable	scientific method
conclusion	

18. The goal of _____ is to discover _____ that the universe obeys by using evidence to create testable predictions.

19. A/An _____ is a situation specifically set up to observe what happens under certain conditions.

20. A tentative explanation for an observation is called a/an _____.

21. Learning through questioning is called _____, and it is the basis for all scientific discovery.

22. A good experiment must be able to be _____ by other scientists, who will obtain similar results.

23. When making observations in the laboratory, scientists must be _____ about what they record as data.

24. A/An _____ is a quantity that is kept the same during an experiment where other things are allowed (or observed) to change.

25. A/An _____ is a statement of something learned or demonstrated by an experiment.

26. A/An _____ is a series of steps that outlines how to perform a particular experiment.

27. Measurement _____ can be small if the experiment is accurate and precise.

28. An explanation advances to become a/an _____ when it is supported by a substantial body of evidence.

29. All measurements contain some _____, which is unavoidable.

30. A difference is _____ only when it is larger than the estimated error in the measurements.

31. A/An _____ is a quantity that is observed and may change in an experiment.

Section 1.3

energy	phases
kinetic energy	potential energy
matter	conservation

32. _____ is the quantity that determines how much change is possible in a physical system.

33. The law of _____ of energy states that energy can never be created or destroyed.

34. Anything that takes up space and has mass is referred to as _____.

35. Solid is one of the three ordinary _____ of matter.

36. When an arrow is shot from a bow, _____ is transformed into _____.

Conceptual Questions

Section 1.1

37. Is fire a form of matter? Briefly explain your thinking.

38. What is the function of an antioxidant?

39. Describe how vitamins are useful to our bodies.

40. Write two sentences about one difference between solid sugar and sugar dissolved in water.

41. Which is a better value: one gallon of milk for $3.00 or one liter of milk for $3.00?

42. The process of dissolving allows chemical reactions to take place more effectively in the body. Explain why this is so.

43. Which unit represents a larger amount of matter, a kilogram or a gram? Explain your reasoning.

44. If you have a solid chocolate Easter rabbit and a hollow chocolate Easter rabbit of the same size:

    a. Which one contains more matter?

    b. Which one has a larger volume?

45. From the figure below, what is the best measurement that we can make?

    a. 10 mL

    b. 10.0 mL

    c. 10.2 mL

    d. 10.5 mL

    e. 10.00 mL

46. Your measurements are limited by the precision of the equipment you use. Which of the two choices below gives the more precise measurement? Explain using a complete sentence for each part.

    a. A top-loading balance with 2 pennies that reads 6 g

    b. A top-loading balance with the same 2 pennies that reads 6.30 g

47. Explain in words how you would determine how many dozen eggs are represented by 42 individual eggs. (12 eggs = 1 dozen.)

48. Explain the difference between accuracy and precision using the dart board pictures below.

49. Why should a measurement always be recorded to the correct number of significant figures?

50. When you squeeze an inflated balloon in one place, it bulges out in another place. Explain why this happens.

51. Why is an empty bottle sitting on your table not truly empty?

52. Give two observations that show that air has mass.

Chapter 1 Review

Section 1.2

53. Science has its limitations. Give an example of a statement that science cannot explain and tell why.

54. Tell if the following statements about scientific hypotheses are true or false.
    a. Hypotheses are definite and permanent statements that cannot be proven wrong.
    b. Hypotheses should be testable and may not necessarily be supported by evidence.
    c. If a hypothesis is tested for long enough and gathers enough support, it can become a theory.
    d. Hypotheses are more well-established and reliable than theories.

55. Tell if the following statements about scientific theories are true or false.
    a. Scientific theories are based on natural and physical occurrences.
    b. Scientific theories are only tested by one researcher.
    c. Theories cannot change when new areas of science are developed.
    d. Development of new technology has the potential to change a theory.

56. Label each of the following statements as a hypothesis or a theory.
    a. Shining blue light on plants helps them grow taller.
    b. All elements are made of indivisible particles called atoms.
    c. Molecules have 3-D shapes based on how their electrons repel each other.
    d. Adding salt to ice will help it melt faster.

57. What steps are involved in the scientific method?

58. Give an example of how an auto mechanic or a baker might use the scientific method in their daily lives.

59. When you are conducting an experiment, it is important to have only one experimental variable whenever possible. Explain why.

60. When performing experiments, it is important to have several trials and therefore several measurements of the same process. This repetition makes it possible to say that the results are more "accurate" than those of another group that performed the experiment only once. Explain why this is true using the words "error" and "average" in your answer.

61. Chemists were asked to analyze an unknown sample. They were able to determine three physical properties of the sample. When run through a series of tests, a yellow solid was isolated that had a melting point of 402°C and a boiling point of 954°C. Use the Handbook of Chemistry and Physics to determine whether the substance is cadmium iodide, lead iodide, or sodium iodide.

Section 1.3

62. Which of the following are examples of matter: air, a crayon, a cat, you, and/or a pencil?

63. Design a simple experiment to test the temperature at which water boils. Define your system under study (using a simple sketch), the variable that you are testing, and the variables you will hold constant.

64. When we talk about "conserving" energy in a chemical reaction, what are we referring to?

Quantitative Problems

Section 1.1

65. Which number is larger: 0.001 or 1×10^{-4}?

66. What is the volume of a paperback book that is 20 cm tall, 11 cm wide, and 3.5 cm thick?

67. Count the significant figures in each of the following:
    a. 10. swimmers
    b. 11.300 g
    c. 0.0234 g
    d. 6.00 L

68. Calculate the numeric answer to the correct number of significant figures.
    a. 62.4 L − 8.21 L + 4.3 L
    b. 6.43 g − 2.10 g
    c. 1.54 m + 10.44 m

69. Soda is often sold in 12 fluid ounce cans. How many milliliters are in a 12 fluid ounce can? (1 US fluid ounce = 29.57 mL)

70. A liquid occupies a volume of 4.50 gallons and weighs 15.8 kg. What is the density of this liquid? Is it heavier or lighter than water? Will this liquid float on water?

71. Perform the following calculations and report your answer to the correct number of significant figures.
    a. 6.25 m × 0.51 m

    b. 2.46 m / 7.8 m

    c. 3.20 m × 2.5 m

72. If a person weighs 82.5 kg, what is the person's weight in pounds?

73. Perform the following conversions:
    a. 350 mL to quarts (qt)
    b. 3.0 ft to meters (m)
    c. 80 km to miles (mi)
    d. 25 mL to cm^3

74. Write out the following numbers as decimal numbers.
    a. 4.5×10^{-2}
    b. 3.33×10^{-9}
    c. 2.5×10^4

75. Write each of the following numbers in scientific notation.
    a. 450,000
    b. 45
    c. 0.45
    d. 0.0045

76. A bar of aluminum has a volume of 1.45 mL and a mass of 3.92 g. Calculate its density.

77. We add 54 grams of aluminum to a graduated cylinder containing 50 mL of water. What will be the level of water in the cylinder after the aluminum has been added?

78. We add 30 g of titanium (Ti) and 30 g of zinc (Zn) to a test tube that has 75 mL of water. What will be the level of water after the Ti and Zn have been added?

79. The density of silver is 10.5 g/mL.
    a. What volume would 2.86 g of silver occupy?
    b. What is the mass of a 16.3 cm^3 piece of silver?

80. A penny is measured to have a mass of 2.52 g and a volume of 0.35 cm^3. Is this penny made of pure copper?

81. Modern-day pennies are made of zinc with a small covering of copper. The weight of a penny is 2.52 g and the volume it occupies is 0.35 cm^3. Calculate the amount of copper used in the penny.

82. An iceberg has a volume of 650 m^3. What is the mass of the iceberg in kilograms (kg)? (Assume the density of ice = 0.917 g/cm^3.)

83. An iceberg is floating in the ocean. A scientist using a specialized instrument measures the volume of the iceberg that is above the water surface and finds it to be 75.0 m^3. What is the volume of the iceberg below the water surface? (Assume the density of ice = 0.917 g/cm^3 and the density of water = 1.000 g/cm^3.)

84. You are given three rings to test to determine whether they are made of gold or are fake. You decide to measure the mass of each ring by weighing them on a balance and their volume by measuring the water they displace when immersed in water. The measurements for the three rings are as follows:
    Ring A: mass = 3.5 g, volume = 0.18 cm^3
    Ring B: mass = 2.8 g, volume = 0.18 cm^3
    Ring C: mass = 3.9 g, volume = 0.20 cm^3
    Using these data, determine which rings could actually be made of gold.

Challenge Problems

85. Page 26 depicts two different theories about the layout of the solar system. The *geocentric* or Ptolemaic model explained that the earth was the center of the universe and everything orbited around it in circles. Hundreds of years passed before enough evidence was gathered to change this theory. Today, we have the *heliocentric* or Copernican model, which explains that the Sun is at the center and the planet orbits are elliptical.

    Group each of the following pieces of evidence under the theory that it supports. Then, write a few sentences explaining why *you* think one theory is more convincing than the other in explaining the layout of the Solar System.
    • The tilt in the Earth's orbit accounts for the seasons.
    • Objects dropped from a height fall towards earth.
    • Moons orbiting Jupiter were seen using a telescope.
    • The earth does not seem to move.
    • Venus has phases like the moon.
    • Stars and planets appear to remain the same brightness, meaning that they probably stayed the same distance from the earth.

    This is a challenging question! Discuss with your teacher and classmates if necessary.

CHAPTER 2
Matter and Atoms

What is matter made of?

What is the explanation for the diversity of matter?

How do we explain properties such as solid or liquid?

You, the plant, and the coal contain the element carbon

What are you made of? In other words, what are you *physically* made from? What sort of "stuff" makes up your skin, bones, and muscles? Is it the same basic kind of "stuff" that makes up rocks, trees, air, plastic, and the rest of the material world? The technical term for "stuff" is *matter*, and matter is what makes up the physical universe.

Ordinary matter, including you, is made from tiny particles called *atoms*. The atoms of matter in your body are the same as the ones that make up rocks, water, plastic, and even metals. Of course, the *details* are different! The blend and arrangement of different atoms in human muscle tissue is different from a log or a sheet of plastic wrap. The atoms themselves are mostly identical. Your body, a piece of wood, and a sheet of plastic are mostly *carbon* atoms. In fact, it is possible to take *cellulose*, the main ingredient of wood, and turn it into a clear plastic sheet called *cellophane*. Many foods are wrapped with cellophane to preserve freshness.

Cellophane is made from wood!

Chemistry is the science of matter and its changes. Chemistry tells us how matter is formed and how one kind of matter, such as wood, can be turned into a totally different kind of matter, such as a sheet of plastic.

A slimy chemical reaction

Take a small plastic cup and add 30 g of white glue. Add 30 mL of water to the glue and stir it until well mixed. In a second plastic cup, combine 100 mL of warm water with 4 g of borax powder. Stir this until the powder is dissolved.

Mix 30 g of white glue with 30 mL of water in a cup

Measure 4 g of borax and mix with 100 mL of water in a second cup

Both cups hold examples of *mixtures*. A mixture contains more than one kind of matter, which is the same as saying more than one chemical. In one cup the mixture is water and glue. In the other cup the mixture is water and borax.

- How are the mixtures alike?
- How are they different?
- Would you classify them as solid, liquid, or gas?

To get some color, add a drop of food coloring to the glue–water mixture and stir it in. Combine the two mixtures by slowly pouring the glue mixture into the cup with the water and borax while stirring gently. What happens to the mixture now? Pick it up and work it between your fingers. Write down your observations about this new mixture.

Pour the colored glue mixture into the borax and water mixture while slowly stirring

- Is the new mixture a solid, liquid, or gas?

The white glue is a mixture of water and polyvinyl acetate (PVA). PVA is a long molecule made of repeating units of smaller molecules. Glue is so viscous, or thick, because the long strands of PVA stick to themselves like wet spaghetti. Borax is a compound of sodium, boron, and oxygen that is "hydrated" (meaning it includes water molecules). Putting the two together creates a chemical reaction that combines them, linking the polyvinyl acetate molecules together and making the "slime." The more you work it, the more links you get and the stiffer the slime becomes.

What is it?

Why did it change from two liquids into this "slime"?

2.1 Matter and the Elements

Explaining the diversity of matter

There are probably a million different kinds of matter in and around your classroom. Think about every different ingredient in the air, the soil, the walls and floor, the books and desks, and everything else. How do we make sense of such variety? Are the millions of different kinds of matter actually mixtures of a few simpler things?

Substances contain only a single kind of matter

The first step toward finding an answer is to search for **pure substances**. A substance cannot be separated into different kinds of matter by physical means such as sorting, filtering, drying, dissolving, heating, or cooling. Corn oil is a pure substance. Salad dressing is not, because it contains oil, water, spices, and some other substances. In other words, something is a pure substance if it is made of a single chemical throughout.

Oil and vinegar dressing is a *mixture* of substances

Corn oil is a pure *substance*

Mixtures contain more than one kind of matter

"Pure" is a much looser word in every day language. A container might say "pure orange juice." However, to a chemist, orange juice is a **mixture**. Orange juice can be separated into water, different flavoring chemicals, citric acid, sugars, and fruit pulp. A mixture is matter that contains more than one substance. Wood is a mixture because there are many substances in wood, including water, cellulose, tannic acid, lignin, and other chemicals.

Matter

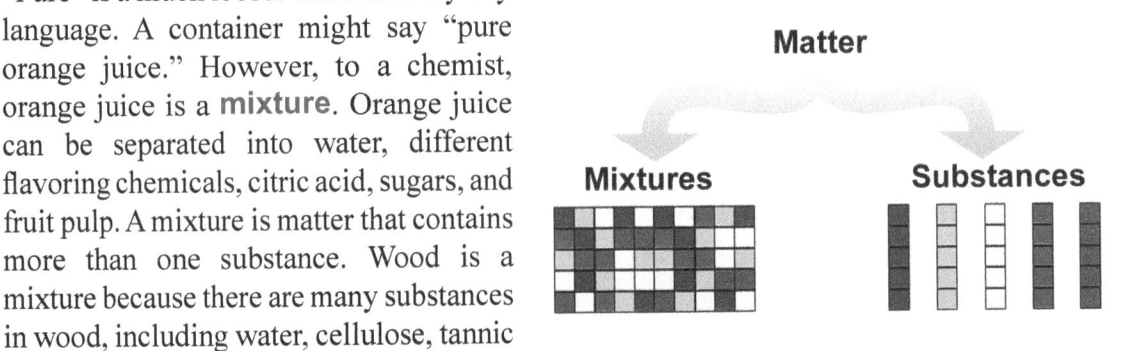

Mixtures   **Substances**

Most ordinary matter is a mixture of substances

Mixtures can be separated by physical means

Mixtures are made of substances. They can be separated into their component substances by physical means such as sorting, filtering, heating, or cooling. Chicken noodle soup, for example, could be separated into its components by using strainers and filters of different sizes. The separation process does not change the characteristics of each substance. You still have water, salt, fats, noodles, and chicken.

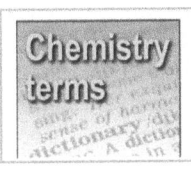

Chemistry terms

pure substance: a kind of matter that can't be separated into other substances by physical means such as heating, cooling, filtering, drying, sorting, or dissolving.

mixture: matter that contains more than one substance.

Physical properties and physical change

Physical properties

Properties that you can measure or see through direct observation are called **physical properties**. For example, water is a colorless liquid at room temperature. The quality of "color" is a physical property. Temperature is another physical property.

Color and Temperature are physical properties

Brittleness and malleability are physical properties

Gold bends easily

Glass shatters

Gold is a shiny, *malleable* solid at room temperature. Malleable materials can be hammered into thin sheets without cracking. The opposite is *brittle*. Glass is brittle. Brittle materials break if you hammer or bend them. Malleability and brittleness are examples of physical properties of solid materials.

Density and phase are physical properties

The density of a material is a physical property. Wood is less dense than water; water is less dense than rock or steel. Wood floats on water because its density is lower than the density of water. The phase (solid, liquid, or gas) of a material is also a physical property.

Wood floats because its density is less than the density of water

Physical changes are reversible

Physical changes include
heating
cooling
melting
freezing
boiling
dissolving
bending
evaporating

Physical changes are changes in the physical properties of matter. Physical changes can be reversed without changing one substance into another. Heating, cooling, dissolving, melting, freezing, boiling, and bending are all physical changes. When water freezes, it undergoes a physical change from a liquid to a solid. This does not change the water into a new substance. The change can easily be reversed by melting the water. Bending a steel bar is another physical change. Bending changes the shape of the bar, but it is still steel.

Chemistry terms

physical property: a property such as mass, density, or color that you can measure or see through direct observation.

physical change: a change in physical properties such as shape, phase, or temperature; for example, grinding, melting, boiling, dissolving, heating, or cooling.

Extensive and Intensive Properties

Extensive properties

Physical properties can be further classified as either extensive or intensive. For example, if we are measuring the mass of a sample of salt, will it change if we have more salt? Of course! The more salt we have, the greater the mass. We call physical properties that depend on how much matter we have **extensive properties**. Examples of extensive properties include mass, weight, volume, and length.

Mass of a substance depends on the amount of substance

Mass is an extensive property

Intensive properties

On the other hand, consider a sample of copper. We can find its density by dividing its mass by its volume. However, it does not matter if we have 1.0 gram of copper or 1.0 kg of copper. The density of copper is always 8.96 g/cm³. We call properties that remain the same no matter how much of something we have **intensive properties**. Examples include density, boiling point, freezing point, conductivity, malleability, and even color and odor!

The density of copper does not depend on the amount of copper.

Density is an intensive property

Intensive properties can help identify substances

Often, we can think of intensive properties as something that helps define a type of matter. For example, we can identify an unknown liquid by its boiling point or a metal by its density. However, just knowing that we have 10 mL of a liquid cannot tell us whether it is mercury or water.

Extensive properties change with how much matter we have

Intensive properties remain the same no matter how much we have

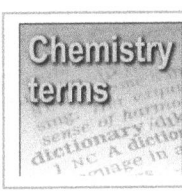
Chemistry terms

extensive property: a physical property that depends on how much matter is present

intensive property: a physical property that does not depends on how much matter is present

Chemical properties and chemical change

Chemical properties

Properties that can only be observed when one substance changes into a different substance are called **chemical properties**. For example, if you leave an iron nail outside, it will eventually rust. A chemical property of iron is that it reacts with oxygen in the air to form iron oxide (rust).

Rust results from a chemical change

Chemical changes are hard to reverse

Any change that transforms one substance into a different substance is called a **chemical change**. The transformation of iron into rust is a chemical change. Chemical changes are not easily reversible. For example, rusted iron will not turn shiny again even if you take oxygen away.

Using chemical changes

We use chemical changes to create useful materials. The slime you made in an experiment is an example of a chemical change. The polyvinyl acetate in the glue was a viscous liquid. Adding the borax links adjacent molecules together like rungs on a ladder. That made the liquid into a semisolid mass, a polymer, that is more able to hold its shape.

The glue and borax together caused a chemical change

Recognizing chemical change

Chemical changes are created by **chemical reactions**. A chemical reaction is any process in which one substance changes into a different substance.

A chemical reaction occurs when you mix baking soda with vinegar. The mixture bubbles violently as carbon dioxide gas, a new substance, is formed. The temperature of the mixture also gets noticeably colder. Bubbling, new substances, and temperature change can all be evidence of a chemical change.

Bubbling

A new gas is forming

Turns cloudy

A new solid is forming

Temperature change

Chemical bonds are changing

Color change

A new substance is forming

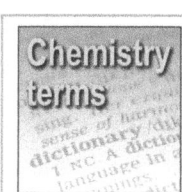
Chemistry terms

chemical property: a property that can only be observed when one substance changes into a different substance, such as iron's tendency to rust.

chemical change: a result of a chemical reaction.

chemical reaction: the process that creates chemical changes.

Scales, Atoms, and Elements

An example of different scales

Is sand a pure substance or a mixture? Although it may look smooth from a distance, a closer look tells us that sand has many small grains. Sand is a *mixture* of different minerals, air, and water.Like sand, all matter shows different and important structures at different *scales*. A **scale** is a typical length, or size, that shows a particular level of detail. For example, at the centimeter scale you can see the shape of the sand pile. At a scale of 0.01 mm you can see the details of each sand grain, but the shape of the pile is completely lost.

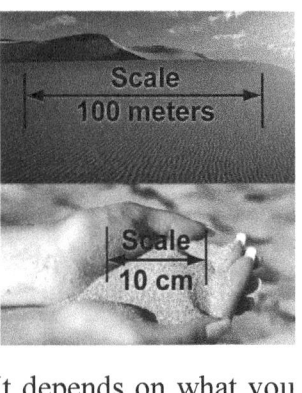

The macroscopic scale

The universe can be understood differently at different scales. It depends on what you are trying to understand. To calculate how much sand fills a bucket, you only need to know about sand's properties on the largest scale. We call this the **macroscopic** scale. Observations are macroscopic when they are large enough for us to see or directly measure in experiments, like mass in grams or the temperature of a pot of water.

The microscopic scale: the scale of atoms

However, to understand temperature and many other aspects of matter, we must look on a scale 200 million *million* times smaller than a grain of sand—the scale of individual atoms! A single atom is about 10^{-10} m in diameter. We call this scale **microscopic.** Macroscopic properties such as temperature ultimately depend on the behavior of atoms.

Elements are unique types of atoms

A pure substance called *feldspar* is common in sand. On the microscopic scale, orthoclase feldspar always contains four different kinds of atoms - potassium, oxygen, silicon, and aluminum. Each different type of atom is one of the **elements**, the most fundamental "pure substances" from which all other matter is made. Think of an element as a unique type of atom. All atoms of the same element have the same structure. Atoms of one element have a structure different from atoms of any other element.

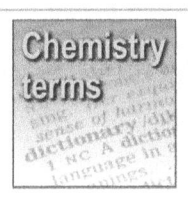

scale: a typical size that shows a certain level of detail.

macroscopic: on the scale that can be directly seen and measured, from bacteria up to the size of a planet.

microscopic: to a chemist, on the scale of atoms, 10^{-9} m and smaller.

element: a substance that cannot be separated into simpler substances by chemical means.

The periodic table

The modern periodic table

As early chemists worked on determining which substances were elements, they noticed that some elements acted like other ones. The soft metals lithium, sodium, and potassium always combine with oxygen in a ratio of two atoms of metal per atom of oxygen. From these kinds of observations, scientists developed the *periodic table of the elements*. The **periodic table** organizes the elements according to how they combine with other elements (chemical properties). When this book was written, we knew of 118 elements, of which 92 occur naturally.

Li Lithium
Na Sodium
K Potassium
O Oxygen

The elements Li, Na, and K all form compounds in a 2:1 ratio with oxygen.

Metals and nonmetals

One big distinction is between metals and nonmetals. Metals tend to be solids at room temperature and are shiny and dense. Metals such as copper or aluminum are good conductors of electricity. At room temperature, nonmetals may be solid like carbon, liquid like bromine, or gas like oxygen. Nonmetals are generally poor conductors of electricity.

Periodic table of the elements

metal

nonmetal

1 H 1.0079 hydrogen																	2 He 4.0028 helium
3 Li 6.941 lithium	4 Be 9.0122 beryllium											5 B 10.811 boron	6 C 12.011 carbon	7 N 14.007 nitrogen	8 O 15.999 oxygen	9 F 18.998 fluorine	10 Ne 20.180 neon
11 Na 22.990 sodium	12 Mg 24.305 magnesium											13 Al 26.982 aluminum	14 Si 28.086 silicon	15 P 30.974 phosphorous	16 S 32.065 sulfur	17 Cl 35.453 chlorine	18 Ar 39.948 argon
19 K 39.098 potassium	20 Ca 40.078 calcium	21 Sc 44.956 scandium	22 Ti 47.867 titanium	23 V 50.942 vanadium	24 Cr 51.996 chromium	25 Mn 54.938 manganese	26 Fe 55.845 iron	27 Co 58.933 cobalt	28 Ni 58.693 nickel	29 Cu 63.546 copper	30 Zn 65.41 zinc	31 Ga 69.723 galium	32 Ge 72.61 germanium	33 As 74.922 arsenic	34 Se 78.96 selenium	35 Br 79.904 bromine	36 Kr 83.80 krypton
37 Rb 85.468 rubidium	38 Sr 87.62 strontium	39 Y 88.906 yttrium	40 Zr 91.224 zirconium	41 Nb 92.906 niobium	42 Mo 95.94 molybdenum	43 Tc (98) technetium	44 Ru 101.07 ruthenium	45 Rh 102.91 rhodium	46 Pd 106.42 palladium	47 Ag 107.87 silver	48 Cd 112.41 cadmium	49 In 114.82 indium	50 Sn 118.71 tin	51 Sb 121.76 antimony	52 Te 127.60 tellurium	53 I 126.90 iodine	54 Xe 131.29 xenon
55 Cs 132.91 cesium	56 Ba 137.33 barium	71 Lu 174.97 lutetium	72 Hf 178.49 hafnium	73 Ta 180.95 tantalum	74 W 183.84 tungsten	75 Re 186.21 rhenium	76 Os 190.23 osmium	77 Ir 192.22 iridium	78 Pt 195.08 platinum	79 Au 196.97 gold	80 Hg 200.59 mercury	81 Tl 204.38 thallium	82 Pb 207.2 lead	83 Bi 208.98 bismuth	84 Po (209) polonium	85 At (210) astatine	86 Rn (222) radon
87 Fr (223) francium	88 Ra (226) radium	103 Lr (262) lawrencium	104 Rf (261) rutherfordium	105 Db (262) dubnium	106 Sg (266) seaborgium	107 Bh (264) bohrium	108 Hs (277) hassium	109 Mt (278) meitnerium	110 Ds (281) darmstadtium	111 Rg (272) roentgenium	112 Cn (285) copernicium	113 Uut (284) ununtrium	114 Fl (289) flerovium	115 Uup (288) ununpentium	116 Lv (293) livermorium	117 Uus (293) ununseptium	118 Uuo (294) ununoctium

57 La 138.91 lanthanum	58 Ce 140.12 cerium	59 Pr 140.91 praseodymium	60 Nd 144.24 neodymium	61 Pm (145) promethium	62 Sm 150.36 samarium	63 Eu 151.96 europium	64 Gd 157.25 gadolinium	65 Tb 158.93 terbium	66 Dy 162.50 dysprosium	67 Ho 164.93 holmium	68 Er 167.26 erbium	69 Tm 168.93 thulium	70 Yb 173.06 ytterbium
89 Ac (227) actinium	90 Th 232.04 thorium	91 Pa 231.04 protactinium	92 U 238.03 uranium	93 Np (237) neptunium	94 Pu (244) plutonium	95 Am (243) americium	96 Cm (247) curium	97 Bk (247) berkelium	98 Cf (251) californium	99 Es (252) einsteinium	100 Fm (257) fermium	101 Md (258) mendelevium	102 No (259) nobelium

Atomic mass values in parentheses indicate the mass of the most stable isotope as reported by Los Alamos National Laboratory in June 2016.

Reading the periodic table

The element symbol

Each element in the periodic table has its own box. The largest item in the box is usually the **element symbol**. This is a one- or two-letter abbreviation of the element. For example, C in a chemical formula or diagram will always stand for carbon because C is the element symbol for carbon.

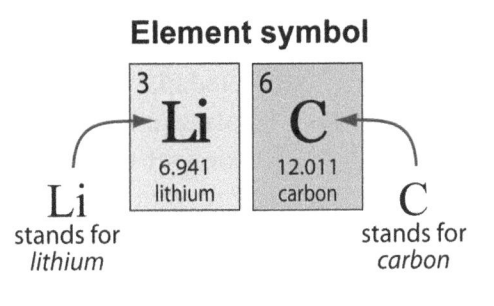

The atomic number is unique for each element

Notice that the periodic table arranges the elements by increasing **atomic number** from left to right, and then from top to bottom. The lightest element is hydrogen, with an atomic number of 1. The heaviest naturally occurring element is uranium, with an atomic number of 92. Heavier elements are not found naturally on Earth, but they have been created in laboratories.

The rows and columns of the periodic table

Each row on the periodic table is called a **period**. Each column is called a **group**.

- The first row (period) has only two elements: hydrogen (1) and helium (2).
- The 2nd and 3rd rows have 8 elements each.
- The 4th and 5th rows have 18 elements.
- The 6th and 7th rows have 32 elements. To fit the table to a page, parts of the 6th and 7th rows (elements 57–70 and 89–102) are usually dropped below the main table.

element symbol: a one- or two-letter abbreviation for each element.

atomic number: the number of protons in an atom's nucleus, unique to each element.

period: a row of the periodic table.

group: a column of the periodic table, all the elements of which have similar chemical properties.

A NATURAL APPROACH TO CHEMISTRY

The mole

The atomic mass unit (amu)

A single atom is so small that you need an equally small unit of mass to describe it conveniently. One **atomic mass unit (amu)** is 1.66×10^{-24} g. A single hydrogen atom has a mass of 1.0 amu. A carbon atom has a mass of 12.0 amu.

Written right below the element symbol is the average atomic mass in amu. You can see that the mass increases with atomic number (with a few exceptions). The atomic mass has two important interpretations:

1. It is the mass of a single atom in *amu*.

2. It is the mass of a *mole* of atoms in grams.

Average atomic mass

Hydrogen has an average mass of 1.0079 g/mol

Carbon has an average mass of 12.011 g/mol

Avogadro's number: 6.02×10^{23}

A mole

We cannot measure masses as small as amu easily. Our average laboratory balances measure in *grams*. How many atoms are in 1.01 g of hydrogen? The answer is 6.02×10^{23} atoms. How about 12.0 g of carbon? The answer is the same, 6.02×10^{23} atoms. The number 6.02×10^{23} is called **Avogadro's number** and it is very important in chemistry. The atomic mass of any element contains 6.02×10^{23} atoms. Scientists have developed the unit of **mole** that expresses the mass of 6.02×10^{23} atoms of any element. One mole of nitrogen weighs 14.0 g and contains 6.02×10^{23} atoms of nitrogen.

Hydrogen atoms
1.01 amu / atom

$$1.01 \text{ g} \left(\frac{1 \text{ atom}}{1.01 \text{ amu}} \right) \left(\frac{1 \text{ amu}}{1.66 \times 10^{-24} \text{ g}} \right) = 6.02 \times 10^{23} \text{ atoms}$$

1 mole of atoms

Carbon atoms
12.0 amu / atom

$$12.0 \text{ g} \left(\frac{1 \text{ atom}}{12.0 \text{ amu}} \right) \left(\frac{1 \text{ amu}}{1.66 \times 10^{-24} \text{ g}} \right) = 6.02 \times 10^{23} \text{ atoms}$$

One mole is the number of atoms in the average atomic mass if the value is assumed to be in grams. The average atomic mass of magnesium (Mg) is 24.31 g. That means 6.02×10^{23} atoms of magnesium have a combined, total mass of 24.31 g.

One mole contains 6.02×10^{23} atoms

The average atomic mass in grams is the mass of one mole of atoms

---

Chemistry terms

atomic mass unit (amu): a mass unit equal to 1.66×10^{-24} g.

mole: an amount of matter containing 6.02×10^{23} particles.

Avogadro's number: the number of particles contained in one mole, 6.02×10^{23}.

Calculating moles

Moles have a measurable mass

Atoms are too small to weigh individually, so chemists often work in moles of atoms. A mole of atoms has a mass that is convenient to measure on a balance. For example, a mole of iron has a mass of 55.85 g. This is about the mass of a few nails.

1 mole of iron

Mole problems tend to be of two kinds:

1. How many moles are in a given mass of a substance?

2. What is the mass in grams of a specific number of moles of a substance?

In both types of problems you can use dimensional analysis to get the answer. Use the ratio of one mole to the atomic weight from the periodic table as a conversion factor. For example, one mole of calcium weighs 40.078 g; one mole of sulfur weighs 32.065 g; one mole of oxygen weighs 15.999 g.

1 mole = the atomic weight from the periodic table

How many moles are in 100 g of sulfur (S)?

16
S
32.065
sulfur

Asked: *The number of moles*

Given: *The element is sulfur and there are 100 g.*

Relationships: *One mole of sulfur has a mass of 32.065 g.*

Solve: $100 \, g \, S \times \left(\dfrac{1 \; mole \; S}{32.065 \; g \; S} \right) = 3.12 \; moles \; of \; S$

Answer: *100 g of sulfur contains 3.12 moles of sulfur atoms.*

How many grams of calcium (Ca) do you need to have 2.50 moles of calcium?

20
Ca
40.078
calcium

Asked: *The mass in grams*

Given: *The element is calcium and there are 2.50 moles.*

Relationships: *One mole of calcium has a mass of 40.078 g.*

Solve: $2.50 \; moles \; Ca \times \dfrac{40.078 \; g}{1 \; mole} = 100.20 \; g \; of \; Ca$

Answer: *2.50 moles of calcium has a mass of 100.20 g.*

2.2 Molecules and Compounds

The smallest piece of matter

Think about a wax candle. Imagine carving off a tiny sliver of wax with your fingernail. Is the small piece still wax? Of course it is. Now think about cutting your sliver of wax in half, and in half again. Keep cutting and eventually you reach a particle of wax so small that if you cut it again, it is no longer wax but something else. That single smallest particle of wax that *retains the identity of wax* is called a **molecule**. Molecules are made of atoms. A single molecule is the smallest particle of a substance that can be.

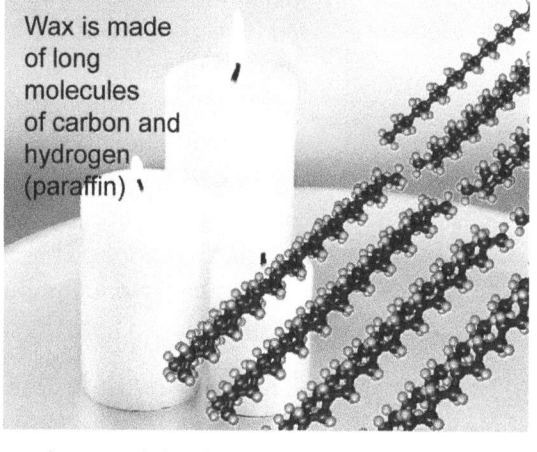

Wax is made of long molecules of carbon and hydrogen (paraffin)

Most matter is in compounds

Wax is a **compound** made of the elements carbon and hydrogen. Pure elements are actually quite rare in nature. Most matter exists as compounds. With a few notable exceptions (such as gold), pure elements quickly combine with other elements to make compounds. For example, water (H_2O) is a compound of hydrogen and oxygen. Virtually everything you eat and everything in your kitchen is a compound (or mixture of compounds). Salt is a compound of sodium and chlorine. Sugar is a compound of carbon, hydrogen, and oxygen. "Pure sugar" is not a pure *element* in the chemical sense.

Most matter is in the form of compounds

Compounds versus mixtures

Compounds and mixtures are different. A mixture of hydrogen and oxygen is a gas at room temperature. The compound H_2O is a liquid. A compound contains two or more different elements that are *chemically bonded* together. In water, the oxygen atoms and hydrogen atoms are bonded together. A mixture contains two or more elements and/or compounds that are *not* chemically bonded together. In fact, most mixtures are mixtures of compounds! Sugar is a compound and soda is mostly a mixture of three compounds, water, sugar, and carbon dioxide gas.

Mixture   **Compound**

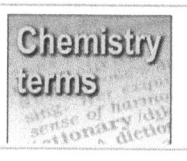

Chemistry terms

molecule: a group of atoms chemically bonded together.

compound: a substance containing more than one element in which atoms of different elements are chemically bonded together.

Millions of substances from 92 elements

Properties of pure elements

Consider three elements: hydrogen, oxygen, and carbon. By itself, pure hydrogen is a light, colorless gas. Hydrogen is extremely flammable, which was unfortunate for the early makers of the airships called zeppelins. The infamous Hindenburg was filled with hydrogen gas and exploded on May 6, 1937, killing 36 people. Pure oxygen is also a colorless gas, making up about 21% of Earth's atmosphere. Pure carbon has two common forms: a black solid called graphite and a hard crystal called diamond.

Properties are determined by the compound, not by the constituent elements

The diversity of matter comes from compounds. That's because *the properties of matter belong to the compound, not the constituent elements*. Consider just a few compounds of these three elements. Combine one carbon atom, one oxygen atom, and four hydrogen atoms and you have methanol, commonly called wood alcohol. Nine carbon, four oxygen, and eight hydrogen atoms make aspirin. Twenty carbon atoms and 42 hydrogen atoms in a long chain make paraffin, or candle wax. Eight carbon and 18 hydrogen atoms make octane, a component of gasoline.

These very different substances contain just carbon, hydrogen, and oxygen atoms

There are trillions of different combinations of 92 elements

This is the explanation for the diversity of matter

What are plastics?

Almost everything we own and use contains some form of the substance known as "plastic." Plastics are human-made polymers. The prefix "poly" means "many" and polymers are chain molecules made of many repeating units. Polyethylene is a polymer used for making bags, children's toys, bottles, and many other items. Polyethylene contains only carbon and hydrogen atoms! Interestingly, the idea for polymers was found when early scientists were looking for a way to make silk. Years ago, silk was a very valuable fabric, used by royalty and the very wealthy. Scientists were hoping to create artificial silk and make lots of money! Rayon was the first artificial silk produced and it was made from cellulose polymers.

The chemical formula

The chemical formula

Compounds are represented by a **chemical formula.** The chemical formula tells you how many of each kind of atom are in the compound. For example, the chemical formula for water is H_2O. The subscript 2 indicates there are two hydrogen atoms for every oxygen atom in water. This is important to know for effective communication in chemistry and in practice if you have to make water from the elements oxygen and hydrogen.

Reading a chemical formula

Element symbol indicates hydrogen

Element symbol indicates oxygen

H_2O

Subscript means there are 2 hydrogen atoms in each molecule

No subscript means there is one oxygen atom in each molecule

Water

Examples of chemical formulas

The diagram below shows another chemical formula. Sodium bicarbonate ($NaHCO_3$) is commonly known as baking soda. This compound contains oxygen, carbon, hydrogen and sodium in a ratio of three oxygen atoms to one atom each of carbon, hydrogen and sodium.

Sodium bicarbonate (baking soda)

$NaHCO_3$

3 oxygen atoms

1 carbon atom

1 hydrogen atom

1 sodium atom

CH_3OH is the chemical formula for methanol, or wood alcohol. This formula is written to show that the carbon and three hydrogen atoms are together. The compound *paraffin* in candle wax is $C_{20}H_{42}$.

Solved problem

Write a chemical formula for a compound that has three hydrogen (H) atoms for each atom of nitrogen (N).

Asked: *Chemical formula*

Given: *3 hydrogen (H) atoms and 1 nitrogen (N) atom*

Relationships: *The subscript tells the number of each element in the compound.*

Answer: *NH_3*

Chemistry terms

chemical formula: a combination of element symbols and subscripts that tells you the ratio of elements in a compound; for example, H_2O is the chemical formula for water and tells you there are two hydrogen (H) atoms for every one oxygen (O) atom.

Molecules

Molecular compounds

In a molecular compound, the atoms are bonded together in molecules. A pure molecular compound contains only identical molecules, each with the same shape and chemical formula. Water is a molecular compound, as are methane (CH_4), ammonia (NH_3), and glucose ($C_6H_{12}O_6$).

Properties come from the molecule

The properties of a compound depend much more on the exact structure of the molecule than on the individual elements from which it is made. For example, aspirin is a molecule made from carbon, hydrogen, and oxygen according to the chemical formula $C_9H_8O_4$. Aspirin relieves swelling and reduces pain in humans.

Acetylsalicylic acid
(aspirin)
$C_9H_8O_4$

Aspirin
acetylsalicylic acid
200 Tablets
100 mg.

O oxygen
C carbon
H hydrogen

Properties depend on the exact chemical formula

By themselves, the elements C, H, and O do not have the property of reducing pain. Other molecules made of the same elements have very different properties. For example, formaldehyde (a toxic preservative) is also made from just carbon, oxygen, and hydrogen. The beneficial properties of aspirin come from the specific combination of exactly eight hydrogen, nine carbon, and four oxygen atoms in the exact structure of the aspirin molecule. Remove even one hydrogen atom, and the resulting molecule would not have the properties of aspirin.

Properties also depend on molecular structure

The structure of a molecule is very important to the properties of a compound. The same 21 atoms in aspirin can even be combined in other structures with the same chemical formula! The resulting molecules are completely different chemicals and they do *not* have the beneficial properties of aspirin. *Both chemical formula and structure determine the properties of a compound.* The shape of a molecule is critical to its chemical and physical properties.

Three different molecules with *the same chemical formula!*

Benzodioxole-5 carboxylic acid, methyl ester
$C_9H_8O_4$

Acetylsalicylic acid
(aspirin)
$C_9H_8O_4$

Acetyl benzoyl peroxide
$C_9H_8O_4$

Describing molecules

To completely describe a real molecule, you need to know both its composition and its structure. Consider acetic acid, which has the chemical formula CH_3COOH. This is what gives vinegar its sour taste and generates a fizzy reaction when mixed with baking soda. The chemical formula tells us which and how many atoms it is made of, but not much about the structure or the exact *shape* in which the atoms combine. However, we need to know more to uniquely describe the chemical known as *acetic acid*. The diagram below shows five different ways to represent the acetic acid molecule. Each kind of representation is best for certain applications.

acetic acid CH_3COOH

1 Chemical formula

3 Ball-and-stick model

5 Molecular surface

2 Structural diagrams

4 Space filling model

The structural diagram

The structural diagram shows the bonds, or connections, between atoms in the molecule. You can see that the two carbon atoms are bonded to each other. Structural diagrams are the easiest way to show how the atoms in a molecule are connected to each other. Notice that some of the lines are double. A double line means a *double bond* between the atoms.

The ball-and-stick model

The ball-and-stick model gives you the best sense of the three-dimensionality of the molecule. Real molecules are rarely flat like a structural diagram. The balls are the atoms and the sticks are the bonds between atoms.

The space-filling model

In reality, atoms are so close that they overlap when they bond. This is not shown by the ball-and-stick model. The space-filling model more accurately shows how the atoms overlap each other in a molecule.

The molecular surface model

The molecular surface model combines the ball-and-stick view with a transparent shape that represents the "surface" of the molecule. Don't be fooled—this isn't really the surface of the molecule! Molecules and atoms do not have hard, shiny surfaces as drawn in diagrams. The true boundary of an atom or molecule is very diffuse.

Ionic compounds

The compound sodium chloride (NaCl) has no molecules

Salt, or sodium chloride (NaCl), is a compound made of sodium (Na) and chlorine (Cl) in a ratio of one sodium atom per chlorine atom. Salt is fundamentally different from aspirin at the atomic level. In aspirin, the atoms in a single molecule are chemically bonded *only* to other atoms in the same molecule. In salt *each* sodium atom is bonded to *every neighboring chlorine atom*. Each chlorine atom is likewise bonded to every neighboring sodium atom. The sodium and chlorine atoms in NaCl are always in a ratio of one sodium per chlorine. However, there are no *molecules* where a single sodium atom is bonded uniquely to a single chlorine atom.

Each atom is only bonded to one or more specific atoms in the molecule

Every chlorine atom is attracted to all its neighboring sodium atoms and vice versa

Ionic compounds

Salt is a good example of a whole class of compounds called **ionic compounds**. Salt still has a chemical formula because there is always one sodium atom for every chlorine atom. However, salt does not have molecules because the bonds that hold salt together form between every neighboring atom, and not just the atoms in the molecule.

An ion is a charged atom

When you dissolve salt in water, the sodium and chlorine atoms come apart. They do not remain bonded together as atoms in a molecule would. In fact, each chlorine atom in salt acquires a negative *electric charge* and becomes an *ion*. An **ion** is a charged atom. The sodium atoms also become ions, but with a positive charge.

Salt in water

Solid salt

Positive and negative charges attract each other

Positive and negative charges attract each other. That is why every positive sodium ion is attracted to all the surrounding negative chlorine ions and vice versa. A compound becomes ionic when either atoms or groups of atoms become electrically charged.

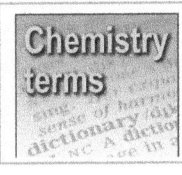
Chemistry terms

ionic compound: a compound in which positive and negative ions attract each other to keep matter together. Salt (NaCl) is a good example.

ion: an atom or small molecule with an overall positive or negative charge as a result of an imbalance of protons and electrons.

The molar mass

Moles of compounds

We know how to determine the number of moles that corresponds to a quantity of an element from its average atomic mass. However, most matter exists in compounds and most of chemistry deals with compounds. Chemistry requires us to be able to calculate the number of moles associated with a specific amount of a compound.

The molar mass

We start with the chemical formula. The **molar mass** is the mass of one mole of a compound with a given chemical formula. As an example, start with water (H_2O). What is the mass (in grams) of one mole of water?

H_2O

1. The chemical formula says one mole of water contains two moles of hydrogen and one mole of oxygen.
2. Add up the mass of two moles of hydrogen (2 g) and one mole of oxygen (16 g).
3. The result (18 g) is the mass of 1 mole of water.

H	1 mol H	1.01 g
H	+ 1 mol H	+ 1.01 g
O	+ 1 mol O	+ 16.00 g
	1 mol H_2O	18.02 g

What is the mass of 1 mole of methane (CH_4)?

Asked: *The mass of 1 mole of methane*

Given: *Methane (CH_4) contains 1 carbon (C) and 4 hydrogen (H) atoms*

Relationships: *The molar mass is the sum of the atomic masses for each atom in the compound.*

Solve: $4H + C = 4(1.0079) + 12.011 = 16.04$ *g per mole of CH_4*

Answer: *One mole of methane (CH_4) has a mass of 16.04 g.*

How many moles are in 100 grams of water (H_2O)?

Asked: *The number of moles in 100 g of water*

Given: *Water (H_2O) contains 2 hydrogen (H) atoms and 1 oxygen (O) atom.*

Relationships: *The molar mass is the sum of the atomic masses for each atom in the compound.*

Solve: $2H + O = 2(1.0079) + 15.999 = 18.015$ *g per mole of H_2O*

$$100 \text{ g} \times \left(\frac{1 \text{ mole}}{18.015 \text{ g}} \right) = 5.55 \text{ moles}$$

Answer: *100 g of water (H_2O) contains 5.55 moles.*

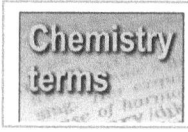

molar mass: the mass of one mole of a compound with a given chemical formula.

Solving problems with moles

Converting back and forth between grams and moles is a very useful skill in chemistry. This is because we weigh substances in grams, but we need to know how many moles there are in order to determine the number of atoms or molecules in that mass. The periodic table allows us to obtain the molar mass for any compound with which we might be experimenting in the lab. You will find unit cancellation to be very important when you are doing this type of calculation. Keeping track of your units helps you to eliminate simple mistakes. To convert from grams to moles we divide by the molar mass.

How many moles are in 25.0 g of copper oxide (CuO)?

Asked: *Moles of CuO*

Given: *25.0 g of CuO*

Relationships: *The molar mass for CuO is 63.55 + 15.999 = 79.55 g/mole.*

Solve: $25.0 \; \overline{g \; CuO} \times \dfrac{1 \; mole \; CuO}{79.55 \; \overline{g \; CuO}} = 0.314 \; moles \; of \; CuO$

Answer: *25.0 g of CuO contains 0.314 moles of copper oxide (CuO).*

How many grams are in 2.300 moles of butane (C_4H_{10})? Butane is used as a lighter fluid in disposable lighters.

Given: *2.300 moles of C_4H_{10}*

Relationships: *The molar mass for C_4H_{10} is 4(C) + 10(H)*
= (4 × 12.011) + (10 × 1.0079) = 58.123 g/mole.

Solve: $2.300 \; \overline{moles \; C_4H_{10}} \times \dfrac{58.123 \; g \; C_4H_{10}}{1 \; \overline{mole \; C_4H_{10}}} = 133.7 \; g \; C_4H_{10}$

Answer: *133.7 g are in 2.300 moles of butane (C_4H_{10}).*

How many moles are in 30.0 g of baking soda ($NaHCO_3$)?

Given: *30.0 g of $NaHCO_3$*

Relationships: *The molar mass for $NaHCO_3$ is*
22.99 + 1.0079 + 12.011 + 3 × 15.999 = 84.01 g/mole.

Solve: $30.0 \; \overline{g \; NaHCO_3} \times \dfrac{1 \; mole}{84.01 \; \overline{g \; NaHCO_3}} = 0.357 \; moles$

Answer: *30.0 g are in 0.357 moles of baking soda ($NaHCO_3$).*

Using Avogadro's number

We can use Avogadro's number to determine how many atoms are in a given mass of a metal, such as lead (Pb).

Solved problem

How many atoms of lead (Pb) are in a lead pipe that weighs 105 g?

Given: *Number of atoms in 105 g of Pb*

Relationships: *The atomic mass of lead is 207.2 g/mole.*

$$105\ \text{g Pb} \times \frac{1\ \text{mole Pb}}{207.2\ \text{g Pb}} \times \frac{6.022 \times 10^{23}\ \text{atoms Pb}}{1\ \text{mole Pb}} = 3.05 \times 10^{23}\ \text{atoms Pb}$$

Answer: *There are 3.05×10^{23} atoms of Pb in a lead pipe that weighs 105 g.*

Sometimes we want to know how many atoms of an element are in a given mass of a compound, as illustrated in the following example:

Solved problem

How many oxygen atoms are in 200.0 g of glucose ($C_6H_{12}O_6$)?

Given: *200.0 g of $C_6H_{12}O_6$*

Relationships: *The molar mass of glucose is $6(C) + 12(H) + 6(O)$*
$= 6(12.011) + 12(1.0079) + 6(15.999) = 180.155$ g/mole.

Solve: *First we find how many moles are in 200.0 g:*

$$200.0\ \text{g}\ C_6H_{12}O_6 \times \frac{1\ \text{mole}\ C_6H_{12}O_6}{180.155\ \text{g}\ C_6H_{12}O_6} = 1.110\ \text{moles}\ C_6H_{12}O_6$$

Next we find how many molecules are contained in 1.110 moles
[Note that it is very important to clearly express your goal in order to be able to comprehend the most challenging questions to follow. Do this at every step of the problem.]

Discussion topic

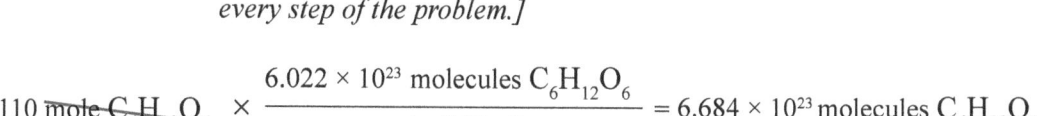

$$1.110\ \overline{\text{mole}\ C_6H_{12}O_6} \times \frac{6.022 \times 10^{23}\ \text{molecules}\ C_6H_{12}O_6}{1\ \text{mole}\ C_6H_{12}O_6} = 6.684 \times 10^{23}\ \text{molecules}\ C_6H_{12}O_6$$

Then we find how many oxygen atoms are contained in 6.684×10^{23} molecules of glucose:

$$6.684 \times 10^{23}\ \overline{\text{molecules}\ C_6H_{12}O_6} \times \frac{6\ \text{O atoms}}{1\ \text{molecule}\ C_6H_{12}O_6} = 4.010 \times 10^{24}\ \text{atoms of O}$$

Answer: *There are 4.010×10^{24} atoms of O in 200.0 g of glucose ($C_6H_{12}O_6$).*

2.3 Mixtures and Solutions

Homogeneous mixtures are the same throughout

Most matter is made of mixtures of many different compounds. A homogeneous mixture is the same throughout. All samples of a homogeneous mixture are the same. For example, stirring food coloring in water can produce a homogeneous mixture. The water near the top of the test tube has the same concentration of food coloring as the water near the bottom. Brass is another example of a homogeneous mixture. Brass is made of 70% copper and 30% zinc. If you cut a brass candlestick into 10 pieces, each piece would contain the same 70% copper and 30% zinc.

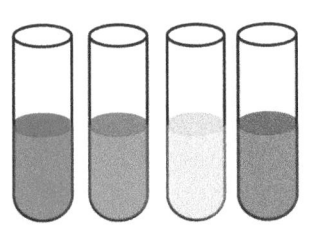

Well-mixed food color in water is a **homogeneous** mixture

Concrete is a **heterogeneous** mixture

Heterogeneous mixtures are not the same throughout

A heterogeneous mixture is one in which different samples are not necessarily made up of exactly the same proportions of matter. One common heterogeneous mixture is concrete. Concrete contains cement and rocks of many different types and sizes.

TABLE 2.1. Summary of the types of matter

Type of matter	Definition	Examples
Homogeneous mixture	A mixture that contains more than one type of matter and is the same throughout.	soda pop, air, metallic alloys
Heterogeneous mixture	A mixture that contains more than one type of matter and is not the same throughout.	chicken soup, soil, fudge ripple ice cream
Element	A substance that contains only one type of atom.	copper metal, oxygen gas, liquid nitrogen
Compound	A substance that contains more than one type of atom.	table salt, rust (iron oxide), carbon dioxide gas

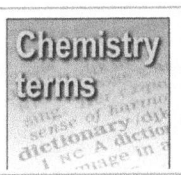

Chemistry terms

homogenous mixture: a mixture that is uniform throughout, in which any sample has the same composition as any other sample.

heterogeneous mixture: a mixture that is not uniform, in which different samples may have different compositions.

Solutions

Defining a solution

A **solution** is a mixture that is *homogenous on the molecular level*. That means there are no clumps bigger than a molecule. The orange juice you drink is partly a solution. The sweetness comes from dissolved sugars. The "orange" taste comes from other dissolved molecules that provide flavor, scent, and color. Orange juice is only *partly* a solution because some substances are *not* dissolved, such as small bits of orange pulp.

Solvent and solute

A solution always has a *solvent* and at least one *solute*. The **solvent** is the substance that makes up the biggest percentage of the mixture and it is usually a liquid. Water is the most important solvent for living things. For example, the solvent in orange juice is water. The **solutes** are the other substances in the solution. Sugar, citric acid, and other flavoring chemicals are solutes in orange juice.

Solvent: water

Solutes: sugar calcium iron ascorbic acid potassium citric acid ... more

Orange juice

Dissolving

When the solute particles are evenly distributed throughout the solvent, we say that the solute has **dissolved**. The picture below shows a sugar and water solution being prepared. The solute (sugar) starts as a solid in the graduated cylinder on the left. Water is added and the mixture is carefully stirred until all the solid sugar has dissolved. Once the sugar has dissolved, the solution is clear again.

Solute (solid sugar)

Solution (sugar dissolved in water)

Solid sugar   Dissolved sugar

The molecular explanation for dissolving

On the molecular level, dissolving of a solid (like sugar) occurs when molecules of solvent collide with, and transfer energy to, molecules of solid solute. This explains why substances dissolve faster at higher temperatures. Hotter solvent molecules have more energy and are more effective at knocking molecules of solute into the solution. You may have noticed that sugar dissolves much faster in hot water than in cold water.

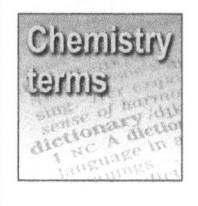
Chemistry terms

solution: a mixture that is homogeneous on the molecular level.

solvent: the substance that makes up the biggest percentage of the mixture, usually a liquid.

solute: any substance in a solution other than the solvent.

dissolved: a term used to describe when molecules of solute are completely separated from each other and dispersed into a solution.

Concentration and solubility

Concentration and dilute solutions

The **concentration** of a solution describes how much of each solute there is compared to the total solution. A solution is **dilute** when there is very little solute. Mixing 1 g of sugar with 99 mL of water makes 100 g of a dilute sugar solution. A 10 gram sample of this solution contains only 0.1 g of sugar compared with 9.9 g of water.

| 1 g | 99 mL | 100 g dilute | 50 g | 50 mL water | 100 g concentrated |
| sugar | water | sugar solution | sugar | | sugar solution |

Concentrated solutions

A solution is **concentrated** when there is a lot of dissolved solute compared to solvent. Mixing 50 g of sugar into 50 mL of water makes a concentrated sugar solution. A 10 g sample of this solution contains 5 g of sugar and 5 g of water.

What is solubility?

Solubility means the amount of solute (if any) that can be dissolved in a quantity of solvent. Solubility is often listed in grams per liters of solvent. Solubility is always given at a specific temperature since temperature strongly affects solubility.

TABLE 2.2. Solubility of common substances in water at 25°C

Name	Solubility (g/L)	Name	Solubility (g/L)
Salt (NaCl)	36	Chalk	0
Sugar (sucrose)	2,000	Vegetable oil	0
Baking soda (NaHCO$_3$)	about 10	Oxygen	8.3×10^{-3}

Insoluble substances do not dissolve

Notice that chalk and vegetable oil have *zero* solubility in water. These substances are **insoluble** in water because they do not dissolve. You can mix chalk dust and water and stir it up indefinitely. You will just have a mixture of chalk dust and water. The water will not separate the chalk dust into individual molecules because chalk is insoluble in water.

Chemistry terms

concentration: the amount of each solute compared to the total solution.

dilute: a term used to describe a solution containing relatively little solute compared with solvent.

concentrated: describes a solution containing a lot of solute compared with solvent.

solubility: the amount of a solute that will dissolve in a particular solvent at a particular temperature and pressure.

insoluble: not dissolvable in a particular solvent.

Calculating solute and solution quantities

Working with concentration in g/L

Many experiments (and recipes) call for precise amounts of dissolved substances. For example, suppose you have an experiment that requires 10 g of sugar. How much solution do you add if the concentration of the sugar solution is 75 g/L? This is a typical chemistry question. To find the answer, we rearrange the concentration formula to solve for liters of solution.

Calculating solution volume from solute mass and concentration in g/L

$$\text{concentration (g/L)} = \frac{\text{mass of solute (g)}}{\text{volume of solution (L)}}$$

$$\text{volume of solution (L)} = \frac{\text{mass of solute (g)}}{\text{concentration (g/L)}}$$

Solved problem

If the concentration of a sugar solution is 75 g/L, how much solution do you need if you want 10 g of sugar?

Asked: *Volume of solution*

Given: *10 g of solute and concentration of 75 g/L*

Relationships: *Volume of solution (L) = mass of solute (g) ÷ concentration (g/L)*

Solve: *10 g ÷ 75 g/L = 0.133 L, or 133 mL*

Working with percent (%) concentration

Each of the concentration formulas can be rearranged to give one of the quantities in terms of the other two. For example, a mouthwash contains 0.05% menthol. Menthol $(C_{10}H_{20}O)$ is a chemical derived from the peppermint plant that gives mouthwash its minty flavor. How much menthol do you need to make 10 kg of mouthwash?

Calculating solute mass* from solution mass* and % concentration

$$\text{concentration (\%)} = \frac{\text{mass of solute}}{\text{mass of solution}} \times 100$$

$$\text{mass of solute} = \text{mass of solution} \times \frac{\text{concentration (\%)}}{100}$$

*The mass units must be the same.

Solved problem

How much menthol do you need to make 10 kg of mouthwash if the concentration of menthol must be 0.05%?

Asked: *Mass of solute*

Given: *10 kg of solution, solute concentration of 0.05%*

Relationships: *Mass of solute = mass of solution × (concentration ÷ 100)*

Solve: *10 kg × (0.05 ÷ 100) = 0.005 kg = 5 g*

Molarity

What is molarity?

The **molarity** or molar concentration of a solution is the number of moles of solute per liter of solution. Molarity is useful because chemists need a way to control the ratios of different molecules in reactions. It's impossible to count molecules one by one. Instead, *chemists make solutions with a known molarity*. Once you know the molarity you can figure out how many moles of each solute there are in a given volume of solution. If you know how many moles you need, you can calculate how many milliliters of solution you have to add. Milliliters are easy to measure and many chemical experiments use solutions of standard molarity for this reason. The molarity is denoted by the unit M.

M: the unit of molarity

Molarity is the number of moles of solute per liter of solution

How to calculate molarity

To find the molarity, you need to know how many moles are dissolved per liter of solution. Citric acid is what gives the sour taste to lemons and limes. Suppose you add 10 g of citric acid to a half liter of water. What is the molarity of the solution? The problem is solved in three steps:

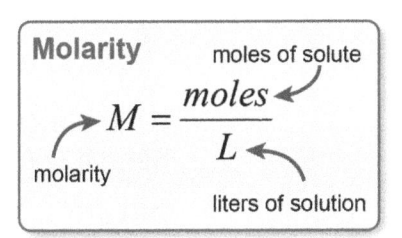

1. Calculate the molar mass so you know the mass of one mole.

2. Use the molar mass to figure out how many moles there are.

3. Calculate molarity by dividing the number of moles by the volume of solution.

Solved problem

If 10.0 g of citric acid ($C_6H_8O_7$) is added to 500 mL of water, what is the molarity of the resulting solution?

Asked:	*The molarity of a solution*
Given:	*The amount of solute, citric acid, and the volume of solution*
Relationships:	*Molarity = moles of solute ÷ volume in L of solution*
Solve:	*Start by calculating the molar mass of $C_6H_8O_7$:*

$(6 \times 12.011 + 8 \times 1.0079 + 7 \times 15.999 = 192.12 \text{ g/mole}$

Next we calculate the number of moles in 10.0 g of $C_6H_8O_7$:

$$\# \, moles = \frac{10.0 \text{ g}}{192.12 \text{ g/mole}} = 0.0521 \, moles$$

Answer: $molarity = \dfrac{0.0521 \, moles}{0.500 \, L} = 0.104 \, M$

Chemistry terms

molarity: the number of moles of solute per liter of solution.

Calculating solution quantities with molarity

Why molarity is useful

Chemical reactions rearrange reactant molecules to form product molecules. For this reason, the *quantity* of molecules is often the most important factor in determining what happens in a reaction. *Molarity* tells you the amount of solute (in moles), so molarity is the best way to describe concentration in many situations.

Vitamins

Vitamin C is a compound called *ascorbic acid* ($C_6H_8O_6$). The ascorbic acid molecule is a sugar (five-sided ring) with a short carbon chain. Besides being a vitamin, ascorbic acid is also a food preservative! It works by accepting electrons (and losing hydrogens) to use up reactive oxygen that might otherwise cause spoiling reactions in food.

Ascorbic acid
$C_6H_8O_6$

Reaction

$$2\,C_6H_8O_6 + O_2 \rightarrow 2\,C_6H_6O_6 + 2\,H_2O$$

Let's look at an example: An ordinary bread bag holds about 2 L of air, which contains about 0.02 moles of oxygen (O_2). Suppose you have a 1 molar (1 M) solution of ascorbic acid. How much do you need to completely react with 0.02 moles of oxygen?

1. Use the balanced reaction to calculate the moles of ascorbic acid you need.

2. Use the molarity formula to find the required volume of 1 M solution.

Solved problem

How much (volume) of a 1 M ascorbic acid solution will completely react with 0.02 moles of oxygen (O_2)?

Asked: *Volume of solution*

Given: *Concentration (1M) and balanced reaction*

Relationships: *Molarity = moles of solute ÷ volume in L of solution*

Solve: *According to the balanced reaction we need 2 moles of ascorbic acid for every mole of O_2.*
That means we need 0.04 moles of ascorbic acid.
volume = moles of solute ÷ molarity = (0.04) ÷ 1 = 0.04 L, or 40 mL

Answer: *40 mL of the solution contains 0.04 moles of ascorbic acid, which is enough to react with 0.02 moles of oxygen (O_2).*

Mixtures of gases

Air is a mixture of gases

Many mixtures are gases. Gases such as air can expand (or contract) to fill any container. For example, 1 g of air can fill a 1 L bottle at 1 atm. The same gram of air can expand to fill 1 m³ at 0.0001 atm or contract to fill 1 mL at 1,000 atm.

	1 g of air at 1,000 atm	1 g of air at 1 atm	1 g of air at 0.001 atm
Volume	1 mL (1 cm³)	1 L	1,000 L (1 m³)
Pressure	1,000 atm	1 atm	0.001 atm
Temperature	0°C	0°C	0°C

Composition of air

20% – 21% oxygen (O_2)

77% – 78% nitrogen (N_2)

1% argon
~ 1% H_2O
0.038% CO_2
+ trace gasses

The molar volume and STP

Concentration in a mixture of gases is usually given as a percent by volume. This is because gases at the same temperature and pressure have the same volume per mole *no matter what kind of gas it is*. For example, a mole of oxygen (O_2) gas at one atmosphere of pressure and 0°C has a volume of 22.4 L. A mole of nitrogen gas at 1 atm and 0°C has the same volume of 22.4 L, and so does a mole of carbon dioxide gas (CO_2). The constant of 22.4 L per mole is called the **molar volume**.

The conditions of 0°C and 1 atm of pressure are called **standard temperature and pressure** (STP).

22.4 liters — 1 mole of oxygen (O_2) at STP

22.4 liters — 1 mole of nitrogen (N_2) at STP

22.4 liters — 1 mole of carbon dioxide (CO_2) at STP

Using volume to determine quantity

Working with gases in terms of volume is necessary because the mass of a gas is hard to measure directly. When you put an "empty" bottle on a balance, you do not get the mass of the air inside the bottle. The most reliable way to determine or specify a quantity of gas is to use volume and pressure to calculate moles, then use moles to calculate mass.

Solved problem

How many moles of oxygen (O_2) are in a 1 liter bottle at STP (1 atm and 0°C)?

Asked: *Number of moles of a gas (O_2)*

Given: *volume and STP conditions*

Relationships: *The molar volume of a gas at STP is 22.4 L / mole*

Solve: $\# \text{moles} = 1\,L \times \dfrac{1\ \text{mole}}{22.4\,L} = 0.045\ \text{moles}$

Answer: *There are 0.045 moles in 1 liter of O_2 at STP.*

Chemistry terms

molar volume: the amount of space occupied by a mole of gas at standard temperature and pressure, equal to 22.4 L per mole at 0°C and 1 atm.

standard temperature and pressure (STP): conditions of one atmosphere of pressure and 0°C.

Partial pressures

Air is a mixture of gases

Air is not an element or even a compound; it is a mixture of gases. Dry air contains roughly (by volume) 78.08% nitrogen, 20.95% oxygen, 0.93% argon, 0.038% carbon dioxide, and trace amounts of other gases. Normal air you breathe is not completely dry; it contains some amount of water vapor, about 1% on average.

Looking at the components of air

The average air pressure at sea level is 101,325 Pa, which is defined to be one atmosphere (1 atm). Because air is a mixture, 101,325 Pa is the *total pressure* from all the gases in air. If you were to separate the different gases in 1 L of air, there are two useful ways to think about the separation. Both are correct and useful.

Equal volumes, different pressures			**Equal pressures, different volumes**		
Nitrogen (N_2)	Oxygen (O_2)	Argon (Ar)	Nitrogen (N_2)	Oxygen (O_2)	Argon (Ar)
1 liter	1 liter	1 liter	0.78 L	0.21 L	0.093 L
79,033 Pa (0.78 atm)	21,228 Pa (0.21 atm)	9,423 Pa (0.093 atm)	101,325 Pa (1.00 atm)	101,325 Pa (1.00 atm)	101,325 Pa (1.00 atm)

Dalton's law of partial pressures

In a mixture of gases, the total pressure is the sum of the partial pressures of each individual gas in the mixture. This rule is called **Dalton's law of partial pressures**. If you divide 1 L of air into *three equal volumes*, the nitrogen gas in each would have a partial pressure of 79,033 Pa, the oxygen gas would have a partial pressure of 21,228 Pa, and the argon gas would have a partial pressure of 9,423 Pa.

How volume divides at equal pressure

If you divide 1 L of air into three volumes of *equal pressure*, the nitrogen has a volume of 0.78 L, the oxygen has a volume of 0.21 L, and the argon has a volume of 0.093 L (93 mL).

Solved problem

If 1 L of helium (75%) and neon (25%) is at STP, what is the partial pressure of helium?

Asked: *Partial pressure of helium*

Given: *75% He and 25% Ne at STP conditions*

Relationships: *The total pressure is the sum of the partial pressures of each gas.*

Solve: *0.75 × 101,325 Pa = 75,994 Pa or 0.75 atm*

Answer: *The partial pressure of helium is 75,994 Pa or 0.75 atm.*

Chemistry terms

Dalton's law of partial pressures: a law that states that the total pressure in a mixture of gases is the sum of the partial pressures of each individual gas in the mixture.

Magical chemical reactions

Perhaps the most magical thing about chemistry is the fact that when atoms of different elements and molecules combine, a new compound is formed that has completely new properties! These new properties are nothing like the original properties of the pure elements.

One example of this involves sodium metal and chlorine gas. Did you know that sodium metal (Na, atomic number 11 on the periodic table) is so reactive that it catches on fire when placed in water? In the laboratory, sodium metal is stored in a glass jar and covered with oil. The oil coats the surface of the sodium metal so that it cannot react with any oxygen or moisture in the air.

Sodium is a very reactive metal. It rapidly oxidizes, which means that it loses electrons in a process similar to rusting. Large amounts of sodium are explosive in water, because the sodium rapidly generates hydrogen gas. This makes it extremely dangerous to handle. Even small amounts of hydrogen gas are highly flammable. The other product, sodium hydroxide, is caustic and can cause serious burns.

Oil

Sodium metal

NaCl
sodium chloride
(salt)

Chlorine   Sodium

Sodium is the most abundant alkali metal, making up about 3% of Earth's crust. In nature, sodium metal does not exist in its pure form. It needs to be extracted from compounds in Earth's crust, such as salt (NaCl).

The most common method used to obtain sodium metal is called electrolysis. Electrolysis uses electricity to separate substances. A voltage is applied to a molten liquid of NaCl, causing electrons to flow in such a manner that the sodium ion (Na^+) becomes Na(s) (where the s means "solid") by gaining an electron. In this case, liquid sodium chloride, NaCl(l), is separated into sodium metal, Na(s), and chlorine gas, Cl_2(g). The chemical reaction is written like this:

$$2NaCl(l) \rightarrow 2Na(s) + Cl_2(g)$$

Chlorine gas can also be obtained from the electrolysis process. During electrolysis, two chlorine ions ($2Cl^-$) release electrons and become a neutral molecule of Cl_2 gas.

Pure elemental sodium metal is toxic to ingest and is hazardous to animals and humans. Elemental chlorine (Cl_2) is a light yellow-greenish gas at room temperature. It is also poisonous to animals and humans if inhaled. Chlorine is an example of a diatomic molecule, meaning its atoms occur in nature as a pair, or in units of two atoms joined together. Chlorine is not stable as an individual atom, much like oxygen is not stable alone. Chlorine is used to make many consumer products, such as plastics, dry-cleaning chemicals, textiles, insecticides, and pharmaceuticals.

Chlorine gas

Both sodium metal and chlorine gas are toxic to us in their *elemental* forms. When these toxic elements react together they produce sodium chloride (NaCl), or table salt, which is a *compound* essential for life. How can this be? Two dangerous chemicals turn into something that is not only safe to consume but is essential to life! This chemical reaction produces a compound (sodium chloride) that is no longer dangerous.

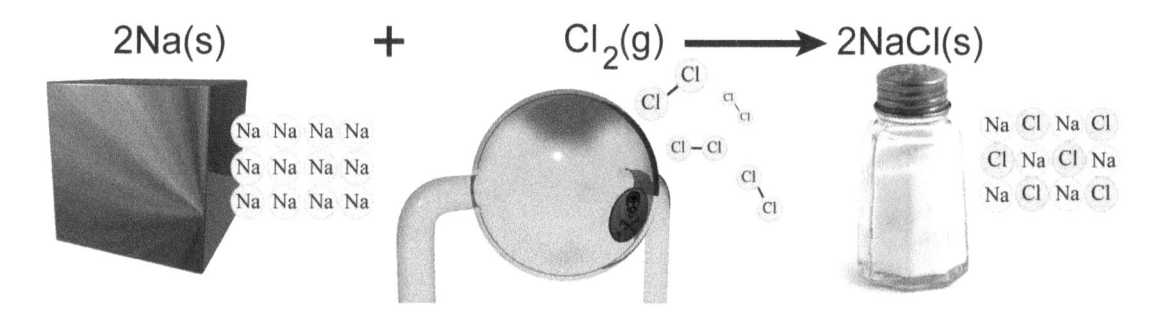

$$2Na(s) \quad + \quad Cl_2(g) \longrightarrow 2NaCl(s)$$

Once the atoms of sodium and chlorine recombine and form a compound, the result is a product (salt) that is common in each of our homes. Salt is required by the body for several important reasons. It helps to maintain the proper fluid concentrations in your tissues, transmits nerve signals, and helps the heart muscle to contract.

Salt is also essential for animals. If you have visited a farm you may have seen salt licks, or salt blocks, that provide cattle and horses with the sodium chloride their bodies need. Some game preserves place them out for deer and other wild animals.

Unlike humans, who obtain salt in their daily diets, animals that eat mostly grass need to be supplemented with salt. Large quantities of sodium chloride (NaCl) are found dissolved in ocean water. Much of our salt is produced by evaporating seawater or by mining for rock salt.

Chapter 2 Review

Vocabulary

Match each word to the sentence where it fits best.

Section 2.1

scale	group
mixture	pure substance
physical property	chemical change
extensive property	physical change
intensive property	macroscopic
chemical property	microscopic
element	mole
period	atomic number

1. A typical size that shows a certain level of detail is called the _____.

2. A substance that cannot be broken down to a simpler substance, and one in which all the atoms have the same atomic number is called a/an _____.

3. A/An _____ is a kind of matter that cannot be separated by physical means.

4. When two or more substances are combined by physical means, a/an _____ is formed.

5. The type of change that transforms one substance into another is _____.

6. Mass is an example of a/an _____ and a/ an _____.

7. The number that represents how many protons are in the nucleus is called the _____.

8. The word _____ on the periodic table refers to the arrangement of the horizontal rows.

9. The _____ is a unit that chemists use to represent a large number of atoms or molecules.

10. A vertical row such as 7A on the periodic table is referred to as a/an _____.

11. A/an _____ is created or caused by the exact molecular structure of a compound.

Section 2.2

molecule	compound
chemical formula	structural diagram
ion	space filling model
ionic compound	molar mass

12. A/An _____ is a substance containing atoms of more than one element bonded together.

13. The _____ is a way to represent the ratio of the different elements in a compound.

14. In a chemical substance, such as water, the single smallest unit is referred to as a/an _____.

15. A/An _____ is an atom that has gained or lost an electron and now carries a charge.

16. The _____ is the weight of all of the atoms represented in the chemical formula added together.

17. A/An _____ is one way to show how all the atoms are connected to one another.

18. When Na^+ and Cl^- are attracted to each other by their opposing charges, they form a/an _____.

Section 2.3

heterogeneous	solvent
homogeneous	solution
solute	concentrated
concentration	dilute insoluble
solubility	molarity
dissolved molar	partial pressure
volume	

19. The substance that is dissolved in a solution is called the _____.

20. The substance that does the dissolving is called the _____.

21. A mixture that does not "mix" in such a way that all substances are evenly distributed throughout is called _____.

22. A solution that has a large quantity of solute particles present is referred to as _____.

23. A mixture that has uniform (evenly distributed) particles throughout is called _____.

24. The value of 22.4 liters per mole is known as the _____ of a gas.

25. When a teaspoon of sugar is added to a cup of warm tea and stirred, we can say that the sugar _____ in the tea.

26. A substance's ability to dissolve is referred to as its _____.

27. Chemists use the unit of _____ to represent how many moles of solute are in one liter of solution.

28. The _____ of a gas in a mixture is the pressure exerted by that gas alone as if it were the only gas in the container.

29. When a substance does not dissolve in a solvent it is said to be _____.

Conceptual Questions

Section 2.1

30. List three examples of physical properties.

31. Explain why breaking a piece of chalk is an example of a physical change and not a chemical change.

32. Compare and contrast the processes of chemical versus physical change.

33. Give an example of a physical change that you observe in your everyday life.

34. Is the burning of magnesium ribbon an example of a chemical or physical change? How do you know?

35. Give an example of a chemical change that you observe in your everyday life.

36. Label the changes as C (chemical) or P (physical):
    a. a match burning
    b. an ice cube melting
    c. metal rusting
    d. salt dissolving in water

37. Find the element magnesium (Mg) on the periodic table.
    a. What period is it in?
    b. What group is it in?
    c. What is its atomic number?

38. A certain element has an atomic number of 18.
    a. What period and group is it in?
    b. List another element that will likely have similar chemical properties.

39. The mole is often referred to as the "chemists dozen." Explain why the unit of a mole is useful to a chemist?

40. What is the mass of 1 mole of copper?

41. Classify each as a mixture or pure substance.
    a. air
    b. soda
    c. diamond
    d. silver
    e. sea water

42. Classify each of the following as an extensive or intensive property.
    a. conductivity
    b. freezing point
    c. weight
    d. odor

Chapter 2 Review

Section 2.2

43. Sketch an example of two different molecules that can be formed by carbon (C) and oxygen (O). Think of some you are familiar with in your everyday life. (Hint: consider the gas you exhale.)

44. Using the chemical formula $C_6H_{12}O_6$ for the sugar glucose, what is the ratio of carbon atoms to oxygen atoms? How about carbon atoms to hydrogen atoms?

45. Write the chemical formula represented for the molecule in the picture.

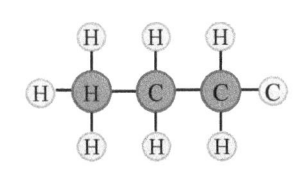

46. Explain why Na^+ is an ion of sodium and not an atom of sodium.

47. The formula mass of methane gas (CH_4) is written as 16 g/mole. Is this correct? Explain.

Section 2.3

48. When sand is mixed with water it can be easily separated. What type of a mixture is this an example of?

49. Describe what happens when you mix 1 teaspoon of salt (NaCl) with 2 cups of water. Explain which substance is the solute and which is the solvent.

50. Compare and contrast a heterogeneous mixture with a homogeneous mixture. Use a table to organize the differences.

51. Given that you have 1 packet of Gatorade® mix and 1 L of water, describe how you would make:
    a. a dilute solution of Gatorade
    b. a concentrated solution of Gatorade

52. Describe how you would prepare 250 mL of a 0.850 M solution of NaCl.

53. Suppose a mixture of gases contained equal masses of nitrogen and oxygen. Would the partial pressures be equal? Explain why or why not.

54. An experiment compares the volume of 1 mol of hydrogen gas (H_2, 2 g/mol) with 1 mol of argon gas (Ar, 40 g/mol). Which of the following is true?
    a. The hydrogen gas has a lesser volume because it has a lower molecular weight.
    b. The argon gas has a lesser volume because it has a higher molecular weight.
    c. The two gases have equal volumes.

Quantitative Problems

Section 2.1

55. How many oranges are in 1 mole of oranges?

56. If you have 9.1×10^{25} oranges, how many moles of oranges are there?

57. Give the mass in grams of:
    a. 1 mole of sulfur (S)
    b. 1 mole of nitrogen (N)
    c. 1 atom of gold (Au)
    d. 1 atom of copper (Cu)

58. Calculate the number of atoms in:
    a. 12.0 g of carbon (C)
    b. 16.0 g of oxygen (O)
    c. 7.0 g of lithium (Li)
    d. 27.0 g of aluminum (Al)

59. Calculate the number of moles in:
    a. 40.5 g of magnesium (Mg)
    b. 25.0 g of copper (Cu)
    c. 10.0 g of aluminum (Al)
    d. 6.0 g of helium (He)

60. How many molecules are in 5.0 moles of water (H_2O)?

61. Calculate the number of grams in 5.0 moles of argon (Ar).

62. How many gold (Au) atoms are in 45.0 g of gold?

63. How may moles are in 1 g of water? How many hydrogen atoms and how many oxygen atoms are contained in 1 g of water?

Section 2.2

64. Determine the molar masses of the following compounds:
    a. sulfur dioxide (SO_2)
    b. methanol (CH_3OH)
    c. ammonia (NH_3)
    d. caffeine ($C_8H_{10}N_4O_2$)
    e. aluminum oxide (Al_2O_3)
    f. lithium oxide (Li_2O)

65. Determine the molar masses of the following compounds:

    a. KNO_3
    b. Na_2CO_3
    c. Ca_3N_2
    d. H_2SO_4

66. Determine the number of moles in:
    a. 20.0 g of ammonia (NH_3)
    b. 30.0 g of sodium chloride (NaCl)
    c. 10.0 g of carbon dioxide (CO_2)
    d. 16.0 g of nitrogen dioxide (NO_2)

67. Calculate the number of grams in:
    a. 0.85 moles of CO_2
    b. 4.30 moles of NO_2
    c. 1.56 moles of NaCl

Section 2.3

68. How much solution should you make using 25.0 g of sugar for a concentration of 60 g/L of sugar?

69. How many grams of alcohol do you need to make 400 g of an antiseptic solution, assuming the concentration of the alcohol is 0.10%?

70. How many moles of KOH are in 45.0 mL of a 6.50 M solution?

71. How many grams of KOH are in 45.0 mL of a 6.50 M solution?

72. How many moles of $CaCl_2$ are present in 60.0 mL of a 0.10 M $CaCl_2$ solution?

73. Calculate the mass in grams of KBr required to prepare 500 mL of a 2.50 M solution.

74. A recipe calls for 1 tablespoon of salt (5 g) in 1 L of water. What is the molarity of the solution?

75. Calculate the molarity of each of the following solutions:
    a. 25.0 g of ethanol (C_2H_5OH) in 455 mL of solution
    b. 14.8 g of sucrose ($C_{12}H_{22}O_{11}$) in 78.0 mL of solution
    c. 9.00 g of sodium chloride (NaCl) in 95.0 mL of solution

76. Calculate the volume in milliliters of a solution required to provide the following:
    a. 3.50 g of NaCl from a 0.45 M solution
    b. 5.0 g of ethanol (C_2H_5OH) from a 1.8 M solution
    c. 0.70 g of acetic acid (CH_3COOH) from a 0.50 M solution

77. The diagram below shows the partial pressures for a mixture of three gases. What is the total pressure in the container?

78. If 10 g of helium gas (4 g/mole) is mixed with 4 g of neon gas (20.1 g/mole) at STP, what is the partial pressure of neon gas in the mixture?

Challenge Problems

79. If 50.0 mL of 0.560 M glucose ($C_6H_{12}O_6$) solution is mixed with 130.0 mL of 2.80 M glucose solution, what is the final concentration of the solution? Assume the volumes are additive.

80. Calculate the number of C, H and O atoms in 2.60 g of glucose ($C_6H_{12}O_6$).

CHAPTER 3

Temperature, Energy, and Heat

What is temperature?

Why is temperature important in chemistry?

How is energy related to temperature?

Is there a difference between heat and temperature?

The coldest place on Earth is in Antarctica, where geologists recorded a temperature of −89°C (−129°F) on July 21, 1983. This is so bitterly cold that an unprotected human would perish in minutes. The Antarctic penguins and sea birds spend most of their lives on the water. The largest purely land-dwelling creature living in Antarctica is an insect no bigger than your fingernail. This insect produces a chemical called *glycerol* in its body, which is a natural antifreeze!

The hottest temperature recorded on Earth was 58°C (136°F) in Libya on September 13, 1922. This narrowly beat the previous record of 57°C set in Death Valley, California on July 10, 1913. Fortunately, the average temperature on the surface of our planet is 15°C, or 59°F. This is perfect for living things, as it is comfortably within the range for which water is a liquid. Above 100°C, water boils and important chemicals break down, or react quickly, as they do in cooking. Below 0°C, pure water is a solid and the chemistry necessary for life cannot take place in a solid.

When an object is *hot*, what is different about its matter compared to the same object when it is *cold*? This chapter explains the concept of temperature and what it really means.

Temperature and state of matter

Dry ice tongs

Dry ice is an amazing substance. Use some heavy gloves or tongs to hold a small piece of it. *Never* touch dry ice with bare skin. *Always* wear proper protection when working with dry ice.

- *How would you describe this material? Is it solid, liquid, or gas?*
- *What is the "smoke" you see? Is it hot or cold?*
- *Does the "smoke" go up or down?*

Place the chunk of dry ice on a balance. Record the mass every 30 s for 2 min.

- *Is dry ice matter? How do you know?*
- *Is the "smoke" matter? How do you know?*
- *What happens to the "lost" mass as the dry ice chunk gets smaller? Where did the mass go?*

Why does the mass decrease?

Where does the matter go?

Place a small piece of dry ice in a beaker of water. Observe what happens. You can touch the vapor with your finger; however, keep your skin away from any solid dry ice that may be floating on the water.

- *What is the vapor that you see?*
- *Is the vapor hot or cold?*
- *Does the vapor flow up or down? Why?*

Dry ice in water

Take about 100 mL of warm water and add a couple squirts of dish detergent. Stir the mixture to thoroughly mix the soap into the warm water. Pour the mixture into a 250 mL graduated cylinder or other tall, thin container.

Add a small piece of dry ice to the mixture and stand back!

- *Explain what caused the explosion of soap suds.*
- *Do the bubbles that form float up or down? Why?*

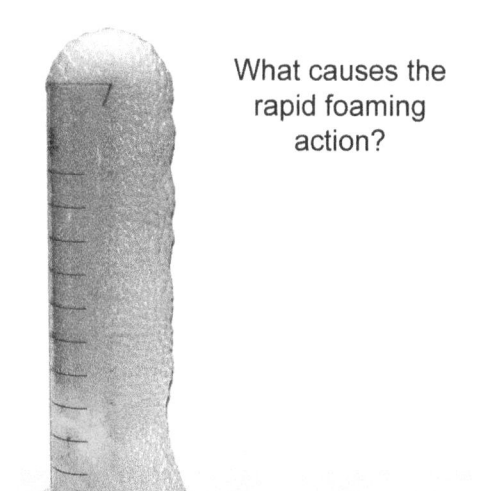

What causes the rapid foaming action?

At room temperature, or 22°C (72°F), air is a gas and water is a liquid. Heat water up to 100°C and it becomes a gas called steam. The water molecules still exist as H_2O. However, the molecules have so much energy that they fly apart from each other to make steam. Carbon dioxide (CO_2) is a gas at room temperature, but it becomes a solid at −79°C. Dry ice is frozen CO_2 gas. It does not melt into a liquid but *sublimates* directly back into gas as the temperature increases.

3.1 Temperature

Particles of matter are in constant motion

Milk looks like a uniform liquid, but it really isn't. Under the microscope, you can see tiny globules of fat suspended in water. These fat particles are in constant motion! The particles jitter around in a very agitated way and *never slow down or stop*. This is strange when you think about it. Motion requires energy. What possible source of energy keeps the fat particles dancing around?

Brownian motion

If you look more carefully at the very smallest particles, you see they don't move smoothly as they would if they were floating. Instead, they move in a jerky, irregular way. The jerky movement of a very small particle in water is called **Brownian motion** and is a direct consequence of atoms and temperature. In 1905, Albert Einstein proved that matter was made of atoms by explaining Brownian motion.

Why Brownian motion occurs

Brownian motion occurs for two important reasons:

1. Matter (including water) is made of atoms.

2. Atoms and molecules are in constant, agitated motion.

If the fat particle is *very* small, collisions with single molecules of water are visible because the mass of a water molecule is not that much smaller. The constant motion of individual water molecules causes Brownian motion.

A human-sized example

Imagine throwing marbles at both a tire tube and a foam cup floating in a pool. The motion of the tube is smooth because each marble has a lot less mass than the tube. The foam cup jerks under the impact of each marble, like the fat particle in Brownian motion. This is because the mass of the cup is not much greater than the mass of a single marble. Brownian motion proves that matter exists in discrete atoms and molecules. It also proves that, *at room temperature*, atoms and molecules are in constant, agitated motion.

Chemistry terms

Brownian motion: the erratic, jerky movement of tiny particles suspended in a fluid caused by the random impacts of individual molecules in thermal motion.

The explanation of temperature

Temperature and energy

Brownian motion demonstrates that atoms are constantly jiggling around. Jiggling implies motion, and motion always involves energy. Ordinary matter, even sitting still, contains energy in the microscopic motion of its constituent atoms. This embedded energy is what **temperature** measures. Temperature is a measure of the average **kinetic energy** of individual atoms (or molecules). When the temperature goes up, the energy of motion increases and the atoms move more vigorously.

Average motion

If atoms are always moving, how can a grain of sand just stand still? The answer to this question has three parts:

1. Atoms are tiny and there are trillions of them in a grain of sand.

2. The motion resulting from temperature is fast, but very short, typically the width of a single atom in liquids and solids (but more in gases).

3. Constant collisions cause the motion of individual atoms to be *random*.

Atoms are typically so close together that they constantly bang into each other and change direction. At any given moment, there are as many atoms bouncing one way as there are the other way. The *average* speed of the whole group is zero. However, no individual atom is ever standing still.

Random motion   Nonrandom motion

Temperature and random motion

Random motion is motion that is scattered equally in all directions. Temperature only measures the energy in the *random* motion of atoms and molecules. Temperature is not affected by energy resulting from motion of the whole group. That is why throwing a rock does not make it hotter. When you throw a rock, you give each atom in the rock the same average motion because all the atoms move together.

Chemistry terms	
	kinetic energy: the energy of motion.
	temperature: a measure of the average kinetic energy of atoms or molecules.
	random: scattered equally among all possible choices with no organized pattern.

Temperature is an average

Molecules at a given temperature have a range of energies

In a given quantity of matter there are trillions of atoms. Some of them have more energy than the average and some have less energy than the average. This is easiest to see in a gas where molecules are not bound together. The graph below shows thermal energy per molecule on the horizontal axis and the number of molecules on the vertical axis. The graph shows that molecules have a wide range of energy. A few have a lot more energy than average and a few have a lot less.

Distribution of molecular energies in a gas at different temperatures

The energy changes with temperature

As the temperature increases, the graph changes in two ways:

1. The average energy of the molecules increases, so the peak of the graph shifts to the right.

2. The graph gets wider, so the range of energy of the molecules increases.

Molecular energy in liquids and solids

In a gas, the average distance between molecules is thousands of times the size of a single molecule. Molecules in a gas interact when they happen to hit each other. This weak interaction is why the graph of molecular energy of a gas spreads out so much.

In a liquid or a solid, the molecules are very close together, separated by less than their own size. Molecules are in continuous motion, making them bump into each other constantly. The constant bumping creates a strong interaction between molecules. In turn, the strong interaction means the energy curve is much narrower. Any molecule with significantly *more* energy quickly bounces into its neighbors and loses some. Any molecule with significantly *less* energy is bumped and jostled by its neighbors and speeds up a little, gaining energy.

Distribution of molecular energy in liquids and solids

Temperature scales

Why is temperature important?

Humans can sense relative temperature through nerves in the skin. Ice feels cold because its temperature is *lower* than the temperature of your skin. A cup of coffee feels hot because its temperature is *higher* than the temperature of your skin. Temperature is important to life because most of the internal processes in living organisms only work in a narrow range of temperatures.

The Fahrenheit scale

There are two commonly used temperature scales: the Fahrenheit scale and the Celsius scale. On the **Fahrenheit scale**, water freezes at 32 degrees and boils at 212 degrees. There are 180 Fahrenheit degrees between the freezing point and the boiling point of water. Temperature in the United States is commonly measured in Fahrenheit. For example, 81°F is the temperature of a warm summer day.

The Celsius scale

The **Celsius scale** divides the difference between the freezing and boiling points of water into 100 degrees (instead of 180). Water freezes at 0°C and boils at 100°C. Most science and engineering temperature measurement is in Celsius. Most countries use the Celsius scale for all descriptions of temperature, including daily weather reports. The same 81°F warm summer day is 27°C.

Fahrenheit degrees   Celsius degrees

27°C is the same as 81°F

Other countries use Celsius degrees for everyday temperature

If you travel to other countries, you will want to know the difference between the two temperature scales. A temperature of 21°C in Paris, France, is a pleasant spring day, suitable for shorts and a T-shirt. A temperature of 21°F would be like a cold January day in Minneapolis, Minnesota! You would need a heavy winter coat, gloves, and a hat to be comfortable outdoors in 21°F. The United States is one of the few countries still using the Fahrenheit scale.

Chemistry terms

Fahrenheit scale: a temperature scale with 180 degrees between the freezing and boiling points of water; water freezes at 32°F and boils at 212°F.

Celsius scale: a temperature scale with 100 degrees between the freezing and boiling points of water; water freezes at 0°C and boils at 100°C.

Converting Fahrenheit to Celsius

Differences between the two temperature scales

Fahrenheit degrees are smaller than Celsius degrees. For example a temperature change of 9°F is the same as a temperature difference of 5°C. Besides the different size of a degree between the two scales, there is also a 32°F *offset* (0°C is 32°F) that must be considered when converting from one scale to the other. Therefore, when we convert from °C to °F, we must first scale the °C by 9/5 and then add 32 degrees. The formulas for the conversions are as follows:

> **Converting between Celsius and Fahrenheit**
>
> $$T_{Fahrenheit} = \frac{9}{5} T_{Celsius} + 32 \qquad T_{Celsius} = \frac{5}{9}\left(T_{Fahrenheit} - 32\right)$$

Fahrenheit to Celsius

To convert from Fahrenheit to Celsius, subtract 32, then multiply by 5/9. Subtracting 32 is necessary because water freezes at 32°F and 0°C. The factor of 5/9 is applied because the Celsius degree is larger than the Fahrenheit degree.

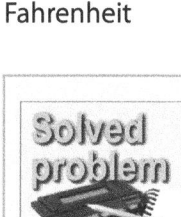
Solved problem

What temperature in Celsius is the same as 100°F?

Asked: *Temperature in °C*

Given: *100°F*

Relationships: $T_C = \frac{5}{9}(T_F - 32)$

Solve: $T_C = \frac{5}{9}(100 - 32) = \frac{5}{9}(68) = 37.8$

Answer: *100°F is the same temperature as 37.8°C.*

Celsius to Fahrenheit

To convert from Celsius to Fahrenheit, multiply by 9/5 then add 32. The factor of 9/5 accounts for the different size degrees and the 32 corrects for the zero offset.

Solved problem

What is the Fahrenheit equivalent of 15°C?

Asked: *Temperature in °F*

Given: *15°C*

Relationships: $T_F = \frac{9}{5} T_C + 32$

Solve: $T_F = \frac{9}{5}(15) + 32 = 27 + (32) = 59°F$

Answer: *15°C is the same temperature as 59°F.*

Measuring temperature

The human
Scientists use instruments to measure temperature because the human sense of temperature is not very accurate. You can feel when something is warm or cold, but you cannot determine its exact temperature. For example, if you walk into a 65°F room from being outside on a winter day, the room feels warm. The same room will feel cool if you come in from outside on a hot summer day.

Thermometers
Our sense of temperature is thus very relative. We can easily compare the temperature of things that we touch, but we can't easily say what the actual temperature is. In science, we try to perform absolute measurements. This means that we need to know the actual value of the temperature. A **thermometer** is an instrument that measures temperature. The common alcohol thermometer uses the expansion of liquid alcohol. As the temperature increases, the alcohol expands and rises

Molecules move around more as the temperature increases. So, the same number of molecules takes up more space at higher temperature

alcohol molecules at 0°C   alcohol molecules at 100°C

up a long, thin tube. The temperature is measured by the height the alcohol rises. The thermometer can indicate small changes in temperature because the bulb at the bottom has a much larger volume than the tube.

How thermometers work
All thermometers are based on a physical property that changes with temperature. A **thermistor** is a temperature sensor that changes its electrical properties as the temperature changes. A **thermocouple** is another electrical sensor that measures temperature. The temperature probe you use in your laboratory experiments uses one of these two sensor types.

The temperature probe uses a thermistor to sense temperature

Some chemicals change color at different temperatures. One type of aquarium thermometer has a stripe that changes color when the water is too hot or too cold.

Chemistry terms

thermometer: an instrument that measures temperature.

thermistor: an electronic sensor that measures temperature by detecting changes in electrical resistance.

thermocouple: an electronic sensor made of two different metals that detects a temperature-dependent voltage across them.

Absolute zero

Absolute zero

As the temperature gets lower, atoms have less and less thermal energy. This implies that a temperature can be reached at which the thermal energy becomes *zero*. This lowest possible temperature, called **absolute zero**, is where atoms have essentially zero thermal energy. Absolute zero is $-273°C$ or $-459°F$. Think of absolute zero as the temperature where even atoms are completely frozen, like ice, with no motion. *It is not possible to have a temperature lower than absolute zero, or $-273.15°C$.*

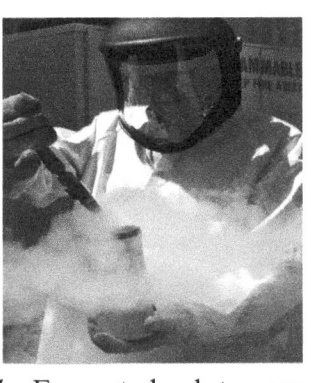

There are no temperatures below absolute zero

Technically, we believe atoms can never stop moving *completely*. Even at absolute zero some tiny amount of thermal energy is left. For our purposes, however, this "zero point" energy might as well be truly zero because the rules of quantum physics prevent the energy from ever going any lower. Figuring out what happens when atoms are cooled to absolute zero is an active area of research.

The Kelvin scale

The **Kelvin** temperature scale is useful for many scientific calculations because it starts at absolute zero. For example, the pressure in a gas depends on how fast the atoms are moving. The Kelvin scale is used because it measures the actual thermal energy of atoms. A temperature in Celsius measures only the *relative* energy, relative to zero Celsius.

Converting to kelvins

The kelvin (K) unit of temperature is the same size as the Celsius unit. Add 273 to the temperature in Celsius to get the temperature in kelvins. For example, a temperature of 21°C is equal to 294 K (21 + 273). Note that the word "degree" is not used with the kelvin scale. A temperature of 300 K is read as "300 kelvin" and is abbreviated without the degree symbol.

$$T_{\text{Kelvin}} = T_{\text{Celsius}} + 273$$

Solved problem

Convert 27°C into kelvins.

Asked: *Temperature in kelvin*

Given: *27°C*

Relationships: $T_{\text{Kelvin}} = T_{\text{Celsius}} + 273$

Solve: $T_K = 27 + 273 = 300\ K$

Answer: *300 K is the same temperature as 27°C.*

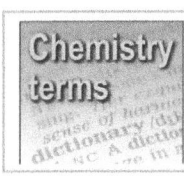

Chemistry terms

absolute zero: the lowest possible temperature, at which the energy of molecular motion is essentially zero, or as close to zero as allowed by quantum theory.

Kelvin scale: a temperature scale that starts at absolute zero and has the same unit intervals as the Celsius scale: $T_{\text{Kelvin}} = T_{\text{Celsius}} + 273$.

3.2 Heat and Thermal Energy

Thermal energy is also called heat

Heat is another word for thermal energy. On the molecular level, thermal energy is the random kinetic energy of a collection of atoms and/or molecules. On a macroscopic level, thermal energy is the energy stored in matter that is *proportional to temperature*. To change the temperature of matter, you need to add or subtract heat. You add heat to warm your house in the winter. If you want to cool your house in summer, you remove heat from it.

Temperature
the average energy per molecule

Heat
the total energy in a collection of molecules

Joules

The **joule** (J) is the fundamental SI unit of energy and heat. A joule is a fairly small unit of energy. Heating 100 mL (100 g) of water from room temperature to boiling requires about 33,000 J of heat.

+ 33,000 J =

100 g at 21°C   100 g at 100°C

Calories

The **calorie** is an older unit of heat used in chemistry. One calorie is the amount of heat required to raise the temperature of one gram of water by one degree Celsius. There are 4.184 J in one calorie so a calorie represents more energy than a joule. To make things more confusing, the Calories listed in foods (with capital "C") are really *kilocalories*. One Calorie (Cal) = 1,000 calories (cal) = 4,184 joules (J).

British thermal units (BTU)

The air conditioner or furnace in your house is rated in **British thermal units (BTU)**. One BTU is the amount of heat required to raise the temperature of one pound of water by one degree Fahrenheit. A typical home-heating furnace can produce 10,000 to 100,000 BTU per hour. One BTU equals 1,055 J.

1 lb of water at 52°F

1,055 J of heat
(1 BTU)

1 lb of water at 53°F

1 BTU raises the temperature of 1 pound of water by 1°F

Chemistry terms

heat: thermal energy, energy resulting from temperature; the total energy in random molecular motion contained in matter.

joule: the fundamental SI unit of energy (and heat).

calorie: an older unit of heat; 1 calorie = 4.184 joules.

British thermal unit (BTU): a large unit of heat. 1 BTU = 1,055 joules.

Thermodynamics and systems

Heat flows from hot to cold (2nd law)

Imagine standing outside on a cold winter day without a coat. Your body feels cold because you are losing energy to your surroundings. That's because your body temperature is higher than the air temperature. Heat (energy) moves from high temperature to lower temperature. This common-sense rule is called the **second law of thermodynamics**.

Choosing a system

To see how heat moves and what it does, we must look carefully at what we are studying. To a chemist, the part of the "universe" under study is called the **system**. In the no-coat example, the system is your body; everything else is called the *surroundings*. By carefully defining the system and the surroundings, you can keep track of how much energy there is and where it goes. For example, if the system is defined as a beaker containing 200 mL of water at 60°C, then the surroundings would be the lab bench on which the beaker is resting and the air surrounding the beaker.

Why heat flow is important

The flow of heat energy is important to virtually everything that occurs in both nature and technology. The weather on Earth is a giant heat recycler among the oceans, the land, and the atmosphere. A car's engine converts heat from burning gasoline to energy of motion of the car.

Open, closed, and isolated systems

Systems can be open, closed, or isolated. In an **open system**, matter and energy can be exchanged between the system and the surroundings. In a **closed system**, only energy can be exchanged between the system and surroundings. An example of a closed system would be a covered coffee cup. Heat can still be exchanged or lost between the air and the coffee, but no matter can be exchanged. In the third type of system, which is **isolated**, the coffee would be inside a perfectly insulated container from which no matter or heat could escape.

Chemistry terms

second law of thermodynamics: law of nature that states that energy (heat) spontaneously flows from higher temperature to lower temperature.
system: a group of interacting objects and effects that are selected for investigation.
open system: a system which can exchange matter and energy with the surroundings.
closed system: a system which can exchange only energy with the surroundings.
isolated system: a system in which neither matter nor energy can be exchanged with the surroundings.

The first law of thermodynamics: energy conservation

The first law of thermo-dynamics

The **first law of thermodynamics** is the law of energy conservation: All the energy lost by one system must be gained by another system. Consider an experiment where you mix 100 g each of hot and cold water. How can the temperature of the mixture be predicted?

COLD + HOT = ?
mix

100 g   100 g
at 10°C   at 80°C

MIXTURE
System

Energy before mixing

=

Energy after mixing

Assume the two cups are an isolated system; no energy or mass is allowed to cross the boundary. That means that the energy after mixing is the same as it was before mixing.

Energy depends on mass and temperature

The amount of heat energy in a quantity of matter, such as a cup of water, is proportional to mass and temperature. More mass means more energy at any temperature, so the higher the temperature, the higher the energy.

Tracing the energy

To find the final mixture temperature, you need to know the total energy of the system. To make things easy, start with 0°C as a reference point. Each gram of water stores 4.184 J of energy for every degree Celsius.

1. The hot water contributes 33,472 J.
2. The cold water contributes 4,184 J.
3. The mixture has a total energy of 37,656 J (hot + cold).
4. The 200 g of water contains 37,656 J of heat at 45°C.

Energy from hot water **33,472 J**

Energy from cold water **4,184 J**

37,656 J — Total energy in mixture

$$\frac{37,656 \text{ J}}{(200 \text{ g})[4.184 \text{ J}/(g \cdot °C)]}$$

Divide the energy over the mixture

= 45°C — Temperature of mixture

How to solve the problem

How did we solve this problem? We added up all the energy in the system. We then analyzed where the energy went. In this case, all the energy went to changing the temperature of the mixture. The problem was solved by calculating what temperature the mixture *had to be* to contain all the energy in the system.

Chemistry terms

first law of thermodynamics: law of nature that states that energy can neither be created nor destroyed, and thus the total energy in an isolated system remains constant; all the energy lost by one system must be gained by the surroundings or another system.

Thermal equilibrium

What stops heat from flowing?

Suppose we pour the hot and cold water into a divided cup so they can't mix, but heat can still flow. Heat flows from the hot water to the cold water. The hot water gets cooler as it loses heat. The cold water gets warmer as it gains the same amount of heat. *When does the heat flow stop?* Why doesn't the hot water keep losing heat until it gets *colder* than the cold water? Obviously, this does not happen; heat flow eventually stops.

Thermal equilibrium

Two bodies are in **thermal equilibrium** when they have the same temperature. In thermal equilibrium, no heat flows because the temperatures are the same. In nature, heat always flows from hot to cold until thermal equilibrium is reached. Making the divider out of insulating foam only slows the process down. Heat still flows, only slower. The hot and cold water take *longer* to reach thermal equilibrium, but the end result is the same.

The rate of heat flow

The rate at which heat flows drops off gradually as the temperatures get closer together. A lot of heat flows quickly when the temperature difference is large, but as the temperature difference gets smaller, the rate of heat flowing gets proportionally smaller, too. As two objects approach thermal equilibrium, the rate of heat flow between them becomes zero because both reach the same temperature.

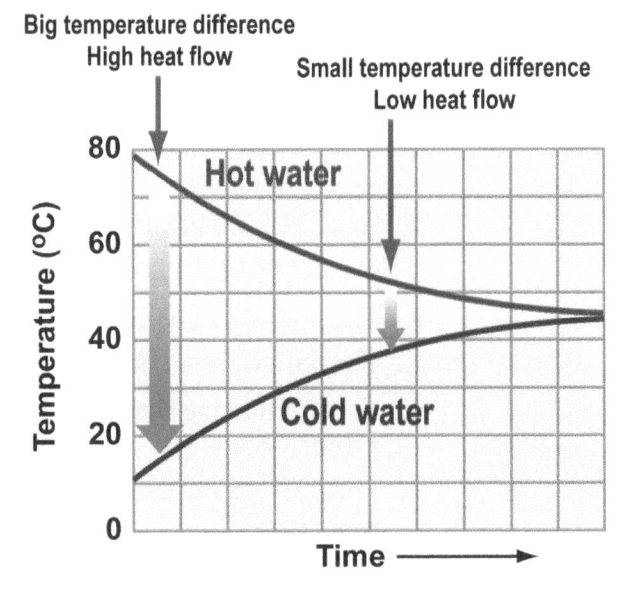

Heat transfer in living things

Heat flow is necessary for life because biological processes release energy. Your body regulates its temperature through the constant flow of heat. The inside of your body averages 37°C. Humans are most comfortable when the air is about 25°C because the rate of heat flow out of the body matches the rate at which the body generates heat. If the air is 10°C, you get cold because heat flows out of your body too rapidly. If the air is 40°C, you feel hot because your body cannot get rid of its excess internal heat.

> **Chemistry terms**
>
> **thermal equilibrium:** a condition in which two systems have the same temperature and no net heat flows from one system to the other.

Specific heat

Differences in materials

The same amount of heat causes a different change in temperature in different materials. For example, it takes 4.184 J of heat energy to raise the temper-ature of one gram of water by one degree Celsius. If you add the same quantity of heat to one gram of gold, the temperature goes up by 32.4°C! The rise in temperature is not the same because different materials have different abilities to store thermal energy.

Specific heat

The **specific heat** in defined as the quantity of energy it takes to raise the temperature of one gram of a material by one degree Celsius. Water is an important example; the specific heat of water is 4.184 J/(g·°C). It takes 4.184 J to raise the temperature of one gram of water by one degree Celsius. The specific heat of gold is 0.129 J/(g·°C). It only takes 0.129 J to raise the temperature of one g of gold one degree Celsius. The specific heat of water is 32 times higher than it is for gold.

TABLE 3.1. Specific heat of some common substances

Material	Specific heat [J/(g·°C)]	Material	Specific heat [J/(g·°C)]
Air at 1 atm	1.006	Oil	1.900
Water	4.184	Concrete	0.880
Aluminum	0.900	Glass	0.800
Steel	0.470	Gold	0.129
Silver	0.235	Wood	2.500

The heat equation

The heat equation is used to calculate how much hear (Q) it takes to make a temperature change ($\Delta T = T_2 - T_1$) in a mass (m) of material with specific heat (c_p).

Heat equation

Mass (g)   Temperature change (°C)

Heat (J)

$$Q = mc_p \Delta T$$

Specific heat [J/(g·°C)]

Chemistry terms

specific heat: the quantity of heat energy, usually measured in J/(g·°C), it takes per gram of a certain material to raise the temperature by one degree Celsius.

Why specific heat varies

Different substances have different specific heats

Substances have a wide range of specific heats. Pure metals, such as gold, tend to have low specific heats. Molecular substances, such as water and oil, tend to have higher specific heats. Specific heat varies for many reasons.

Molecular substances can absorb energy in ways that don't increase the temperature, such as internal motion of the atoms within a molecule. This is because bonds between atoms are not rigid rods, like the diagrams show. Bonds behave more like flexible springs that can bend and stretch. Typically, *only the motion of whole molecules affects the temperature*. The motion of atoms within a molecule, however, may not affect temperature. When energy is absorbed in ways other than motion of the whole molecule, temperature goes up less and the specific heat increases.

Stronger forces between molecules mean it takes more energy to cause a single molecule to move a given amount. This makes the specific heat higher. In general, strong bonds between molecules raise the specific heat because they limit the thermal motion of individual molecules (or atoms).

Why specific heat varies

Materials with heavy atoms or large molecules have lower specific heat compared with materials with lighter atoms. This is because temperature represents the energy per atom. Heavy atoms imply fewer atoms per kilogram. Energy that is divided among fewer atoms means more energy per atom, and therefore more temperature change. Silver's specific heat is 235 J/(kg·°C) and aluminum's specific heat is 900 J/(kg·°C). One gram of silver has fewer atoms than a gram of aluminum because silver atoms are heavier than aluminum atoms. When heat is added, each atom of silver gets more energy than each atom of aluminum because there are fewer silver atoms in a gram. Since the energy per atom is greater, the temperature increase in the silver is also greater.

Why is the specific heat of aluminum almost four times greater than the specific heat of silver?

Silver
Specific heat: **235** [J/(kg·°C)]
1 gram Heavier atoms, mean **fewer** atoms per gram.

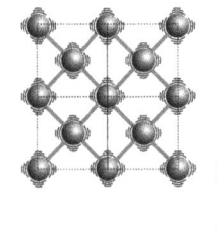

Energy is spread over **fewer** atoms

More energy per atom

Higher temperature gain per joule (lower specific heat)

Aluminum
Specific heat: **900** [J/(kg·°C)]
Lighter atoms, mean **more** atoms per gram.
1 gram

Energy is spread over **more** atoms

Less energy per atom

Lower temperature gain per joule (higher specific heat)

Calculating temperature and heat

Most specific heat problems include one or both of the following two calculations:

1. Calculate the temperature change from a given heat input.
2. Calculate how much heat is needed to reach a specified temperature.

Solved problem

On a sunny day, each square centimeter of the ocean absorbs 180 J of energy from the Sun each hour. Assume all the heat is absorbed in the first 10 m, which has a mass of 1,000 g. How much does the water temperature increase?
This is a lengthy question! Before going on, discuss with your classmates what is asked and what is given. For example, what does "absorb energy from the sun" means?

Asked: *Temperature increase, ΔT*

Given: *Energy input = 180 J,*
mass of water = 1,000 g

Relationships: $Q = mc_p\,\Delta T$

Solve: *180 J = (1,000 g) × 4.184 [J/(g·°C)] × ΔT*
ΔT = 180 ÷ 4,184 = 0.04°C

Answer: *The temperature rise in the top 10 m of the ocean is 0.04°C per hour of full sunlight.*

Solved problem

A metal–working process needs to heat steel from room temperature (20°C) to 2,000°C. If the mass of steel is 100 g, how much heat is required?

Asked: *Amount of heat required*

Given: *100 g of steel, c_p = 0.470 J/(g·°C)*
temperature difference ΔT is
ΔT = 2,000°C − 20°C = 1,980°C

Relationships: $Q = m\,c_p\,\Delta T$

Solve: *Q = (100 g) × 0.470 [J/(g·°C)] × 1,980°C = 93,060 J*

Answer: *It takes 93,060 joules to raise the temperature of 100 g of steel to by 1,980°C, assuming no heat gets lost during the process (which is not a very good assumption!).*

Applying the first law of thermodynamics

Heat flow out of a system equals heat absorbed by surroundings

When you leave a cup of hot coffee on the table, it cools down. Heat flows from the hot coffee to the cooler air in the room. The thermal energy of the hot coffee is decreased, and the thermal energy of the air is increased by the same amount. Everything balances; the increase in thermal energy of the air is exactly the same as the decrease in thermal energy of the coffee.

Solving problems with the first law of thermodynamics

The first law of thermodynamics is useful because it allows you to solve problems quickly and with minimal work. In real life, a hot coffee cup heats up the nearby air, which rises and makes currents that change how fast the heat flows. It would be difficult to calculate precisely how much heat flows every second. By looking at the energy at the start and then after the coffee has completely cooled down, we can get a pretty good answer without knowing the exact details of exactly how the heat went from cup to air.

TABLE 3.2. Applying the first law

Step 1	Step 2	Step 3
Identify the system and all the sources and uses of energy in the system before the change.	Set the total energy of the system after the change equal to the total energy before the change.	Account for all the uses of energy after the change and solve the problem.

Solved problem

A mass of 300 g of water at 80°C cools down to 20°C. Assume all the heat from the water is absorbed by 100 m³ of air (a small room) with a mass of 100,000 g. What is the temperature change in the air?

Asked: *Temperature change in °C*

Given: *300 g of water [$c_p = 4.184 J/(g°C)$], change of 60°C (80°C – 20°C), and 100,000 g of air [$c_p = 1.006 J/(g·°C)$]*

Relationships: $Q = m\, c_p (T_2 - T_1)$

Solve: *Energy lost by the water = (300 g)[4.184 J/(g·°C)](60°C)*
= 75,312 J
Energy gained by the air = energy lost by water = 75,312 J
$$\text{Temperature change of air} = \frac{75,312\ J}{100,000\ g \times 1.006\ J/(g·°C)} = 0.75°C$$

Answer: *The air in the room gets warmer by about 0.75°C.*

Heat transfer

Conduction

Conduction is the transfer of heat *through* materials by the direct contact of matter. Imagine bringing in contact two pieces of material—one hot at 100°C and the other cold at 0°C. When the two pieces come in contact with each other, heat begins to flow. The heat flows from the hot piece to the cold piece. The cold piece warms up and the hot piece cools down. There will be a net heat flow until the two pieces are at the same temperature.

Heat transfer

Thermal conductors

Glass and metal are **thermal conductors.** Think about holding a test tube of hot water. Thin glass conducts heat relatively well so heat flows rapidly through the glass from the hot water to your skin. You cannot hold on for long because the heat raises your skin temperature quickly.

Thermal insulators

A **thermal insulator** is a material that conducts heat poorly. Styrofoam is a good example. You can comfortably hold a hot test pipe surrounded by a centimeter of foam insulation. Heat flows very slowly through the foam so that the temperature of your hand does not rise very much. Plastic foam gets its insulating ability by trapping spaces of air. We use thermal insulators to maintain temperature differences without allowing much heat to flow.

The ability to conduct heat depends on many factors

All materials conduct heat at some rate. Solids usually are better heat conductors than liquids, and liquids are better conductors than gases. The ability to conduct heat often depends more on the structure of a material than on the material itself. For example, solid glass is a thermal conductor when it is made into windows. When glass is spun into fine fibers and made into insulation (fiberglass), the combination of glass fibers and trapped air makes a thermal insulator.

> **Chemistry terms**
>
> **conduction:** the flow of heat energy through the direct contact of matter.
> **thermal conductor:** a material that conducts heat easily.
> **thermal insulator:** a material that resists the flow of heat.

3.3 Phase Changes

Solid, liquid, and gas

During a **phase change**, a substance rearranges the order of its particles (atoms or molecules). Examples of phase change include melting (solid to liquid) and boiling (liquid to gas). The most familiar example is water, which freezes at 0°C and boils at 100°C. All substances experience phase change, even metals such as iron. Iron melts into liquid at 1,535°C and boils into a gas at 2,750°C.

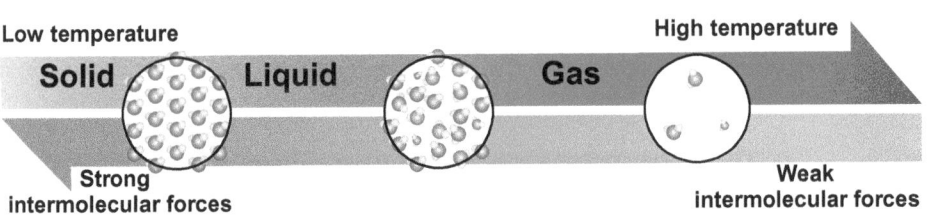

Why phase changes occur

Phase changes come from the competition between temperature and attractive intermolecular forces. On one side of this competition are intermolecular forces, which tend to attract molecules together into rigid structures. On the opposite side is the effect of temperature. Thermal energy is disruptive. Molecules with lots of thermal energy shake back and forth so much they cannot stay in an orderly structure, like a solid.

Melting point

The **melting point** is the temperature at which a substance changes from solid to liquid. Melting occurs when the thermal energy of individual atoms becomes comparable to the attractive force between atoms.

Different materials have different melting points because their intermolecular forces have different strengths. Water melts at 0°C (32°F). Iron melts at a much higher temperature, about 1,535°C (2,795°F). The difference in melting points tells us that the attractive force between iron atoms is much greater than the attractive force between water molecules.

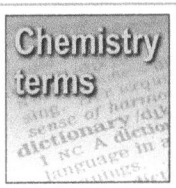
Chemistry terms

phase change: conversion of the organization of molecules in a substance without changing the individual molecules themselves, such as changing from solid to liquid or liquid to gas.

melting point: the temperature at which a substance changes phase from solid to liquid; for example, the melting point of water is 0°C.

Boiling and the heat of vaporization

Boiling point

The **boiling point** is the temperature at which the phase changes from liquid to gas. In a gas, all the bonds between one atom and its neighbors are completely broken. Water boils at 100°C (212°F) at a pressure of one atmosphere. The steam above the teapot is made of water molecules in the gas phase. Iron boils at 2,750°C (4,982°F).

Gas at 100 °C

Liquid at 100 °C

Heat of vaporization

It takes energy for a molecule to completely break its bonds with its neighbors and go from liquid to gas. The **heat of vaporization** is the amount of energy it takes to convert one gram of liquid to one gram of gas at the boiling point. Some representative values are given in Table 3.3. A quick calculation shows it takes 2,256,000 J to turn a kilogram of boiling water into steam! This explains why stoves require so much electric power.

TABLE 3.3. Heat of vaporization for some common substances

Substance	Heat of vaporization, ΔH_v (J/g)
Water	2,256
Alcohol	854
Liquid nitrogen	201
Iron	6,265
Silver	2,336

Comparing heats of vaporization and fusion

Intermolecular force

The heat of vaporization is much greater than the heat of fusion because breaking bonds between atoms or molecules takes much more energy than exchanging bonds. In a liquid, molecules move around by exchanging bonds with neighboring molecules. The energy needed to break one bond is recovered when the molecule forms a new bond with its neighbor.

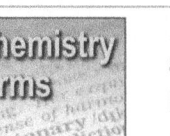
Chemistry terms

heat of vaporization: the energy required to change the phase of one gram of a material from liquid to gas or gas to liquid at constant temperature and constant pressure at the boiling point.

boiling point: the temperature at which a substance changes phase from liquid to gas which is the temperature at which the vapor pressure is equal to the atmospheric pressure. For example, the boiling point of water at atmospheric pressure is 100°C.

The heat of fusion

Temperature does not always rise when heat is added!

Think about heating a block of ice with an initial temperature of –20°C. As heat energy is added, the ice warms. However, once the ice reaches 0°C, *the temperature stops increasing!* This is because ice is melting to form liquid water. As heat is added, more ice becomes water but the temperature stays the same. This can easily be observed with an ordinary thermometer in a *well-stirred* experiment.

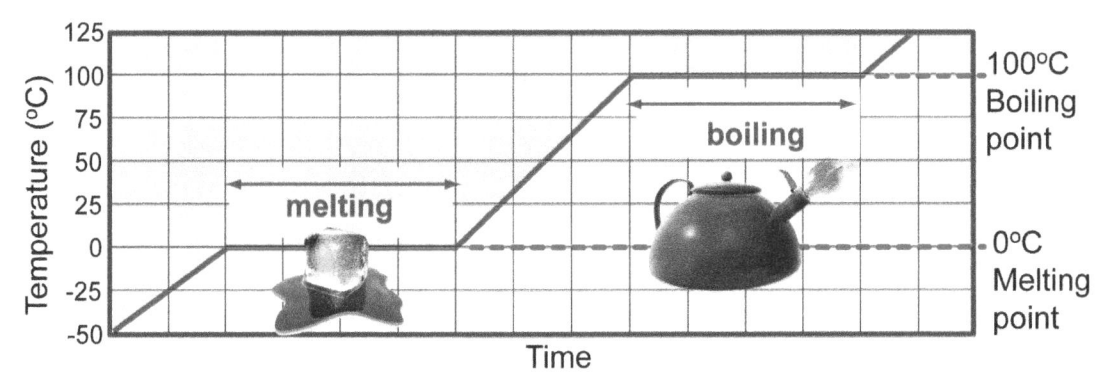

It takes energy to change phase

It takes energy to separate molecules in a solid and make them liquid, *even if the temperature stays the same*. The temperature does not change while the ice is melting because the added energy goes into loosening the bonds between neighboring water molecules. When thermal energy is added or subtracted from a material, either the temperature changes, or the phase changes, but usually not both at the same time. Once all the ice has become liquid, the temperature starts to rise again as more heat is added.

The heat of fusion

The **heat of fusion** is the amount of energy it takes to change one gram of material from solid to liquid or vice versa. Table 3.4 gives some values for the heat of fusion (ΔH_f) for common materials. Note how large the values are. It takes 335,000 J of energy to turn one kilogram of ice into liquid water.

TABLE 3.4. Heat of fusion for some common substances

Substance	Heat of fusion, ΔH_f (J/g)
Water	335
Aluminum	321
Iron	267
Paraffin (wax)	200–220

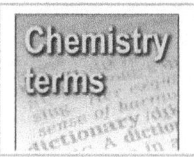

Chemistry terms

heat of fusion: the energy required to change the phase of one gram of a material from liquid to solid or solid to liquid at constant temperature and constant pressure at the melting point.

Solving phase change problems

Condensation releases the heat of fusion

Energy can be released or absorbed in phase changes. For example, condensation occurs when a gas turns back into a liquid again. When water vapor condenses, it gives up the heat of vaporization! Steam at 100°C causes severe burns because each gram of water vapor delivers 2,256 J of energy to your skin from the heat of vaporization. By comparison, a gram of water at 100°C only releases 314 J as it cools down to skin temperature (25°C).

Solving phase change problems

Many problems involving phase changes can be solved by thinking about where the energy is absorbed or released.

1. Energy can be absorbed or released during phase changes.

2. Energy can be absorbed or released by changes in temperature.

The important idea is to realize that energy is conserved. Any energy used to change phase is no longer available to change temperature, and vice versa. For example, if 100 J of energy is applied to a system and 40 J is used to raise the temperature, then only 60 J is available for changing phase.

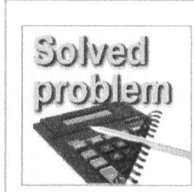

Ice cubes with a temperature of –25°C are used to cool off a glass of punch. Which absorbs more heat: warming up the ice or melting the ice into water? The specific heat of ice is 2.0 J/(g·°C).

Asked: *Which absorbs more heat, warming ice by 25°C or melting it?*

Given: *The ice starts at –25°C. The specific heat of ice is 2.0 J/(g·°C). ΔH_f (water) = 335 J*

Relationships: $Q = mc_p(T_2 - T_1)$ *and* $Q = m\Delta H_f$

Solve: *First, let's calculate the energy that it takes to warm up a gram of ice from –25°C to 0 °C.*
Energy needed to go from T_1 to T_2 is $mc_p(T_2 - T_1)$ = (1 g)[2.0 J/(g·°C)](25°C) = 50 J
So it takes 50 J to warm up 1 g of ice from –25°C to 0°C.
The same gram of ice takes 335 J to melt into liquid water.

Answer: *Changing phase (melting) absorbs 335 J per gram of ice but warming the ice only absorbs 50 J/g. The phase change is responsible for most of ice's cooling effect on drinks!*

Evaporation

Why does cold water evaporate?

Think about wiping a surface with a wet cloth. Over time the water *evaporates*. In **evaporation**, liquid molecules change phase into gas at a temperature far below the boiling point! Virtually all liquids evaporate, some much faster than others. Dampen a surface with alcohol and it evaporates almost immediately. A surface wet with water stays wet for much longer. Why does evaporation occur?

The average energy of molecules

Evaporation happens because there is a surface between liquid and gas. Think about water molecules at the surface compared to molecules deep below the surface. All molecules are in constant jostling motion. The deeper molecules are hit upward by their neighbors as often as they are hit downward. They stay in the water. The molecules on the surface, however, have no molecules on top to send them back down. When a surface molecule is jostled hard enough by a molecule below it, the surface molecule is ejected from the water and becomes a gas. This is the explanation for evaporation.

Explaining evaporation

Molecules near the surface may be bumped right out

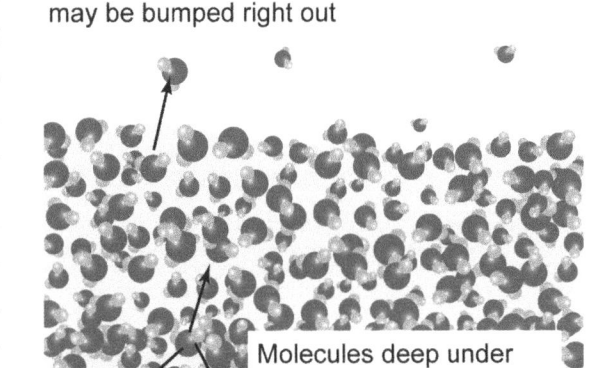

Molecules deep under are bumped up and down

Evaporation cools liquids

How does an evaporating molecule get enough energy to break its connections with the other molecules and escape? The energy is taken away from the molecules just below that did the actual bumping! It actually takes the same amount of energy to evaporate a gram of water at room temperature as it does to boil a gram of water at 100°C! Evaporation transfers thermal energy from a liquid to a gas, and therefore it *cools* the remaining liquid. That is why your wet skin feels cold when you get out of the shower. The evaporating water from your skin takes heat away from your body. This cooling effect is also why you sweat while exercising. The evaporation of sweat from your skin removes heat generated by your muscles.

| Chemistry terms | **evaporation:** a phase change from liquid to gas at a temperature below the boiling point. |

Condensation

Condensation

Have you ever noticed that the outside of a glass of cold water becomes wet on a humid summer day? Where did the water come from? Did it come through the glass?

Where does the water on the outside come from?

The water on the outside of the glass comes out of the air in a process called *condensation*. **Condensation** is the changing of phase from gas to liquid. Water vapor in the air condenses on a cold glass to become liquid. Condensation occurs below a substance's boiling point.

Water cycle

Although all liquids and gases can condense, the process is particularly important with water because evaporation and condensation create the water cycle of Earth. Condensation may occur when a substance in its gas phase is cooled to below its boiling point. Clouds are an excellent example. Water vapor evaporates from the ocean and rises with warm air. The upper atmosphere is colder, so the water vapor condenses into tiny droplets of liquid to make clouds. Clouds are not water vapor, which is a gas. Clouds are condensed liquid water. Evaporation and condensation are responsible for the water cycle in the atmosphere.

Condensation releases heat

Condensation

Evaporation

Condensation is the exact opposite process of evaporation. The energy transferred during condensation is exactly the same, but in the opposite direction, as in evaporation. From Table 3.3 we know that the heat of vaporization of water is 2,256 J/g. When a gram of water evaporates, it carries away 2,256 J of energy, *cooling* any matter left behind. When a gram of water vapor condenses, it gives off 2,256 J of energy, *warming* any matter it condenses on.

Latent heat

The heat energy given off during condensation is often called the **latent heat**. Latent heat is thermal energy associated with a phase change. For evaporation and condensation, the latent heat is the heat of vaporization. For melting and freezing, the latent heat is the heat of fusion. The latent heat released during cloud formation transfers heat from the oceans to the upper atmosphere, warming the atmosphere significantly. This is a very significant component of Earth's energy balance.

Chemistry terms

condensation: a phase change from gas to liquid; a substance in its gas phase may condense at a temperature below its boiling point.

latent heat: thermal energy that is absorbed or released during a phase change.

How pressure affects phase changes

Water boils at a lower temperature at high altitude

Cookbooks often have special instructions to cook food for longer at high altitudes. This is because water boils at different temperatures depending on the air pressure. For example, in Denver, Colorado, water boils at 95°C (203°F) instead of the usual 100°C (212°F). The boiling point is lower because Denver is at an altitude of 1,610 m and the air pressure is lower than it is at sea level.

The phase diagram

The temperature at which a phase change occurs typically depends on pressure. The relationship among the phases of matter, temperature, and pressure is shown on a *phase equilibrium diagram*. Point A is the melting/freezing point which is 0°C at 101,325 Pa (1 atm). Point B is the boiling point, which is 100°C at 1 atm.

Phase equilibrium diagram of water

What the curves mean

Each curve represents a phase change. Crossing the liquid–gas curve means changing from liquid to gas or gas to liquid. This curve represents the boiling point. For Denver, the pressure is 84,000 Pa. Notice that the line for 84,000 Pa crosses the liquid–gas curve at 95°C. Crossing the solid–liquid curve means changing phase from solid to liquid or vice versa. Water freezes or melts at the same temperature from 800 to 200,000 Pa. At higher pressures, water freezes at a temperature below 0°C.

The triple point

Point C on the phase equilibrium diagram is called the *triple point*. The **triple point** of water is at exactly 273.16 K (0.01°C) and a pressure of 611.73 Pa (0.006037 atm). At the triple point, liquid, solid and vapor can all be present at the same time. A sample of water at its triple point can become solid, liquid, or gas with very small changes in pressure or temperature.

Chemistry terms
triple point: the temperature and pressure at which the solid, liquid, and gas phases of a substance can all exist in equilibrium together.

Relative humidity (Rh)

The meaning of humidity

A 90°F day in Houston, Texas, feels much more uncomfortable than a 90°F day in Phoenix, Arizona. The reason is the *relative humidity*. **Relative humidity** describes how much water vapor is in the air compared to how much water vapor the air can hold when it is completely saturated.

Reading the equilibrium vapor pressure

The diagram shows water's phase equilibrium diagram between 0°C (32°F) and 40°C (104°F). The curve represents the boiling point. The curve tells you that water boils at 20°C at a pressure of 2,340 Pa. The curve also represents the equilibrium partial pressure of water vapor in air. For example, at 20°C water vapor has a partial pressure of 2,340 Pa. This is called the *saturation* vapor pressure. Like any saturated solution, if more water vapor is added to air at 20°C, it condenses into liquid. This interpretation is correct because a liquid boils when its vapor pressure is equal to or greater than the ambient atmospheric pressure.

Calculating the relative humidity

Suppose some 20°C air contains less than 2,340 Pa of water vapor. This is an *unsaturated* solution. It means the air could absorb more water vapor without it condensing out. The relative humidity (Rh) is defined as the actual partial pressure of water vapor in air divided by the saturation vapor pressure at the same temperature. For example, the air in Phoenix is very dry, and even at 20°C it might contain only 1,000 Pa of water vapor. The relative humidity is 1,000 ÷ 2,340 = 0.42 or 42%.

The dew point

Another important concept is the *dew point*. The **dew point** is the temperature at which air is saturated with water. For example, suppose air has a partial pressure of 1,000 Pa of water vapor. On the diagram, this corresponds to a dew point of 8°C. At 8°C the relative humidity is 100%. If the air gets cooler than 8°C, the mixture becomes supersaturated and water contained in air will condense. Above 8°C, the relative humidity is less than 100%.

Chemistry terms	**relative humidity:** the actual partial pressure of water vapor in air divided by the saturation vapor pressure at the same temperature.
	dew point: the temperature at which air is saturated with H_2O vapor (Rh = 100%).

Refrigeration by evaporation

Mohammed Bah Abba is a smart, young African teacher who designed a clever refrigerator that needs no electricity! His invention uses earthenware clay pots and the principles of evaporation. As a young man Abba had a fascination with clay pots and their ability to absorb water. He wondered how the clay could absorb so much water, yet still hold together. He had observed that most things that absorb water become soft and lose their shape. He was also curious as to why the clay pots kept things cool. In college, Mohammed took some classes in biology, chemistry and geology and with this background he developed the "pot-in-pot refrigerator."

The pot-in-pot refrigerator is designed using two clay pots of different sizes, one large and the other small. The small pot is placed inside the larger pot and sand is added to fill the space between the walls of the two pots. The sand is moistened with water and a damp cloth is used to cover the top.

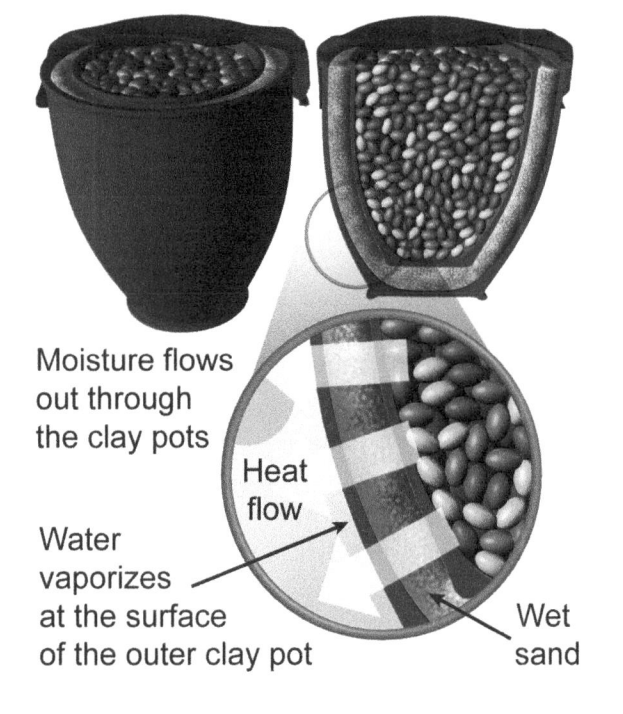

Moisture flows out through the clay pots

Heat flow

Water vaporizes at the surface of the outer clay pot

Wet sand

How does the pot-in-pot refrigerator keep things cool? To explain this, we will use the concepts you have learned about the phase changes of water and why they occur. When water molecules evaporate, they absorb energy because they are going from the liquid phase to the gas phase. Do you recall why this requires energy? It is because the intermolecular forces holding the water molecules together in the liquid phase must be *broken* to allow the water molecules to separate and become a vapor:

$$H_2O \text{ (liquid)} + \text{energy} \rightarrow H_2O \text{ (gas)}$$

The hot climate in Africa provides warm, dry air outside the pot, causing evaporation to occur on the walls of the large outer pot. The moisture from the damp sand is pulled toward the outer pot as evaporation takes place. The porous clay allows the water molecules to travel from the moist interior to the outer pot where they are warmed and evaporate. The warmth outside the pots provides the liquid water molecules with the energy they need to evaporate and change into water vapor.

The heat of vaporization (ΔH_v) for water is 2,256 J/g or 40.6 kJ/mole. This large amount of energy causes significant cooling that results in a temperature drop of several degrees! The more water molecules evaporate, the cooler the temperature becomes. This causes the inner pot to become cool. The cooler temperature of the inner pot preserves foods that would otherwise spoil quickly in the heat.

Throughout human history, single clay pots have been used to keep things cool. Usually the clay pots are soaked in water for 20 minutes or so and then removed. Throughout the next few hours the water absorbed by the clay slowly evaporates. This process is used by street vendors to keep their produce and drinks cool for their customers. The single pot design works, but it is less efficient and does not last as long as Mohammed's pot-in-pot design. His invention shows how important it is to use the ideas behind simple technology in an applied way! Mohammed wanted to help the poor people in the rural regions of northern Nigeria, and his inspiration gave way to this elegant, efficient pot-in-pot refrigerator.

To fully appreciate and understand the significance of Mohammed's invention it helps to understand the people of northern Nigeria. The geography of this area is semi-desert scrubland, and the rural people live in the poorest of conditions. There is no electricity and therefore no refrigeration. Even in the towns, the power supply is not dependable. Most people cannot afford to buy electricity even if it is available. The villagers' way of life is based on agriculture, and young girls have the responsibility of rapidly selling the food that is grown each day before it spoils. Mohammed's invention allows these young girls to attend school more often instead of having to sell food.

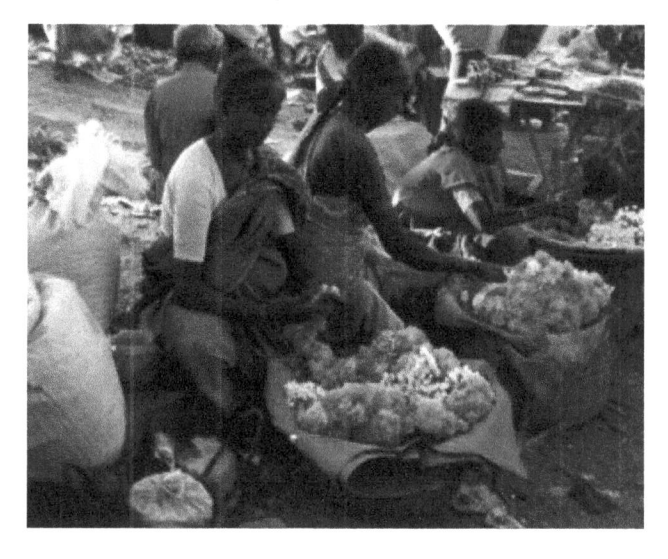

How well does it work? Mohammed did many tests with different fruits and vegetables and found the following results: Eggplant stayed fresh for 27 days instead of three, tomatoes and peppers lasted for three weeks or more, and African spinach, which usually lasts only a day, remained edible for 12 days.

Mohammed worked to refine his invention for two years before beginning to distribute the pot-in-pot. He hired local pot makers to produce the first 5,000 pot-in-pots, which he distributed for free to five local villages in Jigawa. Later, with some limited financial backing, he distributed 7,000 more to another dozen local villages. Educating the illiterate local villagers on how to use the pot-in-pot was a challenge that Mohammed overcame by using a video-recorded play of local actors who acted out how to use the pot-in-pot and demonstrated how food stayed fresh for a much longer time. As a result of the pot-in-pot, the farmers' income levels have risen because they can now sell their produce to consumers based on demand, where before they had to sell quickly because the food would spoil. The number of girls attending local village schools has risen, because they no longer need to sell produce each day to survive. The pot-in-pot has also given rise to healthier food for all people to consume, therefore decreasing disease and illness in these areas.

Mohammed Bah Abba was only in his twenties when his invention won him the Rolex Award for enterprise in 2000. He won the prestigious award not only for his design of the pot-in-pot refrigerator but for his efforts to make it affordable and available to the people who really needed it. These pots sell for thirty to forty cents a set!

Chapter 3 Review

Vocabulary

Match each word to the sentence where it best fits.

Section 3.1

kinetic energy	thermometer
Brownian motion	thermistor
Fahrenheit	absolute zero
random	Kelvin
temperature	Celsius

1. The erratic movement of a small particle in water due to constant collisions of molecules is called _____.

2. _____ is a measure of the average thermal energy of atoms or molecules.

3. The _____ temperature scale, used in the United States, has a boiling temperature of water at 212.

4. The energy of motion is referred to as _____.

5. A device used to measure temperature is called a/an _____.

6. The theoretical temperature where all motion stops is called _____.

7. The SI derived unit of temperature is called the _____. When using this unit, water freezes at zero degrees.

8. Motion that is scattered equally in all directions is called _____ motion.

9. A/An _____ is a temperature sensor that detects changes in electrical properties as the temperature changes.

10. The temperature scale that starts at absolute zero is called the _____ temperature scale.

Section 3.2

specific heat	system
joule	heat
calorie	first law
thermal equilibrium	conductor
second law	insulator

11. _____ is a measure of the thermal energy of a substance.

12. A group of interacting objects and effects that are selected for investigation is called a/an _____.

13. The _____ of thermodynamics states that thermal energy moves from higher temperature to lower temperature.

14. The law of conservation of energy is also called the _____ of thermodynamics.

15. The units of _____ and _____ are used to measure heat energy. The unit of the _____ is larger than the unit of the _____.

16. When the temperature of two systems is the same and heat no longer flows between them, they are in _____.

17. A material that easily permits the flow of heat across it is called a/an _____.

18. The amount of heat needed to raise one g of a substance by one degree is called the _____.

19. A material that does not permit the flow of heat across it is called a/an _____.

Section 3.3

gas	heat of fusion
solid	melting point
liquid	boiling point
triple point	phase change
vaporization	dew point
evaporation	

20. In the _____ phase of matter, the atoms or molecules are able to move and change positions, but are still touching each other.

21. The process of _____ requires a great deal of energy, because it breaks the bonds that hold molecules together in their liquid phase and separates them.

22. In the_____ phase of matter, the atoms or molecules are not able to move or change positions.

23. The amount of heat required to melt one mole of ice is called the _____.

24. Liquids kept in an uncovered container slowly lose volume over time through the process of _____.

25. A substance undergoes a/an _____ when its molecules are rearranged without changing the individual molecules.

26. The temperature at which a substance changes from a solid to a liquid is called the _____.

27. The temperature at which the vapor pressure of a liquid is equal to the atmospheric pressure is called the _____.

28. The _____ phase of matter has no definite volume.

29. The _____ is the temperature at which the partial pressure of water vapor in a sample of air equals its saturation vapor pressure.

30. The _____ is the unique value of pressure and temperature at which the solid, liquid, and gas phases coexist in equilibrium.

Conceptual Questions

Section 3.1

31. Explain why Brownian motion provides evidence that molecules are in constant random motion.

32. Describe the differences between the Fahrenheit and the Celsius temperature scales.

33. What units do we use to measure temperature?

34. How is the kinetic energy of a system related to its temperature?

35. Describe how the random motion of atoms and molecules is related to temperature.

Section 3.2

36. To calculate the heat absorbed by an object, what information is needed besides its specific heat?

37. Objects tend to exchange heat until "thermal equilibrium" is reached. What does this mean? Explain your reasoning.

38. Does the specific heat change when you have a greater mass of a substance, for example, 10.0 g versus 100.0 g? Explain.

39. Copper has a specific heat of 0.34 J/(g·°C). What does this tell you about the structure of copper? (Explain what the unit of specific heat means.)

40. Adding heat to a substance can cause its temperature to increase. Explain why.

41. The specific heat of water is much higher than that of other substances. What does this mean?

42. You have 20.0 g samples of two metals, one with a high specific heat and one with a low specific heat. Upon heating them with the same amount of heat, which one will have the greatest change in temperature? Explain.

43. Suppose you have a flat, hot bar of iron that weighs 25.0 g at 90°C, and you place a 10.0 g bar of copper at 25°C on top of it. What will happen at the molecular level?

44. Tropical islands often have what is referred to as temperate climates, which means the daily temperature is generally the same. It does not get really hot or really cold. Since islands are surrounded by water, explain why the temperature remains relatively constant.

Chapter 3 Review

Section 3.3

45. Make a sketch of the heating curve for water. Label your axes appropriately, and label the solid, liquid, and gas phases.

46. Why are there flat places on your sketch for the heating curve of water?

47. Explain why the heat of fusion is always less than the heat of vaporization for any substance.

48. Explain why your skin feels cool when you sweat.

49. Some substances are liquids at room temperature. What does this tell you about the substances' melting points?

50. Two identical glasses full of water are left in two different rooms. One room is maintained at a temperature of 10°C and the other at 50°C. What would you find when you come back a week later?

51. What phase transition does the red arrow represent in the phase equilibrium diagram shown here?

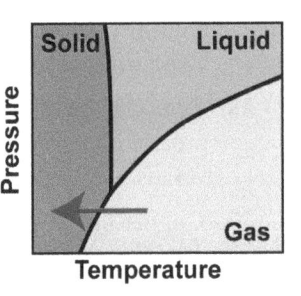

52. Describe the process of evaporation using simple words.

53. Water is the substance with the highest values of heat of fusion (335 J/g) and heat of vaporization (2,256 J/g). Describe the possible role that these large values have for life on Earth.

54. Suppose the air is at a relative humidity of 100%, and then the temperature goes down.
    a. Does the partial pressure of water vapor change? Why or why not?
    b. If the partial pressure changes, what happens to the lost water vapor?
    c. What is the relative humidity at the new temperature?

Quantitative Problems

Section 3.1

55. The normal temperature for a human body is about 98.6°F. Calculate this temperature in Celsius.

56. Ethylene glycol is a liquid organic compound, known as antifreeze. It freezes at –12°C. Calculate the freezing temperature on the Fahrenheit scale.

57. Paper catches on fire at about 451°F. What is this temperature on the Celsius scale?

58. Liquid nitrogen is used as a commercial refrigerant to flash freeze foods. It boils at –196°C. What is this temperature in Fahrenheit?

59. Convert –20°C to Kelvin.

60. Convert 273 K to degrees Fahrenheit.

Section 3.2

61. How many joules (J) are needed to increase the temperature of 15.0 g of lead from 20°C to 40°C? [Use C_p of Pb = 0.128 J/(g·°C).]

62. An unknown metal substance absorbs 387 J of energy. If that substance weighs 50.0 g and changes temperature from 30°C to 50°C, what is the metal? (Refer to your table of specific heats.)

63. A 5.0 g piece of gold (Au) changes temperature from 22 °C to 80 °C. How much heat does the gold absorb? [Use C_p of Au = 0.129 J/(g·°C).]

64. A 6.22 kg piece of copper metal is heated from 21.5 °C to 310 °C. Calculate the heat absorbed in kilojoules by the metal. [Use C_p of Cu = 0.34 J(g·°C).]

65. If 856 J of heat was absorbed by a block of iron that weighs 55.0 g, calculate the change in temperature of the block of iron. [Use C_p of Fe = 0.44 J/(g·°C).]

66. An 80.0 g mass of a metal was heated to 100°C and then plunged into 100 g of water at 24°C. The temperature of the resulting mixture was 30°C. [Use 4.18 J/(g·°C) for the specific heat of water]
    a. How many joules of heat did the water absorb?
    b. How many joules of heat did the metal lose?
    c. What is the specific heat of the metal?

67. One beaker contains 145 g of water at 22°C and a second beaker contains 76.5 g of water at 96°C. What is the final temperature of the water after the beakers are mixed?

68. A 20.5 g piece of zinc was heated to 99.5°C in boiling water. It was then added to a beaker containing 50.0 g of water at 23 °C. When the water and the metal come to thermal equilibrium, the temperature is 25.8°C. What is the specific heat of zinc?

Section 3.3

69. What quantity of heat is released (evolved) when 1.5 L of water at 0°C solidifies to ice at 0°C?

70. The heat energy required to melt 1.0 g of ice at 0°C is 335 J. If one ice cube has a mass of 58.0 g, and you have 12 ice cubes, what quantity of energy is required to melt all of the ice cubes to form liquid water at 0°C?

71. What quantity of heat is required to vaporize 110 g of benzene (C_6H_6) at its boiling point? Benzene's boiling point is 80.1°C and its heat of vaporization is 30.8 kJ/mole.

72. A teacher says the following in a lesson. "The specific heat of water is the highest of all common substances. With a value of 4.18 J/(g°C), water is very important in regulating the temperature of the earth. It takes a lot of energy to change the temperature of water by one degree Celsius. This is true for increasing or for decreasing the temperature of water. The large amount of water that covers the surface of the Earth, provides a very strong buffer both for rasing and for lowering the temperature of the atmosphere."

    Choose the most appropriate notes you might take:

    a. Water has high specific heat.

    b. Water maintain the temperature of the Earth

    c. H_2O has high specific heat.
       Takes a lot of energy to change the temp. of H_2O.
       Water helps to maintain constant Earth temp.

73. What quantity of heat energy, in joules, is required to raise the temperature of 1.50 kg of ethanol from 22.0°C to its boiling point, and then to change the liquid to vapor at that temperature? The boiling point of ethanol is 78.3°C. [The specific heat capacity of liquid ethanol is 2.44 J/(g·°C) and the heat of vaporization for ethanol is 855 J/g.]]

Phase Equilibrium Diagram of Water
(0°C - 40°C)

Use the phase equilibrium diagram above to solve problems 74–78.

74. What is the partial pressure of water vapor in saturated air at 15°C?

75. The water vapor in a sample of air has a partial pressure of 4,400 Pa. At what temperature is this air saturated (what is its dew point)?

76. Some warm air has a temperature of 30°C and a water vapor partial pressure of 2,000 Pa. This air is cooled to 10°C as night falls. Will some liquid condense or not? Explain how you get your answer.

77. Desert air at 35°C has a partial pressure of water vapor of 1,200 Pa. What is the relative humidity?

78. Which has more water vapor?
    a. saturated air (100% relative humidity) at 15°C
    b. air at 28°C with a relative humidity of 50%.

79. A student is planning an investigation to determine if the boiling point of salt solution increases with concentration. To do the investigation and understand the results, which of the following is the most important reason to select a computer?
    a. to email the conclusions to colleagues or the instructor
    b. to collect and graph the data with a spreadsheet program
    c. to record a video of the experimental procedure
    d. to write the lab report using a word processing program

CHAPTER 4
Physical and Chemical Change

What is the difference between physical change and chemical change?

What kinds of chemical changes are there?

How do we recognize chemical changes?

Memory wire is remarkable. Memory wire is made of a special alloy of nickel and titanium that looks like ordinary wire. You can bend it into complex shapes, like springs. What is so special is that, when you heat the wire up, it forcefully returns to the shape it originally had! Something about the metal "remembers" its original physical shape and tries to return once there is a heat source to provide energy. Bending is an example of physical change. Physical changes can be reversed by using physical means, such as changing temperature, filtering, or drying.

Bending is a physical change

Fork

Slinky

This change is not easily reversible

Wood and air   Ashes and smoke

Consider burning a log in a fireplace. The matter in the log changes from wood into ashes, smoke, and water vapor. When the fire cools, the ashes do not spontaneously turn back into wood again! In fact, there is no technical way known to humans to turn the ashes, water, and smoke back into a log again. Given enough time, nature can do it, but only by growing a new tree! Burning is an example of a chemical change. Chemical changes turn one substance into a completely different substance, or substances, which may have very different properties from the starting materials. Chemical changes are *not* reversible by physical means. Some chemical changes can be reversed, but only by inducing more chemical changes!

Observing the effects of chemical reactions

Let's observe some chemical reactions. This will allow us to better appreciate chemical change. Some chemical changes are accompanied by large differences in appearance when the chemicals are mixed. Here we will make some observations of the reactants we start with, followed by observations of the products formed after the chemical reaction takes place.

Measure about 20 mL of 0.50 M silver nitrate ($AgNO_3$) solution, and pour it into a test tube. Silver nitrate solution looks clear like tap water, but it contains little silver ions (Ag^+) floating around that our eyes cannot see. Now take a 10.0 cm piece of copper wire and wrap it around a glass stirring rod (or a pencil). Place the copper wire in the test tube. Make initial observations, and continue to make observations every 5 minutes. The pictures below show the system.

$t = 0$ $t = 2$ min $t = 5$ min $t = 10$ min

$Cu(s) + AgNO_3(aq)$ $Ag(s) + Cu^{2+}(aq)$

As you can see, the silver (Ag) deposits on the copper wire, turning the solution a greenish-blue color after 5 or more minutes.

Why does this color change occur? Our observations allow us to see the grayish, silvery formation on the copper wire and the blue-green color of the solution. During this chemical change, the silver ions (Ag^+) dissolved in the solution *gained electrons* and formed solid silver (Ag). You can see the solid silver forming on the copper wire. Some of the solid copper, Cu(s), *loses electrons* and dissolves in the solution forming Cu^{2+} ions, giving the solution the greenish-blue color. This type of reaction, where chemicals transfer electrons, is an important area of chemistry.

Another type of common chemical reaction is a precipitate reaction. To try this, you will need a dropper bottle of 1.0 M silver nitrate ($AgNO_3$) and a dropper bottle of 1.0 M sodium chloride (NaCl). Set up a test tube with 2.0 mL (20 drops) of NaCl and place it in a test tube holder. Slowly add $AgNO_3$. Make your observations.

The cloudy white solid formed is solid silver chloride (AgCl). If we filtered and dried the solid that settles to the bottom of the test tube, you would have a powdery white substance.

Isn't it amazing that such a brilliant white substance forms from two relatively clear solutions? Let's learn more about why chemicals do this.

4.1 Understanding Chemical Changes

Reversible changes

Physical and chemical change are fundamentally different. For example, consider a burning candle. Some of the wax in a candle is solid, while some is molten. Melting (solid to liquid) and freezing (liquid to solid) are examples of *reversible* changes. If you cool the molten wax, it becomes a solid again. Reversible changes are physical changes.

Chemical change (burning) → Physical change (melting)

Start   15 min   30 min

Over time the chemical change converts wax into water vapor and carbon dioxide

Irreversible changes

What happens inside the candle *flame* is not just melting, however. Over time, the wax vanishes! Burning wax is a very different, *irreversible* kind of change. In the flame, a chemical reaction changes wax into carbon, water vapor, and carbon dioxide—three very different substances. If you cooled the smoke from a burning candle, it would not become wax again. Wax disappears as a candle burns because water vapor and carbon dioxide are gases that float away into the air.

Physical changes are reversible

$C_{20}H_{22}$, a type of *paraffin*, is a major component of candle wax. Each molecule of paraffin contains 20 carbon atoms and 42 hydrogen atoms. If you pour the wax into different shapes, melt it, or cut it up in tiny pieces, each bit will still be made from molecules with 20 carbon and 42 hydrogen atoms. That's because a physical change does not change which molecules make up a substance. *Physical changes are reversible*:

Melting, shaping, cutting, bending, and freezing are all physical changes.

Chemical changes are irreversible

Wax burning in a flame is a chemical change. A **chemical change** is a change in the molecules themselves. In the candle flame, the atoms in paraffin molecules are rearranged into molecules of water and carbon dioxide. Burning candle wax undergoes an **irreversible change**. Chemical changes are irreversible because they rearrange atoms into different substances.

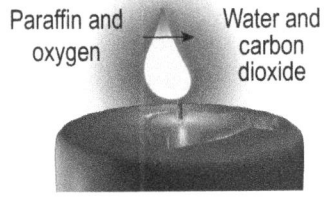

$$2C_{20}H_{42} + 61O_2 \rightarrow 42H_2O + 40CO_2$$

Paraffin and oxygen   Water and carbon dioxide

Chemistry terms

chemical change: a change that affects the structure or composition of the molecules that make up a substance, typically turning one substance into another substance with different physical properties.

irreversible change: a chemical change that rearranges atoms into different substances.

A NATURAL APPROACH TO CHEMISTRY

Energy and change

Energy determines change in matter

Changes in matter involve an exchange of energy. Whether a change is physical or chemical fundamentally depends on the amount of energy. If the energy is great enough to break a molecule apart, then chemical change is possible. If the energy is lower, then only physical change is possible. To understand why, we have to think about the forces between and within atoms and molecules. Strong forces take a lot of energy to change; weaker forces take less energy to change.

Interatomic forces act within a molecule

Let's take water as an example. **Interatomic forces** hold the two hydrogen atoms tightly to the one oxygen atom in a single water molecule. Interatomic forces are relatively strong: They take a lot of energy to break.

Strong
Interatomic forces hold molecules together

Weak
Intermolecular forces act between molecules

Intermolecular forces act between molecules

The fact that water molecules stick together to make ice or liquid means that there are other forces that act between molecules. These forces are called **intermolecular forces**. *Physical changes involve only intermolecular forces.*

Intermolecular forces are much weaker than interatomic forces

Chemical changes involve interatomic forces

The graph shows the relationship between energy and the types of change that occur in water. It takes 333 J of energy to melt 1 g of solid ice into liquid water at 0°C. By comparison, it takes 51,000 J of energy to turn 1 g of water into separated hydrogen and oxygen gases! To make a chemical change requires about 100 times more energy than a physical change.

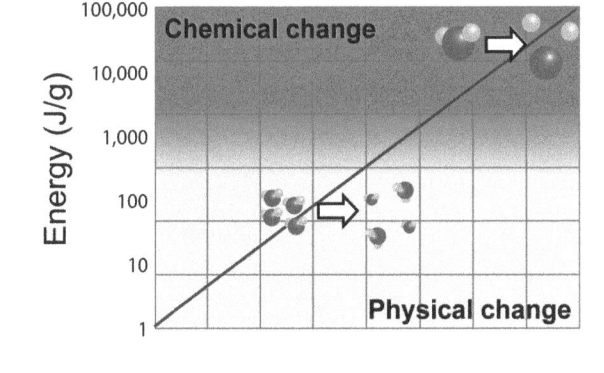

Chemical changes can release energy

The amount of energy needed to break water into hydrogen and oxygen is released if we let the hydrogen and oxygen come back together again to make water. In fact, that is the basic principle behind hydrogen-fueled cars and trucks! A hydrogen car burns hydrogen gas along with oxygen from the air and creates harmless water.

Chemistry terms

interatomic forces: forces that bond atoms together into molecules or ions.

intermolecular forces: forces that act between molecules, typically much weaker than the forces acting within molecules (interatomic forces).

What is NOT a chemical change

Changes in size or shape are physical changes

Any process that changes the shape of a substance is usually a physical change. That means bending or deforming are physical changes. It also means grinding something up into powder is a physical change. Rock candy, granulated sugar, and confectioner's sugar are the same substance, but they have been ground into different textures.

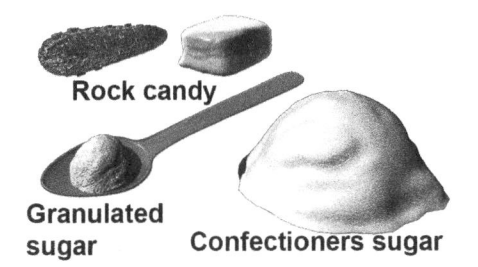

Rock candy

Granulated sugar

Confectioners sugar

Mixing and dissolving are physical changes

Adding food coloring to water spreads dissolved dye molecules evenly through the water, but it does not change the dye molecules into other ones. This is evidence that dissolving is a physical change. Even vigorous mixing is still a physical change. For example, mix some corn oil in water and it floats. Whip it with a whisk and the mixture turns cloudy and white, like milk. Under the microscope, however, you still see a mixture of water and oil. The oil droplets have become very small, but each droplet still contains thousands or millions of atoms. Making bigger drops into smaller drops is definitely a physical change. Milk and mayonaisse are mixtures of oils or fats and water.

Mixing is a physical change

Oil and water

Vigorous mixing

Dispersion of oil in water
(Physical change)

"Drying" may be a chemical or physical change

Drying is the opposite of dissolving. In drying, the water is removed from a mixture, leaving any solutes in their dry forms. Like dissolving, drying is *usually* a physical change. Drying paint for example is not always just a physical change. Certain molecules in latex or acrylic paint react chemically with oxygen to link together. Dried latex or acrylic paint is a solid that does not become liquid again when you heat it or add water back to it. In the sense of chemistry, "drying" means the purely physical process of removing liquid without chemical changes.

Atoms and chemical bonds

Chemistry is explained by the structure inside atoms

Before we can understand chemical change, we need to learn why nearly all ordinary matter exists as compounds and not as single atoms. Why does one oxygen atom bond with two hydrogen atoms to make water? Why not three (H_3O) or even four (H_4O)? Why are pure hydrogen and oxygen found as diatomic molecules (H_2 and O_2) instead of single atoms? The answers to these questions can be found by looking inside the atom, at the structure within. The structure of the atom explains the reason for chemical bonds, which are the source of chemical energy.

Atoms are not hard little balls

We draw atoms as hard, colored balls, but they are not like that at all! A better way to describe an atom is to imagine an extremely tiny, hard core surrounded by a vast, thin cloud. Atoms really have no definite "edge" or "surface."

How we draw atoms

Imaginary "surface"

Electron "cloud"

Nucleus

The nucleus

The core is called the **nucleus**, and it contains 99.8% of the mass of the atom. Compared to the size of a whole atom, the nucleus is extraordinarily tiny. If the atom were the size of your classroom, the nucleus would be the size of a single grain of sand in the center!

Electrons are in the space outside the nucleus

Around the nucleus are tiny particles called **electrons**. Hydrogen has one electron, helium has two electrons, and lithium has three. The number of electrons corresponds to the atomic number of the element, as shown on the periodic table. Chapter 5 will explain more about the structure of atoms. For now, let's look at the basic ideas to begin understanding chemical bonds.

Hydrogen has one electron

Helium has two electrons

Lithium has three electrons

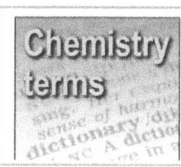

nucleus: the tiny, dense core of an atom that contains all the protons and neutrons.

electron: a tiny negatively charged particle that fills the outer volume of an atom and is responsible for chemical bonds.

Electric charge

Electric charge is a property of matter

Along with mass and volume, matter has a fundamental property called **electric charge**. Electric charge is important because it creates both the forces that hold the atoms together and the forces that cause atoms to combine into compounds and molecules.

There are only two kinds of electric charge: we call them **positive** charge, indicated by the plus (+) sign, and **negative** charge, indicated by the minus (–) sign. Positive and negative charges attract each other. Two positive charges repel each other. Two negative charges also repel each other.

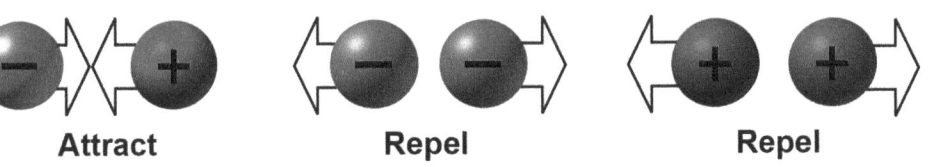

Attract   **Repel**   **Repel**

Protons have positive charge

Positive charge is a property of one of the particles in the nucleus called the **proton**. All of the protons, and therefore all the positive charge in an atom, are in the nucleus. In fact, the atomic number is defined as the number of protons in the nucleus. Hydrogen has one proton in its nucleus, helium has two protons, lithium has three protons, and so on.

Electrons are attracted to the nucleus

Electrons are bound to the nucleus by the attractive force between electrons (–) and protons (+). The electrons don't fall into the nucleus because of their kinetic energy. Think of the Earth orbiting the Sun. Gravity creates a force that pulls the Earth toward the Sun. Earth's kinetic energy causes it to orbit the Sun rather than fall straight in. Although electrons don't really move in orbits, the energy analogy is close enough.

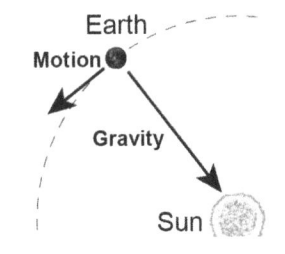

Neutral atoms have zero total charge

The force between electric charges is extremely strong. The electrical attraction between a proton and an electron is approximately 10^{40} times as strong as gravity. This is a 10 with 40 zeros after it! The reason you don't notice electric charge is that atoms are perfectly **neutral**. The positive charge of a proton is *exactly* the same amount as the negative charge on an electron. A carbon atom has six protons and six electrons. Its total electric charge is exactly zero because +6 from the protons and –6 from the electrons add up to zero.

Chemistry terms

electric charge: a fundamental property of matter that comes in positive and negative.
positive: the attribute of charge assigned to the proton.
negative: the attribute of charge assigned to the electron.
proton: a tiny particle in the nucleus that has a positive charge.
neutral: an atom or molecule with zero total electric charge.

A NATURAL APPROACH TO CHEMISTRY

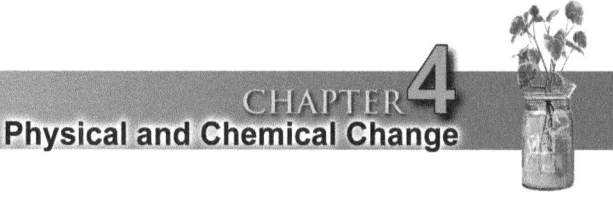

Covalent bonds

Elements and electrons

Each element has a different number of electrons and a unique arrangement of electrons around the nucleus. This different number and arrangement of electrons is what creates each element's unique chemical properties. Hydrogen has a single electron, and that single electron is what makes hydrogen combine with oxygen in a two-to-one ratio to make H_2O. Nearly all the elements form chemical bonds easily. This is why most of the matter you experience is in the form of compounds.

Electrons form chemical bonds

Chemical bonds are created by electrons. Two atoms that are sharing one or more electrons are chemically bonded and move together. In a water molecule, each hydrogen atom shares its single electron with the oxygen atom at the center.

A chemical bond is formed by sharing or transferring electrons

Covalent bonds

The strongest chemical bond is called a **covalent bond**. A covalent bond is formed when two atoms share two electrons. A water molecule contains two covalent bonds, one between each hydrogen and the oxygen. Each bond represents two electrons. In a covalent bond, electrons are shared between atoms, not transferred.

Double bond
O_2
Oxygen

Triple bond
N_2
Nitrogen

NH_3
Ammonia

CH_4
Methane

Molecules

An electrically neutral group of atoms held together by covalent bonds is called a **molecule**. Water is a molecule, and so is glucose. Other examples of molecules are methane (CH_4), ammonia (NH_3), and carbon dioxide (CO_2).

Some elements can share multiple electrons with the same atom. Good examples are oxygen (O_2) and nitrogen (N_2). An oxygen molecule contains a double covalent bond (four shared electrons). A nitrogen molecule has a triple covalent bond (six shared electrons). In diagrams, double and triple bonds are represented as double and triple lines connecting the atoms.

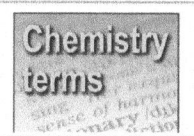
Chemistry terms

chemical bond: a relatively strong connection between two atoms.
covalent bond: chemical bond that consists of two shared electrons.
molecule: a neutral group of atoms chemically bonded together.

Why chemical bonds form

Bonds give an energy advantage to atoms

Chemical bonds form when attractive forces create an advantage in energy. For example, think about two strong magnets as they are brought near each other. When they get close enough, the magnets quickly snap together. Clearly some force pulls the magnets together, but there is another way to look at the situation. The total energy of the two magnets is lower when they are together compared to when they are apart.

Energy is released when bonds form

To pull the magnets apart, you need a force. It takes energy to create forces. If it takes energy to pull them apart, the same energy is released when the magnets come together. In fact, the force that pulls the magnets together is created by the energy difference between being apart and being together. The same is true of chemical bonds. Energy is released when chemical bonds form. Energy is released because chemically bonded atoms have less total energy than free atoms.

Atoms form bonds to reach a lower energy state

A general principle of chemistry is that atoms arrange themselves so they have the lowest possible energy. Like a ball rolling downhill, atoms form compounds because the atoms have lower energy when they are together compared to when they are separate. Consider water for example. One oxygen and two hydrogen atoms have more total energy apart than they do when combined in a water molecule.

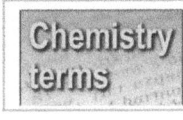

When hydrogen and oxygen combine to make water, 285,000 J of energy is released

The enthalpy of formation

for every mole of water molecules created. This energy is called the **enthalpy of formation**, shown as ΔH_f. Table 4.1 lists the enthalpy of formation for water as negative because energy is given off instead of absorbed. By convention, pure elements are assigned an energy of zero.

TABLE 4.1. Enthalpies of formation for some common substances

Substance	ΔH_f (kJ/mole)	Substance	ΔH_f (kJ/mole)
Hydrogen (H_2)	0	H_2O	−285.5
Carbon (C)	0	CO_2	−393.5
Oxygen (O_2)	0	CH_4	−74.6
Nitrogen (N_2)	0	$C_6H_{12}O_6$	−1266.5

Chemistry terms

enthalpy of formation: the change in energy when one mole of a compound is assembled from pure elements.

Ionic bonds

An ion is a charged atom

Not all compounds are made of molecules. For example, sodium chloride (NaCl) is a compound of sodium (Na) and chlorine (Cl) in a ratio of one sodium atom per chlorine atom. The difference is that, in sodium chloride, the electron is essentially *transferred* from the sodium atom to the chlorine atom. When atoms gain or lose an electron, they become *ions*. An **ion** is an atom that has either lost one or more electrons or gained one or more electrons. By losing an electron, the sodium atom becomes a sodium ion with a charge of +1. By gaining an electron, the chlorine atom becomes a chloride ion with a charge of −1. Notice that when chlorine becomes an ion, the name changes to chloride.

An ionic bond forms when one or more electrons are transferred from one atom to another

Ionic bonds

Sodium and chlorine form an ionic bond because the positive sodium ion is attracted to the negative chloride ion. **Ionic bonds** are bonds in which electrons are transferred from one atom to another. In general, ionic bonds are slightly weaker than covalent bonds.

Ionic compounds do not form molecules

Ionic bonds are not limited to a single pair of atoms like covalent bonds. In sodium chloride, each positive sodium ion is attracted to all of the neighboring chloride ions. Likewise, each chloride ion is attracted to all the neighboring sodium atoms. Since the bonds are not just between pairs of atoms, ionic compounds do not form molecules! In an ionic compound, each atom bonds with all of its neighbors through attraction between positive and negative charge.

Sodium chloride (NaCl) is an ionic compound

The chemical formula for ionic compounds

The chemical formula for an ionic compound such as salt is used in the exact same way as the formula for a molecular compound such as water. The chemical formula for salt (NaCl) means that there is one sodium atom per chlorine atom. You calculate the formula mass of salt (58.5 g/mole) by adding the atomic masses of sodium (23.0 g/mole) and chlorine (35.5 g/mole).

Sodium chloride involves the transfer of one electron. However, ionic compounds may

Ions may be multiply charged

also be formed by the transfer of two or more electrons. A good example is magnesium chloride ($MgCl_2$). The magnesium atom gives up two electrons to become a magnesium ion with a charge of +2 (Mg^{2+}). Each chlorine atom gains one electron to become a chloride ion with a charge of −1 (Cl^-). The ion charge is written as a superscript after the element (Mg^{2+}, Fe^{3+}, Cl^-, etc.).

Chemistry terms

ion: an atom or small molecule with an overall positive or negative charge due to an imbalance of protons and electrons
ionic bond: an attraction between oppositely charged ions. This attraction occurs with all nearby ions of opposite charge.

Reactivity

Elements that react strongly are rarely found in pure form

Some elements react so strongly that they are never found in nature by themselves as pure elements. Examples are lithium (Li), sodium (Na), and potassium (K). These are very common elements, but they are always found in compounds such as salt (NaCl), minerals in rocks such as petalite ($LiAlSi_4O_{10}$), and even chemicals in your body.

Petalite
$LiAlSi_4O_{10}$

Salt
NaCl

Some elements do not react

Other elements such as helium, neon, and argon are always found as pure elements. These elements, called noble gases, are not reactive because of their electronic structure. Noble gases do not form chemical bonds with other elements.

Reactivity and the periodic table

What does it mean for an element to be "reactive"? In a literal sense, it means that it forms bonds with anything it touches! If you look at the periodic table, you see that the three most reactive metals (Li, Na, and K) are in the same group (column). The unreactive elements (He, Ne, Ar, Kr, and Xe) are also in a group, but on the far right of the table.

1	2	3	4	← Electrons away from noble gas →				4	3	2	1	

The halogens are reactive elements

To the immediate left of the noble gases is another group of very reactive elements—the halogens, which include fluorine (F), chlorine (Cl), and bromine (Br).

If we look at the two example compounds of salt (NaCl) and the mineral petalite ($LiAlSi_4O_{10}$), we see an important pattern. Sodium and lithium from the left of the periodic table are bonded with elements from the right half of the periodic table: chlorine, aluminum, oxygen, and silicon.

Elements on the far left and far right of the periodic table are more likely to form chemical bonds

Reactivity and the periodic table

The more reactive elements in the periodic table tend to form chemical bonds more easily. For example, sodium readily bonds with chlorine and the reaction releases a large amount of energy. Sodium and chlorine are on opposite sides of the periodic table.

Chemistry terms

reactivity: the tendency of elements to form chemical bonds.

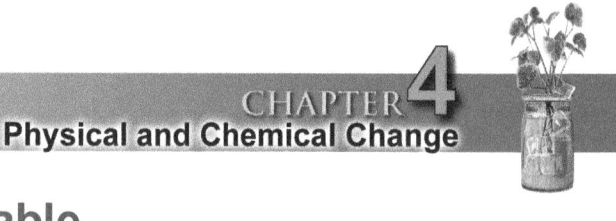
Reactivity and the periodic table

The two main classes of chemicals that we work with in general chemistry are ionic and molecular compounds. The periodic table helps us tell the difference between these two types of compounds.

Ionic compounds contain a metal and a nonmetal

Ionic compounds, which are often referred to as salts, form between metals and nonmetals. You have learned that atoms in ionic compounds transfer electrons. In the case of an ionic compound, the metal loses the electron(s) and the nonmetal gains the electron(s). Let's look at the periodic table below to see how this pattern works.

When dealing with a chemical compound, you can look at the periodic table to see whether there is a metal bonded to a nonmetal; if so, you can classify the compound as ionic.

Molecular compounds contain two or more nonmetals

Molecular compounds are made up of two or more nonmetals bonded together. You can see from the periodic table that these elements appear in the upper right corner. Molecular compounds share electrons. For example, carbon dioxide (CO_2) is made of carbon and oxygen, and both are nonmetals.

Use the periodic table to help determine whether a compound is ionic or molecular

Hydrogen (H) has both metallic and nonmetallic behavior. The fact that it only has one electron and one proton makes the hydrogen atom very small in size. This is why it is a unique element on the periodic table. In most compounds, hydrogen shares its one electron and forms a molecular compound. This is because hydrogen holds its one electron very tightly to the nucleus.

Is the compound CF_4 ionic or molecular? We start by locating carbon (C) and fluorine (F) on the periodic table, and we find that they are both nonmetals. This indicates that CF_4 is a molecule. We know it shares its electrons in the bonds it makes.

4.2 Chemical Reactions

Examples of chemical change

Chemical changes turn one substance into a different substance. We already mentioned that the digestion of food is a process of chemical changes. The substances that leave your body are definitely not the same substances that went in! Here is another (cleaner) example. The device in the diagram performs *electrolysis*. In electrolysis, an electric current transfers a relatively large amount of energy to water molecules. The water molecules change slowly into gas.

Electrolysis is not the same as boiling

Over time the mass of water goes down, and the volume of gas goes up. However, this is not boiling because *the gas is not water vapor*.

1. When you cool the gas, it does not condense back into droplets of water.
2. One of the gases burns! Water vapor (steam) does not burn.
3. The other gas causes flames to get much brighter! This is also not characteristic of water vapor.

Water is different from hydrogen and oxygen

On the molecular level, each particle (or molecule) of water contains one oxygen atom bonded to two hydrogen atoms. The chemical reaction that occurs in electrolysis splits up the water molecule into separate atoms of hydrogen and oxygen. Hydrogen and oxygen are different substances than water. For example, both hydrogen and oxygen are gases at room temperature, whereas water is a liquid at room temperature.

Chemical reactions

A chemical change is caused by a **chemical reaction**. A chemical reaction is usually written as an equation that has the molecules you start with on the left and the molecules you finish with on the right. The reaction for electrolysis starts with two water molecules and produces two hydrogen (H_2) molecules and one oxygen (O_2) molecule.

chemical reaction: a process that rearranges the atoms in any substance(s) to produce one or more different substances.

chemical change: a result of chemical reaction.

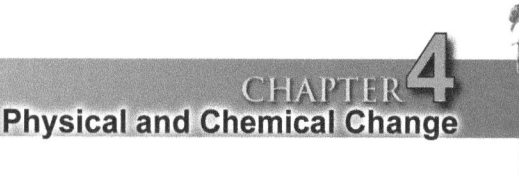
The chemical equation

Reactants and products

The chemical formula for water is H_2O. How do we represent the reaction that assembles hydrogen and oxygen to make water? The answer is with a chemical equation. The **reactants** are the compounds that you start with. The reactants are chemically changed into the **products**. The products are the compounds that are formed by the reaction. In this example, the reactants are hydrogen and oxygen, and the product is water.

Reactants	Products
H_2O	H_2 + O_2

$$H_2O \rightarrow H_2 + O_2 \quad \textit{unbalanced equation}$$

Reading a chemical equation

To read a chemical equation, you need to understand its numbers. The *subscripts* tell you how many atoms of each element are in the molecule. For example, the 2 in H_2O tells you there are two hydrogen atoms per oxygen atom in a water molecule. Pure oxygen (O_2) and hydrogen (H_2) gas are molecules of two atoms each (*diatomic molecules*).

Unbalanced chemical equations

But this equation is not *balanced*. The equation shows two hydrogen atoms and two oxygen atoms on the reactant side. There are two hydrogen atoms but *only one oxygen atom* on the product side. That leaves one oxygen atom unaccounted for.

Reactants	Products
$2H_2O$	$2H_2$ + O_2

$$2H_2O \rightarrow 2H_2 + O_2 \quad \textit{balanced equation}$$

Balanced chemical equations

The **balanced equation** combines two molecules of hydrogen with one molecule of oxygen to make two molecules of water. Notice that all the atoms on the reactant side of the equation are used on the product side. No atoms are left over. The **coefficient** tells you how many molecules participate in the balanced reaction. The coefficient is the number "2" in front of H_2O. It tells you there are two molecules of water in the balanced equation.

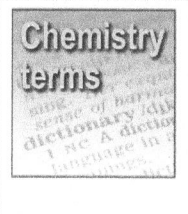

Chemistry terms

reactant: a substance that is used or changed in a chemical reaction.

product: a substance that is created or released in a chemical reaction.

balanced equation: an equation in which the total numbers of atoms of each element are the same on both the reactant side and the product side of the equation.

coefficient: the number that tells you how many of each molecule participate in the balanced reaction.

The balanced chemical equation

Rules for balancing equations

When balancing a chemical equation, you want to get the same number of each type of atom on both the reactant and product sides. Here are the rules for doing it.

1. *Do not* change the subscripts, because this would change the identity of the substances in the reaction. For example, H_2O is water but H_2O_2 is hydrogen peroxide.

2. *Do* change the coefficients to adjust how many molecules of each substance appear as either products or reactants.

Balancing the reaction for rust

The process is often trial and error. You start with an unbalanced reaction that shows the correct chemical formula for each substance. You then try different coefficients to see what works. Here is an example: Iron (Fe) reacts with oxygen (O_2) in the air to form rust (Fe_2O_3). The balanced and unbalanced reactions are shown below.

unbalanced reaction

$$Fe + O_2 \rightarrow Fe_2O_3$$

Reactants	Products
$Fe + O_2$	Fe_2O_3

balanced reaction

$$4Fe + 3O_2 \rightarrow 2Fe_2O_3$$

Reactants	Products
$4Fe + 3O_2$	$2Fe_2O_3$

It is useful to make a table showing the atoms of each element on each side. Try different coefficients until the table shows the same numbers on both sides.

Atoms (or moles)

	Reactants	Products
Iron	1	2
Oxygen	2	3

Atoms (or moles)

	Reactants	Products
Iron	4	4
Oxygen	6	6

Solved problem

When magnesium metal (Mg) reacts with oxygen (O_2) it forms magnesium oxide (MgO). Write the balanced equation for this reaction.

Given: *The unbalanced reaction is $Mg + O_2 \rightarrow MgO$.*

Relationships: *The same number of each type of atom must appear on each side.*

Solve: *There are two oxygen atoms on the left side but only one on the right side. Oxygen is unbalanced.*

Adding a 2 in front of water ($2H_2O$) balances the oxygen atoms.

Adding a 2 in front of magnesium ($2Mg$) balances the Mg atoms.

Answer: *The balanced chemical equation is $2Mg + O_2 \rightarrow 2MgO$.*

A NATURAL APPROACH TO CHEMISTRY

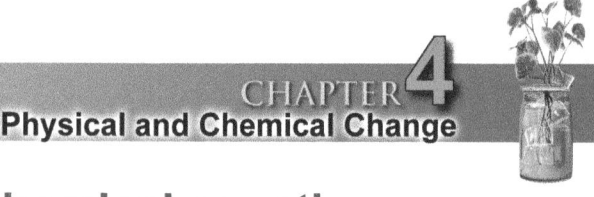

The meaning of a balanced chemical equation

The photosynthesis reaction

The basis of most life on Earth is the *photosynthesis* reaction. This reaction takes place inside plants, combining water from the soil with carbon dioxide from the air to make glucose (sugar) and oxygen. Plants use the sugar for energy and to build starch and cellulose, the larger molecules that make up plants' cell walls. Animals breathe oxygen and eat plants to get sugar and other plant molecules.

Photosynthesis

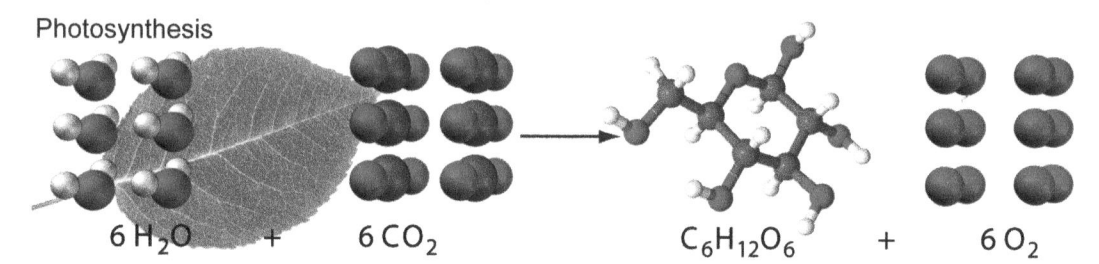

$$6\,H_2O \quad + \quad 6\,CO_2 \quad \longrightarrow \quad C_6H_{12}O_6 \quad + \quad 6\,O_2$$

Reading the reaction

The equation tells us that six molecules of water and six molecules of carbon dioxide react to produce one molecule of glucose and six molecules of oxygen. Molecules are so tiny though; how does the equation relate to the macroscopic (real) world?

Coefficients represent moles

The answer is that the coefficients also represent *moles* of each substance. Remember, a mole always has the same number of atoms. We can interpret the coefficients to mean *six moles* of water combine with *six moles* of carbon dioxide to produce *one mole* of glucose and six moles of oxygen. This is the real power of the balanced equation. It tells us precisely how many moles of each substance are used (reactants) or produced (products). A mole is a measurable quantity, often amounting to grams or even kilograms.

Converting from moles to grams

We use the formula mass to convert from moles to grams. For example, the formula mass for water is approximately 18 g/mole. That means 6 moles of water has a mass of $6 \times 18 = 108$ g. The balanced reaction says 108 g of water combines with 264 g of carbon dioxide to produce 180 g of glucose and 192 g of oxygen.

Photosynthesis

6 H₂O	6 CO₂	C₆H₁₂O₆	6O₂
6 moles x18 g/mole	6 moles x44 g/mole	1 mole x180 g/mole	6 moles x32 g/mole
108 g	**264 g**	**180 g**	**192 g**

Conservation of mass

Note that both products and reactants add up to the same total mass. Because the same atoms appear on both the reactant and product sides of the balanced equation, the total mass on each side must be the same. This is called the law of **conservation of mass**.

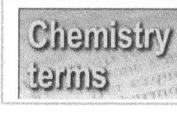
Chemistry terms

conservation of mass: law that states that, in any chemical reaction, the total mass remains the same: the total mass of reactants equals the total mass of products.

Endothermic reactions

Energy is also part of reactions

If you mix water and carbon dioxide together, you do not produce sugar. There is carbon dioxide in the atmosphere, and there is plenty of water, yet we do not see puddles spontaneously turn into sugar! That tells us there is something missing from the chemical equation. You may have guessed that the "something" is *energy*. Energy is both the cause of chemical change and also what limits change from happening.

Including energy in photosynthesis

Let's consider the photosynthesis equation *including energy*.

Photosynthesis is endothermic

2,800,000 J from sunlight

$$2,800,000 \text{ J} + 6H_2O + 6CO_2 \rightarrow C_6H_{12}O_6 + 6O_2$$

The photosynthesis reaction takes a lot of energy

This equation tells us that energy is one of the reactants. Energy needs to be supplied for this reaction to proceed. In fact, a lot of energy is required. One mole of glucose has a mass of 180 g. It takes an *input* of 2,800,000 J to make 180 g of glucose from water and carbon dioxide. This is enough energy to lift a small car 300 m in the air, or almost 1,000 ft up. All that energy is needed just to make a small cupful of sugar from water and carbon dioxide. Puddles of water do not become sugar because there is normally not enough energy to do it.

Energy for photosynthesis comes from the Sun

Glucose is made inside plants, so where does the energy come from? You probably already know the answer: the Sun. Plants use the energy in sunlight to assemble glucose molecules from carbon dioxide and water in the environ-ment. At night, plants do not make glucose because there is no adequate source of energy.

Endothermic reactions

Photosynthesis is an example of an **endothermic** reaction. An endothermic reaction absorbs energy as it goes from reactants to products. Energy needs to be supplied or the reaction does not work. Many of the reactions in your body are also endothermic reactions, as are many of the reactions that occur when food is cooked.

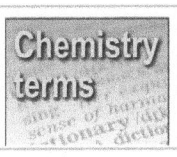

Chemistry terms

endothermic reaction: a chemical reaction that requires an input of energy to go from reactants to products; endothermic reactions absorb energy.

Exothermic reactions

The cellular respiration reaction

The opposite reaction of photosynthesis is *cellular respiration*. In cellular respiration, glucose is combined with oxygen to make water and carbon dioxide. The chemical reaction is written just like photosynthesis written backward, *including the energy*.

Respiration is exothermic

$$C_6H_{12}O_6 + 6O_2 \rightarrow 6H_2O + 6CO_2 + \boxed{2,800,000 \text{ J}}$$

Exothermic reactions give off energy

In cellular respiration, oxygen is used and energy is released. A reaction that releases energy is called **exothermic**. The exothermic reaction that combines glucose with oxygen is how animals, including you, derive energy from food. In every cell in your body, glucose is being broken down into carbon dioxide and water. The exact reactions are more complex, but the result is what is written above. Every mole (180 g) of glucose your body burns releases 2,800,000 J of energy. The reaction requires six moles of oxygen to proceed, which must be obtained from the air you breathe.

Glucose stores chemical energy like a molecular "battery"

In many ways, the glucose molecule is a natural *battery*. Plants "charge" the battery with energy from sunlight by combining carbon dioxide and water. Animals (and plants) use the energy by breaking the molecule back down into carbon dioxide and water again. The energy is stored in the chemical bonds between atoms.

Glucose
$C_6H_{12}O_6$

Enthalpy

The energy potential of a chemical reaction has a special name: **enthalpy**. Enthalpy is measured in joules per mole (J/mole) or kilojoules per mole (kJ/mole). If the enthalpy is positive, the reaction increases the total energy of the constituent atoms. Reactions with positive enthalpy are always endothermic, because they need to absorb energy to proceed. Photosynthesis has an enthalpy of +2,800 kJ/mole. Reactions with negative enthalpy release energy. Exothermic reactions always have negative enthalpy because they release energy. Respiration has an enthalpy of –2,800 kJ/mole.

Chemistry terms

exothermic reaction: a chemical reaction that releases energy in going from reactants to products.

enthalpy: the energy potential of a chemical reaction at standard temperature and pressure, measured in joules per mole (J/mole) or kilojoules per mole (kJ/mole).

System and surroundings for reactions

The big picture of energy flow

Let's think about the two reactions of photosynthesis and respiration together. The energy it takes to make the glucose molecule is exactly the same as the energy released when the molecule is broken down again. As mentioned earlier, the first law of thermodynamics says that energy cannot be created or destroyed; it is always conserved. Another way to say this is that the total energy of the universe is a constant. Energy that is stored in one place has to be taken away from some other place.

$$2,800,000\ J + 6H_2O + 6CO_2 \rightarrow C_6H_{12}O_6 + 6O_2$$

$$C_6H_{12}O_6 + 6O_2 \rightarrow 6H_2O + 6CO_2 + 2,800,000\ J$$

The system includes what we are interested in

It's impossible to do experiments using the whole universe, so we choose a small portion to be our **system**. We choose the system to include just the specific matter and energy we are interested in investigating. Very often the system will be the products and reactants of the reaction.

The surroundings are everything else

The rest of the universe all around the system is called the **surroundings**.

1. The total mass and energy of the system plus the surroundings is constant.

2. Any matter or energy *gained* by the system must be *lost* by the surroundings.

3. Any matter or energy *lost* by the system must be *gained* by the surroundings.

The system is often the reactants and products of a reaction

The surroundings are everything except the products and reactants

$$C_6H_{12}O_6 + 6O_2 \rightarrow 6H_2O + 6CO_2 \qquad \textbf{Energy}$$

System
Products and reactants

Surroundings
lab equipment
air in room
water in solution

Chemistry terms

system: an interrelated group of matter and energy that we choose to investigate.
surroundings: everything outside the "system."

Activation energy

Why don't exothermic reactions occur spontaneously?

The respiration reaction releases energy by breaking down glucose into carbon dioxide and water. The reaction is not endothermic, so why doesn't a tablespoon of glucose turn into CO_2 and H_2O by itself? The answer has to do with the microscopic details of how chemical reactions occur. The hydrogen, carbon, and oxygen atoms in $C_6H_{12}O_6$ must first be separated before they can regroup to form the new molecules of CO_2 and H_2O. Separating the atoms means breaking the *chemical bonds* that hold the glucose molecule together.

It takes energy to break chemical bonds

Think of two chemically bonded atoms like two magnets that are stuck together. It takes energy to pull the magnets apart. Similarly, it takes energy to break the chemical bonds and separate the atoms in glucose.

It takes energy to separate two magnets

It takes energy to separate two bonded atoms

Activation energy

In an exothermic reaction, the atoms arranged as the products have lower energy than they had when they were arranged as the reactants. However, to get to the lower energy state, the molecule needs enough input energy to get "over the hump." This energy is called the **activation energy**. Activation energy is the energy needed to start a reaction and break chemical bonds in the reactants. Without enough activation energy, a reaction will not happen, even if it releases energy if it were to happen. That is also why a flammable material, such as gasoline, does not burn without a spark or flame. The spark supplies the activation energy to start the reaction.

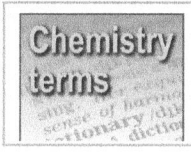

activation energy: the energy necessary to break bonds in the reactants so a chemical reaction can occur, measured in units of joules per mole (J/mole) or kilojoules per mole (kJ/mole).

4.3 Chemical Reactions in the Lab

Many reactions occur in solution

Many reactions occur between chemicals dissolved in water. This includes all of the reactions that sustain life in your body. Why are solutions so important in reactions?

The answer is not complicated. *Reactions can only occur if molecules can move around and touch each other.* For example, sodium sulfide (NaS) is a powdery, white mineral salt. Copper sulfate ($CuSO_4$) is a bright blue powder. If you mix the two chemicals as powders, nothing really happens.

Dry
NaS + $CuSO_4$
White powder   Blue powder
Light blue powder mixture (no reaction)

In solution
+
NaS (aq) $CuSO_4$(aq)

Dark brown precipitate
Chemical reaction

The result is quite different if you dissolve the powdered chemicals in water and then mix the solutions. The copper sulfate is a bright blue solution. The sodium sulfide is a colorless solution. When you mix the two, a deep brown, almost black sludge forms and settles at the bottom. If the quantities are right, the blue color may almost disappear.

Aqueous solutions

A solution with water as the solvent is called an aqueous solution. Aqueous solutions are so important that chemists consider being dissolved in water to be like a fourth state of matter! When we write reactions, we use the symbols (s), (l), (g), and (aq) to show what state of matter the reactants and products are in:

- (s)   indicates a solid.
- (l)   indicates a liquid.
- (g)   indicates a gas.
- (aq)   indicates a substance dissolved in water.

Precipitates

The brown sludge is an example of a *precipitate*. A **precipitate** is a compound that is not soluble in water. Precipitates are evidence that a chemical reaction has occurred. In this reaction, the insoluble compound is copper sulfide (CuS). Aqueous means dissolved in water.

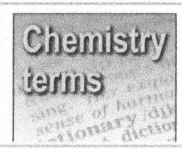

Chemistry terms

aqueous (aq): dissolved in water.

precipitate: an insoluble compound that forms in a chemical reaction in aqueous solution.

Oxidation and reduction

Salts are ionic compounds that dissolve to form ions

In the next few chapters, you will see how the electrons in atoms are directly responsible for their chemical properties. For example, when sugar is dissolved in water, the molecules become separated from each other but remain whole. This is not true for *salts* such as copper sulfate ($CuSO_4$). **Salts** are ionic compounds that form ions when dissolved in water. If you look at the molecular level, you would find that, in aqueous solution, copper sulfate dissociates into copper ions (Cu^{2+}) and sulfate ions (SO_4^{2-}). This happens because each single copper atom transfers two electrons to the sulfate ion.

$CuSO_4(s)$

$CuSO_4(aq)$

Sulfate ion

Copper ion

Oxidation means losing electron(s)

Pure zinc is a relatively soft, gray metal. Copper is also a soft metal, but it is reddish-gold in color. When zinc metal is placed in a solution of copper sulfate, the zinc slowly disappears! The zinc disappears because it is being oxidized. In chemistry, **oxidation** means losing an electron and becoming more positive. The zinc metal atoms become Zn^{2+} ions, and these go into the solution.

Reduction means gaining electron(s)

Zinc has to give up two electrons to become Zn^{2+}. So, where do these electrons go? They go to the copper ions. A Cu^{2+} ion accepts two electrons to become a copper (Cu) atom. Copper atoms are no longer soluble in water, so they drop out of the solution as copper metal. The reddish-brown sludge that appears in the test tube is pure copper metal. In chemistry, **reduction** is the process of gaining electrons and becoming more negative. The copper ion (Cu^{2+}) accepts two electrons and loses its positive charge to become copper metal.

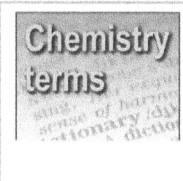
Chemistry terms

salt: an ionic compound that dissolves in water to produce ions.

oxidation: a chemical reaction that increases the charge of an atom or ion by giving up electrons.

reduction: a chemical reaction that decreases the charge of an atom or ion by accepting electrons.

Acids and bases

The dissociation of water

When pure water is carefully examined, we find that, on average, one out of every 550 million molecules of water is *dissociated*, or separated, into a hydrogen (H^+) ion and a hydroxide (OH^-) ion.

$$H_2O \xrightleftharpoons[]{dissociation} H^+ + OH^-$$

The dissociation reaction is written with a double arrow to show that the ions can recombine to make a normal water molecule. In equilibrium, the constant dissociation and recombination leaves (on average) one out of 550 million water molecules broken apart into H^+ and OH^-.

Properties of acids

An **acid** is a compound that dissolves in water to make a solution that contains *more H^+ ions* than there are in pure water. Acids have the following properties:

- Acids give some foods such as lemons their sour taste.

- Acids react with metals to produce hydrogen gas (H_2).

- Acids can corrode metals and burn skin through chemical action.

Acids create the sour taste in food

When hydrochloric acid (HCl) dissolves in water, it ionizes into hydrogen (H^+) and chlorine (Cl^-) ions. The fact that the H^+ ion is created is what makes HCl an acid.

Properties of bases

A **base** is a compound that dissolves in water to make a solution with *more OH^- ions* than there are in pure water. Some of the extra OH^- combines with H^+ to make water again, so another way to think about bases is that they reduce the concentration of H^+ ions. Bases have the following properties:

- Bases create a bitter taste.
- Bases have a slippery feel, like soap.
- Bases can neutralize acids.

Common bases

Ammonia

Soap

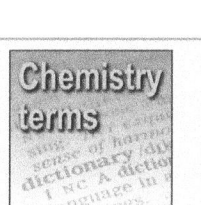

Chemistry terms

acid: a chemical that dissolves in water to create more H^+ ions than there are in neutral water.

base: a chemical that dissolves in water to create fewer H^+ ions than there are in neutral water (or equivalently, more OH^- ions).

Acid–base reactions

Acids and bases react to form salts and water

When acids and bases are combined in aqueous solution, they react to make water and salt. In fact, the chemical definition of *salt* is any compound formed from the positive ion from a base and the negative ion from an acid. For example, hydrochloric acid (HCl) is a common laboratory acid; it is also found in your stomach where it helps to break down food. Sodium hydroxide (NaOH) is a common base. Sodium hydroxide is found in drain cleaners and industrial processes.

Acids and bases react to produce water and a salt

$$HCl + NaOH \xrightarrow{\text{aqueous solution}} H^+ + Cl^- + Na^+ + OH^- \rightarrow H_2O + NaCl$$

| hydrochloric acid | sodium hydroxide | H$^+$ ion | chloride ion | sodium ion | hydroxide ion | water | sodium chloride (salt) |

Table salt (NaCl) is formed by the positive sodium ion from sodium hydroxide (a base) and the negative chloride ion from hydrochloric acid.

Acids are important because of the H$^+$ ion

The H$^+$ ion is very important in chemistry, mainly because it is a *single bare nucleus, with no electrons*. Earlier in the chapter we said that chemical bonds come from the interactions of electrons, in the outer part of the atom. This is true with one big exception—the H$^+$ ion. Since H$^+$ is chemically powerful, and it is *always* present in water, acids play a crucial role in chemistry. Many reactions that occur in aqueous solutions are sensitive to the concentration of H$^+$ ions, including nearly all the reactions in your body.

The pH scale

Because acids and bases are so important, they have a special measurement—the *pH scale*. The **pH scale** tells you whether a solution is acidic or basic. A pH less than 7 indicates an acid. An acid has higher concentration of H$^+$ than pure water. A pH greater than 7 indicates a base. A base has an H$^+$ concentration less than that of pure water.

The pH scale

Acids ← → Bases

0 1 2 3 4 5 6 7 8 9 10 11 12 13 14

Pure water

> **Chemistry terms**
>
> **pH scale:** a measurement of the H$^+$ ion concentration that indicates whether a solution is acidic or basic; pure water has a pH of 7; solutions with pH < 7 are acidic.; solutions with pH > 7 are basic.

Chemistry in the movies

When you go to the movies, chances are there are chemical reactions involved in making the special effects you see. Computers are used to generate some effects, but chemicals are still used when a realistic or more dramatic effect is needed. Action movies and movies that involve magic seem to use the most chemical reactions.

Chemical reactions are often used to generate convincing explosions and fires. On a Hollywood movie set, these chemical reactions need to be safely contained and easily extinguished. To accomplish this, just the right amount of chemical is added to achieve the desired effect. To carry out a chemical reaction with some precision requires skill and experience. For this reason, creating special effects is often called an "art."

How are these effects created? Fire scenes are created using combustible gases such as propane. As you have learned, fire is the result of a chemical reaction between two gases—a hydrocarbon made of C and H atoms and oxygen (O_2). When a spark or heat is added to this mixture, it provides the energy necessary for some of the bonds to be broken between atoms. These atoms then recombine with oxygen atoms to form CO_2, H_2O, and more heat, which further increases the combustion process. Sometimes other chemicals such as lithium (Li) and strontium (Sr) are added to the flames to achieve a more red-colored flame. When these effects are required on a Hollywood film set, the amounts of fuel are small and contained. Fire extinguishers are handy just in case. Fire blazes can also be filmed separately and then added to the film scene using computer technology.

Explosions seen in movies are created by *pyrotechnics*. The stunt crew in charge of pyrotechnics has special training and certification for using explosives. Small amounts of C-4 explosive are used and placed in areas that will provide the desired visual effect. C-4 explosives are made of approximately 90% RDX, which is a chemical composed of nitrogen, carbon, and hydrogen. Plastic explosives made of C-4 are used because they can be molded and shaped to fit easily where they are needed, and the size of the explosion can be controlled by how much RDX is added.

Different explosions require different chemical mixtures, and this takes time to perfect!

In a movie involving magic and sorcery, chemicals may be used to create an eerie smoke when entering a mysterious cave. The smoke can be white, gray, or even colored. A variety of methods have been used in Hollywood to make smoke. The first method was to use dry ice (solid CO_2). Dry ice sublimes readily at room temperature, giving a smoky effect. However, CO_2 gas from subliming dry ice displaces oxygen in the air. When too much dry ice is used, actors could experience nausea and dizziness from a lack of oxygen.

Liquid nitrogen (N_2) is sometimes used for fog and smoke. Liquid nitrogen creates a low-lying fog effect. Liquid nitrogen is pumped into a machine that contains hot water (near boiling), creating rapid condensation and a thick white fog. Today glycols are used for the most part. Glycols are also called "fog juice." Fog juice consists of glycol, glycerin, mineral oil, and distilled water. The mixture is heated and forced into the air under pressure, creating a fog. Glycols are chemicals containing C, H, and O;

propylene glycol ($C_3H_8O_2$) at a concentration of 90% produces a thick, dense fog. Glycerin has the chemical formula of $C_3H_5(OH)_3$ and, when mixed with distilled water, produces more of a haze. The precise mixture of these ingredients can produce a fog that is more or less dense.

Flying sparks and glowing potions are all part of the magic of chemistry. Potassium nitrate (KNO_3) and potassium perchlorate ($KClO_4$), along with metals such as steel and aluminum, create a sparkling flash effect when burned or combusted with oxygen in the air. Glow-in-the-dark goop or slime contains hydrogen peroxide and phenyl oxalate ester (a compound containing C, H, and O) and a fluorescent dye. When hydrogen peroxide reacts with oxalate ester, the reaction releases energy, exciting the electrons in the dye. These excited fluorescent atoms release light upon returning to their ground state. The different colors are made by adding different dyes.

The next time you go to the movies and see a fire, an explosion, or even some fog, think about how chemistry has made these special effects real and believable. Special effect technicians have a very cool science job!

Chapter 4 Review

Vocabulary

Match each word to the sentence where it best fits.

Section 4.1

interatomic forces	intermolecular forces
irreversible	electric charge
physical change	electron
chemical change	neutral
covalent bond	proton
ionic bond	nucleus
molecule	enthalpy of formation
chemical bond	reactivity

1. _____ comes from a competition between temperature and attractive intermolecular forces.

2. When _____ happens, the molecules of the substance do not change.

3. _____ exist between molecules.

4. When _____ happens, the molecules of the substance change.

5. _____ exist between atoms and are much stronger than intermolecular forces.

6. A/An _____ change rearranges atoms to form different substances.

7. The _____ of an atom contains 99.8% of its mass.

8. _____ have negative charge and are responsible for chemical bonds.

9. The _____ has a positive charge.

10. When a chemical bond between two atoms is formed by sharing a pair of electrons, it is called a/an _____.

11. _____ is a fundamental property of matter. It can be positive or negative.

12. A/An _____ forms when one or more electrons is transferred from one atom to another.

13. A neutral group of atoms that are covalently bound is called a/an _____.

14. The connection between two atoms is called a/an _____.

15. The _____ is the change in energy when one mole of a compound is assembled from pure elements.

Section 4.2

chemical reaction	endothermic
reactants	exothermic
products	enthalpy
balanced equation	activation energy
coefficient	system
conservation of mass	surroundings

16. The process of chemical change is represented by a/an _____.

17. The initial compounds involved in a chemical reaction are called the _____.

18. The compounds generated by a chemical reaction are called the _____ of the reaction.

19. All chemical reactions must satisfy the property of _____.

20. The number that tells us how many of each molecule participate in a chemical reaction is called the _____.

21. A chemical reaction that releases energy is known as _____.

22. A chemical reaction that absorbs energy is known as _____.

23. The _____ is the energy potential of a chemical reaction.

24. The energy required to start a reaction is called the _____.

25. A chemical equation that conserves mass is called a/an _____.

26. A group of matter and energy that we choose to investigate is known as the _____.

27. Everything around a system is called the _____.

Section 4.3

aqueous solution	oxidation
precipitate	reduction
salt	acid
pH scale	base

28. The insoluble compound that results from a chemical reaction that takes place in an aqueous solution is called a/an _____.

29. A/An _____ is an ionic compound that forms ions when dissolved in water.

30. _____ happens when an atom gains electrons.

31. When a compound dissolves in water forming an increased amount of H^+ ions it is called a/an _____.

32. A/An _____ is a compound that dissolves in water to make a solution with a large number of OH^- ions.

33. _____ happens when an atom loses electrons.

34. The _____ is a way to measure the H^+ ion concentration. It tells us whether a solution is an acid or a base.

35. A solution with water as the solvent is called a/an _____.

Conceptual Questions

Section 4.1

36. Give examples of a reversible and an irreversible process.

37. Why are physical changes reversible?

38. What happens during a chemical change that makes them irreversible?

39. Describe the difference between interatomic and intermolecular forces.

40. Describe what happens when you take a glass of water and add one drop of blue food coloring at the top. Explain this at the molecular level.

41. An atom is electrically neutral. What does that mean?

42. Why do different elements have different chemical properties?

43. What particle plays the dominant role in chemical bonds?

44. What is a covalent bond, and how is it formed?

45. What is the primary reason that chemical bonds form?

46. What is the relation between energy and chemical bonds?

47. What is the difference between covalent and ionic bonds?

Section 4.2

48. Hydrogen and oxygen combine to form water. Describe the general process by which this happens.

49. Describe the main components of a chemical equation.

Chapter 4 Review

50. Many chemical reactions release energy. Where does this energy come from?

51. Why do some reactions release more energy than others?

52. Describe the concept of mass conservation. Use the following chemical equation to demonstrate how it is used:
$$4Fe + 3O_2 \rightarrow 2Fe_2O_3$$

53. An ice pack used by athletic trainers becomes cold when activated. Is this the result of an exothermic or an endothermic reaction? Explain.

54. Explain the photosynthesis reaction. Is it an exothermic or an endothermic reaction?

55. Give two simple examples each of exothermic and endothermic chemical reactions.

56. Describe the concept of enthalpy. How is enthalpy related to the energy of a chemical reaction?

57. Describe what the activation energy of a chemical reaction is in your own words.

58. Why do different chemical reactions have different activation energies?

59. Why is it important to specify what makes up a system when we study chemical reactions?

Section 4.3

60. What is an aqueous solution?

61. Describe which element groups in the periodic table have the highest reactivity.

62. What happens to an atom or an ion when it is oxidized?

63. What happens to an atom or an ion when it is reduced?

Quantitative Problems

Section 4.1

64. The melting of ice is a physical change. Separation of water into hydrogen and oxygen is a chemical change. How much energy is required to melt 10 g of ice, and how much energy is required to break up 10 g of water into hydrogen and oxygen?

65. If you combine 10 g of oxygen gas and 10 g of hydrogen gas, how many grams of water would you obtain?

Section 4.2

66. Acid rain contains sulfuric acid, which is formed when sulfur dioxide reacts with water and oxygen in the air. Write the balanced equation for this reaction.

67. Another pollutant in acid rain is nitric acid, which is formed when nitrogen dioxide reacts with oxygen and water. Write the balanced equation for this reaction.

68. When wood or gasoline is burned, we may say that the following reaction occurs:
$$C + O_2 \rightarrow CO_2$$
If we burn 1 ton (1,000 kg) of carbon, how many kilograms of CO_2 is produced?

69. The burning of ethanol, the alcohol in alcoholic drinks, follows the reaction $C_2H_5OH + 3O_2 \rightarrow CO_2 + H_2O$
Is this reaction balanced? If so, show why. If not, balance it.

70. Balance the following chemical equations:
   a. $N_2O \rightarrow N_2 + O_2$
   b. $HBr \rightarrow H_2 + Br_2$
   c. $CH_4 + O_2 \rightarrow CO_2 + H_2O$

71. The following figures show graphical schematics of balanced chemical equations. Write the equation for each schematic.

   a. _____

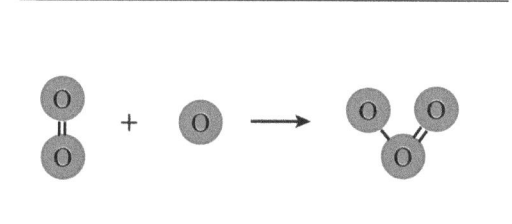

   b. _____

   c. _____

   d. _____

72. The following figures show graphical schematics of chemical equations that are not balanced. Write and balance the chemical equation in each schematic using the concept of mass conservation.

   a. _____

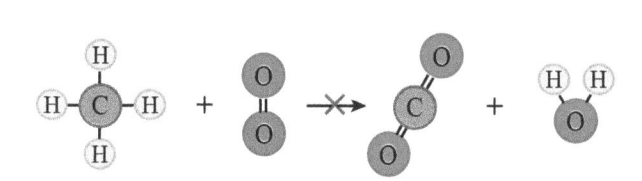

   b. _____

   c. _____

   d. _____

CHAPTER 5
The Structure of the Atom

What are atoms?

What are their properties?

Why are atoms important in chemistry?

What would happen if you took a piece of aluminum foil and tore it in half again and again? Then, when that piece of aluminum became too small to hold, imagine that you could keep cutting it in half again and again. Keep thinking of smaller and smaller pieces of aluminum. Could you keep cutting forever, or do you reach a limit that is the smallest possible piece of aluminum? The answer to this question has far-reaching consequences. Either there is a smallest piece, which means the aluminum is made from tiny particles (atoms), or the aluminum is one smooth substance that can be cut in half forever.

Over time, starting with the ancient Greeks, scientists struggled with this question, each building upon the work of others. Today we know that everything is made from atoms: There *is* a smallest piece of aluminum. Our modern view of the atom is the culmination of 2,500 years of scientific thinking and experimentation. Our understanding of the properties of the atom has led to major chemical discoveries that have improved our lives from medicine to energy.

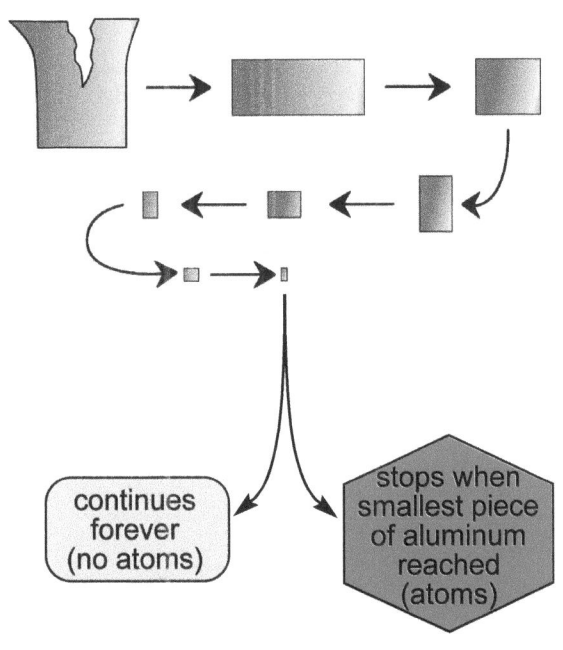

Repeated dividing of aluminum foil

continues forever (no atoms)

stops when smallest piece of aluminum reached (atoms)

Light, color, atoms, and electrons

When you pass high-voltage electricity through a gas, it can light up. This is how a neon sign works. In the lab we use glass tubes filled with gas in a high-voltage power supply.

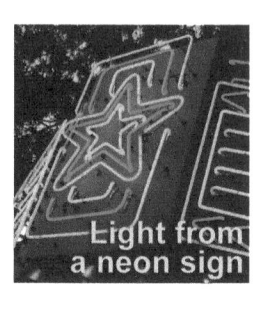

Light from a neon sign

Different elements give off noticeably different colors of light. The most interesting thing happens when you observe this light through a special lens called a *diffraction grating*. You may know that "pure white" light is really an equal mixture of all colors together. The light from a gas discharge tube is also a mixture of colors. A diffraction grating separates the light into its component colors.

To the eye, the light from nitrogen gas looks purple and helium looks pink. However, through the diffraction grating, the purple and pink are not so simple! Instead of a single color, the diffraction grating shows us that the light is really many colors. Each color shows up as a vertical line in what chemists call a line spectrum.

Nitrogen Helium

Do you notice how nitrogen and helium are different? Each element has its own unique line spectrum. In fact, the unique patterns of spectral lines are often called the "fingerprints" of the elements.

Helium

Nitrogen

Oxygen

How are these line spectra different?

Do the line spectra remind you of a barcode used at the checkout counter of a store? It is a good analogy! Line spectra contain information about the structure of each element just as barcodes contain information about product numbers. Compare the line spectra of helium, nitrogen, and oxygen. What differences do you see? What similarities do you see?

- There are areas of the rainbow in which no color is emitted (black).
- Nitrogen and oxygen have more lines than helium.
- All three spectra are noticeably different.
- Some of the lines are thicker than others.

The number of spectral lines is related to the number of electrons in each atom. Helium has two electrons and nitrogen has seven electrons. Could it be that nitrogen has more spectral lines because it has more electrons? In this chapter we will learn how to categorize atoms according to their electron structures in a table called the periodic table, which is the major reference document of chemistry.

5.1 The Atom Has a Structure

Elements and compounds

In the previous chapters, we learned that ordinary matter is made of atoms of the 92 naturally occurring elements. These atoms usually form compounds, such as salt (NaCl) or sodium bicarbonate ($NaHCO_3$). Compounds explain how we get millions of types of matter from 92 elements, but 92 is still a relatively large number. Are the 92 different types of atoms (i.e., the elements) made of even smaller things? The answer is *yes*.

Atoms are made from smaller particles called protons, neutrons, and electrons

How can three particles explain the universe?

This is an *extraordinary* fact! How can the incredible variety of matter in the universe come from only *three particles*? Think about making all the words in the dictionary with only three letters or all the paintings in the world with only three colors. It may seem incredible, but it is true nonetheless. The atoms of all 92 elements (and more) are created from three basic particles: electrons, protons, and neutrons. The beautiful variety of nature arises from how the three particles come together in rich and complex ways.

Each element is a unique type of atom

Before we delve into the depths of the atom, let's review what we know. There are 92 naturally occurring elements, plus 20 to 30 other elements that have been created in a laboratory. Each element represents a unique type of atom. For example, all oxygen atoms are similar to each other but different from carbon atoms or hydrogen atoms.

The 92 naturally occurring elements

The beginning of atomic theory

Democritus (460–370 BC): the beginning of atomic theory

Democritus (460—370 BC) was an ancient Greek philosopher who proposed the idea that you can't divide something in half forever. He argued that eventually you must reach the smallest indivisible part. He called this smallest piece of matter an *atom*. Democritus correctly deduced the existence of atoms, but he could go no further in discovering any of their properties. For the next 2,000 years *atomism* was an interesting idea, but there was no good scientific evidence to support its truth or falsehood.

John Dalton (1768–1828) - first "modern" atomic theory

In 1808, John Dalton, an English school teacher, put together many ideas in his four postulates of the atomic theory. Dalton's four postulates were a brilliant synthesis based on what little evidence there was at that time. They remain true today.

1. All elements are made of tiny indivisible particles called atoms.

2. All atoms of the same element are alike but different from atoms of other elements.

3. Chemical reactions rearrange atoms but do not create, destroy, or convert atoms from one element to another.

4. Compounds are made from combining atoms in simple whole number ratios.

Cathode rays

In the mid 1800s it was discovered that high voltage made a "glow" in a sealed glass tube from which most of the air had been taken out. In 1870, William Crookes invented a tube in which virtually *all* of the gas was removed. The glow inside the tube disappeared, but *the glass glowed at one end*. An invisible ray called a *cathode ray* was being emitted, and scientists debated--were they another kind of light or a stream of particles?

High voltage electricity creating cathode rays inside a Crookes tube

J.J. Thomson (1856–1940) - the discovery of the electron

Thomson

In 1897, J. J. Thomson showed that cathode rays were deflected toward a positively charged plate and away from a negatively charged plate. He deduced that cathode rays must

Cathode rays deflected away from negative plate and toward positive plate

be negative. He also found that they could be deflected by magnetic fields, unlike any ordinary ray of light. He tried using different metals or filling the tube with different gases, but he always got the same cathode rays.

Thomson's discovery stunned the scientific world. Cathode rays were made of particles 2,000 times lighter than the lightest atom (H)! How could there be a particle smaller than an atom? Because Thomson got the same cathode rays regardless of which metals he used for the electrodes, he named the new particle an *electron*, and proposed that electrons were inside *all* atoms.

The discovery of the nucleus

Thomson: the plum-pudding model

If electrons were inside atoms, then atoms could not be the most elementary particles of matter. Furthermore, electrons were *negative* and atoms were *neutral*, so there had to be something *positive* to cancel out the charge of the electrons. Therefore, Thomson proposed a model where the electrons were scattered throughout the atom, surrounded by a soup of positive charge. He named this the *plum-pudding model*, since the electrons resembled plums in plum pudding, surrounded by positively-charged "pudding."

The "plum pudding" model

Atom

⊖ Negative electron
＋ Positive "pudding"

Ernest Rutherford: the gold foil experiment

However, in 1910, Ernest Rutherford disproved Thomson's plum-pudding model. Marie and Pierre Curie had discovered that uranium was radioactive and released energetic alpha particles at high velocity. Alpha particles were positively charged and had a mass about 8,000 times that of an electron. Rutherford devised an experiment to shoot alpha particles through a thin gold foil and observe what happened as they collided with gold atoms. He expected most of the alpha particles to be deflected a little as they crashed through the gold atoms.

Rutherford

The gold foil experiment

α particle

Most a particles passed straight through, but a few were deflected to the side and once in a while one would bounce straight backward!

very thin sheet of gold

Rutherford's discovery of the atomic nucleus

Rutherford's results were completely unexpected. Although most of the alpha particles went straight through the gold foil with no deflection at all and a few were deflected slightly off their original path, about 1 of every 20,000 reversed direction, bouncing back from the foil! Rutherford determined that atoms have nearly all their mass concentrated in a very tiny, very dense, positively charged nucleus. This was his reasoning:

1. The deflected alpha particles were repelled by something with a similar charge, so the nucleus must be positively charged.

2. Very few alpha particles were deflected, so it must be rare for one to come close to a nucleus. This meant the nucleus had to be tiny, about 1/10,000 the diameter of the atom.

3. The alpha particles were travelling at such high velocity that only something with significant mass could deflect them.

The interior of an atom

The big ideas

The three most important ideas in this chapter are these:

1. Atoms are made of neutrons, protons, and electrons. The number of protons and elec-trons is always equal.
2. The number of protons determines the element. All atoms of hydrogen have one proton, all atoms of helium have two, lithium has three, and so on.
3. Most of the properties of atoms are determined by their electrons. Atoms interact with each other via their electrons.

Of course, there are many interesting details! Electrons are quirky particles and they behave in very strange ways, but that is what makes chemistry so interesting.

The nucleus

Neutrons and protons make up the *nucleus*. The **nucleus** is at the center of the atom. There are no electrons in the nucleus, only protons and neutrons. The nucleus is extremely small, even compared to an atom. If the atom were the size of your classroom, the nucleus would be the size of a single grain of sand in the center of the room!

Atom

Nucleus

Particle	Mass (kg)	Charge (C)	Relative mass	Relative charge
Proton	1.673×10^{-27}	$+1.602\times10^{-19}$	1,835	+1
Neutron	1.675×10^{-27}	0	1,837	0
Electron	9.109×10^{-31}	1.602×10^{-19}	1	−1

Mass of protons, neutrons, and electrons

Look at the masses of the three particles. The masses are very small. The mass of a single electron in kilograms has 30 zeros between the decimal point and the first nonzero digit. More important are the *relative* masses. The proton and neutron are much more massive than the electron. The protons and neutrons have essentially all the mass of the atom.

Mass and the nucleus

Nucleus
99.97%

Electrons
0.03%

Most of an atom's mass is concentrated in the nucleus. The number of electrons and protons is the same, but electrons contribute very little mass. For example, a carbon atom has six protons, six electrons and six neutrons. Of the carbon atom's mass, 99.97% is in the nucleus and only 0.03% is electrons.

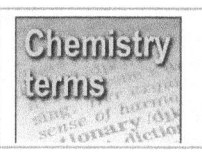
Chemistry terms

nucleus: the tiny dense core of an atom that contains all the protons and neutrons, measuring about 1/10,000 the diameter of the atom.

Atomic number and atomic mass

The atomic number

The **atomic number** of each element is the number of protons in its nucleus. All atoms of the same element have the same number of protons in the nucleus. For example, every atom of helium has two protons in its nucleus. Every atom of carbon has six protons in its nucleus. The periodic table arranges the elements in increasing atomic number. Atomic number one is hydrogen with one proton. Atomic number 92 is uranium with 92 protons.

Helium — Nucleus 2 protons 2 neutrons

Carbon — Nucleus 6 protons 6 neutrons

Neutrons act like glue

All protons have positive electric charge. That means they repel each other. So how does the nucleus stay together? The answer is neutrons. Think about neutrons as "glue" particles that help the nucleus stay together. Every element heavier than helium has at least as many neutrons as protons in its nucleus.

Isotopes

All atoms of the same element have the same number of protons in the nucleus. However, they do not necessarily have the same number of neutrons. Three different *isotopes* of carbon are found on Earth. **Isotopes** are atoms of the same element that have different numbers of neutrons in the nucleus.

Isotopes of carbon

Carbon-12
$^{12}_{6}\text{C}$

Carbon-13
$^{13}_{6}\text{C}$

Carbon-14
$^{14}_{6}\text{C}$

The mass number

The most common isotope of carbon is carbon-12, written as ^{12}C. A nucleus of ^{12}C contains six protons (making it carbon) and six neutrons. The superscript "12" before the symbol "C" tells you the *mass number* of the nucleus. The **mass number** is the total number of protons plus neutrons. The two other isotopes of carbon are carbon-13 (^{13}C) and carbon-14 (^{14}C). These isotopes are carbon because they have six protons in the nucleus, but ^{13}C has seven neutrons and ^{14}C has eight neutrons. Thus, the number of neutrons in an atom is equal to the mass number minus the atomic number.

Atomic mass unit (amu)

Because the mass of a proton is tiny by normal standards, scientists use **atomic mass units** (amu). One amu is 1.661×10^{-27} kg, or slightly less than the mass of a proton.

Chemistry terms

atomic number: the number of protons in the nucleus, unique to each element.

isotopes: atoms or elements that have the same number of protons in the nucleus, but different number of neutrons.

mass number: the total number of protons and neutrons in a nucleus.

atomic mass unit (amu): a mass unit equivalent to 1.661×10^{-27} kg.

Average atomic mass

The average atomic mass may not be a whole number

Let's examine the element lithium. Lithium has two isotopes that are found in nature. Lithium-6 has three protons and three neutrons. Lithium-7 has three protons and four neutrons. The periodic table lists the atomic mass of lithium as 6.94. How is that possible? Do lithium atoms have 0.94 neutrons?

Lithium-6 — Nucleus 3 protons 3 neutrons

Lithium-7 — Nucleus 3 protons 4 neutrons

Elements in nature contain a mix of isotopes

It is not possible to split a proton or a neutron in ordinary matter. Lithium atoms have either six or seven *whole* neutrons. The reason the atomic mass is 6.94 is that, on average, 94 out of 100 atoms of lithium are ^{7}Li and 6 out of 100 are ^{6}Li. The *average* atomic mass is 6.94 because of the mixture of isotopes. No lithium atom has a mass of 6.94 amu.

Radioactivity

Not all isotopes exist in nature. For example, suppose scientists create a nucleus with three protons and five neutrons. This would have an atomic number of 3, making it lithium. The mass number would be 8. Lithium-8 is unstable and quickly decays into two atoms of helium instead! When an atomic nucleus decays or gives off energy, the process is called **radioactivity**. It means that the nucleus undergoes a spontaneous change called **decay**, often turning one element into a different element.

Lithium-8 is radioactive and decays into other elements

$$^8\text{Li} \rightarrow {}^4\text{He} + {}^3\text{He} + n$$

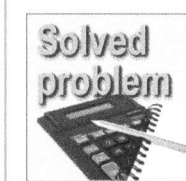

Solved problem

Calculate the average atomic mass for lithium, given that Li-6 has an abundance of 6% and Li-7 has an abundance of 94%.

Asked: *The average atomic mass of lithium, Li*

Given: *Lithium-6 and Lithium-7, their percent abundance*

Relationships: $Avg = \dfrac{(\text{mass of isotope \#1})\,(\%) + (\text{mass of isotope \#2})\,(\%)}{100}$

Solve: $Avg = \dfrac{(6)\,(6) + (7)\,(94)}{100} = 6.94$

Answer: *The average atomic mass of Li is 6.94 amu.*

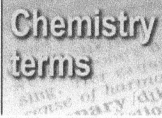

Chemistry terms

radioactivity: a process by which the nucleus of an atom spontaneously changes itself by emitting particles or energy.

decay: the process during which a nucleus undergoes spontaneous change.

The electron cloud

The electron cloud

Compared to protons and neutrons, electrons are much lighter. This has the effect of making the electron much faster, with a much wider range than either protons or neutrons. Because electrons are so fast and light, scientists call the region outside the nucleus the *electron cloud*. Think about a swarm of bees buzzing in a cloud around a beehive. It is not easy to precisely locate any one bee, but you can easily see that, on average, the bees are confined to a cloud of a certain size around the hive. On average, electrons are confined to a similar cloud around the nucleus.

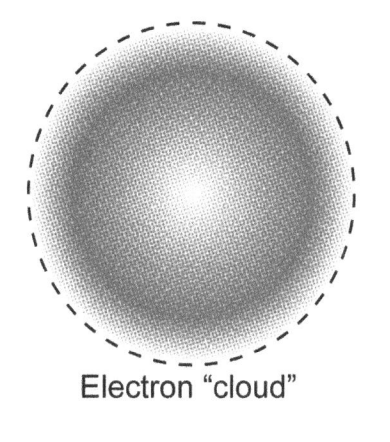

Electron "cloud"

Drawing electrons

Electron orbit

Old "orbit" representation

Electron cloud representation

Electrons are not really particles in the same way a dust particle is a particle. Although electrons have a definite mass, *they do not have a definite size*. The matter in an electron spreads out over a relatively large volume within an atom. In early drawings of atoms, scientists represented electrons like tiny planets in an **orbit** around the nucleus of the atom. Today we draw atoms with a tiny hard nucleus surrounded by a wispy electron cloud.

Electrons determine the size of atoms

The size of an atom is really the size of its electron cloud. When we talk about the size of atoms, what we really mean is how close atoms get to each other. Unless the atoms are chemically bonded together, the electron cloud of one atom does not normally overlap the electron cloud of another.

The "size" of an atom is really the size of its electron cloud

Except for mass, virtually every property of atoms is determined by electrons, including size and chemical bonding

The electrons determine virtually everything about how one atom interacts with another. For this reason, most of chemistry will be concerned with electrons and their unusual organization within atoms. The nucleus is buried deep inside, contributing mass, but not much else, as far as chemistry is concerned.

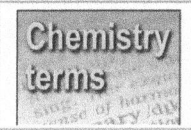
Chemistry terms

orbit: the imaginary path of an electron around the nucleus of an atom.

A NATURAL APPROACH TO CHEMISTRY

Electric charge

Comparing charge and mass

Charge is a difficult idea to grasp, so let's start by comparing mass and gravity with electric charge. Mass is a fundamental property of matter. Any two objects that have mass attract each other through a force called gravity. Mass is the property that determines an object's response to the force of gravity. The more mass there is, the stronger the force of gravity.

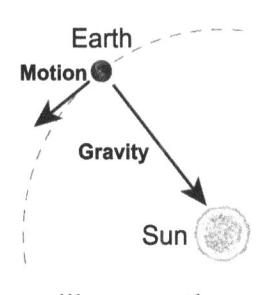

Positive and negative

Electric charge is another fundamental property of matter. However, unlike mass, there are two kinds of charge: positive and negative. Like gravity, there is a force that acts on electric charge called the electromagnetic force. Unlike gravity, however, the *electromagnetic force can attract or repel*.

The charges of the three particles

The electric charge on a proton is what scientists define to be *positive*. The charge on an electron is defined as *negative*. Neutrons are neutral and have zero charge. That means that two protons repel each other, and so do two electrons. Protons and electrons attract each other. Neutrons feel no electromagnetic forces from either protons or electrons.

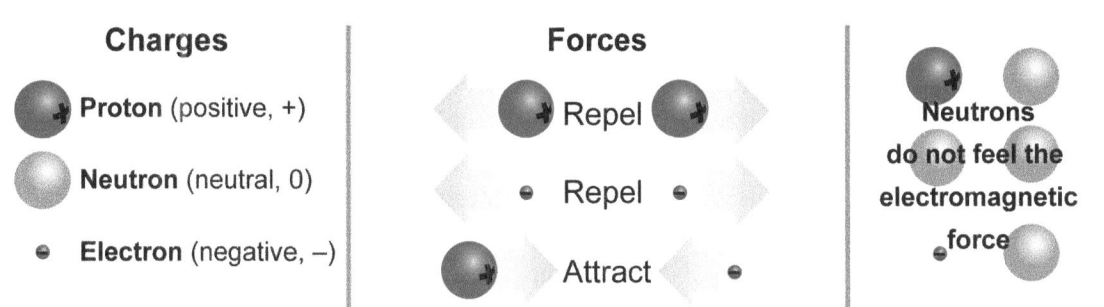

A complete atom has a charge of zero because the charge of the proton is exactly equal but opposite to the charge of the electron

Complete atoms have zero net charge

The charges on the electron and the proton are *exactly* equal and opposite. If you put a proton and an electron together, the total effective charge is zero. For this reason, the charge on a complete atom is always zero because a complete atom contains the same number of protons as electrons. For example, the positive charge from six protons in a carbon nucleus is exactly cancelled by the six electrons in the electron cloud.

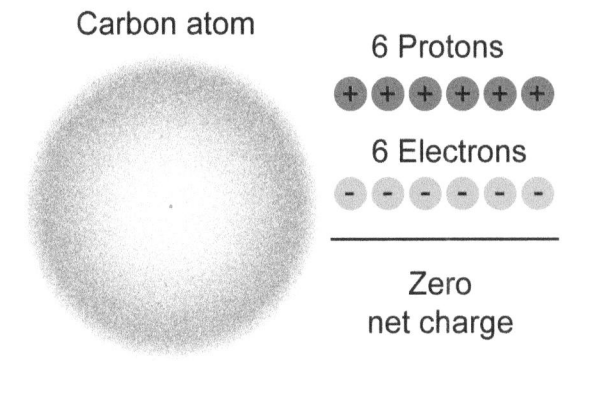

Forces in the atom

Why an atom stays together

The attractive electromagnetic force between protons in the nucleus and electrons is what holds an atom together. The electromagnetic force between electrons is also what creates chemical bonds between atoms, as we shall see. In fact, almost all of the chemistry we learn is driven by the electromagnetic force.

Forces in the nucleus

There is a force in the nucleus that is even stronger than the electromagnetic force, but it does not affect chemistry directly. It is called the *strong nuclear force* and it attracts protons to protons, neutrons to neutrons, and protons and neutrons to each other. If there are enough neutrons in the nucleus, the attractive strong nuclear force can overcome the repulsive electromagnetic force between protons. This is the reason most elements have equal numbers or slightly more neutrons than protons in the nucleus.

The **strong nuclear force** attracts protons to protons, neutrons to neutrons, and protons to neutrons

Attract

Attract

Attract

There is no effect on electrons

Electrons are both attracted and repelled

Let's think about the electron cloud in an atom like carbon. Electrons have energy, so they cannot just "fall in" to the nucleus, but they must be constantly in motion. Each of carbon's six electrons is attracted to the nucleus, but each is also repelled by all the other electrons! The combination of energy with attraction and repulsion is one reason behind the peculiar behavior of electrons in an atom.

Carbon atom

Electrons

Nucleus

Electrons are responsible for the chemical bonds between atoms. When a water molecule forms, the oxygen atom shares electrons with two hydrogen atoms. Each shared electron is a chemical bond. The molecule has its bent shape because eight of the ten electrons in a water molecule repel each other in four pairs. Two pairs are shared with hydrogen atoms and two pairs are not shared.

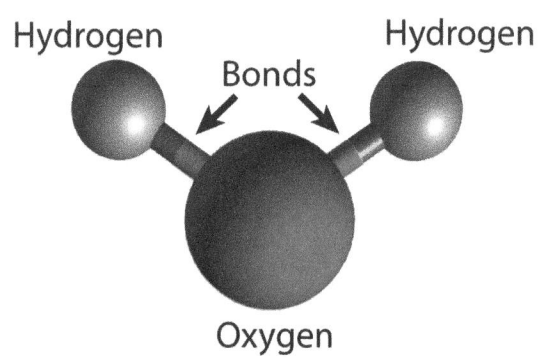

Hydrogen

Hydrogen

Bonds

Oxygen

Ions

All matter contains charge

The fact that everything is made from atoms and atoms are made from electrically charged particles means that everything, including you, is just a big bundle of electric charge. This fact becomes more obvious in the winter when you scuff your feet across a carpet and get shocked by touching a metal doorknob. Static electricity and lightning are examples of how we are made of, and are surrounded by, electrically charged particles.

Electric charges in the atoms of our bodies can cause sparks.

Neutral matter has equal positive and negative charge

If the numbers of electrons and protons in an atom are not equal, the atom will have an overall charge. Let's consider sodium as an example. Sodium has an atomic number of 11, so that means all sodium atoms have 11 protons. Each proton has a positive charge of +1. If these same atoms have 11 electrons, each with a −1 charge, then the −11 charge from the electrons exactly cancels out the +11 charge from the protons, and the atom is neutral.

A neutral sodium atom

Na
The protons and electrons cancel each other out

11 protons: ●●●●●●●●●●●
11 electrons: ●●●●●●●●●●●

Ions

However, if there were only 10 electrons, then the total charge from the electrons would be −10 while the charge from the protons would be +11. That means there is one proton that is not being cancelled out by an electron. This gives the atom an overall charge of +1. Charged atoms are called **ions**. Whenever the numbers of protons and electrons are not equal, an overall positive or negative charge will occur, and an ion will be formed. Ions can be single atoms or small molecules with an overall charge.

A positive sodium ion

Na^{1+}
One proton is not neutralized by an electron, making this a +1 charged atom

11 protons: ●●●●●●●●●●●
10 electrons: ●●●●●●●●●●

A negative oxygen ion

O^{2-}
Two electrons are not neutralized by protons, making this a -2 charged atom

8 protons: ●●●●●●●●
10 electrons: ●●●●●●●●●●

Ionic compounds

Positive and negative ions attract each other, just as protons and electrons do. The ionic compounds we introduced in Chapter 4 are examples. Sodium ions (Na$^+$) have one less electron and are attracted to chloride ions (Cl$^-$), which have one extra electron. The overall compound, sodium chloride (NaCl), is electrically neutral because there are equal numbers of sodium and chloride ions.

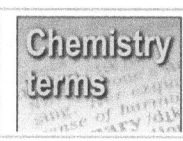
Chemistry terms

ion: an atom or a small molecule with an overall positive or negative charge as a result of an imbalance of protons and electrons.

5.2 The Quantum Atom

Why is it that the noble gases do not react?

How do the chemical properties of the elements arise from the structure of atoms? We have seen that electrons are the components in atoms that are near the "surface" and interact with other atoms. Why is it that the noble gases (helium, neon, argon, and krypton) do not react with other elements or among themselves? Note that these elements have 2, 10, 18, and 36 electrons, respectively. The elements hydrogen, fluorine, chlorine and bromine have 1, 9, 17, and 35 electrons. They have one fewer electron than their respective noble gas group. These elements tend to form negative ions; they *accept* electrons from other atoms.

Elements just before or just after the noble gases are very reactive

Form positive ions	Form negative ions	Form no ions
3 Li 6.941 lithium	**9** F 18.998 fluorine	**2** He 4.0028 helium
11 Na 22.990 sodium	**17** Cl 35.453 chlorine	**10** Ne 20.180 neon
19 K 39.098 potassium	**35** Br 79.904 bromine	**18** Ar 39.948 argon

The elements with one more electron than the noble gas group are lithium, sodium, potassium and rubidium with 3, 11, 19 and 37 electrons, respectively. These elements tend to form positive ions; they *donate* electrons to other atoms.

Modern atomic theory

The basic understanding of the electronic structure in the atom started in the early 1900's with the experiments of Rutherford and the experimental observations of the discrete frequencies of light coming from hydrogen. In 1913 Niels Bohr developed a new theory of the atom that explained these phenomena and laid the foundation for the development of modern atomic theory. The Bohr model had many limitations which were in turn addressed by a new theory called **quantum theory** which was developed in the 1920's. Quantum theory describes the physics in the scale of the atom and gives us a way to understand why and how the elements make the bonds that they do when they combine to form chemical compounds. Quantum theory makes the following statements about matter and energy on the scale of atoms, and particularly about electrons in atoms.

Some findings of quantum theory

1. On the scale of atoms, a particle of matter such as an electron is not solid but is smeared out into a *wave* over a region of space.
2. When electrons are confined in an atom, their wave properties force them into a *pattern* that minimizes their energy.
3. Each unique "place" in the pattern is called a **quantum state**, and each can hold one single electron.
4. Electrons are always found to be in one quantum state or another and are not found between states.
5. No two electrons can be in the same quantum state at the same time.

Chemistry terms

quantum theory: a theory of physics and chemistry that accurately describes the universe on very small scales, such as the inside of an atom.

quantum state: a specific combination of values of variables such as energy and position that is allowed by quantum theory.

Waves and particles

Our intuition is often wrong in the quantum world

The most basic idea of quantum theory is that our intuitive notion of a particle cannot be applied to the tiny world of the atom. To most of us, a particle is a tiny speck of matter that has a definite size, mass, and position, like a tiny ball. A ball-like particle can be either here or there, but it cannot be in two places at the same time. The quantum theory tells us *this intuition is wrong when things are as small as an atom*. In the quantum world, a particle is not like a tiny ball at all. Instead, the mass, size, and even the location is spread out into a *wave*.

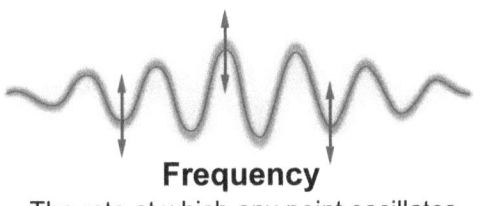

Intuitive "particle"
Mass and position are at a definite point

Wave "particle"
Mass and position are spread out over space

Heisenberg's uncertainty principle

The fact that particles are "smeared out" into waves can be explained by Heisenberg's uncertainty principle. In 1927 Werner Heisenberg proposed that it is not possible to know certain parameters of a particle, such as its position and velocity, accurately at quantum scales. The better you determine one by experiment, the more you perturb the other and thereby increase its uncertainty. The quantum world is a world of statistics and probability, instead of exact certainty.

Frequency

The oscillations of a wave have *frequency* and *wavelength*. The **frequency** is the number of times per unit of time that any point on the wave goes back and forth. A light wave has a very high frequency, 10^{12} times per second or more! A water wave might oscillate one or two times per second.

Frequency
The rate at which any point oscillates

Wavelength
The separation of successive peaks (or valleys)

Wavelength

When a wave moves through space, the successive peaks (or valleys) are separated by a distance called the **wavelength**. The wavelength is the same from one peak to the next. Like the frequency, it is a characteristic of a particular wave. The wavelength of light is very small, only 10^{-8} m or so.

Chemistry terms

frequency: the rate at which an oscillation repeats; one hertz (Hz) is a frequency of one oscillation per second.

wavelength: the distance (separation) between any two successive peaks (or valleys) of a wave.

Planck's constant

Wave energy increases with frequency

Waves in water carry energy, as anyone who has seen waves from a storm crashing on a beach can vividly remember. The same is true of light waves and particle waves, such as electrons. You might intuitively think that the faster something oscillates, the more energy it has. You would be right! The energy carried by a wave is proportional to how fast it oscillates, or its *frequency*. High frequency means faster oscillation and more energy.

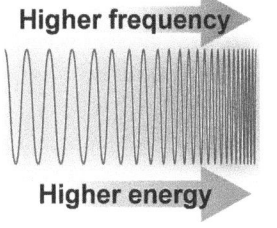

A photon is the smallest quantity of light energy

Before quantum theory, the ideas of "particle" and "wave" were distinct. Light was a wave, and an electron was a particle. Today we know that an electron is also a *matter wave*, and light waves come in tiny bundles of energy called *photons*. A **photon** is like a particle because it has a definite energy and moves with a certain speed and direction. However, a photon has no mass, just pure energy. You don't see light as a stream of photons for the same reason you don't see individual atoms. A small 3 W flashlight beam emits 10^{19} photons per second!

Planck's constant

The scale at which the granular nature of matter and energy becomes evident is determined by *Planck's constant*. **Planck's constant** has the symbol h and a value of 6.626×10^{-34} joule-seconds (J·s). The energy and wavelength of both electrons and photons are calculated from Planck's constant.

---

de Broglie wavelength

Wavelength (m)

Planck's constant
6.626×10^{-34} J·s

$$\lambda = \frac{h}{\sqrt{2mE}}$$

Mass (kg) —— Energy (J)

Photon Energy

Planck's constant
6.626×10^{-34} J·s

Energy (J)

$$E = h\nu$$

Frequency (Hz)

The connection among atoms, light, and electrons

In his 1924 Ph.D. thesis, Louis de Broglie proposed that the wavelength of a particle is inversely proportional to the square root of its mass and energy. The de Broglie wavelength of an electron is very small. If the electron had the same energy as green light $(3.82 \times 10^{-19}\text{J})$, its de Broglie wavelength would be 7.94×10^{-10} m. *This is the same size as an atom,* which explains the close connection between light and the behavior of electrons in atoms.

3.82×10^{-19} J

Energy of a green photon

Chemistry terms

Planck's constant (h): the scale of energy at which quantum effects must be considered, equal to 6.626×10^{-34} joule-seconds (J·s).

photon: the smallest possible quantity (or quanta) of light.

Electrons in the quantum atom

The wavelength of an electron in an atom

Most of the properties of the elements are caused by what happens to the wavelength of an electron when it is bound up inside an atom. To help understand this, consider a ball bouncing around in a box. At any instant, there is only one ball at one particular place in the box. When the ball hits the walls of the box, it bounces off it.

Waves versus balls

A wave reflects when it hits a wall, just like a ball in a box. However, waves are very different from balls. A ball is only in one place, but a wave can occupy all the space in the box. So can its reflection! One ball plus one ball is two balls, but one wave plus another wave can add up to *zero*. If one wave is "up" when the other is "down," then they cancel each other out! When averaged over time, the only waves that survive in a box are the ones whose wavelength fits the size of the box. All the others interfere with their own reflections and average out to zero.

The sum of two waves can be zero (no wave)

Waves that exactly "fit" in the box with their own reflections

Waves that do not exactly "fit" in the box with their own reflections

The atom is a "box" for electrons

Now replace the box with an atom and let the wave be an electron. Electrons are "boxed" inside atoms by the attraction from the positive nucleus. The walls of the box are soft to an electron because the electron never hits a hard surface, but it needs more and more energy to get farther away from the nucleus. Given a limited amount of energy, an electron is confined to be within a certain distance from the nucleus. This confinement acts just like a soft-walled box.

The key idea of the quantum atom

Here is the main idea of the quantum atom. *The wavelength of the electron must be a multiple of the "size" of the atom.* If it is not, then the electron wave cancels with its own reflections over time. The diagram shows three "allowed" electron waves and two that are "not allowed." To be stable inside an atom, an electron must have one of the allowed wavelengths that exactly fits the size of the atom. The elements differ because the "size" of the atom depends on the strength of the attraction from the nucleus, which depends on the atomic number.

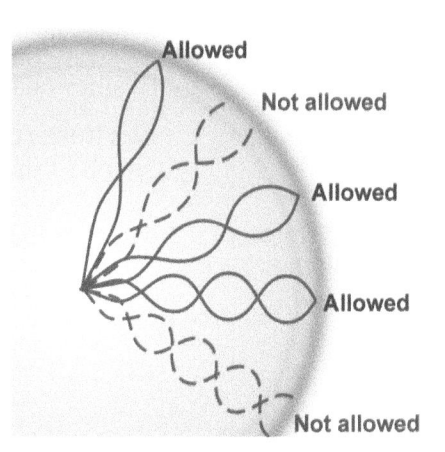

Allowed
Not allowed
Allowed
Allowed
Not allowed

Quantum states

Consequences of restricting the electron wavelength

What does it mean to say that an electron can only have a wavelength that matches the size of an atom? The most important consequence comes from the relationship between wavelength and energy. If you know the energy of an electron, then you also know its wavelength. Conversely, if the wavelength of the electron is fixed, you also fix its energy as well. *Electrons inside atoms can only have specific energies that match the wavelengths they are allowed to have.*

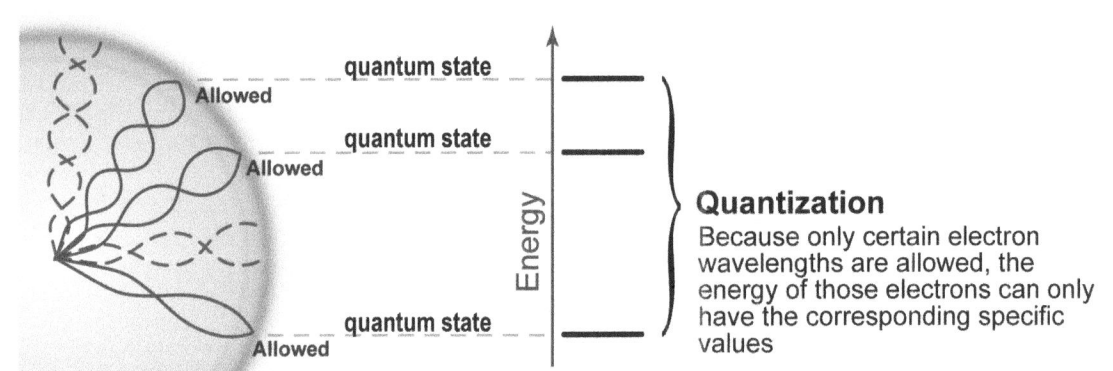

Quantization
Because only certain electron wavelengths are allowed, the energy of those electrons can only have the corresponding specific values

Quantization

The restriction of energies to specific discrete values is called *quantization*. This is one of the most important consequences of quantum theory. An electron trapped inside an atom *cannot* have any value of energy. The electron can have only those specific values of energy that correspond to the allowed wavelengths.

We now have a way to define a *quantum state*. A quantum state is one of the allowed wavelengths in an atom. Because of the connection between wavelength and energy, each quantum state has a specific energy. This is the key idea of the quantum atom.

Real quantum states

The details of real quantum states inside an atom are complicated for these reasons:

- Atoms are three-dimensional, not two-dimensional boxes.

- Besides charge and mass, electrons have a purely quantum property called *spin*.

- Electrons repel each other, so in atoms with more than one electron, the size and shape of the "box" depend on both the nucleus and the other electrons in the atom.

Multiple states can have the same wavelength

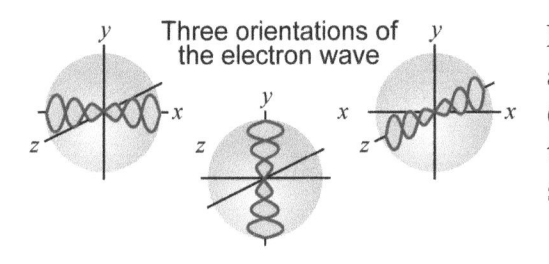

Three orientations of the electron wave

For example, because the electron wave can be aligned along any of the three coordinate axes (x, y, or z), there are three different quantum states that have the same wavelength, and therefore the same energy. This is a three-dimensional effect.

Orbitals

The origin of s, p, d, and f
The allowed quantum states are grouped in a peculiar, yet historically interesting way. When scientists first started using spectroscopy to explore the elements, they noticed that the spectra of the metals (Li, Na, and K) had four characteristic groups of spectral lines. They named the groups *sharp*, *principal*, *diffuse* and *fundamental*, but they had no real idea what caused the differences among the four groups. Today we know each group is associated with a quantum state in a particular shape. In deference to history, the four types of shapes are known by the letters s, p, d, and f.

Orbitals
Orbitals are groups of quantum states that have similar shapes in space. To understand what these shapes look like, consider the single electron in a hydrogen atom. With no other electrons to repel it, this electron has an equal chance to be at any angular position around the nucleus. Hydrogen's lone electron is in an s orbital. The s orbitals are spherically symmetric, and each one can hold two electrons.

The shapes of the s, p, and d orbitals

s	p	d	
			5th energy level
			4th energy level
			3rd energy level
			2nd energy level
			1st energy level

Why some orbitals have strange shapes
Carbon has six electrons. With this many electrons, repulsion between electrons changes the shape of the electron cloud. The p orbitals are shaped like dumbbells along each of the three coordinate axes. The three p orbitals can hold six electrons all together. The d orbitals are more elaborately shaped and can hold a total of 10 electrons.

Orbitals create 3-dimensional molecules
The three-dimensional shape of the orbitals represents the real three-dimensional shape of the electron cloud. The orbital shapes are directly responsible for the three-dimensional shapes of molecules. Methane (CH_4) is tetrahedral because of the way the s and p orbitals form chemical bonds between carbon and hydrogen.

Methane CH_4

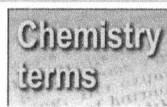
Chemistry terms
orbital: group of quantum states that have similar spatial shapes, labeled s, p, d, and f.

Energy levels

The quantum states are grouped into energy levels

Since several quantum states have the same energy, the states are grouped into **energy levels**. The diagram below shows how the quantum states are arranged in the first five energy levels. There is an even number of quantum states because they occur in spin-up/spin-down pairs. The first energy level has two quantum states. The second and third energy levels have eight quantum states. The fourth and fifth levels have 18 states each.

Organization of the energy levels

Sixth energy level
(32 electrons)

Fifth energy level
(18 electrons)

Fourth energy level
(18 electrons)

Third energy level
(8 electrons)

Second energy level
(8 electrons)

First energy level
(2 electrons)

○ **One quantum state holds 1 electron**

The Pauli exclusion principle

Electrons confined to the same atom obey a quantum rule called the *Pauli exclusion principle*. The **Pauli exclusion principle** states that two electrons in the same atom may never be in the same quantum state. Electrons fill quantum states from the lowest energy to the highest. Lithium, with three electrons, cannot have all three in the first energy level because there are only two quantum states (spin-up and spin-down). The third electron has to go into the second energy level.

Lithium's 3rd electron has to go into the 2nd energy level

Lithium: 3 electrons

Hund's rule

Electron-electron repulsion forces affect the way electrons are distributed in orbitals. According to *Hund's rule*, electrons with the same-spin must occupy a different equal-energy orbital, before additional electrons with opposite spins can occupy the same orbitals. Here we see how the electrons of N and O are distributed in orbitals.

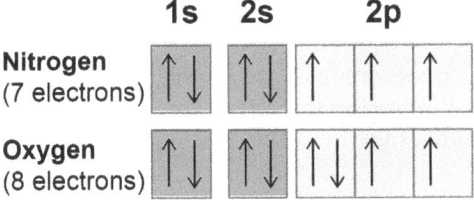

Nitrogen
(7 electrons)

Oxygen
(8 electrons)

1s   2s   2p

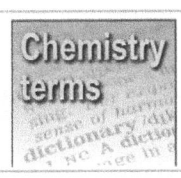
Chemistry terms

energy level: the set of quantum states for an electron in an atom that have approximately the same energy.

Pauli exclusion principle: principle that states that two electrons in the same atom may never be in the same quantum state.

150

The periodic table

Rows correspond to energy levels

The rows of the periodic table correspond directly to the energy levels for electrons. The first energy level has two quantum states. Atomic hydrogen (H) has one electron, and atomic helium (He) has two electrons. These two elements are the only ones in the top row of the periodic table because there are only two quantum states in the first energy level.

The second row

The next element, lithium (Li), has three electrons. Lithium begins the second row because the third electron goes into the second energy level. The second energy level has eight quantum states and there are eight elements in the second row of the periodic table, ending with neon. Neon (Ne) has 10 electrons, which exactly fill all the quantum states in the first and second levels.

The third row

Sodium (Na) has 11 electrons, and it starts the third row because the 11th electron goes into the third energy level. The third row ends with the noble gas, argon, which has 18 electrons. Eighteen electrons completely fill the third energy level.

Energy levels correspond to bonding properties

If you compare the energy level diagram with the periodic table, you find that all the noble gases have completely filled energy levels. All the elements that tend to form negative ions (F, Cl, and Br) have one electron *less* than a full energy level. All the alkali metals that tend to form positive ions (Li, Na, and K) have one electron *more* than a full energy level. This is a strong clue that the energy levels are crucial to the chemical properties of the elements.

Rows of the periodic table correspond to filling of the energy levels

5.3 Electron Configurations

Organization
of the energy
levels

All the elements share a common organization for how the quantum states are grouped into energy levels. Because each element has a different nuclear charge, the actual energies of each level are unique to each element. However, the overall pattern is the same for all the elements and determines the organization of the periodic table.

Energy levels and quantum states   **The periodic table**

○ **One quantum state holds one electron**

Electrons fill up
lowest energy
orbitals first

Every proton in the nucleus of an atom will attract one electron. Each of those electrons must exist in one of the quantum states in the diagram. Like a ball rolling downhill, each electron settles into the lowest unoccupied quantum state.

Electrons settle into the lowest unfilled quantum states

How the first
few elements
fill the energy
levels

The first (and lowest) energy level holds two electrons. Hydrogen has one electron, so it belongs in the first energy level. Helium has two electrons, and they completely fill the first energy level.

Beginning the
second row

Lithium has three electrons. Two of lithium's electrons go into the first energy level. The Pauli exclusion principle forbids lithium's third electron from occupying either of the occupied states on the first energy level. The third one has to go into the second energy level.

Ending the
second row

Fluorine has nine electrons. They fill all but the last quantum state on the second energy level. Neon has 10 electrons, which completely fill the first and second energy levels.

152

Electron configuration

The principal quantum number

The **principal quantum number** (or quantum number) defines certain properties of the quantum states. The diagram below shows the first four quantum numbers and the quantum states associated with each. The quantum states are further divided into the orbital types s, p, d, and f. The key at the right shows how the quantum states fall into energy levels. Note that the *energy level* is not the same as the quantum number!

Principal quantum #	Quantum states				Electrons	Energy levels
	s	p	d	f		
1	↑↓ 1s				2	☐ First
2	↑↓ 2s	↑↓ ↑↓ ↑↓ 2p			8	☐ Second
3	↑↓ 3s	↑↓ ↑↓ ↑↓ 3p	↑↓ ↑↓ ↑↓ ↑↓ ↑↓ 3d		18	☐ Third
4	↑↓ 4s	↑↓ ↑↓ ↑↓ 4p	↑↓ ↑↓ ↑↓ ↑↓ ↑↓ 4d	↑↓ ↑↓ ↑↓ ↑↓ ↑↓ ↑↓ ↑↓ 4f	32	☐ Fourth ☐ Fifth ☐ Sixth

Electron configuration

The **electron configuration** is a quick way to describe how electrons in an atom are distributed among the orbitals. The first number is the principal quantum number. The letter identifies the orbital, and the superscript is the number of electrons in that orbital. Quantum number 1 contains only a single s orbital which can hold two electrons. Quantum number 2 can hold up to two "s" electrons and six "p" electrons for a total of eight.

Electron configuration

Element	Number of electrons	Electron Configuration	Description of electron locations
Hydrogen	1	$1s^1$	One electron at the 1s level.
Helium	2	$1s^2$	Two electrons at the 1s level
Lithium	3	$1s^2 2s^1$	Two electrons at the 1s level and one electron at the 2s level
Beryllium	4	$1s^2 2s^2$	Two electrons at the 1s level and two electrons at the 2s level
Boron	5	$1s^2 2s^2 2p^1$	Two electrons at the 1s level, two electrons at the 2s level, and one electron at the 2p level

Chemistry terms

electron configuration: a description of which orbitals contain electrons for a particular atom.

principal quantum number: a number that specifies the quantum state and is related to the energy level of the electron.

Finding the electron configuration

Here is the complete list of orbitals and the filling order for all of the currently discovered elements:

1s, 2s, 2p, 3s, 3p, 4s, 3d, 4p, 5s, 4d, 5p, 6s, 4f, 5d, 6p, 7s, 5f, 6d, 7p

The table is arranged according to the structure of the atoms and orbitals

This order tells a chemist exactly how the electrons are structured in an atom. It may seem somewhat random, but using the periodic table as your guide, there is a way to remember the orbital filling order. This is because the structure of the periodic table is actually based on the structure of the atoms. By understanding the connection between the orbitals and the periodic table, we learn about both the structure of the atom and its connection to chemical and physical properties. First, let's look at how the periodic table would be laid out if we didn't place the rare earth elements below the table.

Periodic table showing which orbital typically contains the highest energy electrons for that element

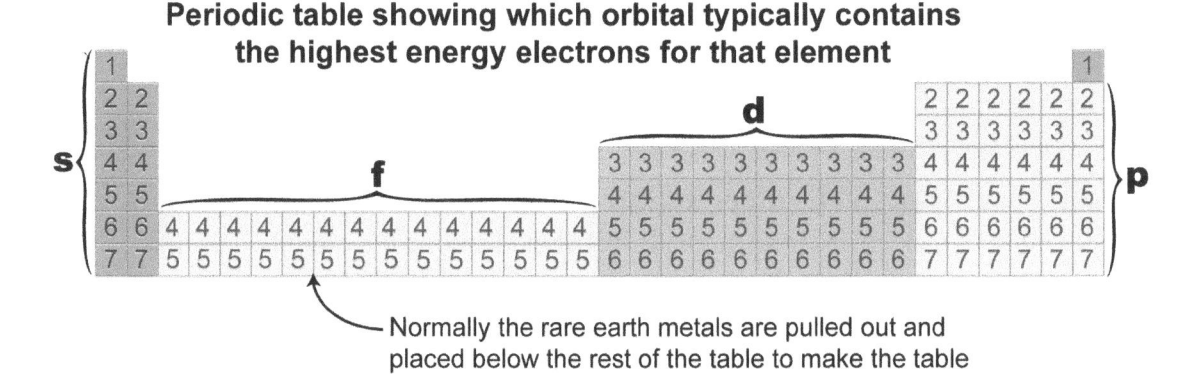

Normally the rare earth metals are pulled out and placed below the rest of the table to make the table more compact. This is only done to save space.

Finding the electron configurations

To find an electron configuration, start with the number of electrons (the atomic number). Use the chart below to find the largest number of electrons that is still less than the configuration you are trying to find. Subtract that number from the number of electrons you have, and the remainder is the superscript on the unfilled orbital. For noble gases, the chart will give you the exact electron configuration.

Electron configuration chart

$1s^2$,	$2s^2$,	$2p^6$,	$3s^2$,	$3p^6$,	$4s^2$,	$3d^{10}$,	$4p^6$,	$5s^2$,	$4d^{10}$,	$5p^6$
2	4	10	12	18	20	30	36	38	48	54

Total number of electrons for full orbitals

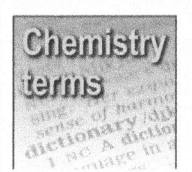

Write the electron configuration for silicon (atomic number 14).

Solve: *There are 14 electrons. The chart shows that 12 electrons fill up to $3s^2$. Therefore, the remaining 2 electrons must go into a 3p orbital, making the electron configuration $1s^2 2s^2 2p^6 3s^2 3p^2$.*

5.4 Light and Spectroscopy

Visible light

Light is a form of electromagnetic energy that comes mainly from electrons in atoms. If you are reading this book under a fluorescent light, then you are seeing the energy levels in the atom right now! In fact, we "see" when the light that enters our eyes is absorbed by electrons in molecules at the back of our eyes. When these molecules absorb light, the cells that contain them send electrical signals to your brain and you "see."

Only visible light interacts with molecules in the eye.

The spectrum of visible light

Energy and color

The different colors of light come from the energies of different photons. Red is the lowest energy photon that humans can see. The highest visible energy is violet. All the colors between red and violet form the *visible spectrum*. A **spectrum** is a representation of the different energies present in light. Since energy depends on frequency and wavelength, the colors of light also depend on frequency and wavelength. The spectrum often specifies wavelength on the x axis. One nanometer (nm) is 10^{-9} meters.

Lower energy   **Higher energy**

Infrared   Visible light   Ultraviolet

Wavelength (nm)

White light is a mixture of colors

The white light from a lamp is actually a mixture of many different colors and energies. White light from the Sun is not truly white. You can split white light into a spectrum of colors by using a prism. A device that splits light into its spectrum is called a **spectrometer**. These instruments provided one of the first and best clues to unraveling the mystery of the structure of the atom.

Analyzing starlight with a prism
(one of the first spectrometers)

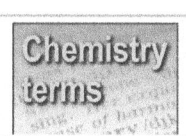
Chemistry terms

spectrum: a representation of a sample of light into its component energies or colors, in the form of a picture, a graph, or a table of data.

spectrometer: a device that measures the spectrum of light.

The electromagnetic spectrum

There are many types of light

The light that we can see (visible light) is really only a small subset of a much larger spectrum of electromagnetic energy. The full **electromagnetic spectrum** includes lower energies (radio and microwaves) and higher energies (ultraviolet and x rays). Many scientists use the word "light" loosely to mean the entire electromagnetic spectrum. This includes radio waves, microwaves, x rays, and even gamma rays.

- Radio waves
- Microwaves
- Infrared
- Visible light
- Ultraviolet
- X-rays
- Gamma rays

low energy

high energy

infrared lasers read CDs

microwaves for cell phone communication

radio waves

visible light

Energy and frequency

The energy of a photon depends on its frequency and wavelength according to the Planck relationship $E = h\nu$. The Greek symbol ν (pronounced "nu") is used to represent frequency in hertz (Hz). Because photon energies tend to be small (10^{-18} J), scientists define the **electron volt** (eV) as 1.602×10^{-19} J. Electron volts are also about the size of energy changes in an atom. For example, the difference between the second and third energy levels in hydrogen is 1.89 eV.

Photon energy

Planck's constant

Energy (J or eV)
6.626×10^{-34} J·s
4.136×10^{-15} eV·s

$$E = h\nu$$

Frequency (Hz)

Energy, frequency, and wavelength of various forms of electromagnetic radiation

infrared

visible light

radio

microwave

ultraviolet

x rays   gamma rays

Energy (eV)
10^{-9} 10^{-6} 10^{-3} 10^{0} 10^{3} 10^{6}

Frequency (Hz)
10^{6} 10^{9} 10^{12} 10^{15} 10^{18}

Wavelength (m)
10^{3} 10^{0} 10^{-3} 10^{-6} 10^{-9} 10^{-12}

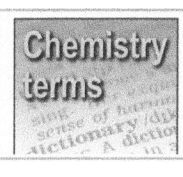

Chemistry terms

electromagnetic spectrum: the complete range of electromagnetic waves, including visible light.
electron volt: a unit of energy equal to 1.602×10^{-19} J.

The speed of light

The speed of a wave is its frequency times its wavelength

Photons and other waves move one wavelength with each oscillation. Since the number of oscillations per second is the *frequency*, and one wavelength is the distance the wave advances, the *speed* of a wave is its frequency multiplied by its wavelength. This relation-ship allows us to calculate the frequency if we know the wavelength and vice versa.

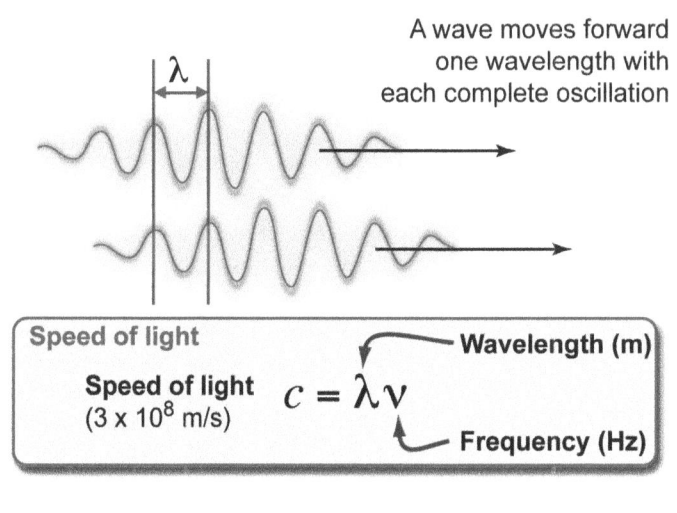

A wave moves forward one wavelength with each complete oscillation

Speed of light

Speed of light (3 x 10⁸ m/s) $c = \lambda \nu$ Wavelength (m)
Frequency (Hz)

The speed of light

Photons move *very* fast at a speed of 3×10^8 m/s, or 186,000 miles per second! This is the ultimate speed limit in our universe. Nothing can move faster than light. The **speed of light** is so important it has its own special symbol, a lowercase letter c.

c is a constant

The speed of light in a vacuum is a *constant*. That means it is the same for all frequencies and wavelengths. In chemistry, the speed of light is very useful for converting between frequency and wavelength. If you know the wavelength of light, then you can calculate its frequency from the speed of light.

Solved problem

The wavelength of red laser light is 652 nm. What is its frequency? How much energy does a photon of this light have in electron volts?

Asked: *Frequency and energy*

Given: $\lambda = 652 \times 10^{-9} \ m$

Relationships: $c = \lambda\nu$, $E = h\nu$

Solve: $c = \lambda\nu$ therefore $\nu = \dfrac{c}{\lambda} = \dfrac{3 \times 10^8 \ \text{m/s}}{652 \ 10^{-9} \ \text{m}} = \dfrac{4.6 \times 10^{14}}{\text{s}} = 4.6 \times 10^{14}/\text{s}$

$E = h\nu = (4.136 \ 10^{-15} \ \text{eV} \cdot \text{s}) (4.6 \times 10^{14}/\text{s}) = 1.9 \ \text{eV}$

Answer: *Since 1 Hz=1/s, the frequency is 4.6×10^{14} Hz and the energy is 1.9 eV.*

Chemistry terms

speed of light (c): a constant speed at which all electromagnetic radiation travels through a vacuum, including visible light; the speed of light in a vacuum is 299,792,458 m/s or approximately 3×10^8 m/s.

Interactions between light and matter

Experimenting with excited electrons

Light from an incandescent light bulb shows a continuous spectrum of colors. This tells us that the atoms that produced the light can absorb and release any amount of energy. Light from pure hydrogen does something completely different. Instead of a continuous rainbow, *we see a few very specific colors and nothing but darkness in between.*

Electrons losing energy in the visible light range

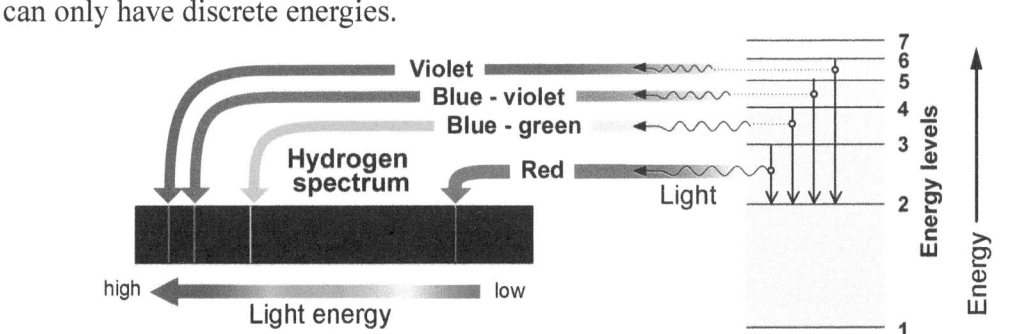

No fixed energy levels

Using a prism to separate the light emitted by an electron as it jumps between all possible energy levels would show a complete rainbow

Specific fixed energy levels

Fixed energy levels would only allow the electron to emit specific types of photons, with each photon having an energy equal to the energy lost by specific jumps in energy levels

The spectrum tells us there are energy levels

The spectrum from hydrogen tells us that hydrogen atoms can only absorb and emit light of very specific energies. It is like viewing the inner workings of a hydrogen atom. The fact that the spectrum shows discrete colors tells us that electrons in the hydrogen atom can only have discrete energies.

Interactions between matter and light

As a wave of light moves through matter, any electrons inside atoms oscillate in response to the wave. On the atomic scale, two kinds of interactions can occur: absorption or nothing. If a photon is absorbed, another photon with the same energy may be reemitted. The scattering of light is actually a two-step process of absorption and reemission.

Energy levels

Photon

If the photon energy matches a gap between levels it can be absorbed by the atom

If the photon energy does *not* match a gap between levels it passes right through the atom

Electrons can get excited

Which of the two interactions occurs depends on how the energy of the photon compares to the energy levels in the atom. If the photon energy matches a difference in the atom's energy levels, the photon may be absorbed. If not, the photon typically passes right through. If a photon passes through, we say that atom is *transparent* to that light.

Spectroscopy

Different elements have different energy levels

Quantum theory tells us that any electron confined to a small space, like an atom, results in energy levels. The specific energy levels depend on the strength of the force between the nucleus and the electrons. This depends on the number of protons in the nucleus, and on the number of other electrons in the atom that might be shielding the attractive force from the nucleus. For this reason, *the energy levels are different and unique for each element*.

Each element has unique energy levels

Every element and compound has a unique spectrum

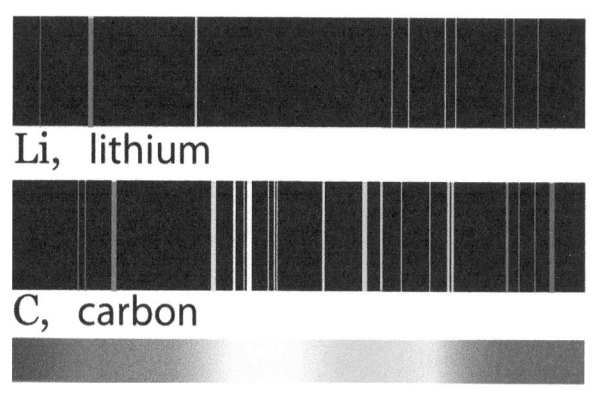

If the energy levels of electrons are different for different elements, then the light emitted from each element must also be unique. In fact, each element emits a characteristic spectrum. Chemists refer to the emission spectrum as the fingerprint of an element. Chemistry laboratories identify elements and compounds by their spectra.

Emission and absorption spectra

Atoms both emit and absorb light at the energies corresponding to their energy levels. If white light is passed through a sample of matter, some light will be absorbed by the atoms in the sample. Not all light will be absorbed. Only colors corresponding to specific energy levels are strongly absorbed, resulting in dark lines in a continuous spectrum. This is called an absorption spectrum. Can you see the similarities between the absorption spectrum and emission spectrum?

Spectroscopy

Using spectra to analyze substances is called **spectroscopy**. Spectroscopy can tell you what elements produced the light being observed. Spectroscopy is a tool to find out what distant stars are made of, identifying unknown compounds at a crime scene, and even discovering forgeries. Right now, satellites are searching for water on Mars and astronomers are studying the composition of distant stars and galaxies by using spectroscopy. Even the makeup of our own atmosphere and global scale environmental research is done via satellites using spectroscopy.

Chemistry terms	**spectroscopy:** the science of analyzing matter using electromagnetic emission or absorption spectra.

Fireworks and color

Almost everyone loves the festive display of fireworks. Fireworks have long been associated with special occasions and annual holidays like Independence Day. The brilliant display of colors and the fantastic explosions attract crowds from miles around. Fireworks similar to the ones we use today were first discovered in China in the early 1800s. The use of fireworks first began after the discovery of gunpowder. Gunpowder is an explosive mixture of sulfur (S), charcoal (primarily carbon), and potassium nitrate (KNO_3), also known as saltpeter. The gunpowder mixture was used to heat chemicals that made the flames and sparks turn different colors.

What do fireworks have to do with chemistry? Certain chemicals release light in the visible spectrum when they are heated. The chemicals that do this are positive ions, or cations, of ionic compounds (or salts). For example, the copper ion (Cu^{2+}) in $CuCl_2(s)$ gives off a green color when heated in a high temperature flame. Which wavelength corresponds to green?

You might remember that the heat from the flame causes the copper electrons to gain energy and become excited. This excitation is temporary, and when the electrons return to their original energy levels, they release the excess energy in the form of light. In this example, Cu^{2+} releases light at around 550 nm, so we can see it. The amount of energy determines the color of light emitted, and the amount of energy emitted is characteristic of the element. What chemicals are responsible for these colors?

Color	Wavelength (nm)	Compounds
Purple	430	Mixture of $SrCl_2$ (red) + CuCl (blue)
Blue	500	CuCl, other copper compounds
Green	550	$BaCl_2$, other barium compounds
Yellow	600	NaCl, other sodium salts
Red	650–700	$SrCO_3$, other strontium salts, $LiCO_3$ or other lithium salts

Chemists have learned which salts to add to achieve just the right color. To make fireworks, these metallic salts are added to a "star." A star is a small lump of clay or a cube that holds the metallic salts together with binding agents. The appearance of a firework is determined by the stars, which are handmade and packed with care inside the cardboard shell. The stars are ignited by a time-delay fuse.

Quite a lot happens when a firework is lit! First, the power to lift each firework is provided by the gunpowder, or black powder. The exothermic reaction provides the thrust to lift the firework into the air. The firework compartment is designed to trap the gases produced inside the shell until the force is enough to shoot the firework upward. The firework actually has two fuses. One goes to the gunpowder; this one burns very quickly. The second one, which is a time-delay fuse, goes up toward the stars. The second fuse is designed not to go off until the firework is high in the air.

Fireworks actually require some careful choreography! The charge of gunpowder is supposed to run out at exactly the same time that the second fuse ignites the stars. The colors become visible as they heat up, and loud bangs are heard simultaneously. Sometimes, if the timing is off, fireworks detonate too early near the ground or too late as they are beginning to fall back down. These are the variables that make fireworks dangerous to people who are not trained to handle explosives.

The old saying "what goes up must come down" is an issue with fireworks and the environment. When a firework combusts, it leaves behind particulate matter and chemical by-products that find their way into the nearby soil and water. Of primary concern is the perchlorate anion (ClO_4^-). Chemicals that produce a hotter, more exothermic reaction are required to energize the metal ions inside the stars. Here chemicals such as potassium chlorate ($KClO_3$) and potassium perchlorate ($KClO_4$) are used. These chlorate (ClO_3^-) compounds are more dangerous to handle than perchlorate (ClO_4^-) compounds. The fact that chlorate has one fewer oxygen atom in its structure causes this instability. Fireworks containing chlorate compounds can even explode if they are dropped by accident! These have caused many deadly explosions. Because of this, we now use perchlorate (ClO_4^-) compounds, which are far more stable than chlorate (ClO_3^-) compounds. However, perchlorates are toxic to the environment and have been shown to be a human health hazard. Perchlorate (ClO_4^-) is very water soluble, finding its way into the water supplies very easily. When consumed in drinking water, perchlorate is known to cause thyroid problems. In several lakes tested after fireworks displays, the perchlorate levels were up to 1,000 times the normal base level, and it took up to 80 days for the levels to return to normal. There are many alternatives being developed that will make fireworks safer for our environment. Researchers have found that by cutting down on the smoke given off by a firework, fewer chemicals are needed to get a strong visual effect. They are also substituting other chemicals for the perchlorates.

Chapter 5 Review

Vocabulary

Match each word to the sentence where it best fits.

Section 5.1

ion	isotope
radioactivity	nucleus
atomic mass unit	mass number
atomic number	decay
orbit	

1. An atom may have more than one _____ if it can have different numbers of neutrons.
2. The mass of one carbon atom is 12.011 _____ _____.
3. Most of the mass of an atom is located in the _____.
4. In an atomic model, a/an _____ is the imaginary path an electron travels around the nucleus.
5. During _____, an element spontaneously changes into a new element.
6. The _____ tells us what kind of element an atom is.
7. A/An _____ is an atom (or small molecule) that has an unequal number of protons and electrons.
8. _____ is when the nucleus of an atom spontaneously changes and energy is released.
9. The _____ of an atom describes the number of protons and neutrons in its nucleus.

Section 5.2

photon	orbital
frequency	quantum state
wavelength	quantum theory the
energy level	Pauli exclusion
Planck's constant	principle

10. There can be a maximum of 8 electrons in the second _____.

11. The _____ tells us how often a wave moves up and down per unit time.
12. Chemists use _____ to describe phenomena that occur at subatomic scales.
13. _____ allows us to find particle's frequency based on its energy.
14. A short _____ indicates a higher energy wave.
15. According to _____, two electrons can never be in the same quantum state.
16. Each _____ can only hold one electron.
17. A/An _____ describes where you are likely to find an electron.
18. The smallest quantity of light possible is called a/an _____.

Section 5.3

electron configuration	principle quantum number
spectrum	spectrophotometer

19. The _____ of visible light spans from about 400 nm to 750 nm.
20. The _____ of an atom describes how the electrons are organized among the orbitals.
21. The _____ tells us the quantum state and energy of a particular electron.
22. Light measurements can be done using a/an _____.

Section 5.4

electromagnetic spectrum	spectroscopy
electron volt	speed of light

23. The _____ includes low energy radio waves, as well as high energy gamma rays.
24. The _____ refers to the time it takes for electromagnetic radiation to travel through a vacuum.
25. A/An _____ is a very small unit of energy that can be used to describe light energy.

26. Using _____, astronomers can determine the composition of distant stars.

Conceptual Questions

Section 5.1

27. Draw a time line showing the development of atomic theory starting with Democritus and ending with Heisenberg. Be sure to mention the person, a date, and their contribution to our current knowledge of the atom.

28. Give at least two experiments that support the idea that everything is made from atoms, and explain why.

29. Which parts of Dalton's atomic theory are now known to be untrue?

30. What was the first subatomic particle to be discovered?

31. Describe the connection between cathode rays and electrons.

32. Describe the experiment performed by J. J. Thomson using cathode rays tubes. What were his conclusions?

33. Given Rutherford's results, why did he determine the nucleus of an atom was small, dense and positively charged?

34. From what particles are atoms constructed, and where are they located in the atom?

35. Which subatomic particle has almost no mass relative to the others: the proton, the neutron or the electron?

36. Why do we need to use probability maps like the orbital picture to show where the electron is? Why can't we say the electron orbits the nucleus like a planet?

37. What number is the same for all oxygen atoms?
    a. the number of protons
    b. the number of neutrons
    c. the number of electrons

38. What is the number on the periodic table that tells you which kind of element an atom is?

39. If you have an atom of carbon-12 and an atom of carbon-14 then you have:
    a. two different ions
    b. two different elements
    c. two different isotopes

40. Describe the difference between the mass number for an atom and the atomic mass of an element.

41. Explain why rubbing almost anything together can cause an electric charge to build up and give an example.

42. If something is electrically neutral, then which one of the following must be true?
    a. It is constructed only from neutrons.
    b. The positive and negative charges are exactly balanced.
    c. It has been discharged by touching something metallic.
    d. It is made from an equal number of protons and neutrons.

43. What must be true of the lithium atoms in a lithium ion battery—the kind that power most laptops?

44. Explain why you don't need the atomic symbol to determine the number of electrons.

Section 5.2

45. Describe the Bohr model of the atom. How did it differ from previous models? Which experimental observations did it explain?

46. Using the diagram below, compare the wavelength, frequency and energy of the two waves:

wave A   wave B

47. Describe the difference between an orbit and an orbital.

48. Which has more energy: radiation with a wavelength of 250 nm or radiation with a wavelength of 400 nm?

Chapter 5 Review

Section 5.3

49. The atom lithium has the electron configuration of $1s^22s^1$. Describe what each number represents.

50. What is interesting about the 3d orbital?

Section 5.4

51. Which type of electromagnetic radiation carries more energy per photon, microwaves or visible light?

52. Which type of photon has more energy: a red photon of visible light or a blue photon of visible light?

53. Explain why shining an intense red laser at a particular metal does nothing, while a very weak ultraviolet light can cause electrons to be ejected from the atoms.

54. How does an electron absorb energy? a. It jumps to a higher energy level.
    b. It heats up.
    c. It moves closer to the nucleus.
    d. It jumps to a lower energy level.

55. How does an electron emit a photon of light?
    a. It jumps to a higher energy level.
    b. It heats up.
    c. It moves farther away from the nucleus.
    d. It jumps to a lower energy level.

56. What is spectroscopy, and how can it help us learn about distant stars, planets and our own atmosphere?

57. If you shine a light into a prism, it:
    a. creates new types of light so you see photons other than the color of the original light.
    b. separates the photons that were mixed together in the original beam of light.
    c. subtracts some of the photons that were in the original light.

58. If an electron has four possible different energy levels, how many different photons of electromagnetic energy could be given off by that electron, assuming it keeps absorbing and releasing energy so that it visits every possible energy level?
    a. two
    b. four
    c. six
    d. eight

Quantitative Problems

Section 5.1

59. If the nucleus of an atom is about 1/10,000th the radius of an atom, what percentage of the volume of the atom is empty space, assuming the atom is a perfect sphere?

60. Make up some analogy that gets across how big an atom is compared to its nucleus. For example: If the nucleus were as big as a baseball (about 3.5 cm radius), the outer edge of the atom would be about 3.5 football fields away (about 350 meters or 35,000 cm).

61. How many protons does a nitrogen atom have?
    a. 7
    b. 14
    c. 28
    d. It depends on the charge of the atom.

62. How many electrons does a nitrogen atom have?
    a. 7
    b. 14
    c. 28
    d. It depends on the charge of the atom.

63. Below is a table of several different isotopes used in medical imaging and research. Fill in the table with the appropriate numbers.

Element	Isotope	Protons	Neutrons
potassium	$^{40}_{19}K$		
potassium	$^{39}_{19}K$		
oxygen	$^{15}_{8}O$		

64. Below is a table of ions or atoms. Fill in the table with the appropriate numbers.

Element	Isotope	Protons	Electrons
lithium	Li^{1+}		
argon	Ar		
nitrogen	N^{2+}		
nitrogen	N^{5-}		

65. Calculate the approximate atomic mass for sulfur, given the following isotopes and abundances:
sulfur-32: 94.93%
sulfur-33: 0.76%
sulfur-34: 4.29%
sulfur-36: 0.02%

Section 5.2

66. A particle has a frequency of 2.0×10^{15} Hz. What is its energy in joules (J) and in electron volts (eV)?

67. Suppose alpha particles are emitted from a reaction and have an energy of 5.2 eV. Calculate the de Broglie wavelength in nm for one particle. The mass of an alpha particle is 6.64×10^{-27} kg.

Section 5.4

68. If you have an instrument that uses microwaves with a frequency of 10^{12} Hz, what is the energy in (ev) and the wavelength in (nm)?

69. Below is a diagram showing which kinds of electromagnetic radiation are produced when an electron jumps from a higher energy level to a lower one. Why does it make sense that when an electron jumps from a higher level to level 3 that it emits infrared photons, but when it jumps to level 1, ultraviolet photons are emitted?

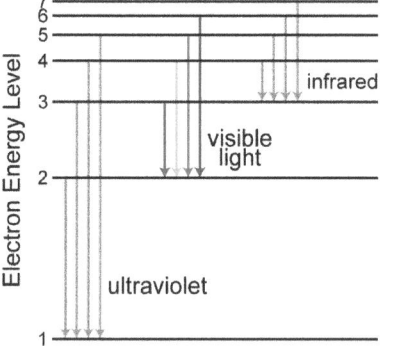

70. An electron absorbs an amount of energy equivalent to 12.75 eV, and three photons are emitted as the electron loses energy and returns to its ground state. The first photon has an energy of 0.66 eV, and the second photon has an energy of 1.89 eV. What is the energy of the last photon emitted by that electron?

71. Of the following subsets of the electromagnetic spectrum, which is **NOT** ordered by *decreasing* frequency?
    a. Gamma rays, visible light, infrared, radio waves
    b. X-rays, ultraviolet, microwaves, radio waves
    c. Gamma rays, x-rays, infrared, ultraviolet
    d. X-rays, visible light, microwaves, radio waves

72. Classify each of the following wavelengths under the correct part of the electromagnetic spectrum (gamma rays, x-rays, etc.). If it falls under "visible light," write what color it is.
    a. 8.8×10^{-13} m
    b. 4.4×10^{-7} m
    c. 1.2×10^{0} m
    d. 2.5×10^{-8} m

CHAPTER 6
Elements and the Periodic Table

Where did all the different elements come from?

How is the periodic table organized, and how is it used?

Which elements are essential for life here on Earth?

Where did matter come from? The answer is found in astronomy! The universe contains billions of galaxies full of stars and planets. When astronomers look with powerful telescopes, they find that all the galaxies are rushing away from each other. The universe is expanding. An expanding universe means galaxies that are far apart today must have been closer together in the distant past. We believe that about 14 billion years ago, all matter in the entire universe was concentrated in a single point. That point exploded into the vast expanse of matter we see today in a cataclysmic event astronomers call the *Big Bang*.

Because of some complex physics, only four different elements were made in the Big Bang. Hydrogen accounted for 75% of all atoms. Helium accounted for almost all of the remaining 25%, with tiny amounts of lithium and beryllium. So, where did carbon, oxygen, iron, and the other elements come from?

Stars release their huge amount of energy by nuclear reactions that fuse hydrogen and helium into heavier elements, such as carbon and oxygen. When a star explodes in a *supernova*, even heavier elements are created, such as iron, silver, and gold. The supernova blows all the heavy elements that it made back into space, where they eventually can condense into a new star and planets, such as our own Solar System. The picture shows the remnant of a supernova that occurred in AD 1054. It was so bright that it was visible during the day for almost a month.

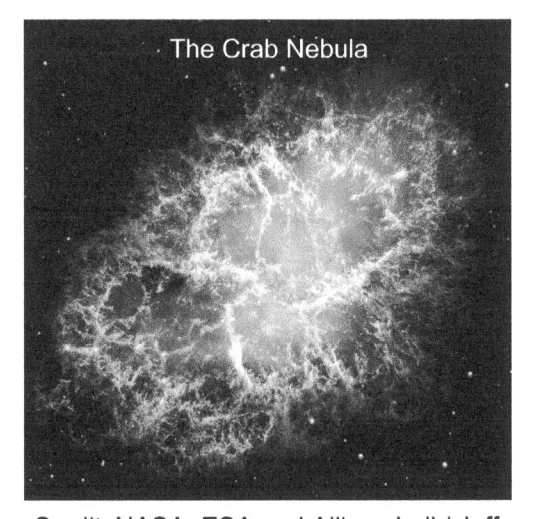

The Crab Nebula

Credit: NASA, ESA and Allison Loll / Jeff Hester (Arizona State University).

Testing properties of elements

How does the periodic table help us to understand the properties of the elements? By making some simple observations, we can begin to see patterns in the way elements are organized on the periodic table. Here we will experiment with four metals—calcium (Ca), magnesium (Mg), copper (Cu), and zinc (Zn)—to see how they react with water.

To begin you will need four test tubes in a test tube rack.

- Fill each test tube with about 10.0 mL of water.
- Place a small piece of each metal in the test tubes using a metal spatula. (Use caution as some of the test tubes may get quite hot during the experiment!)
- Look carefully at the test tubes and record some observations over the next 3–5 minutes.
- After the reactions have stopped, touch the test tubes to see which ones are warm.

You many have noticed that calcium and magnesium had the most vigorous reactions. Where are they on the periodic table? They are both in group 2 (the second column). Which one had the most impressive reaction? Look at where these elements are placed relative to each other. Could it be that the further down a group, the more reactive the metal? If the metal is more reactive, that means it caused the most observable change; for example, it showed the most bubbling and got warm.

Where are copper and zinc located? They are in the middle of the periodic table in group 11 (Cu) and group 12 (Zn). Neither of these seemed to react with water much, if at all. What could be different? These metals are located closer to the middle of the periodic table. Perhaps metals located on the left side react more with water.

Which metal would you select to cover the hull of a ship?

You will learn in this chapter that elements are grouped in columns based on the number of outer electrons they have. Group 2 elements, such as Ca and Mg, react more with water than elements with more electrons in their outer shells, such as Cu and Zn. Sodium (Na) is a metal in group 1 that bursts into flames when it comes into contact with water! Perhaps you can go online and see an example of this reaction.

6.1 The Periodic Table

The elements can be divided into metals, nonmetals, and metalloids

There are about 118 known elements. Based on their physical and chemical properties, they belong to one of three broad categories: metals, nonmetals, and metalloids. Metals are malleable and shiny and conduct electricity, and they are generally solid at room temperature. Examples include aluminum and copper. Nonmetals do not conduct electricity. Many nonmetals are gases or liquids at room temperature. Examples include nitrogen and oxygen. Metalloids have some properties similar to metals and some similar to nonmetals. Silicon is an important metalloid.

Atomic mass values in parentheses indicate the mass of the most stable isotope as reported by Los Alamos National Laboratory in June 2016.

Some elements are synthetic

Technetium (number 43), promethium (number 61), and all of the elements above atomic number 92 do not have any stable isotopes. These elements are highly radioactive. They were synthesized in a laboratory by bombarding the nuclei of existing atoms with high-energy particles such as neutrons or other fast-moving atomic nuclei.

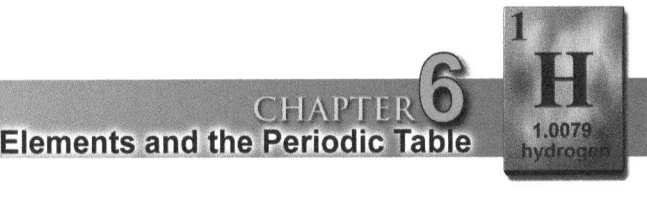
The periodic table and you

You are made mostly of hydrogen, carbon, oxygen, and nitrogen

Take approximately 44,000,000,000,000,000,000,000,000,000 atoms of the right kind, bond some of them together, mix the resulting bunch of molecules and ions together, and you could end up with a typical person weighing about 75 kg (or 165 lb). Of those atoms, over 99% of them would need to be only four different elements: hydrogen, carbon, oxygen, and nitrogen. Other elements are also essential for life, but they exist in much smaller numbers.

TABLE 6.1. Elemental composition of the human body

Element	% by mole
Hydrogen	63.0
Oxygen	26.0
Carbon	9.0
Nitrogen	1.25
Calcium	0.25
Phosphorus	0.19
Potassium	0.06
Sulfur	0.06
Sodium	0.04
Chlorine	0.025
Magnesium	0.013
Iron	0.00004
Iodine	0.000002

There would also be **trace amounts** of almost every element on the table, because "you are what you eat" (and what you breathe), absorbing everything from your environment.

You are made from star dust

Although hydrogen is the most common atom in your body, virtually all of the hydrogen in the universe was created in the Big Bang, so you have atoms in you that were present at the beginning of space and time. Even more incredible is the fact that almost all of the other atoms in your body must have been produced in the cores of exploding stars. These stars eventually provided the material from which the Earth was formed. You are literally made out of star dust!

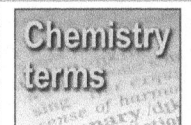

Chemistry terms

trace amount: a very small quantity.

Essential elements

Macronutrients and trace elements

While traces of almost all naturally occurring elements exist in your body, there are a small number that are considered essential to life. To maintain a healthy body, there are some elements you need to have a lot of; these are called **macronutrients**. These are the ones that form the bulk of your body. Macronutrient elements such as Na, Mg, P, S, Cl, K, and Ca are come from mineral sources, while others such as C, H, N, and O are found in organic matter. There are also some elements that are beneficial in trace amounts but can be toxic if you have too much.

Essential elements

H																	He
Li	Be		macronutrients								B	C	N	O	F	Ne
Na	Mg		trace elements								Al	Si	P	S	Cl	Ar
K	Ca	Sc	Ti	V	Cr	Mn	Fe	Co	Ni	Cu	Zn	Ga	Ge	As	Se	Br	Kr
Rb	Sr	Y	Zr	Nb	Mo	Tc	Ru	Rh	Pd	Ag	Cd	In	Sn	Sb	Te	I	Xe
Cs	Ba	Lu	Hf	Ta	W	Re	Os	Ir	Pt	Au	Hg	Tl	Pb	Bi	Po	At	Rn
Fr	Ra	Lr	Rf	Db	Sg	Bh	Hs	Mt	Ds	Rg	Cn	Uut	Fl	Uup	Lv	Uus	Uuo

The molecules of life

To make fats, carbohydrates, DNA, and proteins, you need hydrogen, carbon, nitrogen, oxygen, phosphorus, and sulfur. Calcium is needed to build your bones, and it functions in many other ways as dissolved ions. Sodium, magnesium, potassium, and chlorine all exist as dissolved ions. They help to transport other molecules into and out of cells, firing your nerves so you can see, smell, hear, and touch, and controlling the amount of water that enters and leaves your cells. These are only a few of the functions done by these other macronutrients.

Trace elements play special roles

The **trace elements** tend to have more specialized functions and are only present in extremely small amounts. You might be surprised to see chromium (Cr) on the list of essential elements. Some forms of Cr are know to cause cancer. However, in small amounts, Cr^{+3} ions are necessary to enhance insulin function, helping to control blood sugar levels. Other trace elements work together with enzymes to help them perform necessary biological functions. You would not be able to live without functioning enzymes.

Dotted lines represent interactions between purple Mg ions, ATP, water and enzyme.

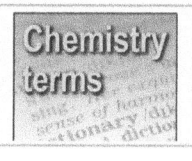
Chemistry terms

macronutrients: elements needed in large quantities by your body.

trace elements: elements that are needed in very small quantities to maintain optimum health.

Periodic properties of the elements

Searching for order in the elements

Back in 1869, when the science of chemistry was still young, a scientist and teacher of chemistry named Dimitri Mendeleev was trying to figure out whether there was an organization to the elements. He was searching for a pattern he could use to organize them in a logical way. At that time little was known about atoms. He knew that elements had an atomic mass and some other physical and chemical properties. Mendeleev tried arranging elements in order of atomic mass. Protons had not yet been discovered, and atomic number was not known at that time.

Mendeleev

When he graphed the density of the elements versus their atomic mass he saw a pattern.

Density is a periodic property

He observed that the density of the elements followed a **periodic** pattern, meaning that the pattern would repeat at regular intervals. Here he saw the density increase and then decrease in a repetitive pattern. The periodic table is named for this because the rows are organized by repeated patterns found in both the atomic structures and the properties of the elements.

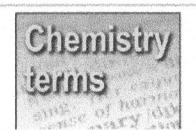
Chemistry terms

periodic: repeating at regular intervals.

Atomic level periodic properties and atomic radius

Atomic level and observable properties match patterns

In the Mendeleev's time, the internal structure of atoms was unknown. Only certain physical and chemical properties were known, such as density and melting point, or how one element would combine with another. However, it would probably not surprise Mendeleev that atomic level properties would follow the same periodic patterns as the observable properties mentioned above.

Atomic radius as a periodic property

One simple example of a periodic atomic property is atomic radius. The **atomic radius** describes the distance from the center of an atom to its "outer edge," where the likelihood of finding its electrons in the electron cloud gets very low. The image below shows the relative size of atoms from the first 18 elements on the periodic table.

Relative size of atomic radii for the first 18 elements

Relative atom size arranged in a periodic table view

Explanation of atomic radius trend

We can see that atomic radius increases down a column and decreases across a row. Why? Protons in the nucleus attract the negatively charged electrons. Electrons also interact with each other—by repelling each other. This decreases the attractive force between protons and outer electrons. The more electrons there are in the innermost shells, the stronger this shielding effect. As the number of protons increases, the attractive force between positively and negatively charged particles increases, and the atomic radius decreases.

172

Ionic radius, electronegativity, and ionization energy

Ionic radius: the size of an ion

Closely related to atomic radius is ionic radius. When an atom loses an electron to become a positively charged cation, it becomes smaller. This is because there are more protons than electrons, so the electrons are pulled in closer to the nucleus. Similarly, when an atom gains an electrons to become a negatively charged anion, it becomes larger because the protons cannot hold on to the increased number electrons as well. .

Electronegativity: how well one atom grabs electrons from another

When atoms bond, they may share electrons equally or almost equally, causing a covalent bond to form. In other cases the sharing is so uneven that we consider one atom to have taken electrons from the other. This causes the formation of ions. An atom's **electronegativity** (EN) is the measure of how well it can attract electrons from another atom to which it is bonded. EN increases across a row and decreases down a column. Metals have low EN and become cations when bonding; halogens have high EN and become anions when bonding.

Ionization energy: how well an atom holds onto its own electrons

On the other hand, ionization energy measures how well an atom holds onto its own electrons. The **ionization energy** (IE) is the minimum energy it takes to remove an electron from an atom, forming an ion. This can be done by hitting the atom with a photon of light. IE follows the same pattern as EN. Across a row, number of protons increases and the electrons are bound more tightly, so it is harder to remove an electron and IE increases. Down a column, electrons are added to a larger shell, so the protons cannot hold onto the electrons as tightly and IE decreases..

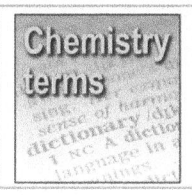
Chemistry terms

atomic radius: the distance from the center of an atom to its "outer edge."
electronegativity: the ability of an atom to attract another atom's electrons when bound to that other atom.
ionization energy: the energy required to remove an electron from an atom.

The first periodic table

Chemical properties have a repeating pattern

Density was a physical property of the elements that Mendeleev used in looking for patterns, but he also used chemical properties. For most of the elements, the ratio of how they react with either hydrogen or oxygen was already well known. Again, the elements were arranged in order of increasing atomic mass as with density, but this time the oxide or hydride formula was written instead of the value for density. Another pattern emerged.

Oxides and hydrides of first 35 elements known in 1869

In the diagram, the vertical green lines represent a place where the pattern of chemical combination with oxygen (or hydrogen) begins to repeat. If you take the same set of elements and start a new row each time the pattern repeats and make sure elements that react in the same way are in the same column you get the following:

Oxides and hydrides sorted into rows

The first periodic table as suggested by Mendeleev in 1869

How the first periodic table was created

If you take a look back at the density graph, you will find another reason to start a new row with Li, Na, K, Cu, and Rb. All of them, except for Cu, are at a point when the density is lowest and the pattern of densities starts to repeat. So, the repeating physical property of density seems to match up well with the repeating chemical properties of the elements. Mendeleev noticed this periodic pattern in both chemical and physical properties, so he arranged the elements into a table like the one you see above, with columns representing elements with similar chemical properties.

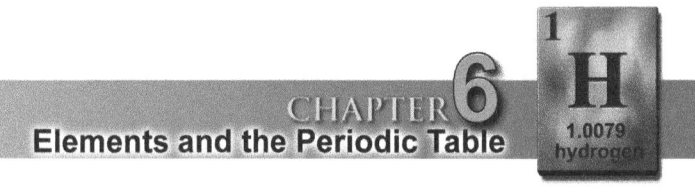

The modern periodic table

The modern periodic table is organized by atomic number

Nothing was known about the internal structure of atoms in Mendeleev's time. Protons hadn't been discovered yet, so the more logical ordering by atomic number was not possible. Today's periodic table includes many more elements and is ordered not by atomic mass but by atomic number.

However, two things are still true of the periodic table. Each column still represents a group of elements with similar chemical properties, and each row (or period) still marks the beginning of a repeated pattern of physical or chemical properties. Elements can be broadly categorized into metals, nonmetals and metalloids, and an understanding that each column has similar chemical properties has led to names for some of these element groups. Groups of particular interest are the *alkali metals* (group 1), the *alkaline earth metals* (group 2), the *halogens* (group 17), and the *noble gases* (group 18).

Periodic table colored by element groups

metals
- alkali metals
- alkaline earth metals
- transition metals
- rare earth metals
- other metals

nonmetals
- halogens
- noble gases
- other nonmetals

metalloids
- metalloids

group 1																	group 18
1 H 1.0079 hydrogen	group 2											group 13	group 14	group 15	group 16	group 17	2 He 4.0028 helium
3 Li 6.941 lithium	4 Be 9.0122 beryllium											5 B 10.811 boron	6 C 12.011 carbon	7 N 14.007 nitrogen	8 O 15.999 oxygen	9 F 18.998 fluorine	10 Ne 20.180 neon
11 Na 22.990 sodium	12 Mg 24.305 magnesium	group 3	group 4	group 5	group 6	group 7	group 8	group 9	group 10	group 11	group 12	13 Al 26.982 aluminum	14 Si 28.086 silicon	15 P 30.974 phosphorous	16 S 32.065 sulfur	17 Cl 35.453 chlorine	18 Ar 39.948 argon
19 K 39.098 potassium	20 Ca 40.078 calcium	21 Sc 44.956 scandium	22 Ti 47.867 titanium	23 V 50.942 vanadium	24 Cr 51.996 chromium	25 Mn 54.938 manganese	26 Fe 55.845 iron	27 Co 58.933 cobalt	28 Ni 58.693 nickel	29 Cu 63.546 copper	30 Zn 65.41 zinc	31 Ga 69.723 gallium	32 Ge 72.61 germanium	33 As 74.922 arsenic	34 Se 78.96 selenium	35 Br 79.904 bromine	36 Kr 83.80 krypton
37 Rb 85.468 rubidium	38 Sr 87.62 strontium	39 Y 88.906 yttrium	40 Zr 91.224 zirconium	41 Nb 92.906 niobium	42 Mo 95.94 molybdenum	43 Tc (98) technetium	44 Ru 101.07 ruthenium	45 Rh 102.91 rhodium	46 Pd 106.42 palladium	47 Ag 107.87 silver	48 Cd 112.41 cadmium	49 In 114.82 indium	50 Sn 118.71 tin	51 Sb 121.76 antimony	52 Te 127.60 tellurium	53 I 126.90 iodine	54 Xe 131.29 xenon
55 Cs 132.91 cesium	56 Ba 137.33 barium	71 Lu 174.97 lutetium	72 Hf 178.49 hafnium	73 Ta 180.95 tantalum	74 W 183.84 tungsten	75 Re 186.21 rhenium	76 Os 190.23 osmium	77 Ir 192.22 iridium	78 Pt 195.08 platinum	79 Au 196.97 gold	80 Hg 200.59 mercury	81 Tl 204.38 thallium	82 Pb 207.2 lead	83 Bi 208.98 bismuth	84 Po (209) polonium	85 At (210) astatine	86 Rn (222) radon
87 Fr (223) francium	88 Ra (226) radium	103 Lr (262) lawrencium	104 Rf (261) rutherfordium	105 Db (262) dubnium	106 Sg (266) seaborgium	107 Bh (264) bohrium	108 Hs (277) hassium	109 Mt (278) meitnerium	110 Ds (281) darmstadtium	111 Rg (272) roentgenium	112 Cn (285) copernicium	113 Uut (284) ununtrium	114 Fl (289) flerovium	115 Uup (288) ununpentium	116 Lv (293) livermorium	117 Uus (293) ununseptium	118 Uuo (294) ununoctium

57 La 138.91 lanthanum	58 Ce 140.12 cerium	59 Pr 140.91 praseodymium	60 Nd 144.24 neodymium	61 Pm (145) promethium	62 Sm 150.36 samarium	63 Eu 151.96 europium	64 Gd 157.25 gadolinium	65 Tb 158.93 terbium	66 Dy 162.50 dysprosium	67 Ho 164.93 holmium	68 Er 167.26 erbium	69 Tm 168.93 thulium	70 Yb 173.06 ytterbium
89 Ac (227) actinium	90 Th 232.04 thorium	91 Pa 231.04 protactinium	92 U 238.03 uranium	93 Np (237) neptunium	94 Pu (244) plutonium	95 Am (243) americium	96 Cm (247) curium	97 Bk (247) berkelium	98 Cf (251) californium	99 Es (252) einsteinium	100 Fm (257) fermium	101 Md (258) mendelevium	102 No (259) nobelium

Atomic mass values in parentheses indicate the mass of the most stable isotope as reported by Los Alamos National Laboratory in June 2016.

Orbitals and atomic radius

The electron cloud in overlapping orbitals is what gives an atom its size

One of the atomic level properties that we looked at previously was atomic radius, which is an indication of the size of an atom. The nucleus is tiny, so the size of the atom is really the space occupied by the electron cloud surround-ing the nucleus. To the right is a view of a boron atom showing a unique color for each orbital containing electrons. The cloud of electrons created by the overlapping 1s, 2s, and 2p orbitals is what gives a boron atom its size.

Overlapping orbitals of boron

two electrons located in the orange 1s orbital

two electrons located in the green 2s orbital

one electron located in the purple 2p orbital

$$1s^2 2s^2 2p^1$$

Here is another version of the table showing which orbitals are the last to be filled as the electrons fill up around an atom's nucleus.

Orbital view of the periodic table

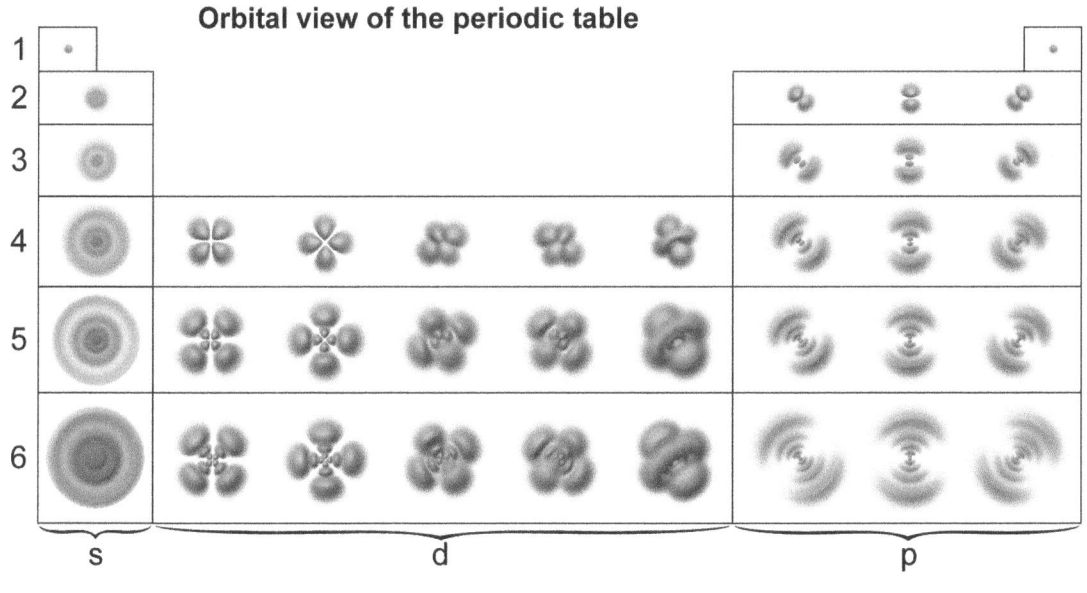

Atomic radii match orbital sizes

Compare the table above with the chart to the right. Each time you start a new row, the atom gets bigger because you start filling a new primary energy level with bigger orbitals. As you go across a row, atoms get smaller because the increased number of protons pulls electrons at the same primary level closer to the nucleus.

Atomic radius

H																	He
Li	Be											B	C	N	O	F	Ne
Na	Mg											Al	Si	P	S	Cl	Ar
K	Ca	Sc	Ti	V	Cr	Mn	Fe	Co	Ni	Cu	Zn	Ga	Ge	As	Se	Br	Kr
Rb	Sr	Y	Zr	Nb	Mo	Tc	Ru	Rh	Pd	Ag	Cd	In	Sn	Sb	Te	I	Xe
Cs	Ba	Lu	Hf	Ta	W	Re	Os	Ir	Pt	Au	Hg	Tl	Pb	Bi	Po	At	Rn
Fr	Ra	Lr	Rf	Db	Sg	Bh	Hs	Mt	Ds	Rg	Cn	Uut	Fl	Uup	Lv	Uus	Uuo

small ☐▇ large

A NATURAL APPROACH TO CHEMISTRY

6.2 Properties of Groups of Elements

Column 1 forms the alkali metal family

Alkali metals

Group 1 is known as the alkali metals. Hydrogen is in this column, but because of its peculiar properties, it is not considered to be part of the alkali metals. The most abundant alkali metals include lithium (Li), sodium (Na), and potassium (K). Less common are rubidium (Rb), cesium (Cs), and francium (Fr).

Alkali metals form positive ions with a charge of +1

The elements in group 1 all lose electrons easily. For example, in many compounds sodium becomes a positive ion (Na^+) by giving up an electron. Lithium and potassium also become positive ions (Li^+ and K^+). Sodium never becomes a negative ion, and neither do lithium or potassium. This characteristic comes directly from their electron structures. Can you see what the alkali metals have in common from the diagram?

Electron configuration of the alkali metals

$1s^2, 2s^1$

Lithium: 3 electrons

$1s^2, 2s^2, 2p^6, 3s^1$

Sodium: 11 electrons

$1s^2, 2s^2, 2p^6, 3s^2, 3p^6, 4s^1$

Potassium: 19 electrons

Electron structure

All the alkali metals have a single electron in the highest unfilled energy level. Lithium has a full first energy level, and its third electron is alone on the second energy level. Sodium has its first and second energy levels full, and its 11th electron is alone on the third level. Potassium has its first, second and third energy levels full, and its 19th electron is alone on the fourth level.

Oxides and chlorides

All of the alkali metals combine with oxygen in a 2:1 ratio. For example, lithium oxide is Li_2O, sodium oxide is Na_2O, and potassium oxide is K_2O. The alkali metals all combine with chlorine in a 1:1 ratio to make ionic salts. Examples are sodium chloride (NaCl) and potassium chloride (KCl), both of which are common in food.

Li O Li
Li_2O

Li Cl
LiCl

Na O Na
Na_2O

Na Cl
NaCl

K O K
K_2O

K Cl
KCl

Properties of the alkali metals

The alkali metals are soft and react explosively with water. Many of the alkali metals have interesting biological functions. Their ions are used in nerve signalling, proper water retention, and maintaining correct blood chemistry levels.

The alkaline earth metals

The alkaline earth metals

Alkaline earth metals

Group 2 is known as the alkaline earth metals. The most commonly found ones are beryllium (Be), magnesium (Mg), and calcium (Ca). Like the alkali metals, these elements also tend to lose electrons easily. However, they tend to lose two electrons, making their ions Be^{2+}, Mg^{2+}, and Ca^{2+}.

Electron structure

Looking at the electron structures of the group 2 elements provides a clue to why they make ions with a charge of +2.

Electron configuration for the alkaline earth metals

$1s^2, 2s^2$

Beryllium: 4 electrons

$1s^2, 2s^2, 2p^6, 3s^2$

Magnesium: 12 electrons

$1s^2, 2s^2, 2p^6, 3s^2, 3p^6, 4s^2$

Calcium: 20 electrons

All the group 2 metals have a two electrons in the highest unfilled energy level. Beryllium has a full first energy level, and its third and fourth electrons are on the second energy level. Magnesium has the first and second energy levels full, and its 11th and 12th electrons are on the third level. Potassium has the first, second and third energy levels full, and its 19th and 20th electrons are on the fourth level.

Oxides and chlorides

The alkaline earth metals combine with oxygen in a 1:1 ratio. For example, beryllium oxide is BeO, magnesium oxide is MgO, and calcium oxide is CaO. The alkaline earth metals all combine with chlorine in a 1:2 ratio to make ionic salts. Examples are beryllium chloride ($BeCl_2$), magnesium chloride ($MgCl_2$), and calcium chloride ($CaCl_2$).

Group 2 metals in the body

Both magnesium and calcium are crucial for life. Calcium is one of the main structural components of bones and teeth. The disease *osteoporosis* is caused by a lack of calcium in bones. Your nervous system also relies on calcium. A flood of calcium ions is the electrical impulse that triggers the contraction of your muscles. Magnesium ions are crucial to the chemistry of many enzymes in your body. Without sufficient magnesium, these enzymes would not be able to function efficiently, if at all.

The transition metals

About the transition metals

Transition metals

In the center of the periodic table are the transition metals. These include familiar metals such as titanium (Ti), chromium (Cr), iron (Fe), nickel (Ni), and copper (Cu). All the transition metals are solid at room temperature except for mercury (Hg). All are excellent conductors of electricity. Osmium (Os) is the densest metal with a density of 22.61 g/cm^3.

The transition metals

The transition metals start on the fourth row of the periodic table because *they all have electrons in partly filled d orbitals*. There are no d orbitals in the first, second, or third rows of the table.

Electron configurations for the transition metals

$1s^2, 2s^2, 2p^6, 3s^2, 3p^6, 4s^2, 3d^6$

Energy

s   p   d

Iron: 26 electrons

$1s^2, 2s^2, 2p^6, 3s^2, 3p^6, 4s^2, 3d^{10}, 5s^2, 4d^9$

s   p   d

Silver: 47 electrons

How the orbitals are filled

The transition metals illustrate a peculiar fact: The 3d orbitals have higher energies than the 4s orbitals! This is true even though the principal quantum number (3) of 3d is less than the 4 in 4s. Energy is the real, physical quantity that determines how the electrons act in atoms. The real energy levels correspond to the rows of the periodic table.

The quantum number is an important mathematical construction, but it is not the same as the energy level

Bonding properties of transition metals

The bonding properties of the transition metals are complicated. For example, iron can form three different compounds with oxygen: FeO, Fe_2O_3, and Fe_3O_4. The second compound (Fe_2O_3) is what you know as *rust*. The third compound is magnetite, or lodestone. Silver bonds with oxygen in a ratio of two silver atoms to each oxygen atom (Ag_2O). The dark tarnish on fine silverware is silver oxide.

Rust (Fe_2O_3)

Silver tarnish (Ag_2O)

Carbon, oxygen, and nitrogen

C, N, and O: important elements

Groups 13 through 16 contain some extremely important elements. Carbon (C) is the backbone of the chemistry of life. Proteins, fats, carbohydrates, and even DNA are carbon-based molecules. Nitrogen (N) makes up 78% of Earth's atmosphere in the form of a diatomic gas (N_2). Oxygen makes up 21% of the atmosphere, also in the form of a diatomic gas (O_2).

Bonding properties

The electron structures of these elements make them very flexible in their chemistry. Oxygen and nitrogen tend to accept electrons, rather than donate them. Carbon can go either way, sometimes accepting electrons and sometimes donating them.

Electron configurations for carbon, nitrogen, and oxygen

$1s^2, 2s^2, 2p^2$ $1s^2, 2s^2, 2p^3$ $1s^2, 2s^2, 2p^4$

Carbon: 6 electrons   **Nitrogen:** 7 electrons   **Oxygen:** 8 electrons

Electron configuration is partially filled p orbitals

All the elements in groups 13 through 16 have partly filled p orbitals. Boron has a single electron in the 2p orbital. Carbon, nitrogen and oxygen have two, three, and four electrons in their 2p orbitals. The heavier elements in groups 13–16 have similar electron configurations—partly filled p orbitals.

Example compounds

The chemistry of these three elements is extraordinarily rich. Carbon bonds to many elements as well as itself. Carbon is so important that there are two entire chapters of this book devoted to the chemistry of carbon and its compounds (Chapters 17 and 18). Diamond, methane gas, and sugar are carbon compounds. Nitrogen and oxygen likewise form bonds with many other elements and with themselves. Ammonia and laughing gas (nitrous oxide) are nitrogen compounds.

Nitrous oxide N_2O

Glucose $C_6H_{12}O_6$

Methane CH_4

Ammonia NH_3

Diamond C

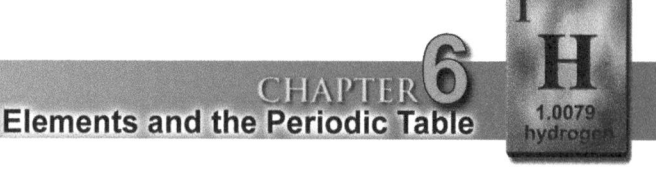
The halogens

Column 17 forms the halogen family

Halogens

Group 17 is known as the halogens. This group includes fluorine (F), chlorine (Cl), and bromine (Br). The halogens tend to be colored gases at room temperature. Those that aren't gases at room temperature tend to vaporize when heated slightly. The pure forms of these gaseous elements are not healthy to inhale. Chlorine gas was once used as a poison gas. However, chlorine in its ionic form is essential for life.

Halogens form negative ions

Unlike metals, the halogens tend to grab one electron instead of giving any away. For this reason, they all form singly charged negative ions. Examples include chloride (Cl^-) and fluoride (F^-) ions. Let's look at their electron configurations to see why they tend to grab only one electron. Notice that each of the halogens has only one open quantum state in its highest energy p orbital. Atoms with this configuration have a high affinity for electrons to fill up that last open space and reach a full energy level.

Electron configurations of the halogens

$1s^2, 2s^2, 2p^5$ $1s^2, 2s^2, 2p^6, 3s^2, 3p^5$ $1s^2, 2s^2, 2p^6, 3s^2, 3p^6, 4s^2, 3d^{10}, 4p^5$

Fluorine: 9 electrons

Chlorine: 17 electrons

Bromine: 35 electrons

Pure halogens are toxic but compounds are not

In their pure forms, these elements form diatomic molecules such as Cl_2 and F_2. If pure, the halogens are so reactive that they are highly toxic to many organisms. For example, chlorine is used in drinking water and swimming pools to kill bacteria and other harmful microorganisms. Pure chlorine is a greenish, foul-smelling gas that does not occur in nature, even though chlorine compounds are very common. When combined with a metal, the resulting compound is generally an ionic salt, such as sodium chloride (NaCl).

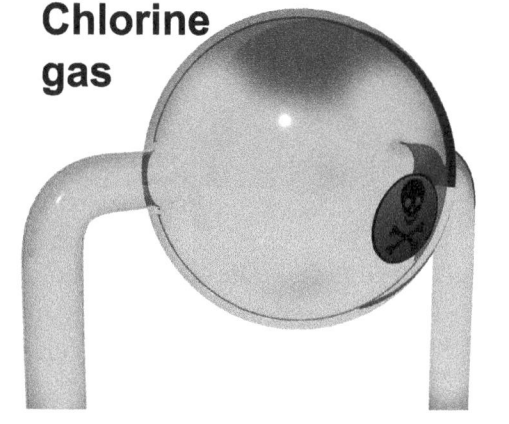

Chlorine gas

The noble gases

Column 18 forms the noble gas family

Noble gases

Group 18 is known as the noble gases. The four lightest members of this group are helium (He), neon (Ne), argon (Ar), and krypton (Kr). They are "noble" because they don't chemically bond with *any* of the other elements (with a few rare exceptions). The name "noble" came from not mixing with the "lower" elements, like royalty not socializing with the peasants!

Why the noble gases are important

The noble gases are extremely important, because understanding why they *don't* form chemical bonds is the key to understanding why other elements *do* form chemical bonds. Look carefully at the electron configurations of neon, argon, and krypton. What do they have in common?

Electron configurations of the noble gases

$1s^2, 2s^2, 2p^6$

$1s^2, 2s^2, 2p^6, 3s^2, 3p^6$

$1s^2, 2s^2, 2p^6, 3s^2, 3p^6, 4s^2, 3d^{10}, 4p^6$

Neon: 10 electrons   **Argon:** 18 electrons   **Krypton:** 36 electrons

Electrons in noble gases are all located in completely filled energy levels

When chemical bonds may or may not occur

Elements that have completely filled energy levels do not make chemical bonds. The converse is also true. Elements that have unfilled energy levels do make chemical bonds. This observation leads to two very important ideas.

Only electrons in an unfilled energy level are available to make bonds

Electrons in completely filled energy levels do not make bonds

The outermost electrons determine chemical properties

These observations are the key to explaining the periodic table, and also many other properties of the elements. Remember what we said earlier: Electrons determine all the properties of an element except its mass. Now we can refine that statement, because not all electrons are important to chemical behavior. Only the outermost electrons in the highest energy level interact with other atoms. These outermost (highest energy) electrons are the ones that determine chemical behavior.

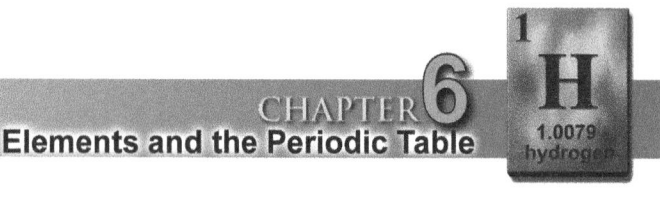
Why compounds form

The "nobility" of the noble gases

The noble gases are called "noble" because they have only completely filled or completely empty energy levels. This electron structure makes the noble gases chemically inert, so we only find them as pure, single atoms in the environment. Every other element has a partially filled energy level. These other elements are found bonded to each other (such as O_2) or to other elements in compounds (for example, NaCl or H_2O).

| Chlorine atom | Sodium atom | Chloride ion | Sodium ion |
| 17 electrons | 11 electrons | 18 electrons like argon | 10 electrons like neon |

Why sodium chloride forms

Consider the electron structures of sodium and chlorine side by side. The pure elements have partially filled energy levels. However, by exchanging electrons to form the ionic compound sodium chloride, *both sodium and chloride ions achieve a noble gas electron structure!*

Compounds give each participating atom a noble gas electron structure

Electron structures explain why chemical bonds form

Electron structures are important because they explain why chemical bonds form. The noble gases have the most stable, lowest energy configurations for electrons in an atom. Noble gases don't form bonds because they have nothing to gain. Other elements do form bonds, and they do it so they too can have noble gas electron configurations. The diagram below shows how one oxygen atom gets a noble gas electron structure by sharing electrons with two hydrogen atoms (which explains the 2 in H_2O).

Hydrogen
1 electron

Oxygen
8 electrons

Water (H_2O)

Hydrogen   **Oxygen**   **Hydrogen**

6.3 Valence

The meaning of valence

In the last section we learned that only the electrons in the highest unfilled energy level form chemical bonds. Think of the electrons in any completely filled energy levels as permanently grounded! This greatly reduces the problem of understanding chemical bonding. We don't need to care about electrons in filled energy levels. We need only concern ourselves with the electrons in the highest unfilled level.

Sulfur has six valence electrons

For example, sulfur has 16 electrons. Ten of these are in the completely filled first and second energy levels. That leaves six electrons in the unfilled third energy level. *Sulfur's chemical properties come from the six electrons in the highest unfilled energy level.*

Electron configurations for oxygen and sulfur

Oxygen has six valence electrons

Oxygen has eight electrons. Two of these are in the completely filled first energy level. That leaves six electrons in the partly filled second energy level. All of oxygen's chemical properties are due to having six electrons in the highest unfilled energy level.

Valence electrons

Oxygen and sulfur have the same number of valence electrons. **Valence electrons** are the special name given to electrons in the highest energy level. Because oxygen and sulfur have similar valence electrons, they form similar chemical compounds.

Oxygen and sulfur form similar chemical compounds

Aluminum sulfide
Al_2S_3

Magnesium sulfide
MgS

Carbon disulfide
CS_2

Sodium sulfide
Na_2S

Aluminum oxide
Al_2O_3

Magnesium oxide
MgO

Carbon dioxide
CO_2

Sodium oxide
Na_2O

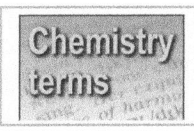

valence electrons: electrons in the highest unfilled energy level, responsible for making chemical bonds.

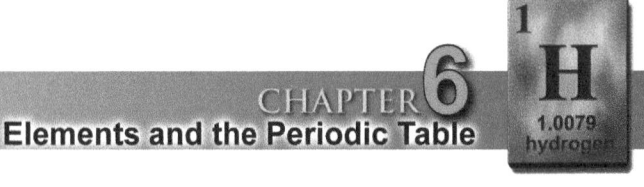
Determining valence electrons

Identifying valence electrons

The electrons that are in the highest energy level are the valence electrons. To determine how many there are, start with an element's electron configuration.

1. Write down the electron configuration.
2. Count how many electrons are in the highest s and p orbitals. You should get a number between one and eight.
3. These are the valence electrons.

Counting valence electrons

$$2 + 5 = 7 \text{ valence electrons}$$

$$Cl = 1s^2 2s^2 2p^6 3s^2 3p^5$$

level 3 is the highest principal energy level

$$2 + 1 = 3 \text{ valence electrons}$$

$$Ga = 1s^2 2s^2 2p^6 3s^2 3p^6 4s^2 3d^{10} 4p^1$$

level 4 is the highest principal energy level

d orbitals do not count

For elements *other than the transition metals*, electrons in d-orbitals do not count as valence electrons. For a complicated reason of quantum theory, the s and p orbitals become mixed when atoms bond with each other. This has the technical name *hybridization*. During bonding the separate s and p orbitals become a hybrid sp orbital.

Solved problem

How many valence electrons does tin (Sn) have?

Given: *Valence electrons are the electrons found in the highest principal energy level orbitals.*

Relationships: *Tin is in the fifth period (or row) of the periodic table, so the highest principal energy level electrons will be in level five.*

Solve: *The electron configuration of tin is*

$$Sn = 1s^2 2s^2 2p^6 3s^2 3p^6 4s^2 3d^{10} 4p^6 5s^2 4d^{10} 5p^2$$

or in shorthand notation,

$$Sn = [Kr]5s^2 4d^{10} 5p^2$$

Answer: *There are a total of four electrons in level five s and p orbitals, so tin has four valence electrons.*

The main group elements

The main group elements

Valence is such an important concept that many chemists prefer to label the periodic table groups according to valence electrons. In this scheme, groups 1A through 8A are called the *main group elements*. The transition metals are placed in a separate category according to how the d-orbital electrons form bonds (groups 1B–8B).

1	2		Valence electrons										3	4	5	6	7	8

1A

Main group elements

1 H 1.0079 hydrogen	**2A**																	2 He 4.0028 helium

Transition metals (valence electrons vary)

8B

3 Li 6.941 lithium	4 Be 9.0122 beryllium														**3A**	**4A**	**5A**	**6A**	**7A**

| 11 Na 22.990 sodium | 12 Mg 24.305 magnesium | **3B** | **4B** | **5B** | **6B** | **7B** | | | | **1B** | **2B** | | 5 B 10.811 boron | 6 C 12.011 carbon | 7 N 14.007 nitrogen | 8 O 15.999 oxygen | 9 F 18.998 fluorine | 10 Ne 20.180 neon |

| 19 K 39.098 potassium | 20 Ca 40.078 calcium | 21 Sc 44.956 scandium | 22 Ti 47.867 titanium | 23 V 50.942 vanadium | 24 Cr 51.996 chromium | 25 Mn 54.938 manganese | 26 Fe 55.845 iron | 27 Co 58.933 cobalt | 28 Ni 58.693 nickel | 29 Cu 63.546 copper | 30 Zn 65.41 zinc | 13 Al 26.982 aluminum | 14 Si 28.086 silicon | 15 P 30.974 phosphorous | 16 S 32.065 sulfur | 17 Cl 35.453 chlorine | 18 Ar 39.948 argon |

| 37 Rb 85.468 rubidium | 38 Sr 87.62 strontium | 39 Y 88.906 yttrium | 40 Zr 91.224 zirconium | 41 Nb 92.906 niobium | 42 Mo 95.94 molybdenum | 43 Tc (98) technetium | 44 Ru 101.07 ruthenium | 45 Rh 102.91 rhodium | 46 Pd 106.42 palladium | 47 Ag 107.87 silver | 48 Cd 112.41 cadmium | 31 Ga 69.723 galium | 32 Ge 72.61 germanium | 33 As 74.922 arsenic | 34 Se 78.96 selenium | 35 Br 79.904 bromine | 36 Kr 83.80 krypton |

| 55 Cs 132.91 cesium | 56 Ba 137.33 barium | 71 Lu 174.97 lutetium | 72 Hf 178.49 hafnium | 73 Ta 180.95 tantalum | 74 W 183.84 tungsten | 75 Re 186.21 rhenium | 76 Os 190.23 osmium | 77 Ir 192.22 iridium | 78 Pt 195.08 platinum | 79 Au 196.97 gold | 80 Hg 200.59 mercury | 49 In 114.82 indium | 50 Sn 118.71 tin | 51 Sb 121.76 antimony | 52 Te 127.60 tellurium | 53 I 126.90 iodine | 54 Xe 131.29 xenon |

(continued bottom row): 81 Tl 204.38 thallium | 82 Pb 207.2 lead | 83 Bi 208.98 bismuth | 84 Po (209) polonium | 85 At (210) astatine | 86 Rn (222) radon

Valences of main group elements

All of the elements in the same column (group) in the main group elements have the same number of valence electrons. For example, carbon, silicon, germanium, tin, and lead all have four valence electrons.

Valences of transition metals

The number of valence electrons for the transition metals does not follow a simple pattern. Many act as if they have two valence electrons, like the group 2A elements. However, there are more exceptions than rules, and it depends strongly on what other elements are in a compound. For example, chromium makes bonds that involve from two to even six electrons.

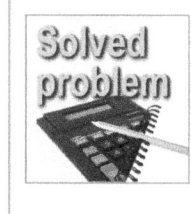

Solved problem

How many valence electrons does magnesium (Mg) have?

Given: *Magnesium (atomic number of 12)*

Relationships: *Mg is a group 2A element; all group 2A elements have two valence electrons.*

Answer: *Magnesium has two valence electrons.*

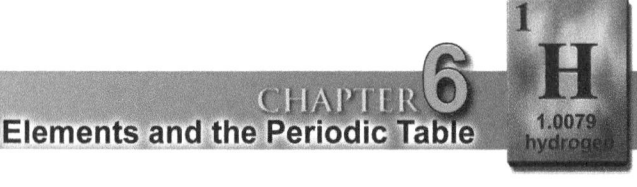
Introduction to Lewis dot notation

Lewis dots show valence electrons

Because valence electrons are the most important electrons involved in bonding, a special graphic notation called a *Lewis dot diagram* was invented to represent them. A **Lewis dot diagram** shows each valence electron as a dot surrounding the element symbol. There can be up to eight dots in a Lewis dot diagram. Electrons in filled energy levels don't count because they do not participate in bonding.

Lewis dot diagram for carbon

C $1s^2 2s^2 2p^2$
4 valence electrons

Draw individual dots before pairing them

What if there are more than four valence electrons? Where do they go? Once each side of the atom symbol has one valence electron, you start to pair them up. Drawing the dots this way, by first drawing them individually and then pairing them up when necessary, will become important when we learn about covalent bonding in the next chapter. Below is a part of the periodic table, showing you how many valence electrons each atom has.

Lewis dot diagram → Ḣ

compound with oxygen or hydrogen → H_2O

Same number of valence electrons causes similar bonding patterns

								He
								n/a
Li	Be.		B.	·C.	·N.	·O:	·F:	:Ne:
Li_2O	BeO		B_2O_3	CO_2	N_2O_5	H_2O	HF	n/a
Na	Mg.		Al.	·Si.	·P.	·S:	·Cl:	:Ar:
Na_2O	MgO		Al_2O_3	SiO_2	P_2O_5	H_2S	HCl	n/a
K	Ca.		Ga.	·Ge.	·As.	·Se:	·Br:	:Kr:
K_2O	CaO		Ga_2O_3	GeO_2	As_2O_5	H_2Se	HBr	n/a
Rb	Sr.		In.	·Sn.	·Sb.	·Te:	·I:	:Xe:
Rb_2O	SrO		In_2O_3	SnO_2	Sb_2O_5	H_2Te	HI	n/a

indicates no reaction

Elements in the same group have the same number of valence electrons

Atoms in the same family (or column) have the same number of valence electrons. They also react with oxygen in the same way, forming the same kind of chemical formula when bonding with oxygen. By understanding the underlying structure of the electrons, especially the valence electrons, we are now set up to better understand why atoms bond together the way they do. The next chapter will take a deeper look at bonding.

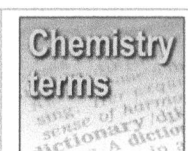
Chemistry terms

Lewis dot diagram: a diagram showing one dot for each valence electron an atom has, these dots surround the element symbol for the atom.

More about valence electrons

Why valence electrons bond

Valence electrons participate in bonding because they are the most loosely bound electrons in an atom. The loosely bound electrons are the easiest to share. Electrons in completely filled energy levels are tightly bound to an atom. That explains why the noble gases don't form chemical bonds. There are no loosely bound electrons left to bond with.

Valence electrons and Lewis dots

All the alkali metals have a single valence electron. Their Lewis dot diagrams all have a single dot representing the single electron available for bonding. All the alkali earth metals (group 2) have two valence electrons. Elements in boron's group have three valence electrons. Carbon's group has four valence electrons. Nitrogen has five, oxygen has six, and fluorine has seven. The second row ends with neon, which has eight valence electrons.

Lewis dot diagrams

Li	•Be	•B•	•C•	•N•	:O•	:F:	:Ne:
1	2	3	4	5	6	7	8

Valence electrons

Filled d orbitals do not contribute valence electrons

For elements in the main groups, electrons in the d orbitals do not count as valence electrons. These elements have only completely filled d orbitals, and the electrons in a completely filled d orbital act like they are in filled energy levels. That is why selenium (Se) has six valence electrons, putting it in the oxygen group. The electron configuration of selenium shows a completely filled d orbital.

Valence electrons for selenium

$2 + 4 = 6$ valence electrons

$1s^2, 2s^2, 2p^6, 3s^2, 3p^6, 4s^2, 3d^{10}, 4p^4$
Filled energy levels

Filled d orbital

Selenium: 34 electrons

The transition metals are different

The situation is different with the transition metals. These elements have partially filled d orbitals. Therefore, transition metals may have more than eight valence electrons. This is one reason why the bonding patterns among the transition metals are so complicated. How many valence electrons there are depends partly on which other element or elements are participating.

Using the periodic table

Who uses the periodic table?

So why should we care about the periodic table and its guide to periodic properties? Chemists, biologists, material scientists, engineers, and physicists use the periodic table every day to help design new drugs, create recyclable construction materials, utilize sources of renewable energy, and invent the next cool electronic device. This is just a tiny fraction of the applications in which the periodic table is a crucial guide.

A stronger type of glass

Let's look at an example—making stronger glass. Standard glass from which drinking bottles and window panes are made contains the element sodium. If you've ever dropped a glass on the floor, you know that it breaks pretty easily.

Common glass is primarily made from silicon and oxygen, but it also contains some sodium, calcium, and aluminum. To make the glass stronger, you could replace the sodium atoms on the surface with another atom that is a little bigger than sodium. However, the replacement atom must have similar chemical properties to sodium to interact with its neighboring atoms in a similar way and be incorporated into the glass. To have similar chemical properties, we would want to choose an element from the same column (or family) as sodium, and the next largest atom would be potassium. If you were a chemist working for a glass maker, choosing potassium would be a good option.

Normal glass can be made stronger by replacing Na with K on its surface

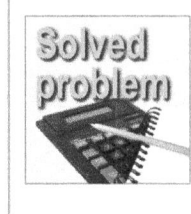

Solved problem

A pottery glaze is made from a mixture of several materials. One of those materials is called flux, which changes the melting point of the glaze. There are several fluxes that are commonly used: MgO, CaO, BaO, and SrO. Why does it make sense that if one of these compounds is a flux, the others might make good fluxes too?

Asked: *Why does is it make sense that MgO, CaO, BaO, and SrO all act as fluxes in pottery glazes if any one of them does?*

Given: *A flux is a component of a pottery glaze. The compounds listed are all commonly used as fluxes.*

Relationships: *Mg, Ca, Ba, and Sr are all from the same family of the periodic table —the alkaline earth metals.*

Solve: *Elements in the same column have similar chemical properties and follow either an increasing or decreasing trend in other properties. If they come from the same column, then they can behave the same way (with slight variations depending on their atomic level properties) in the glaze.*

Group 1 and 2 metal ions and our bodies

Alkali metal ions and alkaline earth metal ions have some very important functions in your body. Among the most biologically important metal ions are Na^+, K^+, and Li^+ (group 1) and Ca^{2+} and Mg^{+2} (group 2). Animals and humans could not survive without the proper amounts of these ions in their blood and tissues.

The biological importance of the metal ions is a marked contrast to their ho-hum behavior in the chemistry lab. For most of us, a chemical reaction is interesting when we notice a dramatic chemical change, such as a color change, an explosion, or the release of light. The group 1 and 2 metal ions are soluble in aqueous solutions, and they usually just play the role of "spectator ions" in most chemical reactions. However, these dissolved ions do very interesting things in the living body that we cannot see directly. They regulate nerve impulses, heart muscle contractions, and proper water retention inside our cells, just to name a few of their important roles.

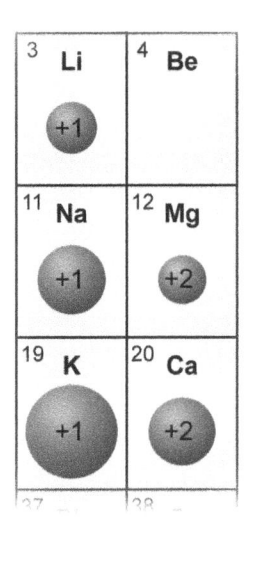

Calcium is a good example. When Ca^{2+} ions are released inside your heart, they stimulate contraction of the heart muscle, causing it to squeeze or push your blood. To relax the heart muscle, the calcium ions are reabsorbed (taken in) by nearby tissues. The presence or absence of the calcium ion (Ca^{2+}) causes contraction or relaxation of the heart!

A nerve impulse is stimulated by an increase in the amount of sodium ions (Na^+) inside the neuron, or nerve cell. When a nerve is "fired" or stimulated it sends a message to a part of our body. In this case the sodium ions allow a message to travel to the proper place in our bodies. Nerve cells are designed to send the message from one cell to another by absorbing and releasing sodium ions. The sodium ions are absorbed into the cell, stimulating it to "fire." The next nerve cell or neuron is then stimulated, and so on. In this way, the message travels from one cell to the next, following a domino effect.

Sodium–potassium ion pump

This protein is located so that it pokes through the cell membrane. It uses the chemical energy in ATP to pump Na^+ out of the cell and K^+ into it.

Electrolytes contain metal ions such as potassium (K^+), sodium (Na^+), and calcium (Ca^{2+}). Sports drinks usually provide electrolytes, and some vitamin waters contain sugars and electrolytes. Metal ions such as Na^+ and K^+ are responsible for regulating how much water is absorbed by our tissues. These ions are major components of blood plasma and intercellular fluids. Scientists have been studying the amounts of these metal ions inside our body tissues for a long time.

It has been discovered that other ions from group 1 have effects on the body. Some of these effects have been discovered through circumstance. Lithium (Li^+) for instance has no known function in the human body. However, in 1817 salts containing lithium were thought to have mystical healing power. The legendary "Fountain of Youth" was a spring that provided magical healing and restored youth to the elderly. This spring was thought to contain lithium ions! In 1927, Mr. C. L. Grigg began to sell a lemon–lime soft drink containing lithium ions, which later became known as 7Up.

Concerns from the Federal Drug Administration (FDA) caused lithium ions to be removed from the drink in the 1950s. Right around this same time it was discovered that lithium ions had a remarkable therapeutic effect on mental illness. Manic depressives and people suffering from bipolar disorder were prescribed lithium drugs to help regulate their mood swings. Lithium when prescribed as a medication can help people function more successfully in their daily lives, because it lessens extreme mood swings. Today lithium is given in the form of lithium carbonate (Li_2CO_3). These drugs are helpful to about 70% of the people experiencing manic depression.

A natural spring in Florida was thought to be the Fountain of Youth by the Spanish explorer Ponce de Leon

Interestingly, scientists are still not sure exactly how the lithium ion helps these patients, but they think it has something to do with its similarities to the sodium ion (Na^+). It is hypothesized that the smaller size of the lithium ion may alter the function of some neurotransmitters, and this may account for its therapeutic effect. One theory is that Li^+ is transported across the cell membrane instead of Na^+, decreasing the amount of Na^+ entering the cell, or neuron. In this way the excitability associated with the release of some neurotransmitters decreases. Periodicity shows us that the lithium ion is smaller in size than the sodium ion, and this has led to some ideas about how it affects the human body.

Lithium ions may help to regulate neurotransmitters, chemicals that allow nerve cells to communicate with each other. See the enlarged synapse, which is the place where one nerve cell "touches" another.

Chapter 6 Review

Vocabulary

Match each word to the sentence where it best fits.

Section 6.1

supernova	macronutrients
trace amounts	trace element
electronegativity	periodic
ionization energy	atomic radius

1. You'll need a significant amount of _____ if you want to stay healthy.

2. Most of the elements in your body were created in a/an _____.

3. Although necessary for life, too much of any one _____ can be toxic.

4. Almost every element on the periodic table can be found in our bodies in _____.

5. The changing of the seasons is an example of a/an _____ shift in weather patterns.

6. In the photoelectric effect, shining a light with high energy photons on a metal can cause the metal to eject electrons. Those photons must have energies equal to or greater than the _____ of the atoms of that metal.

7. If you want to find an element that will strip electrons from another element during a chemical reaction, then you want one with a high _____.

8. The _____ of an atom is a result of the size of the largest orbital occupied by its electrons.

Section 6.3

valence electrons	electron configuration
Lewis dot diagrams	

9. By knowing the _____, we gain a deeper knowledge of the structure of the atom.

10. You find _____ at the highest principal energy level of an atom.

11. When trying to figure out a chemical formula, it is helpful to use _____, a visual representation of the outermost electrons.

Conceptual Questions

Section 6.1

12. What were the two most abundant elements created in the Big Bang?

13. If only two elements were created in the Big Bang (with trace amounts of two other elements), where did the rest of the elements on the periodic table come from?

14. Describe the distribution of metals, nonmetals, and metalloids on the periodic table.

15. No elements higher than atomic number 92 are found in mineral ores, because they don't have any stable isotopes. Without a supernova here on Earth to create heavier elements, how were these elements discovered?

16. Explain what is meant by the phrase "You are made from star dust."

17. Which element in your body was most likely created early in the birth of our universe?
    a. hydrogen
    b. oxygen
    c. carbon
    d. nitrogen

18. Describe what is meant by an "essential element."

19. If you don't eat a well-rounded diet, it may be necessary for you to take mineral supplements often found in multivitamins. These can help provide you with necessary trace elements that may be missing from your diet. Explain why it would not be good to take too many multivitamins at one time.

20. Name two functions performed by essential elements in your body.

Section 6.2

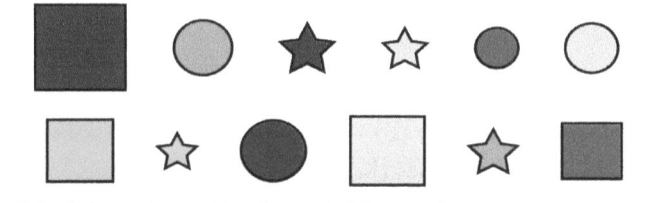

21. Given the collection of objects above, come up with at least one table that organizes them according to their properties of shape, size, and color (a periodic table of objects).

22. There are three missing objects that would complete your table. Describe the properties of size, shape, and color for these missing objects.

23. How did density (a physical property) and reaction patterns (a chemical property) help Mendeleev create the first periodic table? Briefly explain the patterns they follow as well.

24. When Mendeleev first started looking for patterns in elements, he arranged the elements first in order of increasing atomic mass. How is this similar to how we would order the elements today? How is this different from how we would order elements today?

25. What makes a group of elements a "family"?

26. One of the most dangerous radioactive isotopes to get into your body is strontium-90. Strontium-90 tends to be incorporated into your bones and teeth, instead of passing through your system quickly. Why does it make sense that strontium would be captured by your bones and teeth given the family of elements strontium belongs to?

27. Chlorine gas was once used as a chemical weapon. Using the periodic table, suggest another gaseous element that may also be dangerous and explain why you chose this element.

28. Explain the difference between electronegativity and ionization energy.

29. Compare and contrast the periodic properties of atomic radius, electronegativity, and ionization energy. What are some similarities and differences in how these properties map to elements on the periodic table?

Section 6.3

30. Which subatomic particle most directly affects the properties of an atom or molecule?
    a. proton
    b. neutron
    c. electron

31. Explain the reasoning behind your choice for the preceding question.

32. If the primary energy levels for electrons are represented by numbers such as 1, 2, 3, 4, etc., what letters are used to describe the energy sublevels (or orbitals) within these primary levels?

33. What are two differences between a 1s and a 2s orbital? How about a 2p and a 3p orbital?

34. In what order will the electrons fill up the orbitals?
    a. They will fill the lowest energy ones first.
    b. They will fill the highest energy ones first.
    c. The orbitals are filled in a random order.

35. Fill in the table below to show which type of orbital is being filled by the highest energy electron in each of the large block of elements.

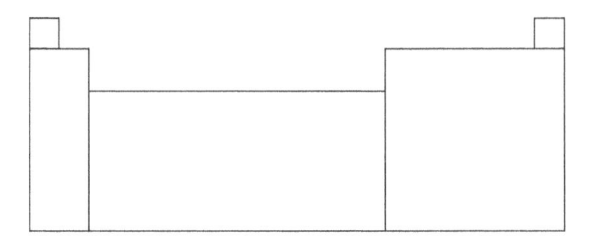

36. Of all the electrons surrounding the nucleus, why are the valence electrons considered to be the most important?

37. What is the best predictor of an element's chemical properties?
    a. atomic radius
    b. density
    c. number of valence electrons
    d. its full electron configuration

Chapter 6 Review

38. What is the relationship between the size of an orbital and the energy level of electrons found in that orbital?

39. Carbon can form the following two compounds: carbon dioxide (CO_2) and methane (CH_4). What does this tell you?
    a. The number of valence electrons on carbon atoms can vary.
    b. The number of valence electrons of hydrogen and oxygen must be different.
    c. Carbon always has the same number of valence electrons.
    d. Both b and c are true.

Quantitative Problems

Section 6.1

40. If a carbon-12 atom fused with a helium-4 atom, what would the resulting new atom be?

41. Of the 4.40×10^{28} atoms in a typical person, 3.96×10^{27} of them are nitrogen. What percent of a typical person is made of nitrogen?

42. Of the 4.40×10^{28} atoms in a typical person, 8.80×10^{20} of them are iodine. Why is iodine considered to be found in "trace amounts" when the typical person has 880 billion billion atoms of iodine in his or her body?

43. Which of the following atoms has the **biggest** radius? Explain why.
    a. H or He
    b. Li or Be
    c. He or Ne
    d. Na or Mg
    e. O or S

44. Which of the following is ordered from **smallest** to **largest** ionic radius?
    a. $S^{2-} < Cl^- < K^+ < Ca^{2+}$
    b. $Ca^{2+} < Cl^- < K^+ < S^{2-}$
    c. $Cl^- < S^{2-} < Ca^{2+} < K^+$
    d. $Ca^{2+} < K^+ < Cl^- < S^{2-}$

45. Explain why Br- is larger than Rb+.

46. Which of the following has the **highest** electronegativity, and why? Refer to the diagram on page 173 if you need help.
    a. Lead (Pb)
    b. Carbon (C)
    c. Fluorine (F)
    d. Potassium (K)

47. Which of the following has the **lowest** ionization energy, and why? Refer to the diagram on page 173 if you need help.
    a. Beryllium (Be)
    b. Cesium (Cs)
    c. Oxygen (O)
    d. Silicon (Si)

48. Place the following elements in the appropriate place on the periodic table outline shown below.
    a. hydrogen (H)
    b. helium (He)
    c. potassium (K)
    d. krypton (Kr)
    e. copper (Cu)
    f. boron (B)
    g. calcium (Ca)
    h. phosphorus (P)
    i. iron (Fe)

Section 6.2

49. How many electrons can fit in an orbital?

50. Give both full and short versions of the electron configurations for each of the following elements:
    a. silicon (Si)
    b. molybdenum (Mo)
    c. cesium (Cs)
    d. uranium (U)

51. Write the electron configuration for the following elements:
   a. nitrogen (N)
   b. neon (Ne)
   c. sodium (Na)
   d. boron (B)
   e. iron (Fe)
   f. chlorine (Cl)

52. What are the similarities and the differences in the electron configurations of the following pairs of atoms?
   a. Ne and Kr
   b. F and Cl
   c. Li and Na
   d. O and N
   e. C and Si

53. Given the graph below of melting points, what would you estimate would be the melting point of titanium (Ti)?

54. A researcher is doing an investigation to determine how the melting point of titanium compares to metals of lower and higher atomic mass. Which of the following devices should the researcher select to create a graphical display of the results similar to the chart in problem 53 (above)?
   a. a high temperature thermometer
   b. a computer and spreadsheet program
   c. a research furnace capable of reaching at least 2,500°C
   d. a wireless data network connecting to colleagues at other labs

55. Match the elements below to the correct group on the periodic table.
   a. Platinum (Pt)
   b. Xenon (Xe)
   c. Strontium (Sr)
   d. Rubidium (Rb)
   e. Fluorine (F)

56. Match the following properties with the correct group, then **explain** why that group has the property using principles of valence or electron configurations.
   a. Form +1 ions
   b. React explosively with water
   c. Form +2 ions
   d. Combine with oxygen in a 1:1 ratio
   e. Have complicated bonding properties
   f. Form -1 ions
   g. Combine with a metal to form an ionic salt
   h. Do not bond chemically

Section 6.3

57. How many electrons can be at primary energy level 3? Explain why.

58. How many valence electrons does each of the following elements have?
   a. Kr
   b. F
   c. Na
   d. Al
   e. Br
   f. Zn

59. Draw the Lewis dot structure for each of the following elements:
   a. N
   b. Ne
   c. Kr
   d. Na
   e. O
   f. Be
   g. Xe
   h. F
   i. Li

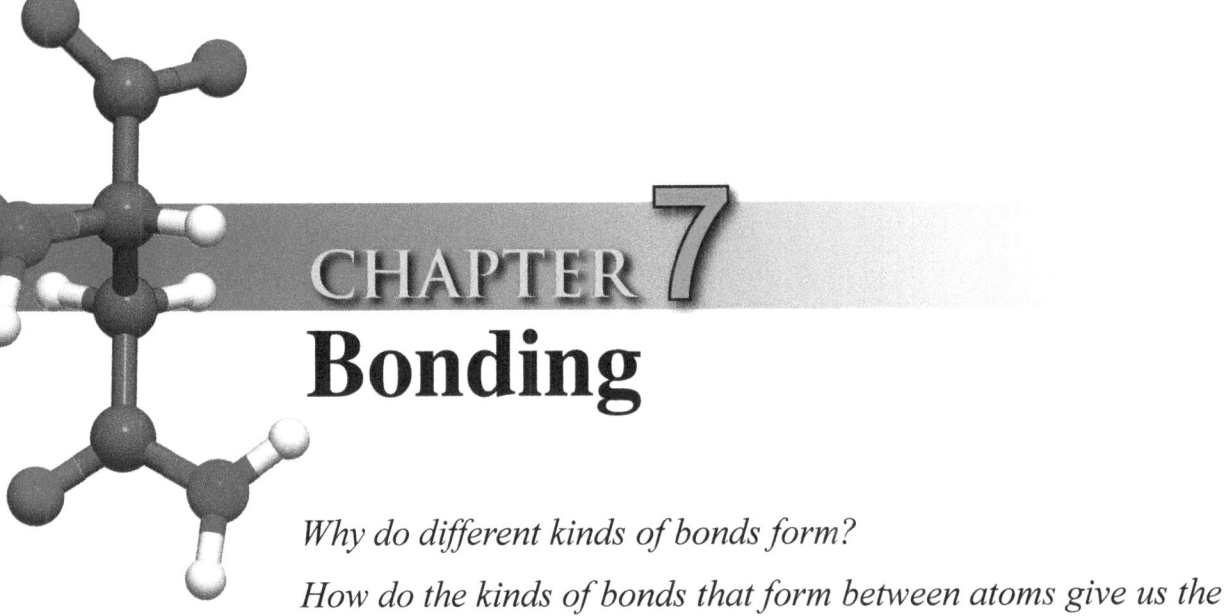

Bonding

Why do different kinds of bonds form?

How do the kinds of bonds that form between atoms give us the entire variety of materials we see all around us?

How can we use the periodic table to predict what will bond?

The elements are not what determines the variety and physical properties of matter. With the exception of the noble gases and some metals, the elements are rarely found in their pure forms on Earth. *Compounds* are the matter we experience. How the elements bond together in compounds is what determines the properties of most of the matter that we observe.

We have learned that sodium chloride (table salt) is essential for life. In solution, NaCl dissociates to form sodium (Na$^+$) and chlorine (Cl$^-$) ions. Both ions are necessary for good health. However, the pure elements sodium and chlorine are both deadly.

Pure sodium is a soft metal that reacts violently with water, producing flames and explosions. Pure chlorine is a yellowish gas that is highly toxic. There are many examples like sodium chloride where a compound is toxic, yet the same elements arranged as another compound are essential nutrients!

This chapter is about how the elements form chemical bonds with each other. Ionic compounds, such as salt, dissociate into ions in solution. Covalent compounds, such as sugar, remain whole molecules even in solution. Metals such as copper and iron are neither ionic nor molecular, but something in between. Solid metals conduct electricity because their electrons are not fixed to any particular atom. Pure ionic and covalent compounds are usually insulators and do not conduct electricity.

Explosive sodium metal   Toxic chlorine gas

Edible table salt

Iron (Fe) is magnetic, iron sulfide (FeS) is nonmagnetic

What do you know about iron and sulfur? Both are present in your body and are essential nutrients. Sulfur is a yellow solid, and its crystals are prized by mineral collectors. The most common form of sulfur in a chemistry lab is a finely ground yellow powder. Biologically, sulfur is found in the amino acids *cysteine* and *methionine*, which are part of many proteins. Sulfur is also associated with many strong-smelling compounds, including the odor of garlic and the smell of a skunk!

Elemental sulfur crystals

Powdered laboratory sulfur

Iron powder on a card above a magnet

Iron powder

Besides being the main ingredient of steel, iron is also the active element in *hemoglobin*, the chemical that transfers oxygen in your blood. As a pure element, iron is a gray metal. The photograph shows iron powder that has been finely ground. One of the interesting properties of iron is that it is magnetic. Iron powder sprinkled on an index card responds to the force created by a magnet held below.

Mixing iron and sulfur powder makes a yellow-gray powder that can easily be separated with a magnet. However, if you heat the two substances past a certain temperature, a chemical reaction occurs. As heat is added, the powders melt and seem to react. However, a magnet shows this is still a mixture of iron and sulfur. The sulfur has melted and dispersed into the iron powder.

Iron and sulfur *do* form chemical bonds to produce the compound *iron sulfide* (FeS), but they have to be near the temperature of red hot steel to do it! Iron sulfide is a gray-brown molecular solid that is found in several naturally occurring minerals. Iron sulfide formed this way is not magnetic! The chemical bond between iron and sulfur atoms, as shown on the picture to the right, changes the magnetic properties of the substance. Magnetism, like all physical properties, depends much more on the specific compound than on the elements it is made of.

7.1 What Is a Chemical Bond?

Chemical bonds and electromagnetic force

In your molecule building kit, a chemical bond is a "stick" joining atoms together. Diagrams show bonds as lines or sticks. Of course, in reality there are no sticks! Sticks and lines are used to represent the bond between atoms so you can "see" them on a macroscopic scale. Inside the atoms, the attraction between positive and negative electric charge is what really does the job. In Chapters 4 and 5, we talked about the *electromagnetic force*. In this chapter we will learn that chemical bonds are not just covalent or just ionic. There is a continuous scale between covalent and ionic, so many bonds have a little of both characteristics.

Bonds shown as "sticks" represent the binding force between atoms

Chemical bond

Vitamin C

Orbital shape and charge

Chapter 5 described the electron cloud, the three-dimensional region of space around an atom where the electrons are found. The electron cloud is held together by the attraction between the negative electrons and the positive nucleus. However, the electron cloud of an atom responds to *any* electric charge, not just the attraction of that same atom's nucleus. If positive and negative charges are brought near an atom, the negative charge repels electrons and attracts the nucleus. The positive charge attracts electrons and repels the nucleus. The result is a distortion of the shape of the atom.

A normal helium atom

Electron distribution distorted by nearby charges

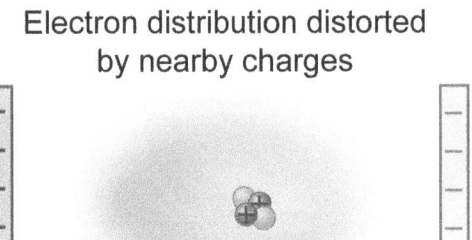

Polarization

The diagram (above left) shows a normal hydrogen atom. The diagram on the right shows the distortion caused by external positive and negative charges. The atom's negative electrons are attracted to the positive plate, and its positive nucleus is attracted to the negative plate. This distortion is called **polarization**. A *polarized* atom has an uneven distribution of positive and negative charge. Polarization occurs whenever anything creates a charge outside the atom, including another atom. Polarization is how many chemical bonds form.

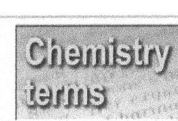

polarization: an uneven distribution of positive and negative charge.

Forming bonds

Overlapping orbitals form a bond

The diagram on the right shows what happens as two hydrogen atoms approach each other. The electrons in each atom are attracted both to their own nucleus and to the nucleus of the other atom.

Nearby atoms polarize each other

As atoms begin to get close, the attraction of the other nucleus slightly polarizes each atom. The result of the polarization is an *attractive force* between the atoms. However, if the atoms get too close, the electrons are also repelled by the electrons of the other atom. The more the electron clouds overlap, the higher the repulsive forces between electrons.

There is a certain distance apart where the attractive forces equal the repulsive forces. If this *equilibrium distance* is close enough, then an electron will be transferred or shared and a chemical bond forms.

Orbitals of approaching hydrogen atoms feel each other's nuclei

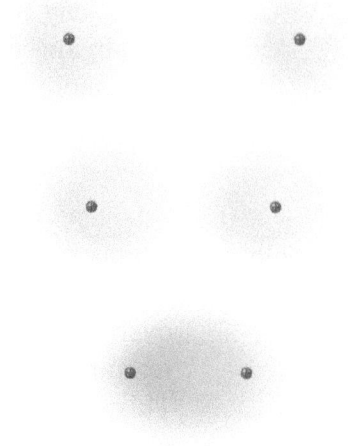

Two bond types

When two atoms approach each other close enough to form a bond, there are two possible things that can occur. One possibility is equal sharing of electrons. Another possibility is for one atom to take electrons from the other.

Covalent bonds

Covalent bonds occur when electrons are shared between atoms. Take two hydrogen atoms as an example (see the image to the right). As the two atoms approach each other, each nucleus begins to tug on the other atom's electron. Eventually, the orbitals of the two atoms overlap, forming a new three-dimensional pattern that we call a *molecular orbital*. Notice that the highest concentration of negative charge is now between the two positive nuclei. The attraction between positive nuclei and negative shared electrons is what holds the atoms together in a covalent bond.

A covalent bond: positive nuclei attracted to negative electrons being shared between them

Negative electrons to which the positive nuclei are attracted

Ionic bonds

The opposite extreme is when one atom takes electrons from the other. Ionic bonds occur when one or more electrons are transferred between atoms, causing the atom that lost electrons to become positive and the one that gained electrons to become negative. Now the two atoms have opposite charges, so they are attracted to each other, again through the electromagnetic force.

An ionic bond: the attraction between + and − ions

Li $^{1+}$ F $^{1-}$

protons = 3   protons = 9
electrons = 2   electrons = 10

Showing bonds in models and diagrams

Model building limitations

Models give you a good intuitive feel for the composition, bonding patterns, and overall shape of molecules. However, the models are approximations of the real thing. As with all approximations, there are limitations to how "real" any model can be to the quantum world. Size is the obvious approximation, but "solidity" and "static" are even more important and less obvious. Real atoms and molecules do not have hard surfaces and are in *constant, vigorous motion*.

Molecular model

Overlapping orbitals for a molecular "surface"

Atoms are not solid balls. They are made of a tiny nucleus surrounded by a cloud of electrons. The electron clouds overlap in a covalent bond, forming a surface most closely resembling the "surface" view in the diagram on the right. This surface represents the boundary within which you are most likely to find all the electrons in the entire molecule.

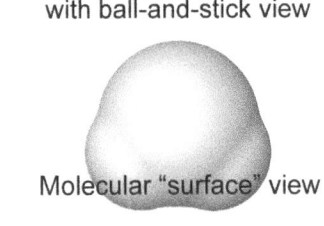

Electron view combined with ball-and-stick view

Using water as a simple example, we can show this surface view in a couple of ways. We can either show a typical orbital view or show a surface that encloses an area where the electrons are likely to be found.

Molecular "surface" view

Surface color shows charge

It helps to add information that shows how evenly or unevenly the electrons are being shared. If we color the surface by charge, then we can see to what degree electrons are shared evenly or unevenly. The diagram below uses blue to represent negative, white to represent neutral, and red to represent positive.

Molecular surfaces colored by charge

The two atoms of hydrogen that make up a hydrogen molecule share electrons equally, so there is no surface charge

hydrogen, H_2

Electrons are unevenly shared between oxygen and hydrogen, causing a surface charge to occur on water molecules

Water, H_2O

Water is a polar molecule

You can see that a diatomic hydrogen molecule (H_2) is neutral all over, or *unpolarized*. A water molecule is quite different. The electrons are attracted more to the oxygen atom than to the hydrogen atoms. That makes the oxygen end of the molecule more negative (blue) and the hydrogen end more positive (red). Unlike hydrogen molecules, water molecules are strongly polarized; they have a separation of charges.

Predicting bond type

Periodic properties and bond type

Since the type of bond is related to how the electrons are shared (or transferred), two of the periodic properties we introduced in Chapter 6 are particularly important. **Electronegativity** describes how strongly an atom attracts electrons from another atom. The higher the electronegativity, the more strongly the element attracts electrons. **Ionization energy** describes how much energy it takes to *remove* an electron from an atom. High ionization energy means it takes a lot of energy to remove an electron. Ionization energy is a measure of how well an atom can hold onto its own electrons.

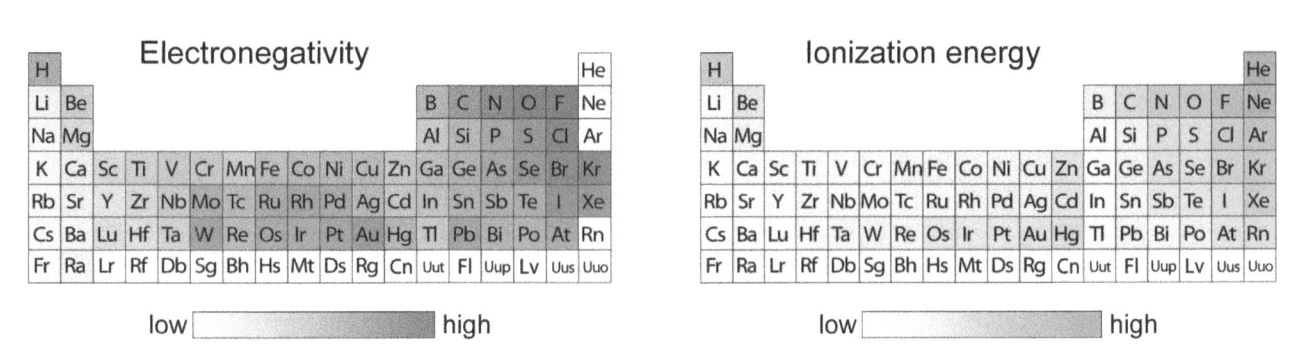

Bond types

The type of chemical bond (if any) between any two elements depends on their relative differences in electronegativity and ionization energy. There are three possible scenarios.

1. Both atoms have similar electronegativity and ionization energy.

2. There is a moderate difference. One atom has medium electronegativity and ionization energy, and the other has high (or low) electronegativity and ionization energy.

3. There is a large difference. One atom has high electronegativity and ionization energy, and one has low electronegativity and ionization energy.

The chart below shows how the different kinds of chemical bonds correspond to the differences in electronegativity and ionization energy.

	Nonpolar covalent bond	**Polar covalent bond**	**Ionic bond**
Atom 1	high electronegativity	high electronegativity	high electronegativity
Atom 2	high electronegativity	medium electronegativity	low electronegativity
Difference in electronegativity	very little difference	a moderate difference	a large difference
Electron sharing	equal or nearly equal sharing	uneven sharing of electrons	transfer of electrons

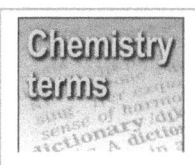

Chemistry terms

electronegativity: a value between 0 and 4 that describes the relative affinity of an element for electrons from other atoms, with high numbers meaning stronger attraction for electrons.

ionization energy: the energy required to completely remove an electron.

Covalent bonds

Definition of a covalent bond

Covalent bonds occur when electrons are shared between atoms. Sometimes the sharing is perfectly equal, and sometimes one atom has a slight advantage over the other in the contest for electrons.

Nonpolar covalent bonds

Let's say you bring two atoms together with high ionization energies and high electronegativities. These tend to be nonmetals, found in the upper right part of the periodic table, as well as hydrogen. They will both pull strongly on each other's electrons and also hold strongly onto their own electrons.

Since their electronegativities and ionization energies are very similar, they will share electrons evenly between them, forming a **nonpolar covalent bond**. Nonpolar means there is no (or very little) charge separation on the surface of the molecule. A good example is molecular oxygen (O_2).

A nonpolar covalent bond

high electronegativity
high ionization energy

high electronegativity
high ionization energy

Cl

Cl

Polar covalent bonds

When one atom has an electronegativity that is moderately different from the other, then the pull for electrons between the two atoms will be unequal. The unequal sharing of electrons makes a **polar covalent bond**. Polar means there are one or more regions of the molecule that have an average positive or negative charge. A good example is water. Water is a polar covalent molecule.

A polar covalent bond

medium electronegativity
medium ionization energy

high electronegativity
high ionization energy

C

O

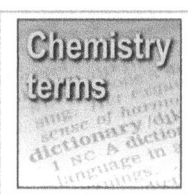

Chemistry terms

nonpolar covalent bond: a bond formed between two atoms in which electrons are shared equally or almost equally between the two atoms.

polar covalent bond: a bond formed between two atoms in which electrons are unequally shared.

Ionic and metallic bonds

Transfer of electrons

If two atoms have electronegativities that are very different, then electron sharing is so uneven that one or more electrons are essentially *transferred* from one atom to the other. This kind of bond often forms between a nonmetal (upper right of the periodic table) and a metal. For example, the bonds in calcium chloride ($CaCl_2$) would involve transferred electrons because chlorine is a nonmetal and calcium is a metal.

Ionic bonds

When an electron is transferred, both atoms involved become charged ions. The atom losing a electron becomes a positive ion and the atom gaining an electron becomes a negative ion. The strong attraction between the positive and negative ions is called an **ionic bond**.

An ionic bond

low electronegativity
low ionization energy

Na

+1   -1

high electronegativity
high ionization energy

Cl

electron transferred from Na to Cl

Ionic substances form crystals

Ionic bonds connect atoms to all neighbors, not just a single neighbor as in a molecule. This is because a positive ion attracts all nearby negative ions and vice versa. For example, in sodium chloride each positive sodium ion attracts all neighboring chlorine atoms. This is very different from what happens in a covalent bond. In a covalent bond, one atom is bonded to only one other atom and the pair stays together as a unit. In an ionic bond, there is no one-to-one pairing of atoms. Each ion is bonded to all of its oppositely charged neighbors.

An ionic crystal

NaCl

Metallic bonds

A metal is sort of like an ionic substance and sort of like a covalently bonded substance. Metals tend to have both low electronegativities and low ionization energies, so they don't attract each other's electrons well, and they don't hold onto their own electrons well. The result is a bunch of atoms that share their electrons with every other atom, forming a **metallic bond**. Electrons are shared like in covalent bonds, but no two atoms are specifically bonded together as in covalent compounds.

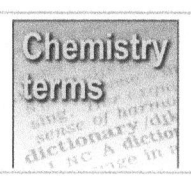

Chemistry terms

ionic bond: an attraction between oppositely charged ions, occurring with all nearby ions of opposite charge.

metallic bond: an attraction between metal atoms that loosely involves many electrons.

Electronegativity

Values of electro-negativity

The periodic table below shows the values of electronegativity for the elements. The values range from a low of 0.7 for francium (Fr) to a high of 3.98 for fluorine (F). The alkali metals are all low since they all have a single valence electron that they try to donate. The halogens are highest since they need one electron to reach the magic number of eight electrons to make a full energy level.

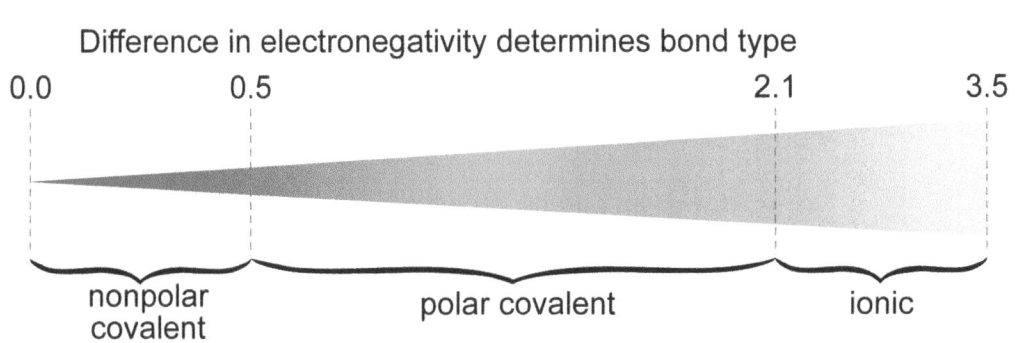

group 1																		group 18
H 2.1 hydrogen																		He -- helium
Li 0.98 lithium	Be 1.57 beryllium											B 2.04 boron	C 2.55 carbon	N 3.04 nitrogen	O 3.44 oxygen	F 3.98 fluorine	Ne -- neon
Na 0.93 sodium	Mg 1.31 magnesium											Al 1.61 aluminum	Si 1.9 silicon	P 2.19 phosphorous	S 2.58 sulfur	Cl 3.16 chlorine	Ar -- argon
K 0.82 potassium	Ca 1.0 calcium	Sc 1.36 scandium	Ti 1.54 titanium	V 1.63 vanadium	Cr 1.66 chromium	Mn 1.55 manganese	Fe 1.83 iron	Co 1.88 cobalt	Ni 1.91 nickel	Cu 1.9 copper	Zn 1.65 zinc	Ga 1.81 galium	Ge 2.01 germanium	As 2.18 arsenic	Se 2.55 selenium	Br 2.96 bromine	Kr 3.0 krypton
Rb 0.82 rubidium	Sr 0.95 strontium	Y 1.22 yttrium	Zr 1.33 zirconium	Nb 1.6 niobium	Mo 2.16 molybdenum	Tc 1.9 technetium	Ru 2.2 ruthenium	Rh 2.28 rhodium	Pd 2.2 palladium	Ag 1.93 silver	Cd 1.69 cadmium	In 1.78 indium	Sn 1.96 tin	Sb 2.05 antimony	Te 2.1 tellurium	I 2.66 iodine	Xe 3.0 xenon
Cs 0.79 cesium	Ba 0.89 barium	Lu 1.27 lutetium	Hf 1.3 hafnium	Ta 1.5 tantalum	W 2.36 tungsten	Re 1.9 rhenium	Os 2.2 osmium	Ir 2.2 iridium	Pt 2.28 platinum	Au 2.54 gold	Hg 2.0 mercury	Tl 2.04 thallium	Pb 2.33 lead	Bi 2.02 bismuth	Po 2.0 polonium	At 2.2 astatine	Rn -- radon
Fr 0.7 francium	Ra 0.89 radium	Lr -- lawrencium	Rf -- rutherfordium	Db -- dubnium	Sg -- seaborgium	Bh -- bohrium	Hs -- hassium	Mt -- meitnerium	Ds -- darmstadtium	Rg -- roentgenium	Cn -- copernicium	Uut -- ununtrium	Fl -- flerovium	Uup -- ununpentium	Lv -- livermorium	Uus -- ununseptium	Uuo -- ununoctium

Electronegativity → 0.93 sodium

low ▭ high

Electro-negativity and bond type

Whether a bond is covalent or ionic mostly depends on the difference in electronegativity between the two bonded atoms. If the difference is low, then you get a nonpolar covalent bond. If it's high, then you get an ionic bond. In reality, there is a sliding scale of bond type ranging between these two extremes. The smallest possible difference in electronegativities is zero, and the largest difference is 3.28 (3.98 − 0.7 = 3.28). The drawing below shows what kind of bond forms over the range of possible differences.

Difference in electronegativity determines bond type

0.0   0.5   2.1   3.5

nonpolar covalent   polar covalent   ionic

Electronegativity and bond type

Classifying chemical bonds

Although there really is no sharp dividing line, most chemists classify bond types into three categories: nonpolar covalent, polar covalent, and ionic. If you take the electronegativities of the two bonded atoms and subtract them, you get a number that tells you how to classify the bond. If the

Bondtype	Electronegativity difference
nonpolar covalent	less than 0.5
polar covalent	between 0.5 and 2.1
ionic	greater than 2.1

difference is less than 0.5, it is considered to be nonpolar covalent. If it is between 0.5 and 2.1, then the bond is considered to be polar covalent. If the difference is greater than 2.1, then the bond is considered to be ionic.

Two examples

Diatomic compounds make the best examples since there are only two atoms to consider. The diagram shows a charge-shaded molecular surface with a ball-and-stick model inside. Diatomic iodine (I_2) is a nonpolar covalent bond, since both atoms have the same electronegativity. Carbon monoxide is a polar covalent bond since the difference in electronegativity is 0.89. The oxygen atom has the higher electronegativity so the bonding electrons spend proportionally more time near the oxygen nucleus than the carbon nucleus. The shaded surface shows that the oxygen end of the molecule is more negative (blue) and the carbon end is more positive (red).

Nonpolar bond calculation

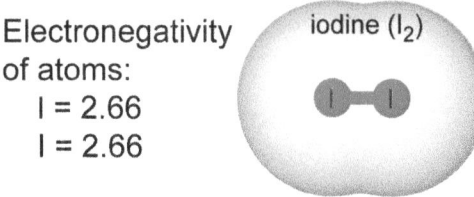

Electronegativity of atoms:
I = 2.66
I = 2.66

Electronegativity difference:
I – I = 2.66 – 2.66 = 0

Polar bond calculation

Electronegativity of atoms:
C = 2.55
O = 3.44

Electronegativity difference:
O – C = 3.44 – 2.55 = 0.89

Solved problem

Water is made by bonding two hydrogen atoms to an oxygen atom. Are the bonds nonpolar covalent, polar covalent, or ionic?

Asked: *The kind of bonds used to make water*

Given: *The electronegativity of oxygen is 3.44.*
The electronegativity of hydrogen is 2.1.

Relationships: *A difference of <0.5 in electronegativities is nonpolar covalent, between 0.5 and 2.1 is polar covalent, and >2.1 is ionic.*

Solve: *3.44 – 2.10 = 1.34*

Answer: *The bond formed between hydrogen and oxygen is polar covalent.*

Polar bonds and polar molecules

Molecules may contain both polar and nonpolar bonds

Most molecules are made up of more than two atoms and have more than one bond. Molecules that have multiple bonds could include all polar bonds, all nonpolar bonds, or some mixture of the two. When chemists talk about substances being polar or nonpolar, they are talking about the *whole molecule*, not a single bond.

Polar bonds versus polar molecules

In a molecule, when electrons are pulled more toward one atom than another, it causes an uneven distribution of the electrons. Since the electrons are negative, this results in an uneven distribution of charge. Polar molecules have at least one area where the electrons are not distributed evenly. Nonpolar molecules have an even distribution of electrons over the entire molecule.

A phospholipid molecule
(found in cell membranes)

some polar bonds

all nonpolar bonds

Polar bonds in a molecule make the molecule polar

Propane
boiling point = – 42°C

Polarity Calculations:
C – C = 2.55 – 2.55
 = 0.00 (nonpolar)
C – H = 2.55 – 2.1
 = 0.45 (nonpolar)

Propanol
boiling point = 97°C

Polarity Calculations:
O – H = 3.44 – 2.1
 = 1.34 (polar)
O – C = 3.44 – 2.55
 = 0.89 (polar)
C – H = 2.55 – 2.1
 = 0.45 (nonpolar)
C – C = 2.55 – 2.55
 = 0.00 (nonpolar)

Polarity and physical properties

Understanding the polar or nonpolar nature of molecules is crucial for understanding the physical properties of substances. For example, on the previous page you calculated that both bonds in water are polar covalent, so that makes water a polar molecule. It is the polar nature of water that makes life on this planet possible. If you want to invent chocolate that will melt in your mouth, but not in your hand, then you need to understand the polar or nonpolar nature of your ingredients!

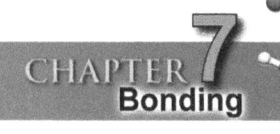

7.2 Valence Electrons and Bonding Patterns

Only valence electrons form bonds

When a chemical bond forms, some valence electrons are either shared or transferred between atoms. Only the *unpaired* valence electrons in an atom participate in chemical bonds. For complex reasons, the fifth, sixth and seventh valence electrons pair up and reduce the number of electrons available for bonding. The diagram below shows the main group elements along with their paired and unpaired valence electrons.

The number of valence electrons affects bond number and ion charge

group 1

Lewis dot diagram → H

group 2

| Li | Be. | | B. | •C. | •N. | •O: | •F: | :Ne: | group 18 He |

group 13 group 14 group 15 group 16 group 17

Li	Be.
Na	Mg.
K	Ca.
Rb	Sr.

B.	•C.	•N.	•O:	•F:	:Ne:
Al.	•Si.	•P.	•S:	•Cl:	:Ar:
Ga.	•Ge.	•As.	•Se:	•Br:	:Kr:
In.	•Sn.	•Sb.	•Te:	•I:	:Xe:

Valence electrons → 1   2   3   4   5   6   7   8*

*All noble gases have 8 except for He

Each unpaired valence electron can form one covalent bond

In a molecular compound, each unpaired valence electron can form one covalent chemical bond. For example, both nitrogen (N) and phosphorous (P) atoms each have three unpaired valence electrons. In molecular compounds, these elements both form three covalent bonds.

Valence electrons, bonds, and charge

•N.   •P.

nitrogen and phosphorous form 3 covalent bonds

In a molecular compound, each unpaired valence electron forms one covalent bond

K   Na

potassium and sodium form +1 charged ions

Ion charge and valence electrons

When forming a positive ion, each valence electron can contribute one unit of positive charge. This occurs when an atom loses its valence electron(s) to another atom, leaving a charge of +1 for every valence electron lost. For example, sodium (Na) and potassium (K) each have a single valence electron and form singly charged ions (+1). Magnesium (Mg) and calcium (Ca) have two valence electrons each. These elements form ions with a charge of +2.

In positive ions, each valence electron can contribute one unit of positive charge

The octet rule

Eight valence electrons = chemical stability

In Chapter 6 you learned that the noble gases have eight valence electrons (except for He, which has two). These elements form no bonds because they are already at the most stable configuration of electrons. From the noble gases we infer that elements with eight valence electrons are chemically stable. The observed behavior of the rest of the elements confirms that elements form chemical bonds to achieve the magic configuration of eight valence electrons. This observation is known as the *octet rule*. The **octet rule** states that elements transfer or share electrons in chemical bonds to reach a stable configuration of eight valence electrons.

Neon forms no bonds or ions

Elements form bonds to reach eight valence electrons

Two valence electrons are most stable for H, Li, Be, and B

The elements hydrogen, lithium, beryllium, and boron have so few electrons that their version of the octet rule is really based on helium as the closest noble gas. Helium fills the first energy level with its two electrons. That means either zero or two valence electrons are also "noble gas" electron configurations. The "octet rule" for hydrogen, lithium, beryllium, and boron is more accurately the "duet rule" or "the rule of 2." These elements form chemical bonds to achieve two valence electrons.

H, Li, Be, and B form bonds to reach two valence electrons

Shared electrons are counted by both atoms

In a covalent bond, a shared electron gets counted as a valence electron by *both atoms*. For example, molecular hydrogen (H_2) shares electrons to get two valence electrons, like helium. In water (H_2O) each of the two hydrogen atoms shares one electron with oxygen, giving each hydrogen two valence electrons and oxygen eight valence electrons.

Water (H_2O)

Hydrogen   Oxygen   Hydrogen

Chemistry terms

octet rule: rule that states that elements transfer or share electrons in chemical bonds to reach a stable configuration of eight valence electrons; the light elements H, Li, Be, and B have He as the closest noble gas, so the preferred state is two valence electrons instead of eight.

A NATURAL APPROACH TO CHEMISTRY

Valence electrons and ion formation

Ionic charge and the periodic table

There are two ways for elements to satisfy the octet rule: by sharing electrons in covalent bonds or by transferring electrons in an ionic bond. When the difference in electronegativity is larger than 2.1, the chemical bond is ionic. Most elements form some ionic compounds. The table below shows the most common charges for ions of the main group elements.

Valence electrons in combination with properties of ionization energy and electronegativity determine specific ionic charge

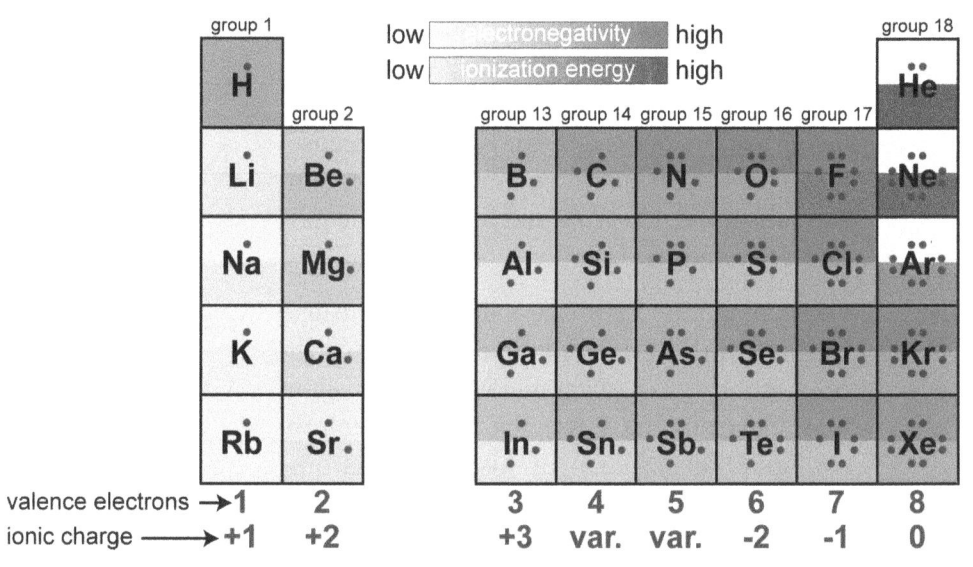

Ion patterns

You should see several patterns:

1. Elements on the left side tend to form positively charged ions, and elements on the right side form negatively charged ions.
2. Elements in the middle sometimes form positive ions and sometimes form negative ions. These are marked as "variable" charge.
3. The alkali metals (group 1) form +1 charged ions because they have one valence electron.
4. The alkali earth metals (group 2) form +2 charged ions because they have two valence electrons.
5. Boron-like elements (group 13) form +3 charged ions because they have three valence electrons.
6. Oxygen-like elements (group 16) form –2 charged ions. These elements have six valence electrons. Their easiest path to the octet rule is to gain two electrons.
7. The halogens (group 17) form –1 charged ions. These elements have seven valence electrons. Their easiest path to the octet rule is to gain one electron.

Electron configuration of ions

Why sodium forms a +1 ion

Sodium is an alkali metal with one valence electron. Sodium usually loses its one valence electron to become Na⁺ to satisfy the octet rule and have an electron configuration like that of a noble gas. Theoretically, sodium (Na) could also gain seven electrons for a charge of –7 to become Na⁻⁷, but losing one is so much more likely. This is why we never see Na⁻⁷ ions in nature. The electron configurations of Na, Na⁺, and Ne are shown to the right. Note that Na⁺ *has the same electron configuration as neon.* Sodium tends to form Na⁺ ions because this is the lowest energy path by which sodium can satisfy the octet rule and reach a noble gas electron configuration.

Neutral sodium

$$Na = 1s^2, 2s^2, 2p^6, 3s^1$$

Lose 1 electron

Sodium ion Na⁺

$$Na^+ = 1s^2, 2s^2, 2p^6$$

Neon

$$Ne = 1s^2, 2s^2, 2p^6$$

Why oxygen forms a –2 ion

Oxygen atoms have six valence electrons. To have an electron configuration like that of a noble gas, oxygen could either gain two electrons to have the same electron configuration as neon or lose six electrons to have the same electron configuration as helium. Given that oxygen has a high ionization energy, it is not likely to lose six electrons. Also, oxygen has a high electronegativity, so it has the ability to grab electrons from other atoms. It makes sense that oxygen will gain two electrons rather than lose six.

Neutral oxygen

$$O = 1s^2, 2s^2, 2p^4$$

Gain 2 electrons

Oxygen ion O²⁻

$$O^{2-} = 1s^2, 2s^2, 2p^6$$

Neon

$$Ne = 1s^2, 2s^2, 2p^6$$

Solved problem

Write the electron configuration for a magnesium ion (Mg²⁺).

Asked: *Electron configuration of Mg²⁺*

Given: *Mg, atomic number of 12, charge of +2*

Relationships: *The electron configuration of magnesium is $1s^2 2s^2 2p^6 3s^2$.*

Solve: *Mg must lose two electrons to become Mg²⁺. Therefore it loses the pair of $3s^2$ electrons.*

Answer: *The electron configuration of Mg²⁺ is $1s^2 2s^2 2p^6$, which is identical to neon.*

Simple ionic formulas

Ionic crystals

Ionic substances typically form crystals, which are large groups of oppositely charged ions arranged in a regular pattern. The calcium chloride ($CaCl_2$) crystal in the diagram is a good example. Calcium chloride is often used to melt ice on roads because it is better for the environment than sodium chloride (also used to melt ice). Ionic crystals are neutral even though they are formed through the attractions of trillions of charged ions. You can have any number of ions in the crystal as long as the positive charges exactly balance the negative charges.

Calcium chloride, $CaCl_2$
two chloride ions for each calcium

$$\left[\;:\ddot{C}\ddot{l}:\;\right]^{-1} \; C\overset{2+}{a} \; \left[\;:\ddot{C}\ddot{l}:\;\right]^{-1}$$

Why calcium chloride has the formula $CaCl_2$

To determine the formula of an ionic compound, you need to balance the positive and negative charges. For example, calcium makes a Ca^{2+} ion. Chlorine makes a Cl^- ion. Each calcium atom loses two electrons and each chloride ion gains only one. This means the compound requires two chloride ions to have the same amount of negative charge as one calcium ion's positive charge. This makes the ratio of calcium to chlorine 1:2, and the formula is therefore $CaCl_2$.

Ca^{2+} ⬅ Each calcium ion comes with a +2 charge

Cl^{1-} ⬅ Each chloride ion comes with a −1 charge

$$\frac{Ca^{2+} \quad Cl^{1-}}{+2 \qquad -2}\quad Cl^{1-}$$

Total charge from ions

$CaCl_2$
Formula shows a 1:2 ratio of calcium to chlorine

Solved problem

What is the correct formula for calcium oxide, a compound used in making paper, and pottery and adjusting the pH of soils?

Asked: *The formula for the ionic compound calcium oxide*

Given: *Calcium oxide is made from calcium and oxygen ions. Calcium forms +2 ions and oxygen forms −2 ions.*

Relationships: *Ca^{2+} and O^{2-} must combine in a ratio that will balance out the positive and negative charges.*

Solve: *The charge on one Ca^{2+} ion will balance out with the charge on one O^{2-} ion. Therefore the ratio is 1:1 and the formula is CaO.*

Covalent bonds

Covalent bond formation

In covalent bonds, electrons are shared between atoms, not transferred. The number of covalent bonds is equal to the number of *unpaired* valence electrons. The diagram below shows the number of covalent bonds by the main group elements.

Valence electrons in combination with properties of ionization energy and electronegativity determine number of covalent bonds formed

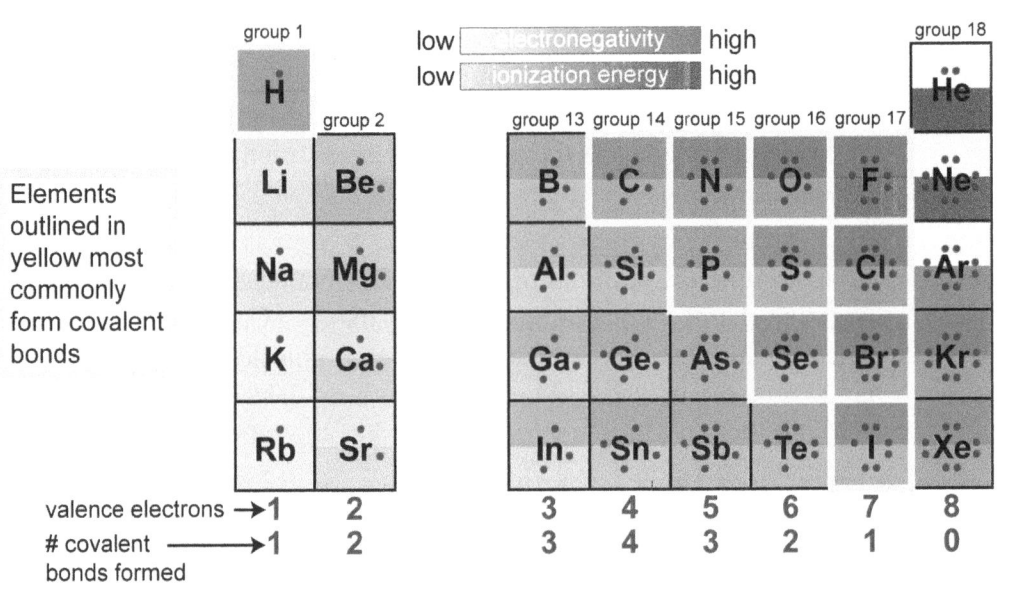

Covalent bond patterns

1. Only nonmetals and hydrogen are commonly found as covalently bonded parts of molecules.
2. Carbon-like elements (group 14) form four covalent bonds.
3. Nitrogen-like elements (group 15) form three covalent bonds.
4. Oxygen-like elements (group 16) form two covalent bonds.
5. Halogens (group 17) form one covalent bond.
6. The number of covalent bonds is equal to the number of unpaired valence electrons.

Paired and unpaired electrons

Going from left to right across the periodic table, notice that nitrogen has three unpaired electrons and *one pair*. The eight electrons in s and p orbitals act like eight strangers filling up four bench seats on a bus. Everyone prefers his or her own seat, so at first each person sits solo. The fifth person must pair up with someone. The same is true of electrons. The fifth valence electron pairs up and is *no longer available for bonding*! For reasons of quantum mechanics, only unpaired electrons form bonds.

Unpaired electrons
(form bonds)

Paired electrons
(do NOT form bonds)

B·   ·C·   ·N·   :Ö·

3   4   5   6

Valence electrons

Bonds and unpaired electrons

Every unpaired electron forms a bond

Take a look at the molecule of vitamin C to the right. This molecule is made from several carbon, oxygen, and hydrogen atoms. Take a close look at each carbon atom. You will see that every carbon atom has four covalent bonds to other atoms. The oxygen atoms each form two covalent bonds, and the hydrogen atoms each form one covalent bond.

Vitamin C

All atoms of the same element form the same number of bonds

Covalent bonds and noble gases

Carbon has four valence electrons, and they are all unpaired. Therefore carbon forms four chemical bonds. Oxygen has six valence electrons. Four of these electrons are paired and two are unpaired. Oxygen always forms two covalent bonds because it has two unpaired electrons. Hydrogen has one valence electron, and its closest noble gas is helium with two valence electrons. Hydrogen needs one more electron to be like helium. It gets this by forming one covalent bond with another atom.

Bonds formed to have same number of valence electrons as noble gas

$\dot{H} = 1s^1$ 1 bond $\ddot{He} = 1s^2$

$\cdot\dot{\underset{\cdot}{C}}\cdot = 1s^2 2s^2 2p^2$ 4 bonds $:\ddot{Ne}: = 1s^2 2s^2 2p^6$

$\cdot\ddot{\underset{\cdot\cdot}{O}}: = 1s^2 2s^2 2p^4$ 2 bonds $:\ddot{Ne}: = 1s^2 2s^2 2p^6$

Acetic acid (vinegar)

By forming bonds, H has 2 valence electrons, while C and O have 8.

Unpaired electrons create very reactive atoms or molecules

One quick way to tell how many covalent bonds an atom will form is to look at its Lewis dot structure. Atoms will form one covalent bond for each unpaired valence electron. Atoms or molecules that have unpaired electrons are highly reactive and are known as **free radicals**. These are the kind of molecules that can be responsible for aging and diseases like cancer. Sometimes free radicals are created as part of our own natural metabolism, and sometimes they are caused by outside sources such as ultraviolet radiation from the Sun. **Antioxidants** are considered an important part of a person's diet because of their role in preventing free radicals from reacting with and damaging DNA.

Chemistry terms

free radical: a molecule or atom that is highly reactive owing to having one or more unpaired valence electrons.

antioxidant: a molecule that reacts easily with free radicals, such as found in brightly colored fruits and vegetables, vitamin E, and chocolate.

7.3 Molecular Geometry and Lewis Dot Structures

Molecular formulas and bonding

Everyone knows that the formula for water is H_2O. This tells us that two hydrogens and one oxygen bond together to form a molecule of water. However, it doesn't tell us *how* they are bonded together. Are the hydrogen atoms attached to each other? You could imagine both possibilities shown in the diagram on the right. One is correct and one is not. Lewis structures are a convenient tool for figuring out the correct way to connect atoms into molecules.

Two ways to bond two hydrogens and one oxygen

Electron dot formulas of ionic and covalent compounds

If you use the Lewis dot diagrams, you can predict that both hydrogen atoms bond to a central oxygen. You can also predict the formula of H_2O. To assemble a molecule from individual atoms, you share one unpaired electron from one atom with an unpaired electron from another atom. Now both electrons "belong" to each atom, and a covalent bond is formed. For an ionic compound, the electron dot formula shows the transfer of electrons between the elements. For example, NaCl is a compound formed with an ionic bond between sodium (Na) and chlorine (Cl). In an ionic compound the elements have an associated charge. In NaCl, Na has a charge of +1 and Cl has a charge of −1.

**Electron dot formulas and Lewis dot diagrams
for covalent and ionic compounds**

Solving the molecule puzzle

You can think of the Lewis structures for individual atoms like puzzle pieces that can be put together to assemble molecules. The goal is to end up with each atom having no unpaired electrons and to be surrounded by eight valence electrons (unless the atom is hydrogen, in which case two paired electrons should be next to each hydrogen atom).

A NATURAL APPROACH TO CHEMISTRY

Isomers

Same molecular formula but different properties

Sometimes there are two or more different but correct ways to fit the atomic puzzle pieces together. This gives you different molecules with the same chemical formula. For example, C_2H_6O can form ethanol, the alcohol that is found in beer, wine, and liquor. The same C_2H_6O can also be *dimethyl ether*, often used in spray cans as a propellant. These two molecules have the same chemical formula but are very different substances with different properties. When you have multiple molecules that can be represented by the same chemical formula, the molecules are called **isomers**. Isomers are formed by bonding the same group of atoms together in different ways. The diagram shows two isomers of C_2H_6O.

Two isomers of C_2H_6O

Ethanol

Dimethyl ether

Solved problem

Give three isomers for the formula C_3H_8O. Show the Lewis dot diagram and the structural formula for each molecule.

Asked: *The Lewis dot diagrams and structural formulas for the three molecules represented by the formula C_3H_8O*

Given: *Carbon has four unpaired electrons, hydrogen has one, and oxygen has two. Three carbons, eight hydrogens and one oxygen form each molecule.*

Relationships: *The atoms will bond together such that all unpaired electrons will be paired up with electrons from other atoms.*

Solve:

Chemistry terms

isomer: a specific structure of a molecule, only used when a chemical formula could represent more than one molecule.

Electron dot formulas for double and triple bonds

Double and triple covalent bonds

Sharing a pair of electrons (one from each atom) is called a *single bond*. It is possible for atoms to share two or even three pairs of electrons. Sharing two pairs of electrons is a double bond and sharing three is a triple bond. Carbon, nitrogen, and oxygen commonly form double and triple bonds.

Ethene   Ethyne

Electron dot formulas and order of bond formation

The process for writing Lewis dot structures for molecules with double and/or triple bonds is very similar to what you have done already. First you single bond all the atoms together. Once you do this you will find that there are still some unpaired electrons left over. If those unpaired electrons are on two atoms that are already sharing electrons, then you can bring those two unpaired electrons into the same region where the first pair of shared electrons is already drawn. *This can only be done with unpaired electrons on two atoms that are already sharing electrons.* If, after single bonding all of the atoms together your unpaired electrons are not on two atoms that are already bonded, then you need to change how you originally put the atoms together to form single bonds.

Acetonitrile (C₂H₃N)   **Formaldehyde (CH₂O)**

Bond atoms together, forming single bonds.

Form double bonds by bringing together single electrons from atoms that are already bonded.

Form triple bonds with any remaining single electrons.

Write final Lewis dot structure and structural formula.

$$H - C - C \equiv N$$
(with H atoms above and below the first C)

$$H - C = O$$
(with H atoms above and below the C)

Molecular geometry

Lewis dot structures are 2D but real molecules are 3D

Lewis dot structures can all be drawn on a flat two-dimensional piece of paper. However, molecules are three-dimensional (3D) objects. In fact, the precise 3D shape of a molecule is very important in determining its physical and chemical properties, such as boiling point and viscosity. For complex molecules like those typically found in biological systems, shape can make the difference between a drug that treats cancer effectively or one that does nothing at all.

A biological molecule involved in regulating the breakdown of sugar

VSEPR

Using Lewis dot structures, we can predict the shapes of simple molecules and gain insights into shapes of larger ones. Using the Valence Shell Electron Pair Repulsion (**VSEPR**) theory, you can make predictions about the angles that attached atoms will form. Since the first three letters of VSEPR stand for "Valence Shell Electron," we are talking about the valence electrons, the ones represented by Lewis dots. The last two letters stand for "Pair Repulsion." Paired electrons are not shared in chemical bonds, but they *do* affect the shape of a molecule. Paired electrons repel each other and also repel shared electrons that *are* involved in a chemical bond.

unshared pair of electrons

shared pair of electrons

Bonds and electron density

Because similar charges repel each other, electrons that are being shared in bonds *and* unshared pairs of electrons will push away from each other. This repulsion is part of what causes a molecule to form a particular shape. Each bond or unshared pair of electrons represents a **region of electron density** around an atom. Depending on how many regions of electron density exist, different shapes will be formed.

Examples of central carbon atom with different regions of electron density

two regions

carbon dioxide

three regions

formaldehyde

four regions

methane

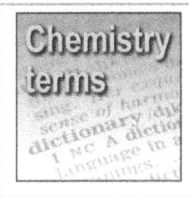
Chemistry terms

VSEPR (Valence Shell Electron Pair Repulsion): a theory that states that the shapes of molecules are dictated, in part, by the repulsion of the shared electrons and the unshared pairs of electrons.

region of electron density: an area represented by shared or unshared electrons around an atom.

Two areas of electron density

**Linear bond shape:
two points form a line**

If you rub a balloon against your hair it will grab some electrons from you, making the balloon negatively charged. If you had two negatively charged balloons and brought them close together, they would repel each other because they are both have the same sign of charge. They push away from each other in opposite directions until they are as far away as possible from each other.

Two charged balloons repel in opposite directions

Repulsion and bond shape

The same thing happens when there are two regions of electron density around an atom. The electrons in both regions push away to be as far apart as possible. For example, consider acetylene (C_2H_2). Around each carbon there are only two areas where electrons are located—the ones being shared in the triple bond between the carbons and the ones being shared in the single bond between the carbon and hydrogen atoms. These electrons repel each other until they are as far away as possible from each other. This causes the molecule to be *linear* around each of the carbon atoms.

Two areas of electron density repel to form linear shapes

These two regions of electron density repel each other forming a 180° angle

same here

The two 180° angles formed around each carbon make the entire molecule straight

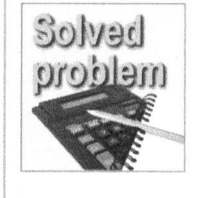

Solved problem

There are two isomers for the formula C_3H_4. Show the Lewis dot diagram for each molecule, and indicate which atoms are at the center of a linear part of the molecules.

Asked: *The linear parts of each isomer of C_3H_4*

Given: *There are two different isomers. Part of each molecule will be linear. The molecules are made from three carbons and four hydrogens.*

Relationships: *Each atom that has two regions of electron density around it will form a linear part of the molecule.*

Solve:

These atoms have two areas of electron density surrounding them

This atom has two areas of electron density surrounding it

Three areas of electron density

Three points form a plane

Now imagine that you have three negatively charged balloons. Again they will repel each other and move as far away from each other as they possibly can. In this case the balloons will point to the corners of a triangle, forming 120° angles between the balloons.

Three charged balloons repel into the corners of a triangle

Trigonal planar

When there are three regions of electron density around an atom, the electrons in all three regions push away until they are as far apart as possible. A good example is ethene (C_2H_4). There are three areas of electron density around each carbon atom. One area is being shared in the double bond between carbons. The other two are shared in the single bonds between the carbon and each of two hydrogen atoms. When three regions of electron density repel each other, a **trigonal planar** shape is formed.

Three areas of electron density repel to form trigonal planar shapes

These three regions of electrons density around each carbon repel, forming 120° angles between the three atoms bonded to each carbon atom

Solved problem

Acetic acid when mixed with water is commonly known as vinegar and has the formula $C_2H_4O_2$. The correct isomer has both oxygens bonded to the same carbon. Draw the Lewis dot structure for this isomer and indicate where the molecule will be trigonal planar.

Asked: *The trigonal planar parts of acetic acid*

Given: *The formula for acetic acid is $C_2H_4O_2$ and both oxygens are bonded to the same carbon.*

Relationships: *Each atom that has three regions of electron density around it will form a trigonal planar part of the molecule.*

Solve:

This carbon has three regions of electron density around it, so the molecule will form a trigonal planar shape around this atom

Chemistry terms

trigonal planar: a flat triangular geometry typical of molecules with three regions of electron density surrounding a central atom. The angle between the atoms is 120 degrees.

Four areas of electron density

Tetrahedral geometry: 3D

You might think that the shape formed by four charged balloons would look something like an "×" or a "+" with all four balloons as far apart from each other as they can get in a plane. However, there is a way to orient the balloons so that they are even farther apart: Have the balloons point to the corners of a *tetrahedron*, a pyramid shape formed from four triangles. If the four balloons lie in a plane then the angle between each balloon is 90°, but pointing the balloons into the four corners of a tetrahedron increases the angle to 109.5°, moving them even farther apart.

Four charged balloons repel into the corners of a tetrahedron, making an angle of 109.5° between them, larger than the 90° angle that could form if they were all in a plane

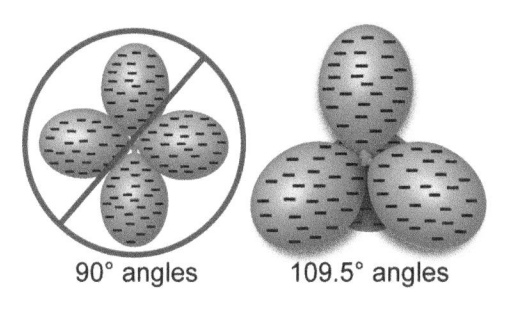

90° angles   109.5° angles

Lone pairs

In all of the Lewis dot structures we have seen so far, all of the electrons have been shared between atoms in covalent bonds. When looking at the 3D version of the molecule, each bond represented one or more pairs of shared electrons. However, atoms such as nitrogen and oxygen have some electrons that are already paired, even before any bonding has occurred. These electrons, known as **lone pairs,** are "invisible" in the ball-and-stick view of a molecule, but their presence affects the geometry of the molecule just as much (if not more) than the electrons being shared in bonds.

Lone pairs of electrons repel just like shared pairs

Lone pair of electrons

Ammonia (NH$_3$) forms a trigonal pyramidal shape

Shared pair of electrons

The lone pair of electrons repels the shared electrons in the H–N bonds, pushing the hydrogens away from the lone pair

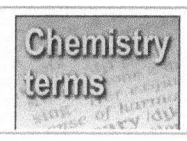

Chemistry terms

lone pairs: electrons that are paired up in a Lewis dot diagram but are not shared between atoms in a covalent bond.

220

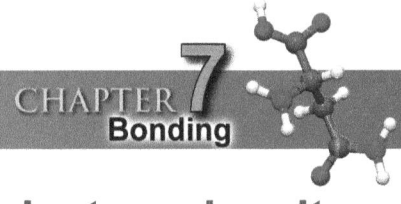
Multiple shapes due to four regions of electron density

Different geometric shapes

There are three shapes that are all based on having electron density in four places around an atom: tetrahedral, trigonal pyramidal, and bent. If there are four single bonds to a central atom, then the four bonded atoms mimic the balloons and form a **tetrahedral** shape. If there are three atoms bonded to a central atom that also has one unshared pair of electrons, then the unshared pair acts just like a shared pair, repelling the other electrons that are being shared in the three bonds. However, because one corner of the tetrahedron is "missing," we call this **trigonal pyramidal**. If there are two atoms bonded to a central atom that has two pairs of unshared electrons, then they all repel as in previous examples, except that the three atoms form a **bent** shape.

Different geometries formed by atoms with four regions of electron density

Tetrahedral   Trigonal pyramidal   Bent

What shapes are formed within the isomer of C_4H_5NO, which has a triple bond connecting nitrogen?

Solve:

These two carbons have three regions of electron density, so a **trigonal planar** shape is formed around them

This carbon has four regions of electron density and is bonded to four atoms, so a **tetrahedral** shape is formed

This carbon has two regions of electron density so the molecule is **linear** here

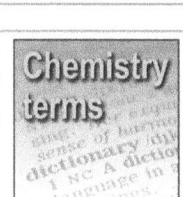

tetrahedral: a shape formed when a central atom is bonded to four other atoms that all point into the corners of a tetrahedron.
trigonal pyramidal: a three-dimensional shape formed when a central atom has one unshared pair of electrons and is bonded to three other atoms whose central plane does not include the central atom.
bent: a shape formed when a central atom has two unshared pairs of electrons and is bonded to two other atoms.

Nutrition Facts

Serving Size 3 oz. (85g)

Amount Per Serving	As Served
Calories 38	Calories from Fat 0

	% Daily Value
Total Fat 0g	0%
Saturated Fat 0g	0%
Cholesterol 0g	0%
Sodium 0g	2%
Total Carbohydrate 0g	3%
Dietary Fiber 0g	8%
Sugars 0g	
Protein 0g	

Vitamin A 270%	•	Vitamin C 10%
Calcium 2%	•	Iron 0%

Percent Daily Values are based on a 2,000 calorie diet. Your daily values may be higher or lower depending on your calorie needs:

		Calories	2,000	2,500
Total Fat	Less than		65g	80g
Sat Fat	Less than		20g	80g
Cholesterol	Less than		300mg	300mg
Sodium	Less than		2,400mg	2,400mg
Total Carbohydrate			300g	375g
Dietary Fiber			25g	30g

The Food and Drug Administration requires that most packaged food and beverages come with a nutrition facts label. You have probably seen labels like the one on the left on cereal boxes, bottled drinks, and other packaging, in stores and on line. But what exactly do the numbers listed mean, and what exactly are calories, fats, carbohydrates, and proteins?

Though you may know that food contains calories and exercise burns calories, you may not know what a calorie is. A *calorie* is a unit of energy, just like a joule. One calorie is defined as the amount of energy needed to raise the temperature of a gram of water by one degree Kelvin at standard atmospheric pressure, and is approximately equivalent to 4.2 joules. However, on food labels, the number of calories listed is actually in terms of the number of Calories (where the "c" is capitalized), where one Calorie is equal to 1000 calories, or 1 kilocalorie.

How are calories related to fats, carbohydrates, and proteins? These three different classes of molecules are contain different amounts of calories per gram. Carbohydrates and proteins provide 4 calories per gram, while fats provide 9 calories per gram. This is why fats are used to store chemical energy and why foods high in fat are also high in calories!

You have probably heard how some fats are good and some are bad for you. Terms such as *saturated*, *unsaturated*, and *trans fats* found on nutritional labels are really describing the structures of fat molecules. Fats and oils are made by both plants and animals to store chemical energy. Each molecule is composed of a glycerol backbone containing three carbons, and each carbon is attached to a long-chain fatty acid.

A chemical reaction between fatty acids and glycerol results in a triglyceride, a typical "fat" or "oil" molecule found in living things

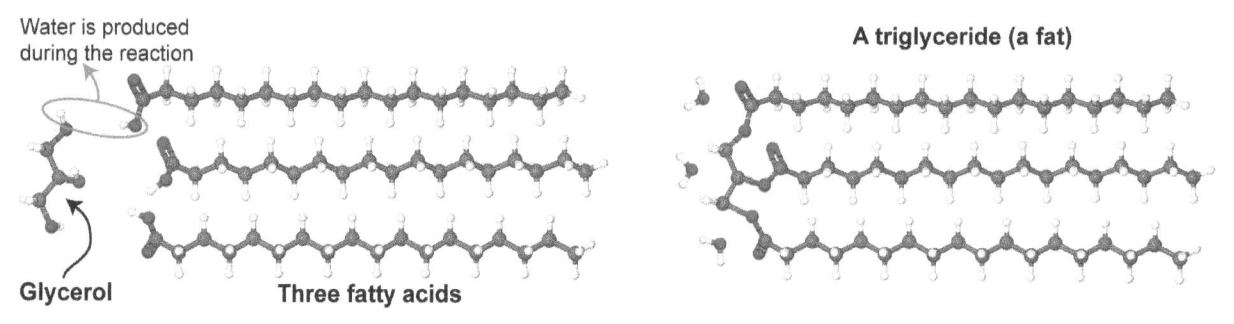

The term "saturated" means each carbon in a fatty acid chain is bonded to the largest number of hydrogen atoms possible, so long straight-chain fatty acids contain only single carbon-to-carbon bonds. This allows them to stack neatly together, so saturated fats such as butter are solid at room temperature..

A NATURAL APPROACH TO CHEMISTRY

The fatty acids in unsaturated fats contain some carbon-carbon double bonds, creating kinks that interfere with the stacking of the molecules. Unsaturated fats, such as olive oil, are liquid at room temperature. Saturated fats can have a negative impact on cardiovascular health. Unsaturated fats, although still high in calories, are beneficial, helping to reduce the bad cholesterol and increase the good type of cholesterol. However, "trans fats," unnatural fats made during the *partial hydrogenation* process, are as bad as or even worse than saturated fats. The difference in this example is the way the carbons are bonded together around the double bond.

Naturally occurring unsaturated fats form *cis* double bonds. "Cis" in Latin literally means "on the same side." This refers to the fact that both hydrogen atoms are on the same side of the double bond. Second, cis fats react more readily with oxygen in the air, resulting in a shorter shelf life for a food product. So manufacturers searched for a way to increase the shelf life of items made with unsaturated fat.

The method of *partial hydrogenation* to create trans fats was developed in the early 1900s, and this process allowed for a longer shelf life for food products. Crisco™ was the first product of this new technology. "Trans" in Latin means "across," which indicates the hydrogen atoms are on opposite sides of the double bond. During the partial hydrogenation process, some of the double bonds are transformed to single bonds . The remaining double bonds are converted from cis to trans. Trans fats are less likely to react with oxygen than the naturally occurring cis fats, and this makes them last longer in food products.

Part of a cis fat molecule   **Part of a trans fat molecule**

What, then, are carbohydrates? Like fats, carbohydrates are also a form of energy and are commonly referred to as sugars and starches. They can be used not only for food storage, but also as protective membranes for many organisms and structural support for plant cell walls. Foods high in carbohydrates include potatoes, bread, and pasta. Carbohydrates are made of the elements carbon, hydrogen, and oxygen, and come in many different types--*monosaccharides, disaccharides,* and *polysaccharides*. A monosaccharide is one unit of carbohydrate ("mono" means one and "saccharide" is another word for sugar). Disaccharides are two monosaccharides bonded to each other. Polysaccharides are chains of at least two monosaccharides.

Finally, *proteins* are larger molecules made of carbon, hydrogen, and oxygen, as well as nitrogen. The basic unit of a protein is the *amino acid*. Proteins have a wide variety of functions, from catalyzing biological reactions to facilitating communication between cells. These molecules are primarily found in meats, eggs, beans, and nuts.

Since all of these molecules play important roles for our body, we must make sure we have well-rounded diets that include all of them! This means that we should eat adequate servings of grains, vegetables, fruits, dairy, and meats and/or beans to stay healthy and make sure our bodies function properly!

Current information about the health effects of trans fat can be found online. Research, and communicate information collected from manufacturers, physicians and government sources. Once you have this information, you may use it to better understand the nutritional health effects of these chemical compounds.

Chapter 7 Review

Vocabulary

Match each word to the sentence where it best fits.

Section 7.1

electrostatic force	polarize
nonpolar covalent bond	polar covalent bond
	ionic bond

1. The _____ is what holds atoms together in bonds.

2. When the electrons are shared unevenly between two atoms they cause the molecule to _____ in that area.

3. A/An _____ forms when electrons are shared unevenly between atoms.

4. If one or more electrons are transferred between atoms causing them to become positively and negatively charged, then a/an _____ forms.

5. If two atoms have the same or very similar electronegativities, then the bond between them will be a/an _____ .

Section 7.2

free radical	antioxidant
octet rule	covalent bonds
unpaired electrons	paired electrons

6. A/An _____ is highly reactive as a result of having one unpaired electron and can do damage to other necessary molecules in your cells.

7. One reason dark-colored fruits and vegetables are considered healthy is their high content of _____ molecules.

8. The _____ states that elements transfer or share electrons in chemical bonds to reach a stable configuration of eight electrons.

9. In _____ electrons are shared between atoms instead of transferred.

10. _____ form bonds and _____ do not form bonds.

Section 7.3

isomer	lone pair
VSEPR	tetrahedral
region of electron density	trigonal pyramidal
	bent
trigonal planar	

11. If an atom has a/an _____ then some valence electrons will not be shared in covalent bonds.

12. You can predict the shapes of simple molecules using _____ theory.

13. Each bond and each pair of electrons not shared in a bond around an atom is considered to be a/an _____ .

14. If you can make more then one molecule from the same set of atoms, then each molecule made from that set is called a/an _____ .

15. The shape typically formed in a molecule around an oxygen atom is _____ .

16. There are two shapes that involve four atoms. The one that has all the atoms lying flat is _____ , whereas the one where they can't be all placed in the same flat surface is _____ .

17. If you had four things that are trying to repel as far away from each other as possible, they will point into the corners of a/an _____ shape.

Conceptual Questions

Section 7.1

18. Why don't all atoms repel each other if the outer part of the atom consists of negative electrons?

19. Describe why sharing electrons causes atoms to bond together.

20. In a ball-and-stick view of a molecule, what do the sticks represent?

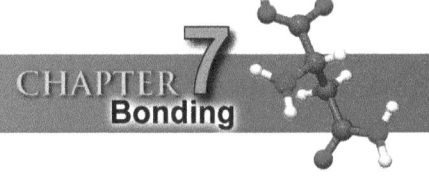

21. Describe the main difference between covalent and ionic bonds.

22. The surface view of a molecule makes it look like the molecule is solid. What does this surface really represent?

23. Describe what the red, white, and blue colors applied to some surface views of a molecule tell you about the charge of the molecule near that part of its surface.

24. If a covalent bond is formed when electrons are shared between two atoms, then what must be true of the electronegativity of both atoms?

    a. The electronegativities must be very different for each atom.

    b. The electronegativities must be exactly the same for each atom.

    c. The electronegativities must be similar, but not necessarily the same.

25. Explain the reasoning behind your answer to the previous question. Be sure to talk about the effect an atom's electronegativity has on the electrons.

26. Describe the difference in how electrons are shared in a nonpolar covalent bond versus a polar covalent bond.

27. Which of the molecules below is bonded together with a polar covalent bond, and how do you know?

 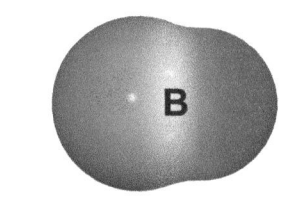

28. Which part of molecule "B" in the previous question is partially negative?

29. Why does having one atom with low ionization energy and low electronegativity paired with an atom that has high ionization energy and high electronegativity result in the formation of ions and an ionic bond?

30. Why do most atomic level images of ionic substances show many atoms forming a crystal, but images of molecular substances usually just show a specific set of bonded atoms?

31. All of the atoms are the same in a chunk of metal, so they all have the same ionization energy and electronegativity; they are both low. Why don't we call the type of bonds formed between the atoms in a metal "covalent bonds"?

32. Most molecules are made from more than two atoms bonded together, so there is more than just a single bond in a typical molecule. If one of the bonds is a polar covalent bond, but the rest of the bonds are nonpolar covalent bonds, then what can you conclude?

    a. The molecule is considered to be nonpolar.

    b. The molecule is considered to be polar.

    c. The molecule has a polar part or may be entirely polar.

Section 7.2

33. Why do atoms of elements in the same group on the periodic table tend to form the same charge if they become an ion, or form the same number of covalent bonds when bonded in this way to other atoms?

34. Using the properties of ionization energy and electronegativity, explain why atoms of elements from the left side of the periodic table tend to form positive ions but atoms from elements on the right side of the table form negative ions.

35. Which valence electrons are the ones involved in ionization and covalent bonding?

    a. the unpaired electrons from the Lewis dot diagram of the neutral unbonded atom b. the paired electrons from the Lewis dot diagram of the neutral unbonded atom

36. How many different isomers are shown below?

37. Are these two molecules isomers of each other or not? Explain.

38. How many valence electrons surround a stable atom in a Lewis dot configuration?

39. Formaldehyde has the formula CH_2O and has one double bond to allow all atoms to form stable valence structures. Explain why this initial attempt to come up with the correct Lewis dot structure will not work.

40. Describe in your own words what Valence Shell Electron Repulsion Theory is and what it is used for.

41. A region of electron density is:
   a. the electrons shared in a bond
   b. the electrons that form the inner core of the atom
   c. the valence electrons that are not shared and are called lone pairs
   d. both A and C

42. Which number of regions of electron density will give you which molecular shapes? Match the correct number with the correct shape.

Regions of electron density	Shape
2	tetrahedral
3	linear
4	trigonal planar

43. Describe the difference between trigonal planar and trigonal pyramidal shapes.

44. What are the three different possible shapes formed around an atom that is surrounded by four regions of electron density?

Quantitative Problems

Section 7.1

45. Polar covalent bonds form when electrons are shared unevenly. Because electrons are not fully transferred, this means they form partially negative and partially positive charges on the atoms. What color indicates a partial positive and what color indicates a partial negative charge on parts of a molecule?

Section 7.2

46. Calculate the type of bond that will form between the following pairs of atoms:
   a. carbon and hydrogen
   b. oxygen and hydrogen
   c. lithium and bromine
   d. carbon and oxygen
   e. fluorine and fluorine

47. Bonds formed between atoms with an electronegativity difference of less than 0.5 are considered to be:
   a. nonpolar covalent
   b. polar covalent
   c. ionic

48. Bonds formed between atoms with an electronegativity difference between 0.5 and 2.1 are considered to be:
   a. nonpolar covalent
   b. polar covalent
   c. ionic

49. Bonds formed between atoms with an electronegativity difference greater than 2.1 are considered to be:
   a. nonpolar covalent
   b. polar covalent
   c. ionic

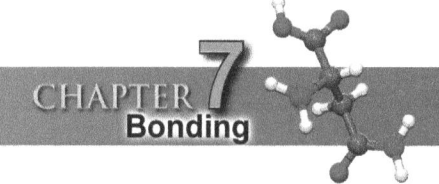

50. Most of the molecules in gasoline have the formula C_8H_{18}. Is gasoline a polar or nonpolar covalent molecule?

51. Some amino acids have polar side chains and some do not. The tyrosine side chain is shown in the green box in the drawing.

   a. Is the side chain for tyrosine polar or not?
   b. If it is polar, are all of the bonds polar or just some of them?
   c. If just some of them are polar which bonds are polar and which ones are not?

52. Describe the relationship between the electron configuration of the noble gases and the charge formed by specific ions. Give at least two examples and use electron configurations to support your answer.

53. Describe the relationship between the electron configuration of the noble gases and the number of covalent bonds formed by specific atoms. Give at least two examples and use electron configurations to support your answer.

54. What is the most stable number of valence electrons to have and how do you know?

55. What ratio of ions will be formed in the following substances, so that the positively charged ions will cancel out the negatively charged ions?
   a. sodium sulfide (Na and S)
   b. magnesium chloride (Mg and Cl)
   c. aluminum oxide (Al and O)

Section 7.3

56. Write the Lewis dot structure and structural formula for PH_3.

57. Write the Lewis dot structure and structural formula for C_2H_6.

58. Write the Lewis dot structure and structural formula for CBr_4.

59. Write the Lewis dot structure and structural formula for CH_5N.

60. Write the Lewis dot structure and structural formula for P_2H_2.

61. Write the Lewis dot structure and structural formula for SiH_3N.

62. Write electron dot diagram and structural formula for calcium chloride $CaCl_2$.

63. Write electron dot diagram and structural formula for the ionic compound potassium oxide K_2O.

64. Write as many isomers of the Lewis dot structure and structural formula for CH_3ON as you can.

65. What is the Lewis dot structure and structural formula for erythrose, shown here?

66. For each of the previous problems (58, 59, 62, and 64) describe how many regions of electron density exist for the carbon atoms in those molecules.

67. If part of a molecule is linear, what is the angle formed between adjacent bonds?

68. If part of a molecule is trigonal planar, what is the angle formed between adjacent bonds?

69. If part of a molecule is tetrahedral, what is the angle formed between adjacent bonds?

CHAPTER 8

Compounds and Molecules

Why are diamonds so hard?

If sugar and salt look so similar, why do they have such different melting points and other properties?

How do water bugs walk on water?

A good, healthy diet consists of a range of foods. You can't survive on only one thing, because there is no single fruit, vegetable, grain, or meat that contains every kind of chemical our bodies need to survive. Eating provides us with four basic things: calories, protein, vitamins, and minerals.

Calories are not an actual substance; they are a measure of the energy we get from eating three types of molecular substances: carbohydrates, fats, and proteins. Most of our energy typically comes from carbohydrates and fats.

We also get energy from eating proteins, but more importantly, proteins get broken down into smaller molecules called amino acids, which we then reassemble into different proteins. The DNA in our body is there for one reason: to provide instructions for building proteins from amino acids. Meat tends to be the food with the highest concentration of protein, but all living things make proteins, so vegetarians can also get the amino acids they need by eating the right combinations of plants.

Multivitamins contain ionic and molecular substances

Magnesium oxide   Vitamin C

The other two necessary "foods" often get grouped together: vitamins and minerals. Many breakfast cereals have these added to them, and many people take a multivitamin supplement that actually provides many minerals as well. Both vitamins and minerals are needed in small quantitates by your body, but going without any one of them for long periods of time can be very bad for your health. Vitamins are actually molecular substances, whereas minerals generally come in ionic form. Most of what we eat is molecular, but minerals and table salt (also considered a mineral) are important ionic components of a healthy diet.

Classifying solids

There are four main categories of solid substances: ionic, network covalent, molecular, and metallic. Chemicals that belong to these different categories share some common physical properties. We will test sand (SiO_2), salt ($NaCl$), sulfur (S), and copper (Cu). You are already familiar with several of the things we will be looking for. For example, we will compare a soft powder to a hard, granular substance.

To begin, make a table with the name of each of the four substances across the top. Next, list the properties down the side. Include texture, solubility in water, malleability (ability to bend), and conductivity.

1. Carefully observe each of the substances below. Record anything interesting about their appearances.

2. Try each of the following tests on the solids.

a. Can they bend? Are they malleable?

b. How do they feel? Soft, smooth, hard, or granular?

c. Place the conductivity apparatus in contact with each substance. Which substance(s) conduct electricity as a solid?

d. Place a small amount of each of them in water and mix. What happens?

e. Repeat the conductivity test on the substances in water from part (d). Record your observations about each substance.

You have just gathered data about all of the **different** classes of solids that we will study in this chapter.

The characteristics of texture, conductivity, and malleability all represent different types of attractive forces and bonding patterns

This information will be a useful guide as you learn about these solids. In this chapter, we will learn how bonding affects a solid's chemical properties.

8.1 Ionic Compounds

Properties of ionic substances

Unlike molecular compounds, ionic substances tend to have very similar properties:
• They are hard and brittle.
• They are solid at room temperature.
• They have very high melting points.
• They conduct electricity if heated to a liquid state.
• They conduct electricity if dissolved in water or some other solvent.

Ionic properties and atomic level structures

The properties we observe can be traced back to the underlying properties and atomic level structures of the ionic substances. An ionic substance is formed when a positively charged ion (resulting from the loss of one or more electrons) is attracted to a negatively charged ion (resulting from the gain of one or more electrons). Ions will attract each other, forming ionic bonds with all neighboring atoms. Let's take a closer look at sodium chloride.

Structure of sodium chloride (NaCl)

Each chloride ion is ionically bonded to six nearby sodium ions

Each sodium ion is ionically bonded to six nearby chloride ions

Ion attraction

Every sodium ion is surrounded by and is attracted to six nearby chloride ions, and every chloride ions is surrounded by and is attracted to six nearby sodium ions. The ions attract each other in very large numbers. In one typical grain of table salt there are about 10^{18} atoms (a billion billion atoms). Since sodium ions have a charge of +1 and chloride ions have a charge of –1, half of the atoms are sodium ions and half are chloride ions.

Positive and negative charges cancel out

In any ionic crystal, the ratio of positive ions to negative ions must allow for all of the positive charge to cancel out all of the negative charge. Otherwise, the ions in the crystal would not be able to hold together. Below are some other ionic substances.

lead(II) sulfide (PbS)   aluminum oxide (Al_2O_3)   copper(II) sulfate ($CuSO_4$)

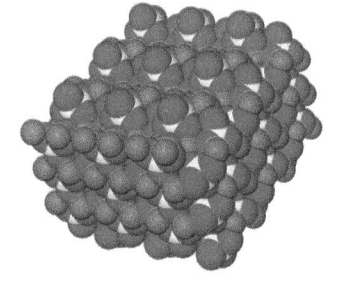

A NATURAL APPROACH TO CHEMISTRY

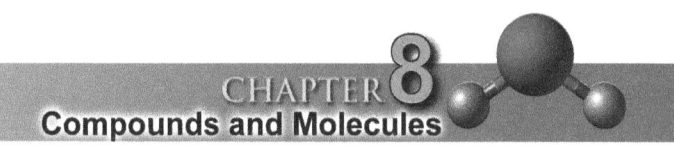
Connecting ionic structure to properties

Bonding patterns of ionic crystals

Now let's consider how ionic structure leads to physical properties. Three properties are related to each other: hardness, melting point, and state of matter.

Ionic substances are hard, have very high melting points, and so are solid at room temperature. All of this can be explained by the bonding patterns found in ionic crystals. Each ion is attracted to and is bonded with all of its neighbors, so the ions have an interconnected network of bonds holding the entire crystal together. This gives the overall crystal strength, making it hard. This also makes it difficult to melt. To be in a liquid state, the ions have to have enough kinetic energy (have a high enough temperature) to continually break free of the attractions, allowing them to flow by each other.

Network of ionic bonds makes ionic compounds hard, and have high melting points.

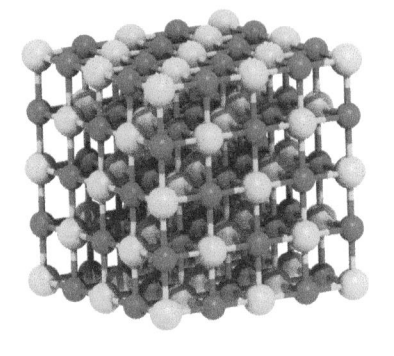

Ionic substances are brittle

Ionic substances are **brittle**. Putting pressure along one edge can cause the ions to shift place so that the positive and negative ions from one layer are not properly aligned with the oppositely charged ions in the next layer. If this happens, then there will be a repulsion between the layers and the crystal will break.

When aligned, the ions attract well, but add enough pressure and the crystal will break.

 Apply force and the ions repel, breaking the crystal.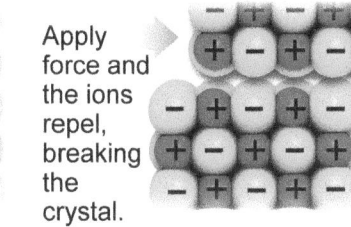

Electric current

An **electric current** is the movement of many electric charges, either ions or electrons, in a particular direction. Solutions of ionic compounds are strong electrolytes because they contain free ions that are capable of conducting electricity.

Ions dissolved in water move in random directions by colliding with water molecules

Overall ion movement toward the electrodes creates an electrical current

Polyatomic ions

An ion can also be a small molecule with a charge

Until now, all of our examples of ionic compounds have been made from ions that are single atoms with either a positive or negative charge. However, an ion can also be a small molecule with a charge. Since something becomes charged when there is an unequal amount of protons and electrons, for a molecule to become charged you need the total number of protons and electrons in the entire molecule to be unequal. One example of a **polyatomic ion** (an ion made from more than one atom) is carbonate, with the formula CO_3^{2-}. In this polyatomic ion, one carbon is bonded to three oxygens, and the entire molecule has a –2 charge.

Structure of the carbonate (CO_3^{2-}) ion

CO_3 molecule needs two extra electrons for all atoms to have eight valence electrons

The two oxygens now have a –1 charge, giving the whole molecule a –2 charge

Calcium carbonate
$CaCO_3$

Ca^{2+} = ⚫ CO_3^{2-} = ⬤

The carbonate ion switches among these three versions of the molecule

Bonding patterns are similar in ionic substances with polyatomic ions

Ionic crystals with polyatomic ions are very similar to the ones we have seen with single atomic ions. They pack together in a regular pattern with each positive ion attracting all of its negative neighbors, and each negative ion attracting all of its positive neighbors. Most polyatomic ions are negative, but there are a few positive ones. To the right is an example of ammonium sulfate, which is made from two polyatomic ions: ammonium (NH_4^+) and sulfate (SO_4^{2-}). It has the formula $(NH_4)_2SO_4$.

Ammonium sulfate $(NH_4)_2SO_4$

NH_4^+ =

SO_4^{2-} =

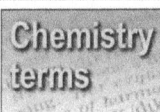
polyatomic ion: a small molecule with an overall positive or negative charge.

A NATURAL APPROACH TO CHEMISTRY

Writing formulas for ionic compounds

Ionic crystals come in many sizes

A grain of table salt is a small piece of an ionic substance, but as we learned earlier, that grain of salt is made from approximately one billion billion ions. Not all grains of salt are the same size. If you carefully grow a salt crystal under the right conditions, there is no limit to how big the grain could be. In an underground cavern in Germany there are single grains that measure over one meter in length on a side. The image to the right shows a large single crystal of table salt from the Fersman Mineralogical Museum in Moscow.

Ionic formulas tell you the ratio of ions in the compound

The formula for table salt is NaCl, but what does that mean if you can have a single crystal that has enormous variations in size? For ionic compounds, the chemical formula tells us the ratio of positive to negative ions in the entire substance. The ratio must be just right so that the total positive charge from all of the positive ions will equal the total negative charge from all of the negative ions.

Balancing positive and negative charge in ionic formula writing

---

Solved problem

Write the correct formulas for the compounds that will form using the following ion pairs: Mg^{2+} and Cl^-, Na^+ and S^{2-}, Al^{3+} and O^{2-}.

Asked: *Ionic formulas for the three different ionic substances*

Given: *The charges on all of the ion pairs*

Relationships: *The positive ions will combine with the negative ions in a ratio so that the positive and negative charges from the ions will be equal.*

Solve: *For each Mg^{2+} we need two Cl^- ($+2 - 1 - 1 = 0$) and the formula is $MgCl_2$. For each S^{2-} we need two Na^+ ($-2 + 1 + 1 = 0$) and the formula is Na_2S.*

To balance charges between Al^{3+} and O^{2-} we need to multiply Al by 2 and O by 3 [$2(+3) + 3(-2) = 0$]. The formula is Al_2O_3.

Writing formulas with polyatomic ions

Formulas with polyatomic ions

Writing ionic formulas using polyatomic ions is basically the same as writing them with simple single atomic ions. The strategy is the same. You need to write a formula that has the correct ratio of positive to negative ions. The only difference is how you show that you want more than one polyatomic ion. Since an ion like nitrite (NO_2^-) is a single unit—a small molecule with a negative charge —we treat that ion like it is a single atom. To write a formula that says you need two or three NO_2^- ions, you need to put parentheses around the ion. For example, three nitrites is written $(NO_2^-)_3$.

Polyatomic ions represent a single unit with a charge just like single-atom ions

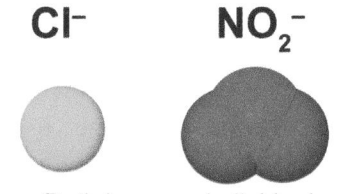

Both ions are individual particles carrying charge

Ionic formula writing with polyatomic ions

The chlorate ion (ClO_3^-) is made by covalently bonding chlorine to three oxygens and adding an extra electron; to indicate more than one chlorate, parentheses must be used

$ClO_3^- = $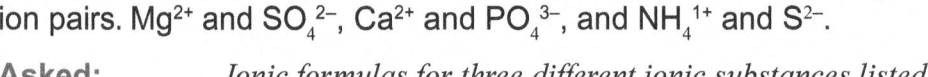

Using Ca^{2+} and ClO_3^- to make calcium chlorate

$$Ca(ClO_3)_2$$

Ca^{2+} ClO_3^-

ClO_3^-

——————
+2   –2

Using Al^{3+} and OH^- to make aluminum hydroxide

$$Al(OH)_3$$

Al^{3+} OH^-

OH^-

OH^-

——————
+3   –3

The hydroxide ion (OH^-) is made by bonding one atom of hydrogen to one atom of oxygen, so it is polyatomic even though the ion has no subscripts

---

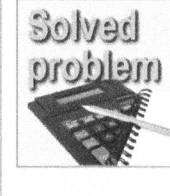

Solved problem

Write the correct formulas for the compounds that will form using the following ion pairs. Mg^{2+} and SO_4^{2-}, Ca^{2+} and PO_4^{3-}, and NH_4^{1+} and S^{2-}.

Asked: *Ionic formulas for three different ionic substances listed.*

Given: *The charges on all of the ion pairs.*

Relationships: *The positive ions will combine with the negative ions in a ratio so that the positive and negative charge from the ions will be equal.*

Solve: *For each Mg^{2+}, we need one SO_4^{2-} (+ 2 – 2 = 0) and the formula is $MgSO_4$.*

To balance charges between Ca^{2+} and PO_4^{3-}, multiply Ca by 3 and PO_4 by 2: [3(+2) + 2(–3) = 0]. The formula is $Ca_3(PO_4)_2$.

For each S^{2-} we need two NH_4^+. The formula is $(NH_4)_2S$.

A NATURAL APPROACH TO CHEMISTRY

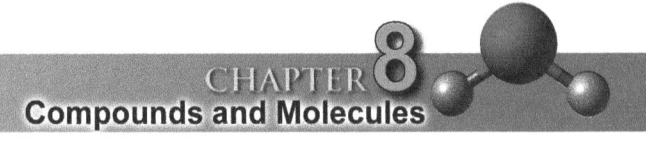

Writing names for ionic compounds

Naming binary ionic compounds

When naming an ionic compound, you just write the names of the ions as they appear in the formula. For simple binary ionic compounds (ionic formulas from two single-atom ions), such as NaCl, the first part of the name is just the name of the element, and the second part of the name is a modified version of the name of the element. Typically, you drop the standard ending and add -ide.

NaF

Use name of element → Change fluorine to fluoride

sodium fluoride

BaCl$_2$

Use name of element → Change chlorine to chloride

barium chloride

Names for polyatomic ions are found on the common ion table

For polyatomic ions you will need to get the name from the table below. Otherwise, it is done the same way as it is for binary ionic compounds. Write the name of the ions in the order that they appear in the formula.

MgCO$_3$

Use name of element → Get name of polyatomic ion from table

magnesium carbonate

(NH$_4$)$_2$SO$_4$

Get name of polyatomic ion from table → Get name of polyatomic ion from table

ammonium sulfate

TABLE 8.1. Common ions

Positive ions				Negative ions			
Aluminum	Al^{3+}	Lead(II)	Pb^{2+}	Acetate	C$_2$H$_3$O$_2$$^-$	Hydrogen sulfate (bisulfate)	HSO$_4$$^-$
Ammonium	NH^{4+}	Lead(IV)	Pb^{4+}	Chloride	Cl$^-$	Hydroxide	OH$^-$
Barium	Ba^{2+}	Magnesium	Mg^{2+}	Carbonate	CO$_3$$^{2-}$	Hydroxide	OH$^-$
Copper(I)	Cu$^+$	Mercury(I)	Hg^{2+}	Chromate	CrO$_4$$^{2-}$	Nitrate	NO$_3$$^-$
Copper(II)	Cu^{2+}	Mercury(II)	Hg^{2+}	Chlorate	ClO$_3$$^-$	Nitrite	NO$_2$$^-$
Calcium	Ca^{2+}	Potassium	K$^+$	Chlorite	ClO$_2$$^-$	Oxide	O^{2-}
Chromium(II)	Cr^{2+}	Silver	Ag$^+$	Cyanide	CN$^-$	Peroxide	O$_2$$^{2-}$
Chromium(III)	Cr^{3+}	Sodium	Na$^+$	Dichromate	Cr$_2$O$_7$$^{2-}$	Phosphate	PO$_4$$^{3-}$
Hydrogen*	H$^+$	Tin(II)	Sn2$^+$	Fluoride	F$^-$	Sulfate	SO$_4$$^{2-}$
Iron(II)	Fe^{2+}	Tin(IV)	Sn4$^+$	Hydrogen carbonate (bicarbonate) HCO$_3$$^-$		Sulfite	SO$_3$$^{2-}$
Iron(III)	Fe^{3+}	Zinc	Zn^{2+}			Sulfide	S^{2-}

*Hydrogen ions rarely exist by themselves. Often they combine with water to form hydronium ions (H$_3$O$^+$).

Ionic naming with transition metals

Roman numerals in the ion name

In the previous table you will see several names for positive ions that are followed by a Roman numeral. This number describes the charge on that ion. Most transition metals can have multiple charges, so to know which charge the ion should have when naming the compound, you need to specify it with a Roman numeral.

A Roman numeral indicates the charge on a positive ion

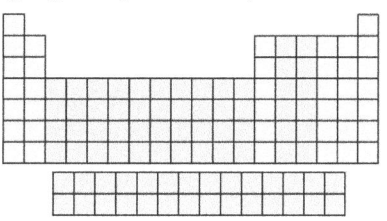

1 = I	6 = VI
2 = II	7 = VII
3 = III	8 = VIII
4 = IV	9 = IX
5 = V	10 = X

The common ion table

Since the transition metals and those metals in groups 14 and 15 can form varying charges, you need to check the common ion table before you write the name of an ionic compound that includes one of those elements. Most transition metals do, but there are two common exceptions: silver and zinc. Silver almost always forms a +1 ion and zinc a +2 ion, so you don't need Roman numerals in names of silver or zinc compounds.

Need to check whether a Roman numeral is necessary for elements in highlighted part of the periodic table

Pb is one of the elements to check for multiple charges. The ion table shows common ions for lead are Pb^{+2} and Pb^{+4}, so you need to use the negative ion to determine the charge on the positive one:

$$Pb^{?+} \quad \begin{array}{c} Cl^- \\ Cl^- \end{array}$$

Total charge from ions ⟶ +2   −2

With only one Pb ion and a total charge of +2 needed, the Pb ion must be lead(II)

PbCl₂

lead(II) chloride

ZnSO₄

Zinc sulfate

Zinc needs to be checked, but the ion table shows it only forms a +2 charged ion, so no Roman numeral is needed

---

Solved problem

Write names for each of the following formulas: $CaCl_2$, $Zn(NO_3)_2$, $Fe_3(PO_4)_2$.

Asked: *Names for the formulas above*

Given: *Three formulas and a common ion table*

Relationships: *The name of each formula is constructed from the name of the ions. If the negative ion is a single atom, modify the name of the element to end in "ide." If the positive ion might form multiple charges, make sure to use a Roman numeral in the name.*

Solve: *$CaCl_2$ is calcium chloride.*

$Zn(NO_3)_2$ is zinc nitrate.

$Fe_3(PO_4)_2$ is iron(II) phosphate.

8.2 Molecular Compounds

Properties of molecular substances

Properties of molecular compounds vary widely compared to those of ionic compounds:

- Some are hard and brittle, but others are flexible, soft, or mushy.
- They could be solid, liquid, or gas at room temperature.
- Their boiling points vary from –253°C to over 4,800°C.
- Most are nonelectrolytes. When dissolved in a solvent, they do not typically conduct electricity.

A molecule is the building block of a molecular substance

The properties of molecular substances depend on two things: the structure of the individual molecule, including the types of covalent bonds formed within the molecule, and the attractions between molecules. Take water for example. The smallest piece of water you can have is a single water molecule. However, when we think of water we imagine a drop, or a cup, or an ocean. One cup of water is made from approximately eight million billion billion (8×10^{24}) water molecules. They bounce off of each other, are constantly in motion, and form no particular crystalline organization when in liquid form. As ice, water can form an organized crystal structure, and in that form it has the property of being hard and brittle like an ionic compound. The great variety of structures possible with molecular substances is what gives them their great variation in properties.

An individual molecule of water

About eight million billion billion (10^{24}) water molecules make up this cup of water

Molecules can be classified into different categories

First we will look at the different types of molecular building blocks. Let's study how their interactions affect the overall properties of the substances made of those molecules. Molecules can be classified as small, medium, or large. Within the large category there are polymers and network covalent substances.

Small

Medium

Large: polymer

Large: network

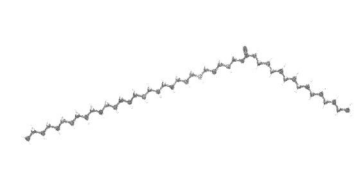

Caffeine, found in tea, coffee, and soda

Wax, one of the main hydrocarbons in beeswax

Protein, molecule on the right shows a thick line tracing the linear chain, with red and blue marking either end

Graphene, layers of which make graphite

Small molecules

Most small molecules are liquids or gases at room temperature

Small molecules are those that are constructed from about a dozen atoms or less. There is no specific number of atoms that puts a molecule in the "small" category, but substances made from small molecules tend to have some similar properties. They are almost always gases or liquids at room temperature and include some of the most important molecules related to the functioning of our entire ecosystem. Often they are over-the-counter drugs, such as acetaminophen, which in its pure form is a liquid.

Acetaminophen

The lower density of ice, compared to liquid water, made the evolution of human life possible

Water is a good example. A single polar water molecule is made from only three atoms, but this molecular substance is essential for life. Water allows the rest of the molecules in our body to organize themselves. When it freezes, the solid form is less dense than the liquid form, a very unusual characteristic. If ice were more dense, then lakes, ponds, and even oceans could freeze solid in cold weather, killing all higher life forms and preventing the evolution of anything beyond the simplest of creatures.

If ice did not float, ponds would freeze from the bottom up killing everything inside.

Most common gases are small molecules

Carbon dioxide and oxygen fall into the small-molecule category as well. These are all gases at room temperature, and it is not by chance that they are all nonpolar. Carbon dioxide is a greenhouse gas, but it is also crucial for the lives of plants, which use the carbon to build up their physical structures and as a temporary chemical storage for the light energy absorbed by their leaves. Typically it is the polarity of the molecule that makes the difference between it being liquid or gas at room temperature.

Some other small molecules you may be familiar with are ethene, which is a nonpolar gas given off by ripening fruit, and ethanol, which is almost the same size but polar and is liquid at room temperature. Ethanol is produced when fruits and other sugar-containing material ferment, making what is commonly called alcohol.

Ethene

Ethanol

nonpolar (gas at room temperature)
boiling point = −103.7°C

polar (liquid at room temperature)
boiling point = 78.4°C

Medium-sized molecules

Liquid or soft solids

Medium-sized molecules are those that are typically formed from more atoms than small molecules, but not much more than 100 atoms. As with small molecules, there is a significant variety of molecule types that fall into the "medium" category, but they tend to share some properties. Typically, they are liquids or soft solids at room temperature, and they often fall into one of two official chemical categories: lipids or long-chain hydrocarbons.

Candle wax is a mixture of medium-sized hydrocarbons

Lipids

Lipids are typically fats or steroids, which are molecules primarily made from carbon and hydrogen. They may include small numbers of other elements. Depending on the size and shape of a fat molecule, the substance made from those molecules might be liquid or solid at room temperature, for example vegetable oil or butter. Lipids are typically nonpolar and insoluble in water.

Linoleic acid, a major component of vegetable oil.

Steroids are another type of lipid

Steroids also fall into the lipid category but have a larger percentage of atoms that are not hydrogen or carbon. Most have four rings of carbon atoms, and could function as hormones, drugs, vitamins, or poisons. Anabolic steroids, which are used as performance-enhancing drugs, all mimic the shape and function of testosterone, a natural steroid.

Testosterone

Hydrocarbons

Hydrocarbons are molecules formed purely from long chains of hydrogen and carbon atoms. They are very similar to fats, except they lack the typical oxygen atoms that are part of the fatty acids produced in living organisms. Medium-sized hydrocarbons tend to form soft solids like petroleum jelly, and ones made from even larger numbers of atoms tend to form harder substances like wax.

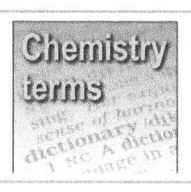
Chemistry terms

lipid: a molecule that typically falls into the category of fat or steroid.

steroid: a molecule with four carbon rings that is biologically active as a hormone, vitamin, drug, or poison.

hydrocarbon: a molecule made entirely from carbon and hydrogen atoms.

Polymers made from a single monomer

Polymers and monomers

The prefix "poly" means "many," which is appropriate for the kinds of molecules we call polymers. **Polymers** are made from many smaller molecules. The smaller molecules that covalently bond together to make polymers are called **monomers**. All of the plastic in the world is made of various kinds of polymers. The recycling numbers on bottles and packages indicate which kind of plastic or polymer the object is made from. Number 3, for example, is polyvinyl chloride (PVC), which is made into pipes and siding. Many vinyl chloride monomers bond together to form long chains, making individual polyvinyl chloride molecules that consist of hundreds or thousands of atoms.

Recycling symbols and polymer codes

$\triangle 1 \triangle$ = PETE $\triangle 4 \triangle$ = LDPE

$\triangle 2 \triangle$ = HDPE $\triangle 5 \triangle$ = PP

$\triangle 3 \triangle$ = PVC $\triangle 6 \triangle$ = PS

$\triangle 7 \triangle$ = Other

A single monomer of vinyl chloride

Polyvinyl chloride (PVC) made by bonding many vinyl chloride monomers together

A single polymer chain typically contains hundreds to thousands of atoms

Polymers can be synthetic

Plastics are synthetic polymers, typically made in labs and factories. However, many natural polymers exist. The simple sugar glucose is a key monomer for making two different natural polymers: starch and cellulose. By bonding the glucose monomers together in a slightly different way, you either get something we can digest, such as starch, which is found in many foods such as bread, pasta, and potatoes, or something we can't digest, such as cellulose, which is what wood, paper, and most plant material are made from.

Glucose
a natural monomer

Starch fragment

Cellulose fragment

Both are polymers of glucose, but the glucose monomer is bonded together slightly differently in starch. Note the pattern of "purple" oxygen atoms where the monomers are bonded together

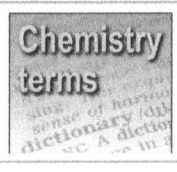
Chemistry terms

polymer: a long chain molecule formed by connecting small repeating units with covalent bonds.

monomer: a small molecule that is a building block of larger molecules called polymers.

A NATURAL APPROACH TO CHEMISTRY

Polymers made from multiple monomers

A single polymer can be made from more than one type of monomer

Each of the polymers we saw on the previous page was made from a single type of monomer. Sometimes more than one monomer is used. DNA is a polymer that uses four different monomers that biologists call nucle-otides. Proteins are constructed from up to 20 different monomers called amino acids. To distinguish between these two types of polymers, we use the term **homopolymer** to refer to polymers made from only one type of monomer; **copolymer** describes polymers made from multiple types of monomers.

DNA fragment colored by base and backbone

- sugar-phosphate backbone
- adenine
- thymine
- guanine
- cytosine

The four monomers used to make strands of DNA
(colored to correspond to the polymer above)

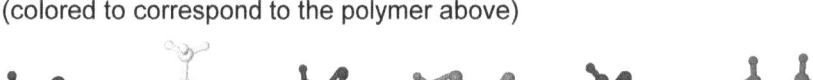

dAMP   dTMP   dGMP   dCMP

DNA: the code for building proteins

DNA is the molecule that provides the code necessary to build proteins. The proteins are built by adding one monomer (amino acid) at a time. The order of the amino acids in the protein polymer is based upon the order of the monomers (bases) in the DNA. Once the full protein is made, various parts of the molecule attract to itself, causing it to form into a particular shape, giving the protein a specific function.

A folded protein molecule

Four of these bind together to form hemoglobin, the protein complex in blood cells that transports oxygen

An unfolded protein fragment

Proteins are made from up to 20 different amino acids. Here they are colored by amino acid, so you can see each monomer clearly.

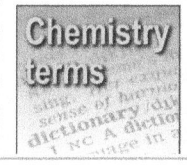

homopolymer: a molecule made from repeatedly bonding the same monomer together.

copolymer: a molecule made from repeatedly bonding more than one type of monomer together.

Network covalent molecules

Network
covalent

Usually, when we think of molecules we think of things so small that we can't even see them with a normal microscope. However, when you see sand, it is likely that at least some of the individual sand grains are actually made from a single individual molecule. Sand is usually a mixture of many different minerals, but the most common one is quartz, which is made from silicon and oxygen. Each silicon atom is covalently bonded to four neighboring oxygen atoms, and each oxygen atom is bonded to two neighboring silicon atoms. Since every atom in quartz is covalently bonded together, the entire grain can be considered a single molecule. Molecules in which large numbers of atoms are covalently bonded in an interlocking way are called **network covalent**.

Silicon dioxide

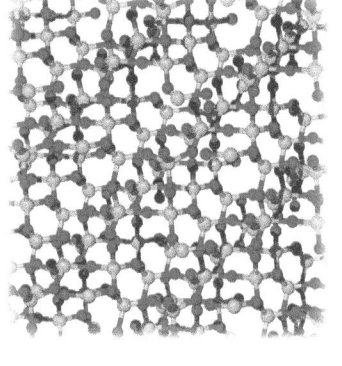

Carbon

Carbon is special because it can form many different kinds of network covalent substances, some of which have amazing properties and were among the first substances to bring about the era of nanotechnology. Below are several forms of carbon. Diamond and graphite are commonly found in nature, whereas buckyballs and nanotubes are primarily synthesized in labs. Buckyballs do occur in nature, but in only small amounts.

Carbon forms many types of network covalent substances

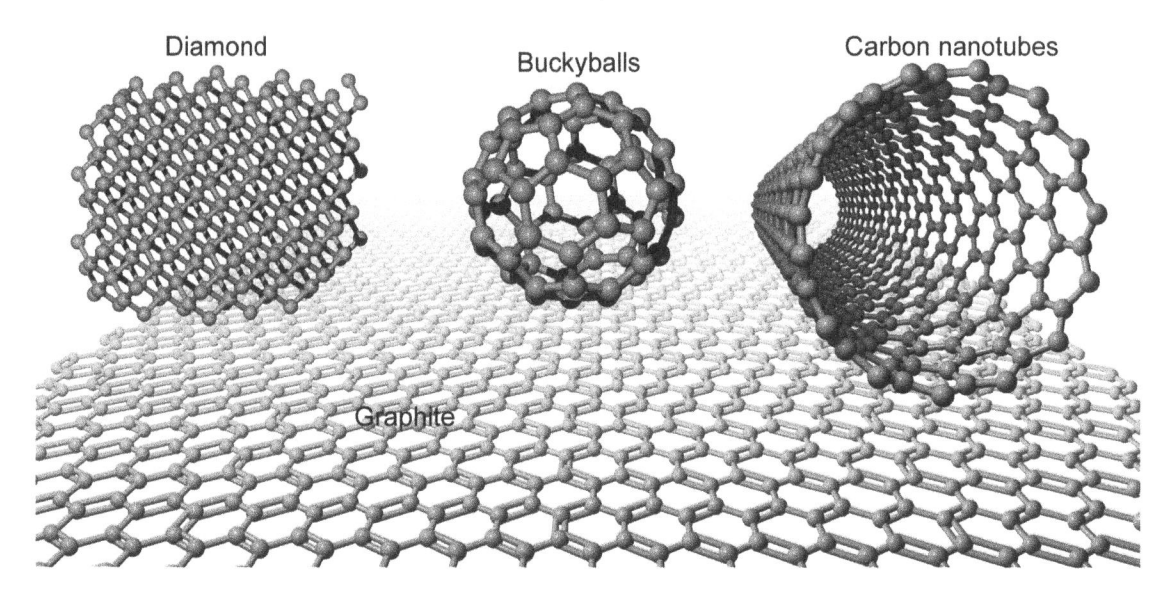

Diamond

Buckyballs

Carbon nanotubes

Graphite

Chemistry terms

network covalent: a type of large molecule, usually made from hundreds to billions of atoms, in which each atom is covalently bonded to multiple neighboring atoms, forming a web of connections.

Chemical formulas of covalent compounds

Molecular substances have a smallest piece

With ionic compounds, the formula indicates the ratio of ions in the compound. This makes sense, because there is no specific boundary between each "piece" of the ionic crystal. In other words, there is no specific group of ions within the larger structure of the substance that we would isolate for any special reason. In molecular substances, such as water or ethanol, there is a "smallest piece" that is significant—a single molecule of that substance.

A sample of ionic or network covalent substance is a single bonded unit of material

Empirical formulas

Network covalent substances are treated more like ionic substances in which the ratio of elements is used. This is because the large number of covalently bonded atoms forms a single unit, just like the large number of bonded ions do in ionic substances. For example, the formula for quartz is SiO_2, indicating that in a grain of typical quartz-based sand, the ratio of silicon to oxygen will be 1:2. A formula that describes the simplest ratio of elements in a substance is called an **empirical formula**.

A molecular (non network) substance is made from weakly attracted molecules

⌐ a molecule of water

Molecular formulas

Chemical formulas for most molecular substances indicate the exact type and number of each atom in a single molecule of that substance. This is called a **molecular formula**. The elements in a molecular formula are ordered alphabetically, unlike in ionic compounds where the positive ion is listed first. Sometimes the empirical formula is the same as the molecular formula, as is the case for water (H_2O), but sometimes the molecular formula is not the empirical formula, as is the case for benzene (C_6H_6).

Benzene

empirical formula: CH
molecular formula: C_6H_6

Solved problem

Write the molecular formula for each of the following molecules:

A   **B**   **C**

Asked: *The molecular formula*

Relationships: *The formula should reflect the exact number and type of atoms in an individual molecule of the substance.*

Solve: *A. C_2H_2 B. NH_3 C. C_2H_5O*

Naming simple binary molecular compounds

Organic
molecules

Molecular substances vary so much in their basic structures that different naming systems are used depending upon the molecule. **Organic molecules** (those made primarily of carbon, hydrogen, oxygen, and the halides) have an entire complex naming system dedicated to that class of substance. In this chapter we will look at naming simple binary molecular substance, or those made from only two elements.

Naming organic
molecules can
be complex.

2-benzyl-1,1-dichlorocyclobutane

Binary molecular
compounds have
simpler names.

carbon dioxide

Naming simple
organic mole-
cules

Naming these simple inorganic molecules is much easier than with ionic substances, because there is a basic two-step procedure for creating the name:

1. Write down the name of the compound as if it were a simple binary ionic compound.

2. Add prefixes to each name that tell you how many of that atom are in the molecule. (Note: If there is only one atom of the first element in the molecule, omit the "mono" prefix from the name.)

Prefix definitions
mono = 1
di = 2
tri = 3
tetra = 4
penta = 5
hexa = 6
hepta = 7
octa = 8
nona = 9
deca = 10

Two phosphorous atoms with three sulfur atoms **P$_2$S$_3$**

Water has another name **H$_2$O**

If there is only one of the first element drop the "mono" **CO**

diphosphorous **tri**sulfide   dihydrogen **mon**oxide   carbon **mon**oxide

Solved problem

Write the name for each of the following formulas: N$_2$O$_4$, S$_2$F$_{10}$, and SO$_3$.

Asked: *Names of the formulas*

Given: *Three formulas and a table of prefix names*

Relationships: *The name of the formula is constructed from the simple ionic name with prefixes before each element, indicating the number of each atom.*

Solve: *N$_2$O$_4$ is dinitrogen tetraoxide.*
S$_2$F$_{10}$ is disulfur decafluoride.
SO$_3$ is sulfur trioxide.

Chemistry terms

empirical formula: the simplest ratio of atoms in a substance.

molecular formula: the exact number and types of atoms in a molecule.

organic molecule: a molecule primarily made from carbon and hydrogen, but often with some oxygen, nitrogen, one of the halides, or some other nonmetal atoms.

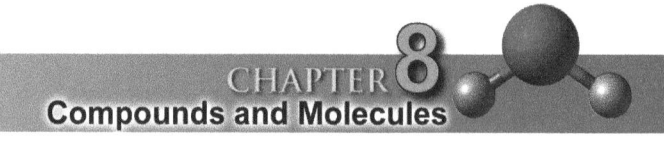
8.3 Intermolecular Forces

Why do molecules stick together in liquids and solids?

Ionic substances stay together through the attraction between positive and negative ions. Network covalent substances stay together because all the molecules or atoms are interconnected. What about water? What force attracts water molecules to other water molecules in a liquid or a solid?

Water is polar, so the partially positive hydrogen atom from one water molecule is attracted to the partially negative oxygen atom on another molecule

intermolecular attraction

Intermolecular and van der Waals attractions

We learned in an earlier chapter that all atoms and molecules are in continuous motion, so why don't the individual molecules, which are moving at extremely high velocity at room temperature, bounce off of each other and form a gas? Why are there liquid and solid molecular substances? The answer must be that the molecules stick to each other. These attractions between molecules are called **intermolecular attractions** and are sometimes referred to as **van der Waals attractions**. These attractions are much weaker than ionic or covalent bonds, which tend to be 100 to 1,000 times stronger than intermolecular attractions.

A tiny drop of water

Dipole–dipole and London dispersion attractions

There are two broad categories of intermolecular attractions: dipole–dipole attractions and London dispersion attractions. All molecules attract to each other using the London dispersion–type attraction. However, for polar molecules the dipole–dipole attraction tends to be the more important intermolecular force owing to higher strength of the dipole–dipole attraction. There is one kind of dipole–dipole attraction that is significantly stronger, so it has been given a special name—hydrogen bonding. We will look at each of these kinds of attractions in more detail on the following pages.

intermolecular attractions → attractions between polar molecules → dipole–dipole and hydrogen bonding

intermolecular attractions → attractions between nonpolar molecules → London dispersion

Chemistry terms

intermolecular attractions: the attractions between molecules.

van der Waals attractions: another term used to describe the attractions between molecules, typically referred to as "intermolecular attractions," but associated with the London dispersion type of intermolecular attraction.

Dipole–dipole attractions

Some molecules are polar and form dipole–dipole attractions

Some molecules are polar because they have some polar covalent bonds as part of their structure. This means that at least one part of the molecule will be partially positive and another part will be partially negative. This allows for the attractions between the oppositely charged parts of different molecules. The attraction between two polar molecules is called a **dipole–dipole attraction**. In the case of very long polymers like proteins, different parts of the same molecule can attract each other, stabilizing its overall structure.

Polar formaldehyde

The polar covalent C=O bond makes the entire molecule polar

Formaldehyde is a substance used as a preservative, and it is a polar molecule. Because the molecule is polar, dipole-dipole attractions will form between the molecules.

The green dotted lines represent dipole-dipole attractions between the molecules, which cause formaldehyde to condense into a liquid at room temperature.

The more polar a molecule is, the stronger it will attract other molecules

The strength of the attraction between polar molecules can be measured by their boiling points. The higher the boiling point, the stronger the individual molecules cluster together, preventing them from separating and forming a gas. More polar molecules have higher boiling points. Usually, when we talk about a molecule being more polar than another, we mean that it has more polar covalent bonds. Oxygen has a high electronegativity, so when oxygen is added to a molecule polar covalent bonds form, causing the molecule to become polar (or more polar). Anytime atoms with high electronegativity are part of a molecule, it is usually a polar molecule.

Higher polarity molecules attract more strongly

propane

boiling point = −42°C

least polar

1-propanol

boiling point = 97°C

1,3-propanediol

boiling point = 214°C

most polar

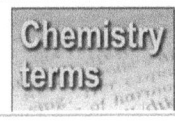

Chemistry terms

dipole–dipole attraction: the attractions between the positive part of one polar molecule and the negative part of another polar molecule.

246

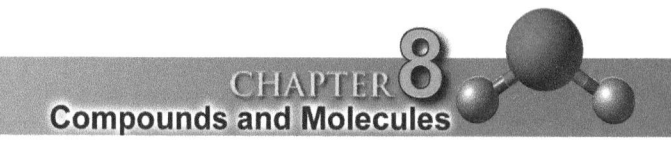

Hydrogen bonding and the special role of water

Hydrogen bonding

In many cases, a polar covalent bond is formed between hydrogen and nitrogen or oxygen. Since there is a moderate difference in electronegativity between hydrogen and either nitrogen or oxygen, you get a polar covalent bond with hydrogen becoming partially positive. When two molecules form a dipole–dipole attraction between hydrogen on one molecule and nitrogen or oxygen on another molecule, the attraction is stronger than other dipole–dipole attractions, so we give it a special name: **hydrogen bonding**.

Hydrogen bonds in liquid water

Water has special properties

Water is composed of only oxygen and hydrogen, so hydrogen bonds form between water molecules and between water and other polar molecules with similar kinds of bonds. The unique physical and chemical properties of water explain why it is so important. For example, when water freezes, it becomes *less* dense! Most materials are *more* dense as solids than as liquids. Ice is less dense than liquid water because hydrogen bonds force water molecules to align in a crystal structure where molecules are farther apart than they are in a liquid.

Iceburg photo curtesy of NOAA

Surface tension

Another feature of water and other polar liquids is **surface tension**. As water molecules pull together they tend to form spherical drops. That's why water drops are round. At the surface of liquid water the molecules pull together, forming a skin. This is how water striders are able to walk across the water instead of sinking into it.

Surface tension from hydrogen bonds allows a water strider to "walk" on water

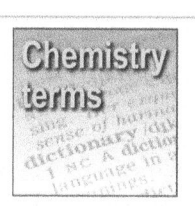
Chemistry terms

hydrogen bonding: in water, the attractions between the partially positive hydrogen from one polar molecule to the partially negative oxygen or nitrogen on another polar molecule.

surface tension: a force acting to pull a liquid surface into the smallest possible area, for example, pulling a droplet of water into a sphere.

Other examples of hydrogen bonding

DNA is held together with hydrogen bonds

When we refer to DNA, we usually mean the spiralling polymer that encodes all the genetic information needed by an organism to function and reproduce. In fact, DNA is really two molecules spiraling around and attracted to each other. To read the code, the two strands of DNA must be separated from each other and then go back together. It is hydrogen bonding that holds the DNA strands together, but not so strongly that they can't be separated and have the genetic code do its job.

DNA uses hydrogen bonds to hold the two strands together

Hydrogen bonds influence protein shapes

In proteins, the shape of the molecule is one of its most important features, giving the molecule a specific function. Many forces help to shape the molecule into its final form, and hydrogen bonding plays a key role. Two common structures that are found in proteins are the alpha helix and the beta sheet. Both of these structures are stabilized by forming hydrogen bonds across different parts of the same molecule.

| **Ball-and-stick view of small protein** | **View with backbone trace to see folding pattern** | **Protein structure stabilized with H bonds** |

PVA

Paper glue is a mixture of the polymer polyvinyl acetate (PVA) and water. When water is present the glue is a liquid, allowing the long polymer molecules to flow by each other. As the water evaporates, the long PVA molecules attract each other directly, forming many hydrogen bonds and locking the molecules in place, forming a solid.

In normal "wet" glue, polymer molecules are "lubricated" by water

As glue dries, many more H-bonds form between the polymer molecules, so the glue hardens

London dispersion attraction

Nonpolar
molecules
can change

Even nonpolar molecules cluster together into liquids and solids, so there must be an attraction between them even if it is usually much weaker than the dipole–dipole-type attractions. In fact, when two nonpolar molecules come very close to each other, they can become very slightly polar and stabilize each other. This polarization is temporary and easily disrupted by the motions of molecules, yet it is enough to allow them to condense together. This attraction between nonpolar molecules is called the **London dispersion attraction**.

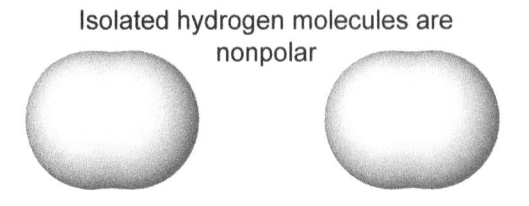
Isolated hydrogen molecules are nonpolar

A temporary, very slight polarity can be induced when nonpolar molecules are close enough
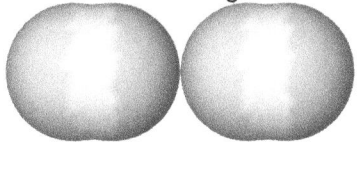

Large-surface-
area molecules

If a molecule is large enough, then there is more surface area over which it can form these temporary attractions, so even nonpolar molecules can be solids at room temperature. However, they tend to be soft solids, such as wax or butter.

Molecules with larger surface area attract more strongly

propane
boiling point = –42°C
least surface area

butane
boiling point = 0°C

pentane
boiling point = 36°C
most surface area

Getting close
counts

The key to stronger overall attractions between nonpolar molecules is not just size. All intermolecular attractions are only felt when molecules are very close, so molecules that can pack together more tightly also have an advantage.

The molecules on the left and right both have about the same surface area. However, the bent shape of the molecules on the right prevents them from forming as strong a London dispersion attraction as the molecules on the left.

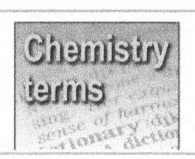
Chemistry terms

London dispersion attraction: the attraction that occurs between nonpolar molecules owing to temporary slight polarizations that occur when the normally equal distribution of electrons is shifted.

8.4 Formula Masses

Chemical forensics

By measuring the different amount of elements used to make a particular substance, we can determine its formula and often identify the specific substance. The field of chemical forensics is focused on determining the identities of unknown substances. Often these are collected at crime scenes, but they might also be found at archeological digs, in a biology lab, during production of new materials, or from other sources.

A scientist working for the National Water Quality Assessment Program

Molar mass and molecular formulas

To be able to understand the data produced from various chemical analyses, we need to clearly understand what a chemical formula tells us. You learned the basics of this in Chapter 2, but we'll look at some more advanced formulas here. For many calculations you need to know the molar mass of a substance. To calculate this, you need to be able to use the formula to determine how many moles of each atom type there are in a mole of that substance.

Atomic mass is the molar mass for that element

Calculating molar mass

Subscripts apply only to the element or group they follow

If the subscript follows a parenthesis, then multiply everything inside the parentheses by the subscript

H_2SO_4

$H = 2 \times 1.0079 = 2.02$

$S = 1 \times 32.07 = 32.07$

$O = 4 \times 15.999 = \underline{64.00}$

molar mass $\rightarrow 98.08 \; \frac{g}{mole}$

$(NH_4)_3PO_4$

$N = 3 \times 14.007 = 42.02$

$H = 12 \times 1.0079 = 12.09$

$P = 1 \times 30.974 = 30.97$

$O = 4 \times 15.999 = \underline{64.00}$

molar mass $\rightarrow 149.08 \; \frac{g}{mole}$

Solved problem

What is the molar mass of aluminum carbonate? *Before going on, discuss with your classmates what the chemical formula for aluminum carbonate is.*

Asked: *The molar mass*

Given: *The name of the formula*

Relationships: *The name of the formula can be used to determine the ratios of elements in the formula. Then the periodic table can be used to get the molar mass of each of the elements used.*

Solve: *Aluminum carbonate is ionic, so the formula is $Al_2(CO_3)_3$.*

$$Al = 2 \times 26.98 = 53.96 \; g/mole$$
$$C = 3 \times 12.011 = 36.03 \; g/mole$$
$$O = 9 \times 15.999 = \underline{144.00 \; g/mole}$$
$$molar \; mass = 239.99 \; g/mole$$

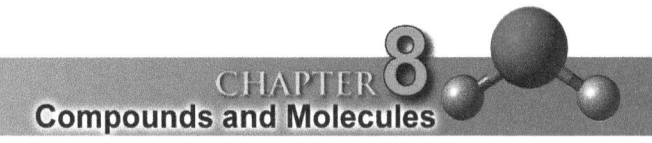

Percent composition

Mass percent composition

One way to identify compounds is by the percent mass of each element. This is like a fingerprint for a particular compound. To calculate the percentage of each element you need to know the total mass of your compound and the mass of each individual element.

% by atom number
Na = 50%   Cl = 50%

$NaCl$

% by mass
Na = 39%   Cl = 61%

Calculating a percent

$$\% \text{ by mass} = \frac{\text{mass of element in the compound}}{\text{total mass of the compound}} \times 100$$

Calculate percent composition

Calculating % using a formula
1. Calculate the molar mass.
2. Calculate the percent of each element in a mole of the substance.

Calculating % with a measured sample
1. Add up the individual mass measurements to get the total mass.
2. Calculate the percentage as above.

Ca_3PO_4

$$
\begin{aligned}
Ca &= 3 \times 40.078 &= 120.24 \text{ g / mole} \\
P &= 1 \times 30.974 &= 30.97 \text{ g / mole} \\
O &= 4 \times 15.999 &= 64.00 \text{ g / mole} \\
& \text{molar mass} &= 149.12 \text{ g / mole}
\end{aligned}
$$

$$
\begin{aligned}
\%Ca &= \frac{120.24}{149.12} \times 100 &= 38.76\% \\
\%P &= \frac{30.97}{149.12} \times 100 &= 19.97\% \\
\%O &= \frac{64.00}{149.12} \times 100 &= 41.27\%
\end{aligned}
$$

Solved problem

A white powder can be broken down into 1.05 g of C, 0.16 g of H_2, and 1.29 g of O_2. Is this powder common table sugar, also known as sucrose ($C_{12}H_{22}O_{11}$)?

Asked: *Whether the unknown powder is sugar*

Given: *The mass of each element in the powder and the formula for sugar.*

Relationships: *The percentage of each element should match the percent composition of sugar if the powder is a sample of that substance.*

Solve: *Calculate the % composition of sugar and the unknown compound.*

sucrose
$$
\begin{aligned}
C &= 12 \times 12.01 &= 144.13 \text{ g/mole} \\
H &= 22 \times 1.0079 &= 22.17 \text{ g/mole} \\
O &= 11 \times 15.999 &= 175.99 \text{ g/mole} \\
& \text{molar mass} &= 342.29 \text{ g/mole}
\end{aligned}
$$

$$
\begin{aligned}
\%C &= \frac{144.13}{342.29} \times 100 &= 42.1\% \\
\%H &= \frac{22.17}{342.29} \times 100 &= 6.5\% \\
\%O &= \frac{175.99}{342.29} \times 100 &= 51.4\%
\end{aligned}
$$

unknown
$$
\begin{aligned}
C &= 1.05 \text{ g} \\
H &= 0.16 \text{ g} \\
O &= 1.29 \text{ g} \\
\text{total} &= 2.50 \text{ g}
\end{aligned}
$$

$$
\begin{aligned}
\%C &= \frac{1.05}{2.50} \times 100 &= 42.0\% \\
\%H &= \frac{0.16}{2.50} \times 100 &= 6.4\% \\
\%O &= \frac{1.29}{2.50} \times 100 &= 51.6\%
\end{aligned}
$$

YES!

The percent composition is very close, so the unknown is probably sugar.

Calculating empirical formulas

The simplest ratio of atoms

An empirical formula gives the simplest ratio of elements in a compound. All ionic formulas and many molecular formulas are empirical. Table salt is a one-to-one ratio of sodium to chloride. A typical grain of salt contains about a billion billion ions. Should we write $Na_{1000000000000000000}Cl_{100000000000000000}$? What about salt crystals that are bigger or smaller? The simplest way is to write the empirical formula, showing the most basic ratio, in this case NaCl.

The empirical formula is the one with the simplest ratio

Not empirical: All show the same ratio, but not in its simplest form	Na_2Cl_2 Na_5Cl_5 $Na_{12}Cl_{12}$
The empirical formula for sodium chloride is a simple 1:1 ratio	NaCl

Finding the mole ratio of atoms

To calculate the empirical formula for a substance, you need to know the ratio of atoms. In one mole of NaCl there will be one mole of Na^+ ions and one mole of Cl^- ions. The way chemists count atoms (or moles of atoms) is by measuring their mass, so you will typically start with a mass that needs to be converted to moles to find the mole ratio.

Calculating an empirical formula

Convert grams to moles
Assume you have a sample that is 0.504 g hydrogen and 4.00 g oxygen

$$H = 0.504\,g \times \frac{1\,mole}{1.01\,g} = 0.500\,mole$$

$$O = 4.00\,g \times \frac{1\,mole}{16.00\,g} = 0.250\,mole$$

Simplify the mole ratio
Divide each answer by the smallest number of moles

$$H = \frac{0.500}{0.250} = 2$$

$$O = \frac{0.250}{0.250} = 1$$

Write the formula

$$H_2O$$

Solved problem

A jar of powder is labeled copper oxide, but you do not know whether the copper is Cu^+ or Cu^{+2}. After taking a small sample you find that it is made from 2.96 g of copper and 0.37 g of oxygen. What is the correct name and formula for the ionic compound in that jar?

Asked: *The correct name and formula for the compound in the jar*

Given: *The mass of each element in a small sample of the powder*

Relationships: *The mole ratio of elements can be simplified to give an empirical formula.*

Solve: *Convert the grams to moles and then simplify the ratio.*

$$Cu = 2.96\,g \times \frac{1\,mole}{63.55\,g} = 0.0466\,mole$$

$$O = 0.37\,g \times \frac{1\,mole}{15.999\,g} = 0.023\,mole$$

$$\frac{0.0466\,mole}{0.023\,mole} = 2.0$$

$$\frac{0.023\,mole}{0.023\,mole} = 1.0$$

The mole ratio is 2 moles of Cu to 1 mole of O, so the formula is Cu_2O, and the name is copper(I) oxide.

Calculating molecular formulas

Sugar and salt crystals

Like a grain of salt, a grain of sugar contains billions and billions of atoms. However, there is a significant difference between the structure of a sugar crystal and that of a salt crystal. In the ionic salt crystal, every atom is bonded with strong chemical bonds to all its neighboring atoms. In the sugar crystal, small clusters of atoms are strongly bonded to form a molecule. These molecules are weakly attracted to each other through intermolecular attractions to form the overall crystal.

A molecule of glucose has six carbon atoms, twelve oxygen atoms, and six hydrogen atoms

Molecular formula

$C_6H_{12}O_6$

Importance of the molecular formula

For the sugar glucose, the cluster of covalently bonded atoms (the glucose molecule) is made from 6 carbons, 12 hydrogens, and 6 oxygens. That means that the smallest possible piece of glucose is a molecule with the formula $C_6H_{12}O_6$. Looking at that ratio of 6:12:6, you will see that by dividing everything by six you can simplify it to 1:2:1, giving the empirical formula CH_2O. For covalently bonded compounds it is the *molecular* formula that is crucial, because CH_2O is the molecular formula for formaldehyde, not glucose. For formaldehyde, the empirical formula is the same as the molecular formula, a situation that is often true even for molecular compounds.

The molecular formula is a multiple of the empirical formula

To find the molecular formula, you need one more piece of information than you needed for finding the empirical formula—the molar mass of the substance. The molecular formula will always be equal to, or a multiple of, the empirical formula.

Empirical formula		Molecular formula
CH_2O	x6	$C_6H_{12}O_6$
$30.03 \frac{g}{mole}$	x6	$180.16 \frac{g}{mole}$

Solved problem

Given the following empirical formulas and molar masses, determine the molecular formula for each one: CH (78.11 g/mole) and H_2O (18.02 g/mole).

Asked: *The molecular formula for two compounds*

Given: *The empirical formula and the molar mass of the compound*

Relationships: *The ratio of molar mass of the empirical formula to the molar mass of the compound will give a factor. Multiply the empirical formula by this factor to get the molecular formula.*

Solve: *Divide the molar mass of substance by the molar mass of the empirical formula; multiply the empirical formula by the result.*

calculate empirical molar mass   determine multiple   calculate molecular formula

$CH = 12.011 + 1.0079 = 13.018$ g/mole $\frac{78.11}{13.02} = 6$ $6 \times CH = C_6H_6$

$H_2O = 2(1.0079) + 15.999 = 18.015$ g/mole $\frac{18.02}{18.02} = 1$ $1 \times H_2O = H_2O$

Nanotechnology: food, cosmetics, and medicine

Nanotechnology is a very important and exciting new area in science. The hope with nanotechnology is that we can build molecules atom by atom! We can't do this yet, but it is quite possible that scientists will be able to soon. Nanotechnology has broad applications in all of the core areas of science.

A nanometer (nm) is 10^{-9} meters, and there are one billion nanometers in one meter. To gain perspective on this small size, a human hair is about 50,000 nm in diameter, a DNA double helix is about 2 nm in diameter, and an average carbon-to-carbon bond length is about 0.15 nm. The term "nanotechnology" usually refers to structures having dimensions around 100 nm or smaller. Although it is difficult, some modern technology has made it possible for chemists to develop materials with these small dimensions.

One of the biggest hurdles for scientists in this field is developing equipment that will work effectively on such a small scale. Much of our current technology is not sensitive enough to handle individual atoms with precision. The field of nanotechnology is very broad and diverse. More than 800 consumer products are already on the market that contain nanotechnology. In most cases consumers are unaware that their products contain nanoparticles.

Eyelash magnified 400 times

Eyelash magnified 2,500 times

What is a nanomaterial? Nanomaterials are generally of two types: fullerenes, such as buckyballs and carbon nanotubes, and inorganic nanoparticles. These substances have many properties of interest to scientists including heat resistance, superconductivity, strong mechanical strength, and special electrical properties. Nanoparticles are made of metals, metal oxides, and superconductor materials and can have catalytic properties. It is very important to note that these materials have very different properties at the nanoscale level than they do in larger everyday amounts. Metals that are nonreactive in normal quantities become very reactive at the nanoscale level. For instance, gold can act as a catalyst in nanoparticle form, but in larger quantities it is nonreactive.

DNA nanorobot

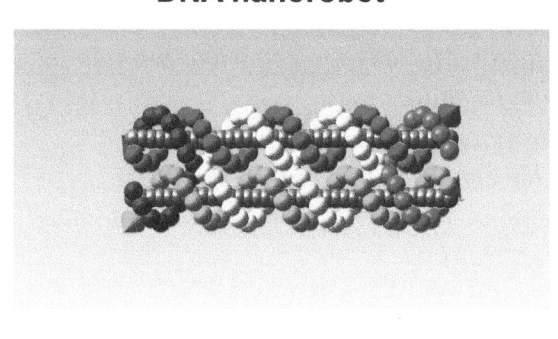

Nanotechnology also holds significant promise for medicine. Scientists are researching ways to use these small particles to deliver drugs to specific tissues and to develop nanorobots that will help repair cells after damage from surgery or disease. Nanosized imaging tools are also being developed that can be placed inside cells and used to monitor cellular changes. Nanoparticles are used as contrast agents to enhance current imaging techniques such as MRIs and ultrasound. By inserting small particles that fluoresce, small areas of tissue can be seen more reliably. For cancer patients, nanoparticles can help to detect tumor growth early on and allow for more effective treatment. Small nanoparticles can penetrate and

travel to hard-to-reach places in the body where they can be absorbed. Researchers link antigens or RNA strands that interact and identify the specific target cell surface. In this way, medicine can reach specific tissues and last longer so that it can work more effectively.

Scientists hope to build molecule-sized biological machines or nanorobots to deliver medication and to repair damaged tissues. Molecular self-assembly is a very important concept in nanotechnology. Since it is difficult to "build" small structures, scientists hope to make the component parts and allow the molecules to form the desired structures on their own based on intermolecular force attractions such as van der Waals forces, hydrogen bonding, and hydrophobic interactions. One application of this approach would be to build regions of nucleic acids and allow them to form sections of DNA or RNA that carry out specific and known functions in the human body. These regions could be used to produce needed proteins and enzymes.

Molecules may be arranged to construct elaborate mechanical devices

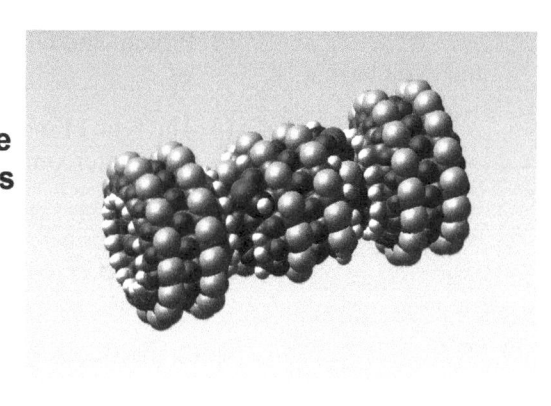

Nano machines may be used to assist targeted drug delivery

The food industry is adding nanosized particles to foods to improve their taste, nutritional value, flavor, and consistency. For example, a chocolate shake with "nanoclusters" gives a richer chocolate flavor without the need to add extra sugar. Certain teas or "nanoteas" offer increased selenium absorption by the body. In this case, a person could drink tea instead of taking a supplement. For children there are nutritional supplement drinks on the market that contain iron nanoparticles.

Cosmetic companies are using nanotechnology to add small oil droplets to make the application of their face creams smoother. Most face creams contain nanosized mineral sunscreen agents, such as zinc oxide or titanium dioxide. The small-sized mineral particles cause sunscreens to be more transparent instead of white. Other common chemicals that are added to face creams such as Retinol A and antiaging chemicals are more easily absorbed by the skin when they are in tiny nanocapusles.

Currently, scientists are working hard to gain the ability to precisely control every atom and nanoparticle so that they can better control the properties and behavior of the nanomaterials they are making.

Chapter 8 Review

Vocabulary

Match each word to the sentence where it best fits.

Section 8.1

brittle	polyatomic ion
electric current	

1. Something that is _____ can be strong but still breaks easily.

2. If you have a/an _____, then you have a small molecule with a charge.

3. When charge moves in a directed way you have a/an _____.

Section 8.2

lipids	copolymers
steroids	network covalent
hydrocarbon	empirical formula
polymers	molecular formula
monomer	organic molecule
homopolymer	

4. A/an _____ will tell you exactly how many atoms there are in an individual molecule.

5. Most of our fuels are one kind of _____ or another, because the carbon and hydrogen they contain have a large amount of chemical energy.

6. Molecules that are made from repeatedly bonding together smaller molecules are broadly called _____.

7. _____ are bonded together to form polymers.

8. Polypropylene is only made from one monomer, so it is a/an _____.

9. For a molecule to be a/an _____ it must be made primarily from carbon and hydrogen with the possibility of some other nonmetals also part of the molecule.

10. An ionic formula is always a/an _____.

11. Some _____ are natural and are necessary for correct biological functioning, and others are sometimes taken as drugs.

12. Some of the highest calorie foods contain _____.

13. Protein and DNA are molecules that are examples of _____.

14. The type of molecular substances that form very large interconnected molecules are called _____.

Section 8.3

intermolecular attractions	hydrogen bonding
van der Waals attractions	surface tension
dipole–dipole attraction	London dispersion attraction

15. _____ is a slightly stronger version of dipole–dipole attraction, but it is not as strong as a covalent bond.

16. Two broad terms that describe why molecules condense into liquids and solids are _____ and _____.

17. When two polar molecules attract each other you have an example of _____.

18. You can "float" a paper clip on water if you very carefully lay it flat on top of the water. This is due to what is known as _____.

19. _____ is particularly important for nonpolar molecules.

Conceptual Questions

Section 8.1

20. What is one property shared by most ionic substances?

21. Why do ionic substances not conduct electricity in their solid form but do if they are dissolved or in their liquid form?

22. Must the positive ion in an ionic compound have the same charge as the negative ion? Explain.

23. Describe the structure of an ionic crystal.

24. In what ways is an ionic crystal like a molecule and in what ways is it different?

25. Describe why you sometimes need parentheses around a polyatomic ion when used in a formula. Give one example of when you need parentheses and one where you don't.

26. Why must the total positive and total negative charge in an ionic compound be equal?

27. Why do some ionic names need a Roman numeral and some don't? Give an example.

28. In this section we learned to name ionic compounds containing transition metals. However, there is a way of naming these without using Roman numerals. Research this and write down a general rule for this previous method of nomenclature as well as both names for the compound $FeCl_3$.

Section 8.2

29. Describe a major difference between the properties of ionic compounds and molecular compounds.

30. What are some common properties of substances made from small molecules?

31. If two small molecules are about the same size, but one is polar, which one will have the higher boiling point? Why?

32. Gasoline is a hydrocarbon. What does that mean?

33. What is a common property of substances made from medium-sized molecules?

34. If you wanted to avoid lipids, what foods should you not eat?

35. Describe the relationship between a monomer and a polymer.

36. How many different monomers are used to make proteins?

37. What do we call a monomer that is used to make a protein?

38. Which kinds of molecular substances most resemble ionic compounds, and in what ways are they similar?

39. Describe the difference between an empirical formula and a molecular formula.

Section 8.3

40. What are the major categories of intermolecular attractions?

41. Is a hydrogen bond more like a dipole–dipole attraction or more like a London dispersion attraction? Explain.

42. Dipole–dipole attractions occur between which types of molecules: a.
   network covalent
   b. polar
   c. nonpolar

43. Explain why water has a boiling point that is so much higher than most molecules that are as small.

44. List three special properties of water, not including its high boiling point.

45. Describe the difference between London dispersion attraction and dipole–dipole attraction.

46. How does the size of a molecule play a role in determining the strength of its intermolecular attractions?

Chapter 8 Review

47. How does the shape of a molecule play a role in determining the strength of its intermolecular attractions?

48. How does the polarity of a molecule play a role in determining the strength of its intermolecular attractions?

Section 8.4

49. What does an empirical formula tell you? Give an example.

50. Give an example of when a molecular formula is the same as its empirical formula.

51. Give an example when the molecular formula is different from the empirical formula.

52. Describe how the percent composition helps in determining the molecular formula of an unknown substance.

Quantitative Problems

Section 8.1

53. What does the formula $BaCl_2$ tell you about the substance barium chloride?

54. Write the formula for each of the following names:
    a. lithium bromide
    a. magnesium fluoride
    b. calcium sulfide
    c. aluminum iodide
    d. aluminum sulfide

55. Write the formula for each of the following names:
    a. chromium(III) nitrate
    b. copper(I) oxide
    c. copper(II) oxide
    d. lithium phosphate
    e. iron(III) sulfate

56. Write the formula for each of the following names:
    a. barium hydroxide
    b. sodium sulfide
    c. tin(IV) carbonate
    d. cobalt(II) chlorate

57. Write the name for each of the following formulas:
    a. K_2O
    b. BeI_2
    c. $SrCl_2$
    d. $PbCl_4$

58. Write the name for each of the following formulas:
    a. FeO
    b. Fe_2O_3
    c. $ZnBr_2$
    d. $AgNO_3$
    e. K_2CO_3

59. Write the name for each of the following formulas:
    a. $NaHCO_3$
    b. $Sn(NO_3)_2$
    c. $(NH_4)_2SO_4$
    d. $Al(C_2H_3O_2)_3$
    e. $CuSO_4$

Section 8.2

60. Write the formula for each of the following names:
    a. dinitrogen monoxide
    b. dichlorine hexoxide
    c. iodine tribromide

61. Write the formula for each of the following names:
    a. iodine heptafluoride
    b. phosphorous trichloride
    c. chlorine monoiodide
    d. dinitrogen tetrafluoride

62. Write the names for each of the following formulas:
    a. SF_2
    b. P_4O_{10}
    c. P_2Cl_4

63. Write the names for each of the following formulas:
    a. Cl_2O_7
    b. PF_5
    c. S_2F_{10}

Section 8.3

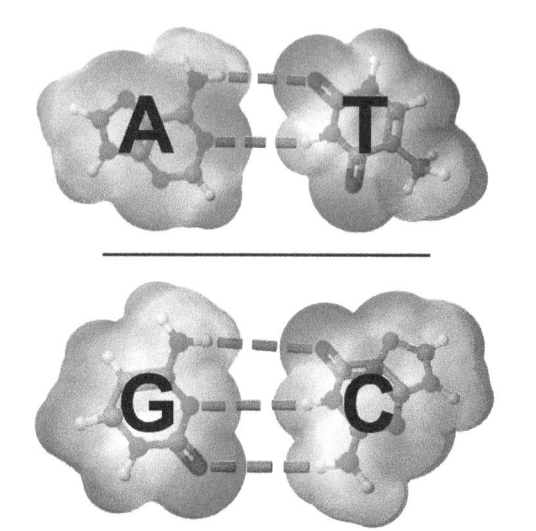

64. There are four DNA bases that are part of the nucleotide monomers that make up the DNA molecule. When two DNA strands wrap around each other they only stick together if there is an "A" on one strand across from a "T" on the other or a "G" on one strand across from a "C" on the other. Which pair do you think sticks together better and why?

65. Why does it make sense that "A" and "T" pair up and "G" and "C" pair up?

Section 8.4

66. Calculate the molar mass for each of the following substances:
    a. H_2O
    b. $NaNO_3$
    c. $(NH_4)_2S$
    d. $Ca_3(PO_4)_2$

67. What is the percent composition by mass for each of the substances in the previous question?

68. If you add up all the percentages of each element in a compound, what number should you get?

69. Calculate how many molecules are in the following:
    a. 6.5 g of H_2O
    b. 19.3 g of C_8H_{10}

70. Give the empirical formula for each of the molecular formulas:
    a. N_2O_4
    b. P_2O_5
    c. P_4H_{10}
    d. H_2O_2
    e. P_3Cl_5

71. Give three possible molecular formulas for the empirical formula CH_2O.

72. If you had a sample of a substance that had 20.23 g of aluminum and 79.77 g of chlorine, what would the empirical formula be for this substance?

73. What is the empirical formula for a substance with the following percent composition by weight:
    40% carbon
    6.7% hydrogen
    53.3% oxygen

74. You have 16.0 g of some compound and you perform an experiment to remove all of the oxygen, 11.2 g of iron is left. What is the empirical formula of this compound?

75. After burning 1.5 g of scandium in oxygen, a new compound is formed that has a mass of 3.1 g. What is its empirical formula?

76. The empirical formula for cyclohexane is CH_2, and its molar mass is 84.18 g/mole. What is its molecular formula?

77. What is the molecular formula for a compound with a molar mass of 34.02 g/mole and empirical formula of HO?

78. A sample of an unknown compound was determined to be made from 8.56 g of carbon and 1.44 g of hydrogen. The molar mass of the compound was found to be 28.03 g/mole. What is its molecular formula?

CHAPTER 9
Water and Solutions

Why is water so important?

What are the chemical properties of water?

How do we describe the things that are mixed into water?

Is steel different from iron? Is 14k gold different from pure gold?

We may not realize it, but we drink solutions every day. Coffee is a solution, as are apple juice, soda, and mineral water. In fact the fluid that makes up our blood is a solution too.

In the environment, sea water is a solution of salt, water, and other dissolved minerals. Solutions are important because they are all around us and within us. In fact, almost all of the chemical reactions that occur in our body only work in solutions.

A solution is a homogeneous mixture of two or more substances. Molecules in a solution are mixed so well that there are no "clumps" of one type of molecule. For example, think about sugar dissolved in water to make a solution. In a true solution, the molecules of sugar are completely separated from other molecules of sugar.

 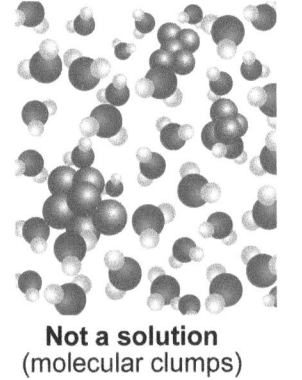

True solution
(*no* molecular clumps)

Not a solution
(molecular clumps)

Most of the solutions we talk about in this chapter will be solutions in water; however, solutions can be solids or gases too! Air is a solution of gases—mostly oxygen and nitrogen. Steel is also a solution—a solid solution of iron and carbon. Fourteen carat gold is a solution of gold and silver. The number "14" in 14k gold means 14 out of every 24 grams are gold (and 10 out of 24 grams are silver).

A NATURAL APPROACH TO CHEMISTRY

When is a solution like a conducting wire?

Dissolve 10 g of salt or sugar in water and what do you get? Both look like clear water, but one tastes sweet and the other tastes salty. Properties other than taste have also changed. Sugar and salt are different types of compounds (ionic and molecular) and they have quite different properties in solution. Both are critical to living things, and many popular sports drinks have both.

Here is an interesting experiment. Start with two solutions that are both made with 10 g dissolved in 100 mL of water. One solution is sugar and the other is salt. Connect a battery to each so that electricity has to pass through the solution before it reaches a light bulb. The results are quite different. Electricity passes right through the salt solution as if it were a conducting metal wire. The sugar solution stops electricity from flowing. A sugar solution is an insulator and the bulb stays dim.

Both the sugar and the salt dissolve completely in water! They are both white granular solids.

Why is the result different for two substances that appear to be so similar?

By itself, pure water is an electrical insulator. The ability to conduct electricity is created by particles in solution. Dissolved salts make conductive solutions because they dissociate into charged ions. Copper sulfate solution is also a good conductor for the same reason. The blue color comes from dissolved copper ions (Cu^{2+}). Dissolved molecular substances make insulating solutions.

This fact could save your life some day! Your body's own electrical control signals travel in conductive salt solutions within and between your cells. The presence of dissolved salts in body fluids explains why wet skin is a more effective electrical conductor than dry skin. In fact, wet skin is more than 1,000 times as conductive as dry skin. That is why your hands should always be dry when working around electrical tools or plugging in appliances.

9.1 Solutes, Solvents, and Water

A true solution

In Chapter 2 we talked about solutions and you have worked with them extensively in the laboratory. This chapter will look at solutions more closely and develop some of their properties. A true solution is *homogenous on the molecular level*. That means there are no clumps bigger than a molecule.

An example solution

Sixteen grams of copper sulfate ($CuSO_4$) in 100 mL makes a deep blue solution when every particle is dissolved. This solution is 1 M because there is one mole of copper sulfate per liter of solution.

Solid copper sulfate
($CuSO_4$)

Copper sulfate solution

In solution the copper ions dissociate from the sulfate ions

Solvent and solute

A solution always has a *solvent* and at least one *solute*. The **solvent** is the substance that makes up the biggest percentage of the mixture. It is normally a liquid. The copper sulfate solution has water as the solvent. The **solutes** are the other substances in the solution. Copper sulfate is the solute in this example.

Dissolving

When the solute particles are evenly distributed throughout the solvent, we say that the solute has **dissolved**. In this example, the copper sulfate starts as a solid powder. Water is added and the mixture is carefully stirred until all the solid powder has dissolved. Once the copper sulfate has dissolved, the solution is transparent again.

All true solutions are transparent

Why solutions are transparent

True solutions are transparent because all the particles are single molecules. Milk is not a true solution because each of the tiny fat particles in milk is made of thousands or tens of thousands of molecules. Particles this size are large enough to block light and scatter it to the side. The scattering of light is the reason milk is opaque.

Chemistry terms

solvent: the substance that makes up the biggest percentage of the mixture, usually a liquid.

solute: any substance in a solution other than the solvent.

dissolved: term used to describe when molecules of solute are completely separated from each other and dispersed into a solution.

The water molecule

Water is critical to life

Your body is about 60% water by weight. In one hour of exercise, you lose as much as two liters of water sweating and breathing! You also lose small amounts of dissolved salts. If the water and dissolved salts are not replaced, your body stops working. The unique physical and chemical properties of water explain why it's so important.

Water is a polar molecule

The water molecule is **polar**. That means the electric charge is unevenly distributed in a water molecule. The two shared electrons from the hydrogen atoms are attracted to the oxygen atom. This makes the oxygen side of the molecule slightly negative and the hydrogen side slightly positive. The diagram on the right shows the surface of the molecule shaded red where it is more positive and blue where it is more negative.

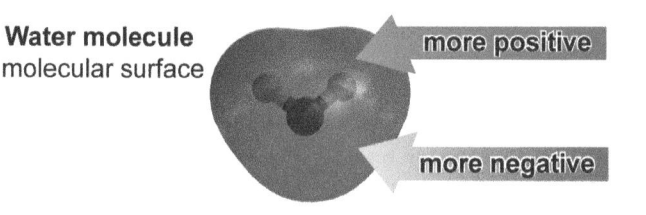

Water molecule
ball-and-stick model

Water molecule
molecular surface
more positive
more negative

Hydrogen bonding

Water molecules tend to stick to each because of their polarity. Positive hydrogen atoms from one water molecule are attracted to the negative oxygen atom in another molecule. This attraction is not as strong as a chemical bond, but it is strong enough that we give it its own name: **hydrogen bonding**. This hydrogen bonding explains some curious properties of water.

Hydrogen bonds

Why ice floats

Ice

When water freezes, it becomes *less* dense! This is unusual; most materials are *more* dense as solids than as liquids. Ice is less dense than liquid water because hydrogen bonds force water molecules to align in a crystal structure where molecules are farther apart than they are in a liquid.

Chemistry terms

polar: a molecule in which there is a charge separation that makes one side (or end) of the molecule more positive or negative than the other side (or end).

hydrogen bond: an intermolecular bond that forms between a hydrogen atom in one molecule and the negatively charged portion of another molecule (or another part of the same molecule).

The importance of hydrogen bonding

Comparing water and methane

Consider two molecules with similar molecular masses. Methane (CH_4) has a molecular mass of 16 g/mole and water (H_2O) has a molecular mass of 18 g/mole. Methane boils at $-161°C$, so at room temperature, methane is a gas. Water has a similar mass, but it boils at an astounding $100°C$! This is far hotter than almost any other low-molecular-weight hydrogen compound. What is the reason? The answer has to do with hydrogen bonding and the *shapes* of the two molecules.

boils at + 100°C   boils at −161°C

Water H_2O 18 g/mole   Methane CH_4 16 g/mole

Hydrogen bonding causes water's high boiling point

Because of its symmetrical shape, a methane molecule is nonpolar! Hydrogen bonding does not occur between neighboring methane molecules. Without hydrogen bonding, it is easier for a methane molecule to escape its neighbors and become a gas. By comparison, water has strong hydrogen bonding between neighboring molecules. Hydrogen bonding is the reason for water's unusually high boiling point. The high boiling point of water is of critical importance to life on Earth. Life needs *liquid* water. If water were a gas at room temperature, it would be impossible for life to exist as we know it.

Making solid steel float!

Try this experiment. Gently place a pin on the surface of water and another on the surface of alcohol. The pin sinks immediately in the alcohol, but the pin *floats* on the water! Pins are made of steel, which is dense enough to *sink* in water. Why can a pin float on water but not on alcohol?

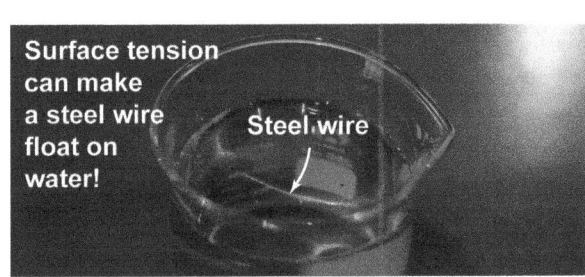

Surface tension can make a steel wire float on water!   Steel wire

Surface tension

The answer is a property called **surface tension**. Surface tension is a force that pulls molecules together along a liquid surface. The high surface tension of water is a direct consequence of hydrogen bonding. The pin floats on water because it has to separate water molecules on the surface to break through and sink. The hydrogen bonds between the water molecules are tight enough that a gently placed pin will float. The fact that water drops pull themselves into spheres is also caused by surface tension. Alcohol has a lower surface tension because it has fewer hydrogen bonds than water, so the pin easily drops through the surface and sinks.

Chemistry terms

surface tension: a force created by intermolecular attraction in liquids, such as hydrogen bonding in water, acting to pull a liquid surface into the smallest possible area, for example, pulling a droplet of water into a sphere.

CHAPTER 9
Water and Solutions

Water as a solvent

The universal solvent

Water is often called the "universal solvent." Although water doesn't dissolve everything, it does dissolve many substances such as salts and sugars. Water is a good solvent for two reasons:

1. Water molecules are small and light.
2. Water molecules are polar.

How water dissolves salt

The polar molecules of water are especially good at dissolving ionic compounds like salt (NaCl). When salt is mixed with water, the polar water molecules are attracted to sodium and chlorine ions in a solid salt crystal. When they touch, they transfer some energy, which causes the ions in the salt crystal to separate.

The negative side of the water molecules are attracted to the Na^+ ions and the positive ends are attracted to the Cl^- ions. Once a Na^+ or Cl^- ion has broken off from the crystal, it instantly attracts oppositely charged sides of nearby water molecules. This process is called **hydration**. The hydrated sodium and chlorine ions stay in solution because of their accompanying polar water molecules, which behave as "private collections."

+ Sodium ion

− Chloride ion

Water dissolves many molecular compounds

Glucose is a covalent molecule, but it dissolves easily in water. The glucose molecule has areas of positive and negative charge. When glucose is mixed with water, the charged areas attract many water molecules. Molecules of glucose do not dissociate into ions but remain together (and neutral) in solution.

Polar water molecules are attracted to charged sites on the glucose molecule

Glucose
$C_6H_{12}O_6$

+ Surface charge −

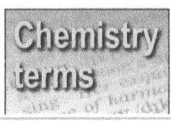
Chemistry terms

hydration: the process by which molecules with any charge separation collect water molecules around them. While not chemically bonded, a hydrated molecule holds fairly tightly its "private collection" of water molecules.

Distilled water versus tap water

Distilled water is used to make solutions

We often use **distilled water** when making solutions with water in the chemistry lab. Distilled water is water that has been purified so that it contains no dissolved substances. The distillation process heats water to its boiling point of 100°C. The steam that forms is collected in a separate clean container. Any ions and solid contaminants are left behind as residue in the original container. Distilled water is sometimes incorrectly referred to as deionized water. However, this is incorrect. **Deionized water** is water that has had its ions removed using a specific filtration process. Deionized water is sometimes used instead of distilled water because it is cheaper to produce and, for most purposes, yields sufficiently pure water.

In contrast, **tap water** often contains dissolved salts and minerals from the groundwater supply, and even from the pipes that carry it from the reservoir. Many minerals that may be present in tap water, such as Fe^{2+}, Ca^{2+}, and Mg^{2+}, are important for our health. Other sources of ions in tap water come from water supplies that are treated with chloride ions (Cl^-) for purification purposes. Chloride ions kill bacteria that may be present in the water supply. Fluoride ions (F^-) are also added at 4 mg/L to help with dental health.

How do we know that tap water contains ions and distilled water does not?

Why do we use distilled water?

When making solutions in the laboratory, we need to know that there are no other chemicals in the solution, besides the ones that we add. Contaminating ions and minerals can interfere with the chemical reaction we are trying to perform. For this reason we use distilled or deionized water when we make our solutions in the chemistry laboratory.

Chemistry terms

distilled water: water purified by heating water to steam and condensing the steam into a clean or sterilized container.

deionized water: water without ions, purified using filtration methods.

tap water: drinking water from the faucet or "tap."

A NATURAL APPROACH TO CHEMISTRY

Reactions in aqueous solutions

Aqueous means dissolved in water
A solution with water as the solvent is called an **aqueous** solution. The word aqueous comes from aqua, the latin word for water. Aqueous solutions are so important that chemists consider being dissolved in water to be almost a fourth state of matter! In writing reactions, we use the symbols (s), (l), (g), and (aq) to show what state of matter the reactants and products are in:

(s) indicates a solid.

(l) indicates a liquid.

(g) indicates a gas.

(aq) indicates a substance dissolved in water.

A good example is the familiar baking soda and vinegar reaction. All four states of matter appear in this reaction.

Identifying the state of matter in a reaction

$$NaHCO_3(s) + HC_2H_3O_2(aq) \rightarrow NaC_2H_3O_2(aq) + H_2O(l) + CO_2(g)$$

Sodium bicarbonate   Acetic acid   Sodium acetate   Water   Carbon dioxide

(solid)   (aqueous solution)   (aqueous solution)   (liquid)   (gas)

Reading the symbols (s), (g), (l), and (aq)
The (s) tells us the baking soda is a solid in the reactants and the (aq) tells us the acetic acid (vinegar) is an aqueous solution. On the product side of the reaction, the first (aq) tells us the sodium acetate is dissolved in the water that was part of the vinegar. The water (l) is a liquid. The carbon dioxide (g) is a gas. The gas is what makes the bubbles. If you are not careful, any product that is a gas quickly escapes, taking its mass with it! If the CO_2 is allowed to escape, we would expect to measure less mass in the products of this reaction compared to the reactants. You can learn a lot about a reaction by knowing how to read these special symbols!

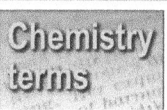**Chemistry terms**   **aqueous solution:** any solution where the solvent is water.

The importance of aqueous solutions

Reactions in solids

In order for a chemical reaction to occur, molecules must *touch* each other. This seems obvious, but think about what it means. In a solid, molecules cannot easily move around. Chemical reactions *do* occur in solids, but they are slow, like changing limestone into marble under heat and pressure in the Earth. This takes thousands of years.

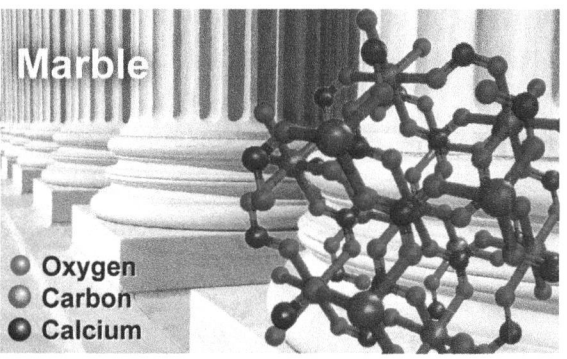

Marble

○ Oxygen
○ Carbon
● Calcium

Reactions in gases

In a gas, molecules move around quickly. Reactions such as combustion can happen quickly in a gas, but there are very few chemicals that are gases at room temperature. Also, gases are not very dense. One milliliter of a gas such as air contains one thousand times fewer molecules as the same volume of a liquid such as water.

Fire is a chemical reaction
that depends on oxygen gas

Reactions in liquids

Liquids combine the advantages of high density and high mobility. In a liquid there are many molecules that are close together. They can easily move around and reach each other. But relatively few chemicals are liquid at room temperature. Sugar is solid, salt is solid, and virtually all proteins and carbohydrates are also solids at room temperature.

Why life requires water

Life involves reactions of thousands of complex chemicals. *This can only happen in aqueous solutions!* Only in a solution can the molecules in living things circulate and reach each other to react. For example, a sequence of reactions called the Krebs cycle occurs in virtually all living things on Earth. In one step of this reaction, malic acid reacts with a chemical called NAD+ to produce oxaloacetic acid and NADH. This is part of how energy is extracted from glucose in every cell of your body.

NAD+ (aq)

Malic acid (aq)

Oxaloacetic acid (aq)

NADH (aq)

Life involves many complex chemical reactions in aqueous solutions

Other solvents

Nonpolar solvents

Water may be the most important solvent to living things, but plenty of other solvents exist, and you will probably use them from time to time in your life. For example, artists thin oil-based paints with odorless mineral spirits. Mineral spirits is the common name for hexane (C_6H_{14}), a linear molecule derived from oil. Hexane is nonpolar, and it is good at dissolving other nonpolar solutes.

Mineral spirits (hexane) are a solvent for oil paints

Hexane C_6H_{14}

Why oil does not dissolve in water

Oil does not dissolve in water because water is a polar molecule and oil molecules are nonpolar. However, oil dissolves easily in mineral spirits. In general, polar solvents dissolve polar solutes, like water dissolving salt. Non-polar solvents dissolve nonpolar sol-utes, such as mineral spirits dissolving oil.

One is a solution and one is not

Oil and water

Oil and mineral spirits

In general, like dissolves like
Polar solvents dissolve polar solutes
Nonpolar solvents dissolve nonpolar solutes

"Solvent" means different things in everyday use

In everyday conversation, the word "solvent" usually means organic liquids such as mineral spirits, acetone (nail polish remover), turpentine, alcohol, and similar chemicals. Many of these chemicals are flammable and harmful when breathed in. In chemistry, the term "solvent" means something that dissolves something else. The common meaning and the chemistry meaning are similar, *so don't get confused*! Water is a solvent in chemistry—the most important one to living things.

TABLE 9.1. Some common solvents other than water

Name	Formula	Typical uses	Hazards
Mineral spirits	C_6H_{14}	paint thinner	flammable, toxic
Methanol	CH_3OH	solvent, fuel	flammable, toxic
Acetone	CH_3COCH_3	nail polish remover	flammable, toxic, carcinogenic
Tetrachloroethylene	C_2Cl_4	dry cleaning chemical	flammable, toxic, carcinogenic

9.2 Concentration and Solubility

Concentration and dilute solutions

The **concentration** of a solution describes how much of each solute there is compared to the total solution. A solution is **dilute** when there is very little solute. A solution is **concentrated** when there is a lot of dissolved solute compared to solvent. The distinction is hard to determine, since even a concentrated solution of acid contains less solute than solvent.

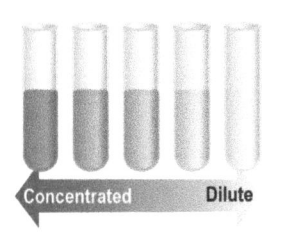

Concentrated   Dilute

What is solubility?

Solubility means the amount of solute (if any) that can be dissolved in a quantity of solvent. The most accurate solubility data are given as a mass percent, which is the mass of solute per 100 g of solution. In the laboratory it is sometimes easier to work with solubility in terms of grams per 100 mL. Solubility is always given at a specific temperature since temperature strongly affects solubility.

TABLE 9.2. Solubility of common solids in water at 20°C

Name	Solubility (% mass)	Solubility (g/100 mL)	Name	Solubility (% mass)	Solubility (g/100 mL)
Salt (NaCl)	26.4	32	Marble ($CaCO_3$)	0	0
Sugar (suc. $C_{12}H_{22}O_{11}$)	67.1	204	Copper sulfate ($CuSO_4$)	16.7	20
Baking soda ($NaHCO_3$)	8.73	9.2	Epsom salts ($MgSO_4$)	25.1	32
Zinc sulfate ($ZnSO_4$)	35	45	Glucose ($C_6H_{12}O_6$)	45.0	81

Comparing mass % to g/mL

Notice that the values in g/100 mL are always larger than the mass percents. This is because the density of a solution varies with concentration. Adding more solute raises the density. This happens for two reasons:

1. Solute molecules fit in between solvent molecules.
2. Solutes may themselves be denser than water.

Adding 1 g of solute always increases the mass of the solution by 1 g. However, adding 1 cm³ of solute does *not* increase the volume by 1 cm³, because solute molecules squeeze between water molecules. The volume of a solution does increase, but not as fast as the mass does, and that is why the density changes.

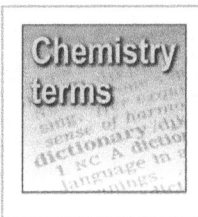

Chemistry terms

concentration: the amount of each solute compared to the total solution.

dilute: term used to describe a solution with relatively little solute compared to solvent.

concentrated: term used to describe a solution with a lot of solute compared to solvent.

solubility: the amount of a solute that will dissolve in a particular solvent at a particular temperature and pressure.

A NATURAL APPROACH TO CHEMISTRY

Concentration

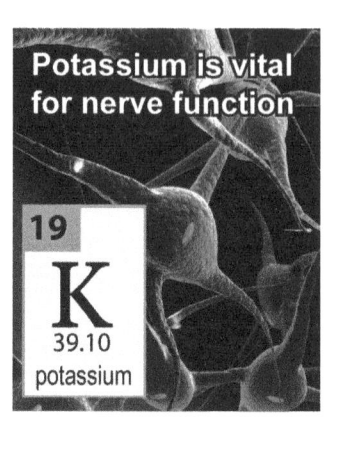

Potassium concentration in your body

Potassium is critical to many of your body's functions, such as transmitting nerve signals. In a healthy person, potassium is dissolved in blood at a concentration of 140 to 200 milligrams (mg) per liter. A blood potassium concentration of less than 130 mg/L causes muscle weakness and heart rhythm instability (*hypokalemia*). A concentration of more than 215 mg/L may also result in heart instability (*hyperkalemia*). Since potassium is lost through excretion and sweat, you need to eat foods containing 4–5 grams of potassium (4,000–5,000 mg) each day. Fruits and vegetables are the best sources.

Different ways to measure concentration

Three common ways to express concentration are

- as a percent, using mass of solute per liter of solution (g/L or mg/L);
- as a percent, using mass of solute divided by total mass of solution; and
- in molarity, which is moles of solute per liter of solution (M).

Three ways to calculate concentration

g/liter	$\text{concentration (g/L)} = \dfrac{\text{mass of solute}}{\text{volume of solution}}$
% mass	$\text{concentration (\%)} = \dfrac{\text{mass of solute}}{\text{mass of solution}} \times 100$
molarity	$\text{concentration (molarity)} = \dfrac{\text{moles of solute}}{\text{liters of solution}}$

Very low concentrations

Environmental scientists often use a variation of percent concentration. Parts per million (ppm), parts per billion (ppb), and parts per trillion (ppt) are commonly used to describe very small concentrations of solutes in the environment. These terms are measures of the ratio (by mass) of one material in a much larger amount of another material. For example, a pinch (gram) of salt in 1,000 tonnes (1 tonne = 1,000 kg) of corn chips is about 1 g salt per billion grams of chips, or a concentration of 1 ppb.

Solved problem

Suppose you dissolve 10.0 g of sugar in 90.0 g of water. What is the mass percent concentration of sugar in the solution?

Asked: *The mass percent concentration*

Given: *10 g of solute (sugar) and 90 g solvent (water)*

Relationships: $concentration = \dfrac{mass\ of\ solute}{total\ mass\ of\ solution} \times 100\%$

Solve: $concentration = \dfrac{10\ g\ sugar}{(10 + 90)\ g\ of\ solution} \times 100\% = 10\%\ sugar$

Molarity: a review

Molarity is the most common unit of concentration

Since we will be using aqueous solutions so often in chemistry, it is important to review what molarity means as well as how to calculate it. Solution concentrations inside living organisms must be carefully maintained. Dehydration is a common side effect of serious illness. Dehydration, or loss of water, can be very dangerous because it affects the concentration of ions inside our cells and tissues. Recall that the **molarity** of a solution is the number of moles of solute per liter of solution. Molarity is useful because chemists need to know the number of reacting molecules. For this reason, *chemists make solutions with a known molarity*. This allows them to make the appropriate concentration, with the correct number of particles for the reaction.

Calculating molarity

To calculate molarity, you will need to know how many moles are dissolved per liter of solution. Let's find the molarity of a salt solution containing 6.0 g of NaCl in 100 mL of water. The problem is solved in three steps:

1. Calculate the formula mass of NaCl so you know the mass of one mole.
2. Use the formula mass to figure out how many moles there are in 6.0 g.
3. Calculate the molarity by dividing the number of moles by the volume of solution in liters.

Calculate the molarity of a salt solution made by adding 6.0 g of NaCl to 100 mL of distilled water.

Asked: *Molarity of solution*

Given: *Volume of solution = 100.0 mL, mass of solute (NaCl) = 6.0 g*

Relationships: $M = \frac{moles}{L}$ *formula mass of NaCl = 22.99 + 35.45 = 58.44 g/mole*

$1000 \ mL = 1.0 \ L$, *therefore* $100 \ mL = 0.10 \ L$

Solve: $moles \ NaCl \ = \ 6.0 \ \overline{g \ NaCl} \times \dfrac{1 \ mole \ NaCl}{58.44 \ g \ NaCl} = 0.103 \ mole \ NaCl$

$M = \dfrac{0.103 \ moles}{0.100 \ L} = 1.03 \ M$

Answer: *1.03 M solution of NaCl*

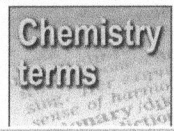

molarity: the number of moles of solute per liter of solution.

Saturation and equilibrium

Saturation

Suppose you add 250 g of sugar to 100 mL of water at 30°C. What happens? According to the table, 219 g will dissolve in the water. *The rest will remain solid.* That means you will be left with 31 g of solid sugar at the bottom of your solution. A solution is **saturated** if it contains as much solute as the solvent can dissolve. The table tells us that 219 g per 100 mL is the saturation concentration of sugar at 30°C. Any amount of solute added in excess of the solubility *does not dissolve.*

Solubility of Sugar in Water

Temp (°C)	Solubility g/100mL	Temp (°C)	Solubility g/100mL
0	177	50	259
10	189	60	284
20	204	70	318
30	219	80	360
40	238	90	410

Equilibrium

A solution is in **aqueous equilibrium** when the concentration does not change over time. If you cover a saturated sugar solution and let it sit, the concentration of dissolved sugar will stay the same. However, the individual molecules that are dissolved do *not* just stay dissolved! Dissolving is really a two-way process.

Dissolving and "undissolving"

Consider a molecule of dissolved sugar that happens to touch some undissolved sugar. That molecule might bounce off and stay dissolved. It might also stick and come out of the solution to become "undissolved" (solid) again. When a solid solute is placed in a solvent, both dissolving and "undissolving" are going on at the same time! If the solution is **unsaturated**, there is more dissolving than "undissolving." The amount of solid solute decreases and the amount of dissolved solute increases.

Solid sugar   Sugar dissolving   Equilibrium   Sugar "undissolving"

Why saturation happens

Of course, the more solute there is in solution, the higher the chance that a solute molecule will come out of solution and become solid again. Saturation happens when the rate of molecules becoming "undissolved" exactly balances the rate of dissolving.

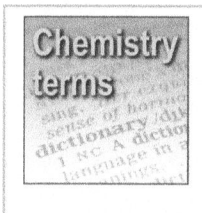
Chemistry terms

saturated: situation that occurs when the amount of dissolved solute in a solution gets high enough that the rate of "undissolving" matches the rate of dissolving.

aqueous equilibrium: condition when the amount of dissolved solutes remains constant over time.

unsaturated: situation in which more of a solute can be dissolved in a solvent at a certain temperature; solute concentration is lower than the solubility

Solubility and temperature

Solubility of solids increases with temperature

A higher temperature normally increases the solubility of solids in liquids. This is mostly because warmer solvent molecules have more energy with which to hit a solid and knock off molecules of solute. A warm solid is also easier to dissolve because the molecules in the solid have more energy and are easier to separate.

Solubility of sugar in water

Solubility (g/100 mL) vs Temperature (°C): 410 at 90

Making a supersaturated solution

Suppose you make a saturated solution of sugar in water at 90°C. According to the graph, you can dissolve 410 g of sugar in 100 mL of water! That's more than four times as much sugar as water (by mass).

Now let the solution cool down to 20°C. What happens? At 20°C only 204 g of sugar can stay in solution. The rest must come out of solution. This is how rock candy is created! The solution becomes supersaturated as it cools. A seed crystal of sugar is put in the supersaturated solution, and the seed crystal grows as sugar solidifies.

100 mL of 90°C water

410 g sugar

Dissolve to make a saturated solution

Cool down

Excess sugar crystallizes into rock candy!

Solubility versus temperature

$ZnSO_4$
$MgSO_4$
$CuSO_4$
NaCl
$NaHCO_3$

The graph shows how the solubilities of some common substances change over a range of temperature. Note that the solubility changes a lot for some solutes, including copper sulfate ($CuSO_4$), but very little for others, such as salt (NaCl).

274

Dissolving rate

Dissolving happens faster when solutes are ground into powder

Dissolving can only happen at the surface between solvent and solute. Most things that are meant to be dissolved, such as salt and sugar, are ground up into a powder to increase the surface area. Increased surface area speeds dissolving because more solute is exposed to the solvent.

Substances are often ground up into powder to make them dissolve faster

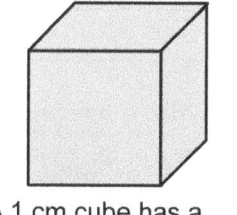

A 1 cm cube has a surface area of 6 cm²

The same volume has a surface area of 9 cm² when divided up into smaller cubes

Powders dissolve faster but not more

Making sugar or salt into a powder does not change the solubility of either compound! It just makes all the dissolving that is going to happen occur *faster*. If you add more powdered sugar to water than can dissolve, the excess will stay powder (solid) in a sludge at the bottom of the beaker.

Temperature increases dissolving rate

Increasing the temperature of a solution will not significantly change the solubility of sodium chloride. Its solubility at 20°C is 26.4% by mass, and at 70°C it is only a little over 27%. However, salt dissolves much faster in hot water than cold water. The same amount of salt will go into solution, but increasing the temperature makes it dissolve faster.

Solid salt

Salt in water

Dissolving is a collision process and slow (cold) molecules are not as effective as fast (hot) molecules

The molecular process of dissolving

The dissolving rate increases with temperature because dissolving is a physical process at the molecular level. Molecules of water literally slam into crystallized (solid) sodium and chloride ions, knocking them out of their solid form and into solution. Higher temperature means that each water molecule has more energy to transfer when it strikes the salt crystal. More energy means more effective dislodging of ions from the crystal.

The solubility of gases in liquids

Gas dissolves in water

Gases can also dissolve in liquids. When you drink carbonated soda, the fizz comes from dissolved carbon dioxide gas (CO_2). Table 9.3 lists the solubility of CO_2 as 1.74 grams per liter of water at room temperature and atmospheric pressure (1 atm).

TABLE 9.3. Solubility of common gases in water at 25°C

Name	Solubility (g/L)	Name	Solubility (g/L)
Oxygen (O_2)	0.04	Methane (CH_4)	0.02
Nitrogen (N_2)	0.02	Hydrogen (H_2)	0.0015
Carbon dioxide (CO_2)	1.74	Helium (He)	0.0015

Solubility of gases in liquids decreases with temperature

The solubility of gases in liquids *decreases* with temperature. The table shows that 0.04 g of oxygen dissolves in a kilogram of water. Dissolved oxygen keeps fish and other underwater animals alive. When water gets warmer, the dissolved oxygen content goes down. Many fish seek deeper, cooler water during the summer. The fish swim deep because there is more dissolved oxygen in the cooler water.

Deeper water is cooler and contains more dissolved oxygen

Solubility of gases in liquids increases with pressure

The solubility of gases in liquids increases with pressure. Soda is fizzy because the carbon dioxide was dissolved in the liquid at high pressure. When you pop the tab on a can of soda, you release the pressure. The solution immediately becomes **supersaturated**, causing the CO_2 to bubble out of the water and fizz. Supersaturation means the solution has more dissolved solute than it can hold. A solution that is supersaturated is always unstable. The excess solute usually drops out of solution, like the CO_2 bubbling out of soda water. Rock candy is made by supersaturating a sugar solution, causing the sugar to "undissolve" back into sugar crystals.

Seltzer water is a supersaturated solution of CO_2 in water

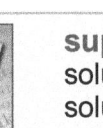
Chemistry terms

supersaturation: term used to describe when a solution contains more dissolved solute than it can hold; supersaturated solutions are always unstable and the excess solute becomes "undissolved," often rapidly.

Preparing a solution

The importance of preparing solutions

Many laboratory experiments require a solution of a specific molarity (M). Preparing solutions for an experiment is an important, frequently used laboratory skill. A solution of known molarity allows us to determine how many particles (ions or molecules) are present quite accurately just by using a graduated cylinder.

How do you begin?

Basic steps for preparing a solution of known molarity:

1. Determine the grams of solute needed by multiplying the moles of solid by its formula mass.

2. Weigh the grams of solute on the balance.

3. Add the solute to a graduated cylinder or a volumetric flask, which chemists use for best accuracy.

4. Fill the flask about two thirds of the way up with distilled water.

5. Mix the solution using a magnetic stirring bar or by shak-ing the bottle up and down until the solid dissolves com-pletely.

6. Fill the volumetric flask or the graduated cylinder up to the correct volume marker. Sometimes it is necessary to use an eye dropper to get the meniscus right on the line. Remix the solution.

Diluting stock solutions

We can also make solutions of known molarity by diluting very concentrated stock solutions. To do this, we use the fact that adding water to a solution does not change how many moles of solute are present. We know that M = moles/L; rearranging we get moles = M×L and thus the formula $M_1V_1 = M_2V_2$, where M_1 is original molarity, V_1 is original volume, M_2 is the new molarity, and V_2 is the new volume.

Safety considerations

When diluting concentrated stock solutions, the procedure differs slightly. Because concentrated acids release a large amount of heat when water is added to them, we always add *acid to water*. Therefore, we should start with a small amount of distilled water and add acid drop by drop until dissolved, then fill to the correct volume.

Solved problem

How can we form 500. mL of 0.1 M HCl by diluting a 8.0 M stock solution?

Asked: *To form a 500. mL solution of 0.1 M HCl*

Given: *8.0 M stock solution of HCl*

Relationships: $M_1V_1 = M_2V_2$

$M_1 = 8.0$ M, $V_1 = ?$, $M_2 = 0.1$ M, $V_2 = 500.$ mL = 0.500 L

Solve: *$V_1 = M_2V_2 / M_1 = (0.1$ M$)(0.500$ L$) / (8.0$ M$) = 6.25$ mL*

Answer: *We place 6.25 mL of the 8.0 M stock solution and dilute to a total volume of 500. mL to form a 0.1 M solution of HCl.*

9.3 Properties of Solutions

Reaction rate and concentration

Caves are formed when the carbonic acid in rainwater dissolves limestone in rock over long periods of time. Suppose you place a sample of solid limestone in a 1 M solution of carbonic acid and place another piece in a 2 M solution of carbonic acid. Will the reactions be the same? How might they be different?

Chemically, the same reaction occurs in both solutions, but the 2 M solution will make the reaction happen *twice as fast* as the 1 M solution. That is because there are twice as many carbonic acid molecules per mL in the 2 M solution. Twice as many molecules means twice the chance of molecules meeting to have a reaction.

Which acid will dissolve the limestone fastest?

Higher concentration generally means a faster reaction rate

Concentration and medicine

$C_9H_8O_4$

The effect of concentration on reaction rate is extremely important in medicine. When you take a medicine, such as aspirin, the molecules in the medicine (acetylsalicylic acid) become dissolved in your blood. Aspirin blocks pain, reduces swelling, and reduces blood clotting; however, if the concentration is too high, aspirin can cause internal bleeding and other problems. Medically, this is called an *overdose*, and it can be fatal. An overdose is a concentration that produces a reaction rate that is dangerous to the body.

Higher temperature generally means a faster reaction rate

Reaction rate is affected by temperature

Reaction rates usually go up with temperature because reaction molecules have more energy. Therefore, less energy has to be added to break the bonds and start the reaction. This effect is stronger in solutions because higher temperature increases the motion of solute molecules. Faster molecules mean more collisions between molecules and therefore a greater chance that molecules meet in a reaction.

278

Energy and solutions

Energy and the heat of solution

Intermolecular bonds are broken when a solute dissolves. Depending upon the type of solute being dissolved, ions are hydrated by water molecules and hydrogen bonds may form between solute and solvent molecules. Since energy is involved whenever bonds form or break, *the overall process of dissolving may use or release energy*. The energy that is used or released in dissolving is called the **heat of solution**.

Negative heat of solution

A solute that *loses* energy when it dissolves has a *negative* heat of solution. The negative sign tells you that energy is released into the solution. The released energy would raise the reading on a thermometer. A good example is calcium chloride ($CaCl_2$). Calcium chloride dissolves in water via the reaction

$$CaCl_2(s) + H_2O(l) \rightarrow Ca^{2+}(aq) + 2Cl^-(aq) + 82.8 \text{ kJ}$$

When dissolving is exothermic

So each mole releases 82.8 kJ of energy! A negative heat of solution means that $CaCl_2$ dissolving is an *exothermic* process. Exothermic means it *gives off energy*.

Heat packs use solutes with negative heat of solution

Dissolving calcium chloride in water makes the solution very hot. That's because the heat lost by the calcium chloride as it dissolves is *gained* by the solution. A *heat pack* contains water and calcium chloride in a thin plastic vial. Breaking the plastic vial allows the calcium chloride to dissolve, and the solution heats up! Skiers often use heat packs to warm cold fingers and toes.

The heat comes from calcium chloride dissolving

Positive heat of solution

Ammonium nitrate (NH_4NO_3) has a positive heat of solution of +25.7 kJ/mole. That means one mole of ammonium nitrate absorbs 25.7 kJ of energy when it dissolves:

$$NH_4NO_3(s) \ + \ 25.7 \text{ kJ} \ \xrightarrow{\ H_2O\ } \ NH_4^-(aq) \ + \ NO_3^-(aq)$$

Cold packs use solutes with positive heat of solution

A thermometer placed in this solution would decrease in temperature. The solution becomes *colder*. A cold pack contains a vial of ammonium nitrate in a bag of water. Breaking the vial allows the ammonium nitrate to dissolve. The solution gets so cold that frost often forms on the surface of the cold pack! Athletes use cold packs to quickly cool injuries.

The cooling effect comes from ammonium nitrate absorbing heat as it dissolves

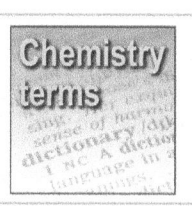

Chemistry terms

heat of solution: the energy absorbed or released when a solute dissolves in a particular solvent.

Measuring heat of solution: coffee cup calorimetry

Experiments with heat and solutions

The amount of heat released or absorbed by a solution can be measured using a simple *coffee cup calorimeter*. A coffee cup calorimeter is a double styrofoam cup that prevents the reaction in solution from losing heat to the environment. You may use this technique in the lab to investigate three types of chemical changes:

1. ionic salts dissolving in solution,
2. neutralization reactions between an acid and a base, and
3. oxidation-reduction reactions between a metal and an acid.

Enthalpy

The heat energy involved in a chemical reaction is given the special name **enthalpy**. Enthalpy is measured in joules per mole (J/mole) or kilojoules per mole (kJ/mole). The symbol for enthalpy change is ΔH, and this is written next to the chemical equation. The enthalpy change tells us how much heat is released or absorbed during the chemical change.

ΔH for endothermic reactions

For instance, if the enthalpy is positive, we write ΔH with a positive sign, indicating the reactants *absorb* heat when forming products:

$$NH_4NO_3(s) + H_2O(l) \rightarrow NH_4^+(aq) + NO_3^-(aq) \quad \Delta H = +25.7 \text{ kJ}$$

In a solution, this absorbed heat results in a decrease in temperature. The temperature decreases because the reaction absorbs thermal energy from the solution. You measure the temperature change of the solution with a temperature probe immediately before and just after mixing the reactants.

ΔH for exothermic reactions

When an acid and a base are mixed, heat is released by the chemical change (an exothermic reaction). The solution becomes warmer. The change in enthalpy (ΔH) is *negative* because the reaction gives off energy to the surroundings:

$$HCl(aq) + NaOH(aq) \rightarrow NaCl(aq) + H_2O(l) \quad \Delta H = -56 \text{ kJ/mole}$$

This reaction takes place under the relatively constant pressure of the atmosphere, because the coffee cup calorimeter is not sealed. The reaction takes place in the solution inside the cups, so if the solution gains heat and the temperature rises, then we can assume that the reaction lost heat based on the first law of thermodynamics. For the short time that we are measuring the heat change in a reaction such as this one, we usually make the assumption that no heat is absorbed by the styrofoam cups.

Chemistry terms	**enthalpy:** the energy potential of a chemical reaction measured in joules per mole (J/mole) or kilojoules per mole (kJ/mole).

A NATURAL APPROACH TO CHEMISTRY

Solution calorimetry

Assumptions

In the laboratory we know that over a long period of time heat would eventually be lost to the cups and surroundings because styrofoam is not a perfect insulator. We know this from our real-life experiences with hot beverages. However, for many experiments the temperature changes over the course of a few minutes, so the actual heat loss can be neglected. For dilute solutions we can also assume that they have the same specific heat as water, because the solute concentration is so low it does not affect the specific heat significantly.

$$\Delta H_{solution} = (\text{grams of solution}) \times (\text{specific heat of solution}) \times \Delta T$$
$$(\text{water})$$
$$\text{where } \Delta H_{solution} = -\Delta H_{reaction}$$

Determining heat lost or gained by the solution

To find out how much heat is lost or gained by the solution, we can use the equation for calculating energy used earlier in Chapter 3.
The reacting chemicals are in the solution; however, the solvent (water) is *not* part of the chemical change. Using the law of energy conservation, we know heat must be conserved. Here, if the reaction is exothermic, the solution temperature will rise because the chemicals released heat.

Heat lost must equal heat gained: net change is zero

$$\Delta H_{solution} = (\text{grams of solution}) \times (\text{specific heat of solution}) \times \Delta T$$
$$(\text{water})$$

$$\text{where } \Delta H_{solution} = -\Delta H_{reaction}$$

When using this equation it is important to remember that you measure the heat change of the solution by weighing your reacting mixture and by measuring the temperature change. You assume that the conditions of temperature and pressure stay the same during the time it takes you to perform these measurements. You are then able to use your data to calculate the heat of the reaction that takes place between the chemicals in the solution. The following pages present a few examples using some realistic data similar to what you will collect in the laboratory.

Coffee cup calorimetry calculations

The first example uses an acid–base reaction. The acid is HCl and the base is NaOH. The reaction is exothermic and heat is released.

Solved problem

When a student mixes 40.0 mL of 1.0 M NaOH and 40.0 mL of 1.0 M HCl in a coffee cup calorimeter, the final temperature of the mixture rises from 22.0°C to 27.0°C. Calculate the enthalpy change for the reaction of hydrochloric acid (HCl) with sodium hydroxide (NaOH). Assume that the coffee cup calorimeter loses negligible heat, that the density of the solution is that of pure water (1.0 g/mL), and that the specific heat of the solution is the same as that of pure water.

$$NaOH(aq) + HCl(aq) \rightarrow NaCl(aq) + H_2O(l) \quad \Delta H = ?$$

Asked: *Amount of heat change (ΔH) for NaOH and HCl reaction*

Given: *Volume of solutions = 40.0 mL + 40.0 mL,*
molarities of solutions are 1.0 M, and ΔT = 5°C

Relationships: $q_{solution} = m_{solution} \times C_{p\ solution} \times \Delta T$

Solve: *First note that the temperature increased, so the reaction released energy to the solution. This means the reaction is exothermic and will have a negative ΔH.*
Total volume of solution is 40.0 mL + 40.0 mL = 80.0 mL.
Total mass of solution is 80.0 g using the density of water (1.0 g/mL).
$q_{solution}$ *= 80.0 g × 4.18 J/(g·°C) × (27.0°C – 22.0°C).*
$q_{solution}$ *= +1,672 J. The positive sign indicates heat is absorbed.*
$q_{solution}$ *= +1.67 kJ, Therefore q_{rxn} = –1.67 kJ, so we reverse the sign as heat gained by the solution is lost by the reaction. To find heat on a per mole basis, we use the molarity times the volume in liters to calculate moles; 1.0 M × 0.040 L = 0.040 moles of both reactants (where NaOH and HCl are in equimolar amounts).*

Lastly, $\dfrac{-1.67\ kJ}{0.040\ mole} = -41.8\ kJ/mole = \Delta H.$
Since the temperature increased, heat was released from the reaction, making ΔH negative.

Answer: *ΔH= –41.8 kJ/mole*

Any time an acid and a base are mixed, heat will be released. The amount of heat depends upon the amount of moles of acid and base that are present in the solution. You will experience firsthand how the solution warms up when doing some neutralization experiments in the laboratory.

More coffee cup calorimetry calculations

This example involves dissolving a salt or an ionic compound in water. In this case, heat is absorbed when the ions separate in water.

Solved problem

In one experiment a student mixed 100.0 mL of water with 1.50 g of ammonium nitrate [$NH_4NO_3(s)$] in a coffee cup calorimeter. The initial temperature of the water was 23°C. After the ammonium nitrate was added, the solution was stirred and the final temperature of the mixed solution was 20.6°C. Calculate the heat change (enthalpy) for the dissolving of $NH_4NO_3(s)$ in kilojoules per mole of solid dissolved. Assume the specific heat of the solution is the same as that of pure water.

$$NH_4NO_3(s) + H_2O(l) \rightarrow NH_4^+(aq) + NO_3^-(aq) \quad \Delta H = ?$$

Asked: *Amount of heat change (ΔH) when dissolving ammonium nitrate (equal to $-q_{solution}$)*

Given: *Mass of water = 100.0 mL, mass of solid $NH_4NO_3(s)$ = 1.50 g*

Relationships: *Molar mass of NH_4NO_3*
= (14.007 × 2) + (15.999 × 3) + (1.0079 × 4)
= 80.04 g/mole, $q_{solution} = m_{solution} \times C_{p\ solution} \times \Delta T$

Solve: *First note the temperature decreased, so the dissolving process absorbed energy from the solution. This means the change is endothermic and the reaction will have a positive ΔH. density of water = 1.0 g/mL for 100.0 mL = 100.0 g.*
total mass of the solution is 100.0 g + 1.50 g = 101.5 g.
$q_{solution}$ = 101.5 g × 4.18 J/g°C × (23 °C – 20.6 °C).
$q_{solution}$ = –1,018.2 J. The negative sign indicates that heat is lost.
$q_{solution}$ = –1.02 kJ, therefore ΔH = 1.02 kJ; we reverse the sign as heat lost by the solution is gained by the reaction. Now we calculate the number of moles in 1.5 g of $NH_4NO_3(s)$:

$$1.50\ g\ NH_4NO_3 \times \frac{1\ mole\ NH_4NO_3}{80.04\ g\ NH_4NO_3} = 0.0187\ mole\ NH_4NO_3(s)$$

Lastly, $\dfrac{1.02\ kJ}{0.0187\ mole} = +54.5\ kJ/mole = \Delta H$

Since the temperature decreased, heat from the surroundings was absorbed by the solution, making q_{rxn} positive.

Answer: *ΔH = +54.5 kJ/mole*

If you recall, ammonium nitrate is the chemical used in cold packs. No wonder it feels cool on our skin—it is absorbing +54 kJ/mole of heat from the warmth of our skin.

Density, freezing, and boiling

Mass and volume of solutions

When you add 25 g of salt to 100 mL of water you do not get 125 mL of solution. That's because the sodium ions (Na^+) and chlorine ions (Cl^-) fit partially in between the water molecules. The volume of the solution is a little greater than 100 mL, but not as much as the added volume of solid salt. The mass of solution, however, is 125 g. The matter has to go somewhere, and 25 g of salt + 100 g of water makes 125 g of solution.

Volumes of solute and solvent do not add up to the volume of solution

20 g salt   80 mL water   87 mL solution!

Density of solutions

If the volume stays about the same and the mass increases, then the *density* of a solution increases. Salt water is denser than fresh water. Almost any solid solute increases the density of the solution above that of the pure solvent. This explains why a can of diet soda floats and a can of sugared soda sinks. Diet soda has only a dilute concentration of sweetener. Sugared soda may have 40 g of sugar in a single can!

Density of gas/ liquid and liquid/liquid solutions

If gases or liquids are dissolved in a liquid solvent, the density can either increase or decrease depending on the solute. Alcohol is less dense than water, so a solution of alcohol and water is less dense than pure water. Carbon dioxide gas is also less dense than water, so soda water is less dense than pure water. However, the amount of CO_2 dissolved in soda water is not very large, so the density change is very small.

Solutes usually lower the freezing point of a solution

The presence of solute molecules usually lowers the freezing point of a solution compared to that of the pure solvent. The freezing point goes down by about 1.86°C for every mole of solute particles. For example, sea water is about 3.5% salt. Since salt dissociates into Na^+ and Cl^- ions, each mole of dissolved salt adds two moles of particles. Pure water freezes at 0°C. The dissolved salt causes sea water to freeze at −2.2°C.

Solutes usually raise the boiling point of a solution

Adding solutes increases the boiling point of a solution (compared to the pure solvent). For water, each mole of solute particles increases the boiling point by about 0.5°C. That means sea water boils at 100.6°C instead of 100°C.

Colligative properties (part 1)

Colligative properties

Why does ice melt when we sprinkle salt on it? Understanding how salt interacts with ice at the molecular level will give us insight into this phenomenon. We know that ice freezes at 0°C (or 32°F), but why does it become a liquid at the same temperature when we add salt to it? To understand this, we need to study **colligative properties**. Colligative properties are the properties of a solution that depend upon the number of dissolved particles collectively, but not on the nature or type of particle. One common colligative property is *freezing point depression*, which is a lowering of the freezing point of a substance. A good point of discussion with classmates and your teacher is the effect of freezing point depression. Use it as an example to practice your speaking and communication skills.

Discussion topic

Lowering the freezing point

For dilute solutions, there is a direct relationship between the increase in the number of solute particles and a decrease in the freezing point of a solution. Why does this occur? First, let's consider a pure solvent such as water. Pure water freezes at 0°C. When water freezes and goes from a liquid to a solid, the molecules are held more tightly. Remember, the particles can vibrate, but they can't slide past one another in the solid phase. The process of solid formation causes a decrease in randomness in the molecules, because they are no longer free to move and slide past one another. Ice is a more ordered structure than water. Solid formation from a liquid is always associated with a decrease in randomness, or **entropy (S)**. When solute particles are introduced into a liquid, the mixing introduces more randomness into the solution. You could think of it as more variation in the types of particles, which increases the disorder of the system. These dissolved particles get in the way of the molecules trying to solidify, and this makes it harder for an ordered lattice to form. This slows down the freezing process.

Entropy

Molality

To calculate the change in the freezing point resulting from a particular solute, it is necessary to use a new unit of concentration called **molality (m)**. Molality is the number of moles of solute per kilogram of solvent. This is different from molarity (M) because the mass of solvent does not vary with temperature. When solutions are undergoing temperature changes, the volume of the solvent can change. Using molality corrects for this.

Chemistry terms

colligative property: a physical property of a solution that depends only on the number of dissolved solute particles, not on the type (or nature) of the particle itself.

entropy (S): a measure of the disorder or randomness of a system.

molality (m): a unit of concentration used when the temperature varies, expressed in moles of solute per kilogram of solvent.

Colligative properties (part 2)

Calculation of molality

Here is the equation that allows us to calculate the molality (m) of a solution:

$$m = \frac{\text{moles solute}}{\text{kg of solvent}}$$

molality

Remember that the density of water is 1.0 g/mL, so 1.0 g = 1.0 mL for this solvent. One practical application of colligative properties is the use of antifreeze in car radiators. The radiator fluid must be able to circulate as a liquid around the engine in order to maintain proper engine temperature. By adding ethylene glycol ($C_2H_6O_2$) to water and mixing, a solution is created that resists freezing at cold temperatures inside the radiator. This happens because the solution has an increased number of ethylene glycol solute particles, which interfere with water's ability to form an ordered solid structure.

Calculating freezing point depression

To calculate the change in freezing point, we need to use the following equation:

freezing point depression constant

$$\Delta T_f = K_f \times m$$

change in freezing point in °C

molarity

Here is an example that explains how you can apply the formula and calculate the freezing point depression for antifreeze in radiator water:

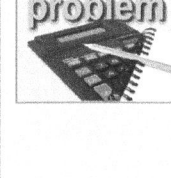
Solved problem

Calculate the freezing point of a 1.8 m aqueous solution of antifreeze that contains ethylene glycol ($C_2H_6O_2$) as the solute.

Asked: *The freezing point of a 1.8 m solution of ethylene glycol*

Given: *Molality m = 1.8 m; K_f = 1.86°C/m (for water the solvent)*

Relationships: $\Delta T_f = K_f \times m$

Solve: $\Delta T_f = K_f \times m = 1.86°C/m \times 1.8\ m = 3.35°C$
Freezing point of antifreeze solution = 0°C – 3.35°C = –3.35°C

Answer: *The freezing point is lowered by 3.35°C.*

By adding sufficient amounts of antifreeze, the solution can withstand temperatures below –25°C, allowing our vehicles to start in colder winter weather. Propylene glycol ($C_3H_8O_2$) is a typical deicer used on aircraft, and it works in a similar way. This substance is sprayed on the airplane to decrease the formation of ice crystals.

Electrolyte solutions

Electrolytes conduct electricity

When salts dissolve in water, they dissociate (or split apart) into their counterpart ions. Aqueous solutions containing dissolved ions are able to conduct electricity. The dissolved ions are capable of transferring an electric charge through a solution. The term **electrolyte** refers to a solute that is able to conduct electricity in an aqueous solution. For example, you know that you are not supposed to blow dry your hair when you are in the tub! This is because your skin contains salt that dissolves in the bath water, the water itself contains some mineral ions, and our blood also contains ions.

Single ion dissolving

Some salts dissolve in a one-to-one ratio, producing the same concentration of individual ions as the original solution. NaCl is a good example:

$$NaCl(aq) \rightarrow Na^+(aq) + Cl^-(aq)$$

$$1.0 \text{ M} \qquad 1.0 \text{ M} \qquad 1.0 \text{ M}$$

Multiple ions dissolving

Other salts dissolve and yield a larger number of ions, and therefore result in a higher concentration of ions. $MgCl_2$ is an example:

$$MgCl_2(aq) \rightarrow Mg^{2+}(aq) + 2Cl^-(aq)$$

$$1.0 \text{ M} \qquad 1.0 \text{ M} \qquad 2.0 \text{ M}$$

On the label of any solution that says 1.0 M NaCl or 1.0 M $MgCl_2$, it is better to think of the ions as already split apart. Imagining the ions apart from each other is representative of how they actually exist in the aqueous solution.

More particles increase the effect

Having more particles in solution increases the strength of its colligative properties. In this case, a salt with three component ions versus a salt with two would have a greater freezing point depression.

TABLE 9.4. Actual number of ions per solute molecule, as a function of solution concentration

Solute	0.10 M	0.01 M	0.001 M
NaCl (Na$^+$, Cl$^-$) (2 ions)	1.530	1.719	1.928
CaCl$_2$ (Ca^{2+}, 2Cl$^-$) (3 ions	1.915	2.473	2.798

Chemistry terms

electrolyte: a solute capable of conducting electricity when dissolved in an aqueous solution.

Evolving from the ocean

For years scientists have speculated that all life forms originated in the ocean. Since life first began, water's role as a solvent was important in bringing chemicals together. When scientists search for life on other planets they search for evidence of water, because they know it must be present for life to exist. Most of our planet is covered by vast oceans. It is in these oceans that scientists find clues to how early life forms evolved and adapted to their environments. The chemical composition of the ocean plays a major role in determining which elements were available for living things to use. At the dawn of time, during the Precambrian era, evidence suggests that life existed only in the ocean.

How could living organisms form from ocean water?

Water's ability to hydrate charged ions and to dissolve minerals and gases made it a mixing pot for elements of life. Ocean water contains nutrients and organic compounds that were formed during energetic reactions. The famous Miller and Urey experiment showed that organic molecules, such as amino acids, sugars and lipids, could be formed from simple molecules such as water, with methane, ammonia, and hydrogen gases. Miller and Urey used electrodes to simulate the energy thought to be provided by lightning. Lightning was an available source of energy sufficient to cause molecules to break apart and reform. There is recent evidence that also suggests that a meteorite impact could have supplied the energy for chemical reactions in the oceans. Experiments suggest that meteorites could have supplied both the energy and the carbon to synthesize key molecules used as building blocks for life. When energy is sent through a solution containing molecules, chemical bonds are broken and reformed. It is hypothesized that some of these new molecules came together and formed unicellular organisms. Water's polarity helped molecules get together and form cell-like structures. Blue-green algae or cyanobacteria were among the first forms of life.

Blood and ocean water

Strong evidence for life evolving from the ocean comes from the observation that blood and ocean water contain similar chemical substances! Blood can be separated into two portions: a liquid layer called plasma and a solid layer containing cells. Blood plasma is about 92% water, and it has a concentration of salt and other ions that is amazingly similar to ocean water. Could it be that, as life evolved, it developed cells that were adapted to the chemical environment of sea water? Blood bathes our tissues inside our bodies. It is responsible for maintaining a very delicate chemical balance inside and outside of our tissues.

Today the ocean's total ionic concentration is several times that of blood, but the ancient oceans are thought to have been more dilute. Like in our blood, the concentration of ions in the ocean is remarkably constant. The ocean is always undergoing localized changes in concentration just like our blood, yet the concentrations of both fluids remain constant overall. Scientists feel that the only way to account for this is by thorough mixing of the water in the ocean.

Plasma (55%)

White blood cells and platelets (<1%)

Blood (45%)

Chemistry of the ancient oceans

To understand the chemistry of the early oceans, scientists have analyzed samples of sedimentary rock dating back to the first half of Earth's history. They found that early oceans had large amounts of dissolved iron in the form of Fe(II) or Fe^{2+} ions. Virtually every living organism we know of requires iron for its life functions. Scientists wonder if this is because organisms evolved in an iron-rich environment. Today's oceans contain very little iron, and organisms have had to develop clever ways to capture it. Once photosynthesis began to make oxygen present in the atmosphere and in the water, it combined with dissolved iron in the oceans to form layers of rust. The rust then settled to the bottom of the ocean. The reaction

$$4Fe^{2+}(aq) + 3O_2(g) \rightarrow 2Fe_2O_3(s)$$

caused the iron to form solid deposits, which can be seen in the geological record dating back to 1.8 billion years ago.

Sulfur became abundant in the oceans as sulfate ions (SO_4^{2-}) and hydrogen sulfide (H_2S). Sulfur is another very important element found in living organisms. Disulfide bridges or covalent sulfur bonds help to stabilize many molecules, such as DNA double helices. In deep water on the ocean floor, where there is no sunlight available for photosynthesis, bacteria get energy by oxidizing hydrogen sulfide (H_2S). These bacteria form the base of the food chain on the ocean floor. The H_2S is made available from volcanic gases that erupt from geothermal vents in the ocean floor. These vents release mineral-rich "smoke." Overall, the elemental composition of the ocean has changed dramatically over time.

By studying which elements were present in the early oceans and comparing these to which elements are present today, scientists are learning about the key elements that may have influenced natural selection of early life forms.

Chapter 9 Review

Vocabulary

Match each word to the sentence where it best fits.

Section 9.1

dissolved	solute
solvent	polar
hydrogen bond	surface tension
hydration	distilled water
tap water	deionized water
aqueous	

1. The biggest percentage of a solution is made up of the _____. Often this is a liquid.

2. A molecule with a charge separation is called _____.

3. A substance is said to be _____ when it completely separates and disperses into the solution.

4. The _____ is the substance dissolved in the solvent.

5. A property named _____ describes when intermolecular forces pull a liquid surface into the smallest possible area.

6. A/An _____ is a type of intermolecular attraction formed when a hydrogen atom bonded to an N, O, or F atom is attracted to a negative charge on another molecule, or even on the same molecule, such as in a protein.

7. The process known as _____ describes how water molecules surround a charged ion or a polar molecule.

8. Water that comes from the sink is called _____, and it conducts electricity.

9. A/An _____ solution is one that has water as its solvent.

10. Water that is condensed after boiling to separate out solute particles is called _____.

11. Water that does not contain ions is called _____.

Section 9.2

concentration	dilute
solubility	concentrated
insoluble	molarity
aqueous equilibrium	saturated
supersaturated	unsaturated

12. A solution that contains *more* dissolved solute than it can "hold" is called _____.

13. A solution that contains *less* dissolved solute than it can "hold" is called _____.

14. A/An _____ has been achieved when the amount of dissolved solute becomes constant over time.

15. A solution is _____ when it is holding the maximum amount of solute that it can.

16. A solution that has very little solute dissolved in it is said to be _____.

17. If a solution is called _____ then it has a large amount of dissolved solute.

18. When the concentration of a solution is measured as moles of solute divided by liters of solution the concentration unit is _____.

19. When a substance will not dissolve it is said to be _____.

20. The amount of solute that will dissolve in a particular solvent is called its _____ (at a given temperature and pressure).

Section 9.3

reaction rate	heat of solution
enthalpy	freezing point
entropy	colligative property
electrolyte	molality

21. A/An _____ is a solute capable of conducting electricity when it is dissolved.

22. When solutions mix, the _____ is affected by the concentration and temperature of the solutions.

23. _____ depression is a common colligative property.

24. The _____ is the energy released or absorbed when a solute dissolves in a solution.

25. _____ is the concentration unit that does not vary with temperature. It is measured as moles of solute per kilogram of solvent.

26. The heat energy of a chemical change is called _____.

27. The _____ of a system is a measure of disorder or randomness.

28. A/An _____ is a property that depends on the number of solute particles in solution, not the type of solute particle.

Conceptual Questions

Section 9.1

29. Suppose you make a solution of ice tea using a mix. What is the solute and what is the solvent. Explain.

30. Describe what happens to the ice tea mix when you mix it.

31. Give an example of a common solid that dissolves in water. Can you explain how it does this?

32. Draw a picture of a water molecule. Label the positive ends and the negative ends of the molecule.

33. Now draw three water molecules and show how they form hydrogen bonds to each other. Label the hydrogen bonds with a different color pen.

34. Describe why hydrogen bonding is important to life on Earth.

35. Look up hydrogen bonding on the Internet. Write down the definition.

36. Give an example of surface tension that you have witnessed in your everyday life. If you have not seen this in your everyday life, ask some friends.

37. When we are told to stay hydrated during exercise, what does that actually mean? Explain.

38. Draw a picture of a potassium ion (K^+) surrounded by water molecules. Show how the water molecules orient themselves around potassium.

39. Sometimes we use distilled water to iron our clothes or to soak our contact lenses in. Why don't we use tap water?

40. Describe the difference between distilled water and deionized water.

41. Give three reasons why aqueous solutions are important.

42. Write out a chemical equation that represents salt [NaCl(s)] dissolving in water. Show the appropriate state of matter for the ions on the products side of your arrow.

43. Write the chemical formula for mineral spirits. Would this substance be soluble in water?

Section 9.2

44. If you were to mix water and chalk, would the chalk dissolve? Explain. Give an example of something that would dissolve (for comparison).

45. Describe how you would make a concentrated solution of lemonade.

46. There are several ways to calculate concentration. List three of them.

47. Pretend you are sitting at the kitchen table with a glass of water and a sugar bowl.
    a. You take a teaspoon of sugar and add it to the water. What happens?
    b. You add two more teaspoons of sugar to the water and stir. What happens now?
    c. Slowly you keep adding small amounts of sugar. What will eventually happen?

48. Refer to the previous question. What would happen if your glass of water were hot? Would this affect what you observe? Explain.

49. Can gases dissolve in water? If so, give an example.

50. Explain why fish swim deeper during the summer months.

51. Describe how you would prepare a 1.0 M solution of copper(II) chloride ($CuCl_2$). List each step and explain as necessary.

52. What would be the difference between a 1.0 M solution and a 6.0 M solution of potassium chloride (KCl)?

53. Explain why it is important to be accurate when preparing a solution of known concentration.

Chapter 9 Review

54. Do you think it would be easy to measure a drinking water supply that contained 1 ppb of lead? Is it important to be able to measure such small amounts accurately?

55. Explain what would happen if you dropped a sugar cube in a cup of water and did not stir. How would this compare to the same amount of granular sugar added to water?

56. What is the density of water? How does this compare with the density of ice? Briefly explain.

Section 9.3

57. Suppose you added a piece of chalk [$CaCO_3(s)$] to a solution of 1.0 M carbonic acid [$H_2CO_3(aq)$] and another piece of chalk to a 3.0 M solution of carbonic acid. Would you expect there to be a difference in what you see? Explain. Describe what you think would be different at the microscopic or molecular level.

58. Describe why sugar dissolves better in hot tea than in iced tea. Discuss the water molecules involved.

59. The ocean does not freeze as easily as a lake or pond. What does an ocean have in it that could explain this behavior? Explain.

60. When we add 2.0 g of a solute to a solution, the mass of the solution always increases by 2.0 g. If we add 2.0 mL or 2.0 cm^3 the volume does not increase by the same amount. Why not? Briefly explain.

61. How does the density of a solution change with the addition of a solute? Explain.

62. Explain why dissolving a salt in water often creates an electrolyte

63. Sometimes there is a change in temperature in a solution when a solute is added to it. For example, the temperature can either increase or decrease when a salt is dissolved in water. Give two practical applications that use this phenomenon.

64. In a case where a salt dissolves and the solution absorbs heat, is the heat written on the products side of the arrow or the reactants side? Explain.

65. Why are styrofoam coffee cups good to use when we are investigating chemical changes in solution?

66. When a chemical change takes place in a solution, the water molecules either absorb heat or emit heat. What are these two processes called?

67. Based on the law of conservation of energy, we can say that $\Delta H_{soln} = -\Delta H_{reaction}$. Explain why.

68. Describe what entropy means in your own words.

69. Why does spreading salt on icy roads make the ice melt, when the temperature is still at the freezing point for ice? Explain to the best of your ability.

70. Compare molality (m) to molarity (M).

71. What is the formula for calculating molality?

72. A student wishes to dissolve solid plant food in water to use with her indoor plants. Which of the following actions is LEAST likely to make the plant food dissolve faster?
    a. cooling the water before mixing
    b. warming the water before using
    c. stirring rapidly while mixing
    d. breaking the fertilizer into smaller chunks before mixing

73. 100 mL of solution can contain a maximum of 44 grams of $MgSO_4$ at 40°C. Which of the following is most likely to be true of a saturated solution of $MgSO_4$ at 20°C?
    a. The 20°C solution contains a lower concentration of $MgSO_4$ than the 40°C solution.
    b. The 20°C solution contains a higher concentration of $MgSO_4$ than the 40°C solution.
    c. Both solutions contain about the same concentration of $MgSO_4$ because both are saturated.

74. Calcium carbonate is used by coral organisms to build their reef structures. The solubility of calcium carbonate in salt water decreases from 10°C to 30°C. Why is this unusual and why might this be helpful to coral?

Quantitative Problems

Section 9.2

75. Suppose you dissolve 12.0 g of sugar in 120.0 g of water.
    a. Calculate the concentration of sugar in the solution by percent mass.
    b. If the density of water is 1.0 g/mL, calculate the concentration in grams per liter.
    c. Calculate the molarity of this solution.

76. Suppose you need to prepare a solution with 20.0 g of $MgCl_2$ in 500 mL of water.
    a. Calculate the percent by mass of $MgCl_2$ in the solution.
    b. Calculate the concentration in grams per liter. Assume the density of water is 1.0 g/mL.
    c. Calculate the molarity of this solution.

77. What is the molarity of a solution that contains 8.5 g of NaCl in 250 mL of water?

78. If 30 g of $CaCO_3$ is dissolved in 2.0 L of solution, what is the mass percent of $CaCO_3$ in the solution? (Assume the density of water is 1.0 g/mL.)

79. Calculate the number of moles and the grams of potassium iodide (KI) needed to make one liter of a 0.75 M solution.

80. An experiment calls for 50.0 mL of 0.700 M NH_3. How much of a 12.0 M stock solution of NH_3 should we dilute?
    a. 2.92 mL
    b. 50.0 mL
    c. 342 mL
    d. 2.92 L

81. We dilute 2.50 mL of a 10.0 M stock solution of H_2SO_4 to a volume of 60.0 mL. What is its final concentration?
    a. 10.0 M
    b. 4.17 M
    c. 2.40 M
    d. 0.417 M

82. Classify each of the following solutions as unsaturated, saturated, or supersaturated. Refer to the table of solubilities on page 270. Assume all solutions are at a temperature of 20°C.
    a. A solution containing 28 g of salt (NaCl) in 75 mL of water
    b. A solution containing 4.5 g of baking soda ($NaHCO_3$) in 50 mL of water
    c. A solution containing 6.0 g of copper sulfate ($CuSO_4$) in 30 mL of water

83. A student is planning an investigation to test a hypothesis that the density of a solution increases linearly with the concentration. Which of the following should be selected to determine how close the relationship is to a straight line?
    a. a graphing calculator
    b. a balance and graduated cylinder
    c. a spectrophotometer for measuring concentration
    d. a temperature probe and constant temperature bath

Section 9.3

84. When a student mixes 50.0 mL of 1.0 M NaOH and 50.0 mL of 1.0M HCl in a coffee cup calorimeter, the final temperature of the mixture rises from 21.0 °C to 25.0 °C. Calculate the acid (HCl) with sodium hydroxide (NaOH). Assume that the coffee cup calorimeter loses negligible heat, that the density of the solution is that of pure water (1.0 g/mL), and that the specific heat of the solution is the same as that of pure water.
    $$NaOH(aq) + HCl(aq) \rightarrow NaCl(aq) + H_2O(l)$$

85. In one experiment a student mixed 100.0 mL of water with 2.60 g of ammonium nitrate [$NH_4NO_3(s)$] in a coffee cup calorimeter. The initial temperature of the water was 24.5°C. After the ammonium nitrate was added, the solution was stirred and the final temperature of the mixed solution was 20.2°C. Calculate the heat change (enthalpy) for the dissolution of $NH_4NO_3(s)$ in kilojoules per mole of solid dissolved. Assume the specific heat of the solution is the same as that of pure water.
    $$NH_4NO_3(s) + H_2O(l) \rightarrow NH_4^+(aq) + NO_3^-(aq)$$

86. In a coffee cup calorimetry experiment, 1.75 g of Zn(s) is added to 100.0 mL of 1.0 M HCl initially at 21.0°C. The temperature rises to 30.1°C. What is the heat of the reaction per mole of Zn? Assume that the specific heat of the acid is the same as that of pure water. $Zn(s) + 2HCl(aq) \rightarrow ZnCl_2(aq) + H_2(g)$

87. Calculate the molality of the following solutions:
    a. a solution containing 2.0 g of NaCl in 500.0 g of water
    b. a solution containing 6.5 g of $CaBr_2$ in 1,200 g of water
    c. a solution of 100 g of sugar ($C_{12}H_{22}O_{11}$) in 2.0 L of water

88. Calculate the freezing point of a 2.20 m aqueous solution of antifreeze that contains ethylene glycol ($C_2H_6O_2$) as the solute. $K_f = 1.86°C/m$ for water.

89. Adding 1.50 g of benzene (C_6H_6) to 80.70 g of cyclohexane (C_6H_{12}) causes a decrease in the freezing point of the cyclohexane from 7.0°C to 3.8°C. What is the K_f (freezing point depression constant) for cyclohexane?

90. Determine the freezing point of a solution containing 0.750 kg of chloroform ($CHCl_3$) and 48.0 g of eucalyptol ($C_{10}H_{18}O$), a compound found in eucalyptus trees. The K_f for $CHCl_3$ is 4.68°C/m and the normal freezing point of $CHCl_3$ is −63.5°C.

CHAPTER 10

Chemical Reactions

How do we represent a chemical reaction?

How do we classify chemical reactions?

How do we evaluate the effectiveness and the economics of chemical reactions?

Chemical reactions occur all around us, including inside our bodies. In fact, the human body is the ultimate chemical factory. Digestion of food is just a number of chemical reactions. The nutrients from the food we eat are then transported to muscle and organ cells, where other chemical reactions extract energy and make life possible.

The atmosphere of our planet is 78% nitrogen (N_2) and 21% oxygen (O_2). However, it was not always this way. We believe that four billion years ago, Earth's atmosphere contained much more CO_2 than it does today and almost no oxygen. All of the oxygen we breathe in the atmosphere today was created by plants! Over millions of years, the photosynthesis reaction gradually changed the entire atmosphere of the planet by turning carbon dioxide into oxygen and organic matter. In the same way that nature uses the energy from the Sun to capture carbon, human technology also uses chemical reactions to make new compounds from existing fundamental elements. From your kitchen to the pharmaceutical laboratories where medicines are produced to the petroleum refining factories where gasoline and plastics are produced, chemical reactions that make something tasty, healthy, or useful are taking place.

Rusting generates heat

Rusting is a process that we are very familiar with. From cars to bridges, we have all seen a shiny piece of iron become covered with the brown flaky substance known as *rust*. The process that turns iron metal to reddish rust is the result of a very common chemical reaction: the reaction of iron with oxygen. This countertop experiment is a quick way to make rust and also to investigate the chemical reaction that occurs. All chemical reactions involve energy, and rusting is no exception. By making the reaction proceed quickly, you can see the energy change with a thermometer. To do the experiment, you need:

- two thermometers,
- a piece of #000 steel wool, and
- a small rubber band for wrapping around the thermometer as indicated in the picture.

Steel wool always has some oil on it from the manufacturing process. This oil must be removed before the iron in the steel can be exposed directly to moist air. Washing the steel wool with dish soap usually does the trick.

Step 1: Wrap one of the thermometers with moist steel wool.

Step 2: Place the two thermometers next to each other as shown in the picture so that you can compare their readings easily.

After some time you should notice that the temperature of the thermometer wrapped with the steel wool starts to increase, while the other thermometer stays constant.

Why does the temperature increase?

Hypothesis #1: There is something going on in the steel wool that releases energy.

Hypothesis #2: There must be another source of heat for the temperature to increase.

The bare thermometer is not in contact with any heat source that doesn't also affect the thermometer with the steel wool. That rules out hypothesis #2. So where does the energy come from? The best explanation is that energy must come from whatever is going on inside the steel wool. In fact, it comes from the chemical reaction between iron (Fe) and oxygen (O_2) that results in the rusting of Fe. The rust is called iron oxide, which has the chemical formula Fe_2O_3. We can write a simple expression that summarizes our observations as follows:

Iron reacts with oxygen to produce rust (Fe_2O_3) and energy.

This is a very good start for a deeper investigation into the subject of chemical reactions because

1. it is a simple reaction that occurs all around us and
2. it shows directly how energy is involved.

In fact energy is involved in all chemical reactions. In some reactions energy is released to the environment, making things hotter, and in others energy is absorbed from the environment, making things colder.

10.1 Chemical Equations

Developing the language of chemistry

Think of the element symbols as the *alphabet* of chemistry and the chemical formulas as the *words* of chemistry. Chemical equations are the *sentences* of chemistry; they tell the story of the material world. All the complex changes we see in the material world are the result of chemical reactions. The "big" story of the world is the interrelationships among all the countless chemical reactions that occur. To understand that story, even in part, we need the language of chemical equations, which really are the sentences of chemistry.

The language of chemistry

Element symbols H, O, Na, Fe	Alphabet of chemistry
Compound formulas H_2O, CO_2, NaCl	Words of chemistry
Chemical equations $2H_2 + O_2 \rightarrow 2H_2O$	Sentences of chemistry

Chemical reactions and chemical change

A **chemical reaction** is any process of chemical change. Chemical reactions convert one or more substances into new substances. Atoms are not created or destroyed in the process. They are simply rearranged to form new substances. In general, we represent a chemical reaction by a **chemical equation** as follows:

Chemical equation

$$Reactants \;\rightarrow\; Products$$

Chemical equations and chemical reactions

The **reactants** are the starting materials used in the reaction. The **products** are the substances that are produced by the reaction. The reactants are always written on the left side of the arrow and the products are written on the right side. The arrow indicates the direction of the chemical reaction, pointing from the reactants to the products. It means that the reactants "give," "yield," or "react to form" the products.

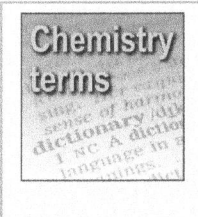

Chemistry terms

chemical reaction: the process that creates chemical changes.

chemical equation: an expression that describes the changes that happen in a chemical reaction.

reactants: the starting materials or substances in a chemical reaction, appearing on the left side of the chemical equation.

products: the materials or substances resulting from a chemical reaction, appearing on the right side of the chemical equation.

A NATURAL APPROACH TO CHEMISTRY

Constructing a chemical equation

An example chemical reaction

Let's construct the chemical equation for one of the reactions that takes place in a fire. In this reaction, oxygen (O_2) from the atmosphere reacts with carbon (C) from wood to produce carbon dioxide gas (CO_2). In this reaction, O_2 and C are the *reactants* since they are consumed by the reaction. Carbon dioxide (CO_2) is the *product*. In words, the reaction can be written as follows:

Carbon reacts with oxygen to produce carbon dioxide.

We can write the expression in a more compact way using an arrow:

carbon + oxygen → carbon dioxide

Chemical equation with formulas

However, the use of the chemical formulas for each substance involved in the reaction is the most accurate and least ambiguous way to describe the reaction. For our reaction, we write the general relationship with the chemical equation using chemical formulas:

$$C + O_2 \rightarrow CO_2$$

Interpreting a chemical equation

The diagram below summarizes the interpretation of the chemical equation.

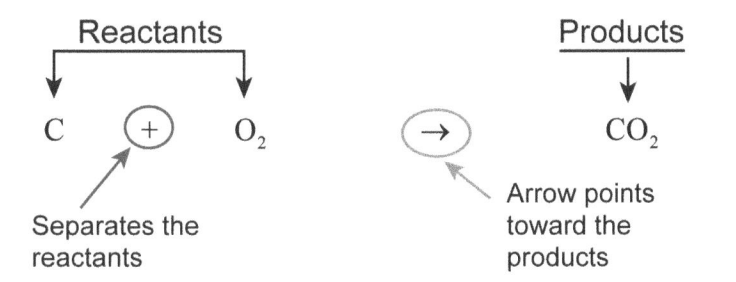

Why we use chemical formulas

Using chemical formulas to write the chemical equation gives us a very compact way to express chemical reactions. It also gives us a clear picture of the types of atoms that are involved in the reaction and how they are bonded together in both the products and the reactants.

Energy may appear on either side of a chemical equation

Does the chemical equation $C + O_2 \rightarrow CO_2$ give a complete representation of burning wood? When we look at wood burning in a fire, we can see that fire gives off light, and we can feel that fires gives off heat. So, if the chemical equation $C + O_2 \rightarrow CO_2$ does represent the phenomenon of wood burning, then *where is the heat* and *where is the light?* Later in the chapter we will add energy to the chemical equation and explicitly recognize the energy as either a reactant (absorbed) or a product (given off).

Conservation of mass

Chemical reactions conserve mass

One of the fundamental properties of chemistry is conservation of mass. In fact, this property is so important that scientists call it the **law of conservation of mass**. The law states that the total mass of the reactants is equal to the total mass of the products. In other words, mass is neither created nor destroyed during a chemical reaction.

The number of atoms in a chemical reaction does not change

The fundamental building block of chemistry and chemical reactions is the *atom*. Conservation of mass really means that a chemical reaction does not change the total number or type of atoms. A chemical reaction rearranges the atoms in the reactants into a new arrangement *of the same atoms* in the products.

> **Law of conservation of mass**
> Each and every atom in the *reactants* must also appear in the *products*.
> Each and every atom in the *products* must also appear in the *reactants*.
>
> *mass of products = mass of reactants*

Burning hydrogen in oxygen

For example, consider hydrogen burning in oxygen. This is a reaction that yields water as the product. It is also the reaction that fuels the space shuttle. The white "smoke" that comes out of the shuttle engines is not actually smoke, but water vapor, which is the product of the reaction.

Developing the equation for a chemical reaction

To start developing a chemical equation we write down the reaction between hydrogen and oxygen with the correct chemical formulas for participating substances.

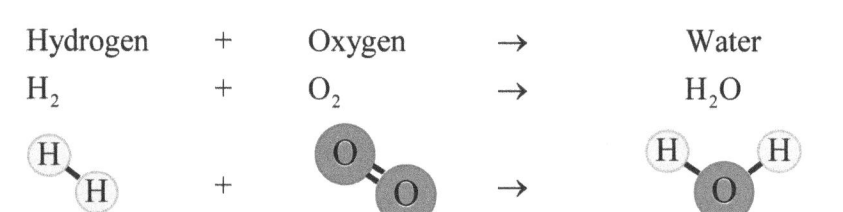

Hydrogen	+	Oxygen	→	Water
H_2	+	O_2	→	H_2O

An unbalanced equation

The above chemical equation correctly shows that water can be created by combining hydrogen and oxygen, but it is *unbalanced* because it does *not* satisfy mass conservation. There are *two* oxygen atoms in the reactants and only *one* in the products!

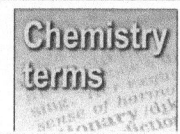
Chemistry terms

law of conservation of mass: law that states that the total mass of reactants (starting materials) and the total mass of products (materials produced by the reaction) is the same.

Reading chemical equations

Why an
unbalanced
equation is
inaccurate

One problem with the equation $H_2 + O_2 \rightarrow H_2O$ is that if you mixed one mole of oxygen and one mole of hydrogen, you would *not* get one mole of water molecules. You would actually get one mole of water molecules and a half a mole of leftover oxygen molecules. You get leftover oxygen molecules because there are more oxygen atoms in the reactants than there are in the products. The chart below summarizes the reaction by counting the numbers of each atom on both sides of the reaction.

"Balanced"
means the same
number of
atoms appear
on both sides

The number of *hydrogen* atoms is the same in both the reactants and the products. We therefore can say that hydrogen atoms are *balanced*.

	Number of Atoms	
	Reactants	Products
Hydrogen	2	2
Oxygen	2	①

missing oxygen⤴

Unbalanced
chemical
equations

The chemical equation $H_2 + O_2 \rightarrow H_2O$ is an **unbalanced chemical equation**. The unbalanced equation tells you what substances are involved in the reaction, but it does *not* tell you how *much* of each are involved. To make it balanced, we need to adjust the number of hydrogen molecules, oxygen molecules, and water molecules until there are the same number of each type of atom on both sides of the chemical equation.

Coefficients

The *number* of molecules in a chemical equation is given by the coefficient in front of the chemical formula. For example, the following might appear in a chemical reaction to describe two hydrogen molecules, one oxygen molecule, or three water molecules:

Coefficient
tells how many
molecules

$2H_2$

Subscript
tells how many
atoms in 1 molecule

		Molecules	Atoms
2 hydrogen molecules	$2H_2$	(H)-(H) (H)-(H)	(H) (H) (H) (H)
1 oxygen molecule	O_2	(O)-(O)	(O) (O)
3 water molecules	$3H_2O$	(H)(O)-(H) (H)(O)-(H) (H)(O)-(H)	(H)(H)(H)(H)(H)(H) (O)(O)(O)

Coefficients
versus
subscripts

The subscript tells you how many atoms are in the molecule. For example the subscript 2 in H_2 tells you there are two hydrogen atoms in a hydrogen molecule. The coefficient tells you how many molecules there are in the reaction. If "$2H_2$" appears in a chemical equation, then you know there are two molecules of hydrogen for a total of four atoms of hydrogen (two molecules × two atoms per molecule).

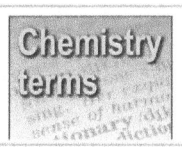
Chemistry
terms

unbalanced chemical equation: a chemical equation that does not satisfy the law of conservation of mass in which the number of each type of atom on the reactant side of the equation does not equal the same number for each atom on the product side.

Writing balanced chemical equations

Using mass conservation to write balanced chemical equations

By multiplying the hydrogen molecule by a factor of 2 and the water molecule by a factor of 2, we obtain a chemical equation that satisfies mass conservation.

Using mass conservation to balance the chemical equation

$$2H_2 \;+\; O_2 \;\rightarrow\; 2H_2O$$

The same number of each type of atom appear in both products and reactants

Balanced equations conserve mass

This chemical equation is **balanced**.

There are two rules for balancing chemical equations:

1. *Do not change* the subscripts in the chemical formulas. This would change the substances involved in the reaction, in essence making a *different* reaction. For example, if we change H_2O to H_2O_2, we change water to hydrogen peroxide.

2. *Do change* the coefficients to adjust the number of each molecule in the reaction. This balances the reaction without changing the substances involved.

OK

$H_2O \quad 2H_2O \quad 3H_2O$

Not OK

$H_2O \quad \rightarrow \quad H_2O_2$

The balanced equation correctly tells you amounts

The balanced equation tells us that when we combine two molecules of hydrogen with one molecule of oxygen, we can obtain two molecules of water. This is the complete recipe for making water. It correctly represents the amount of each substance in the reaction, and it satisfies mass conservation because the same number of each type of atom appears on both the reactant and product sides of the chemical equation.

Chemistry terms

balanced chemical equation: a chemical equation that satisfies the law of conservation of mass, when the total numbers of atoms of each element are the same on both the reactant and product sides of a chemical equation.

A NATURAL APPROACH TO CHEMISTRY

Balancing chemical equations

Why you need to balance chemical equations

The goal of balancing a chemical equation is to get the number of each type of atom to be the same on both the reactant and product sides of the chemical equation. This is really just counting atoms on either side, then adjusting the coefficients until the numbers match. At this point, the process of balancing a chemical equation is trial and error. You must guess and try different coefficients until it works out. For many reactions this approach works fine. However, for reactions that involve a number of reactants and products, a more structured approach is needed. We will develop it in the next few pages.

Coefficients of one

When a single molecule is in a chemical equation, the coefficient of 1 is not written. For example, O_2 in a chemical equation means one *molecule* of oxygen (which contains two atoms).

Coefficients apply to whole molecules

The coefficient of 2 in front of a molecule applies to the entire molecule. For example, $2H_2O$ means that we have two water molecules. Since each water molecule has two hydrogen atoms, the total number of hydrogen atoms is four.

Balance pure elements last

It is always easiest to balance pure elements last. For example, if O_2 appears in a chemical equation, you can change the coefficient to make $2O_2$ or $3O_2$ and change only the number of oxygen atoms. Changing CH_4 to $2CH_4$ changes both the number of carbon atoms *and* the number of hydrogen atoms.

Balance one element at a time

Another good strategy is to start with one element, often carbon. Then check oxygen, and so on, checking and balancing one element at a time. However, every time you change a coefficient, you should make sure you have not unbalanced an element that you already balanced!

Solved problem

The glucose ($C_6H_{12}O_6$) contained in biomass is used as a biofuel to produce ethanol (C_2H_6O) and carbon dioxide (CO_2). Write the balanced equation for this reaction.

Asked: *The coefficients needed to balance the chemical equation*

Given: *The unbalanced chemical equation $C_6H_{12}O_6 \rightarrow C_2H_6O + CO_2$*

Relationships: *The same number of each type of atom must appear on each side.*

Solve: *All atoms involved in the reaction are unbalanced.*
There are 6 C atoms in the reactants and 3 C atoms in the products.
There are 12 H atoms in the reactants and 6 H atoms in the products.
There are 6 O atoms in the reactants and 3 O atoms in the products.
From this accounting, we notice that the number of atoms in the products is half the number of the reactants.
By multiplying the products by a factor of 2 we obtain a balanced chemical equation of the reaction.

Answer: *The balanced chemical equation is $C_6H_{12}O_6 \rightarrow 2C_2H_6O + 2CO_2$.*

10.2 Methods for Balancing Chemical Equations

The respiration reaction

A chemical reaction between blood sugar (glucose, $C_6H_{12}O_6$) and oxygen provides the energy that your body needs. The reaction, called *cellular respiration*, produces carbon dioxide (CO_2) and water (H_2O). Respiration also generates heat.

Cellular respiration: the unbalanced chemical equation

$$C_6H_{12}O_6 \; + \; O_2 \; \rightarrow \; H_2O \; + \; CO_2$$

In this equation we have three different elements to consider: C, O, and H. These elements make up the four substances involved in the reaction.

A general rule

The general rule for developing an effective way to balance chemical equations is to start with the elements that occur in the fewest substances and end with the element that is involved in the most substances.

Start with one element

For our example, both hydrogen and carbon are involved in only one reactant and one product. We could start with either carbon or hydrogen. Let's start with hydrogen. The number of hydrogen atoms in the products is balanced by using a coefficient of 6 in front of the H_2O product.

$$C_6H_{12}O_6 \quad + \quad O_2 \quad \rightarrow \quad 6H_2O \; + \; CO_2$$

Balanced H

Do the next element

Next is carbon, which is involved in two substances. It is balanced by inserting a coefficient of 6 in front of the CO_2 product.

$$C_6H_{12}O_6 \quad + \quad O_2 \quad \rightarrow \quad 6H_2O \quad + \quad 6CO_2$$

Balanced C

Balance pure elements last

The last element to be balanced is oxygen. We have left oxygen for last since it is involved in the largest number of compounds in the reaction. Also, another reason for leaving it for last is that it exists as a pure substance in the reaction.

Let's do some counting of the oxygen atoms as they appear in the equation above:

total number of oxygen atoms in the reactants: $6 + 2 = 8$ total

number of oxygen atoms in the products: $12 + 6 = 18$

Balancing pure elements and checking

Consider the reaction

$$6 + 2 = 8 \text{ oxygen atoms} \qquad C_6H_{12}O_6 \quad + \quad O_2 \quad \rightarrow \quad 6H_2O \quad + \quad 6CO_2 \qquad 6 + 12 = 18 \text{ oxygen atoms}$$

The last step in balancing the equation

The reaction above is balanced for all elements except oxygen. As written, there are 10 more oxygen atoms in the products than in the reactants. To make up the difference we must add ten additional oxygen atoms, or five oxygen molecules (O_2), to the reactants.

The five additional molecules plus the existing oxygen molecule give us a total of six oxygen molecules in the products:

$$C_6H_{12}O_6 \quad + \quad 6\,O_2 \quad \rightarrow \quad 6\,H_2O \quad + \quad 6\,CO_2$$

Check the atom counts

The next step is to check to see that the equation is indeed balanced. We do this by counting the number of atoms for each element on either side of the equation. The equation is balanced when the number of atoms for each element are balanced:

$$C_6H_{12}O_6 \quad + \quad 6O_2 \quad \rightarrow \quad 6H_2O \quad + \quad 6CO_2$$

Reactants	Products
6 carbon	6 carbon
12 hydrogen	12 hydrogen
18 oxygen	18 oxygen

Check that coefficients are not multiples

The last step is to check that the coefficients are the smallest whole numbers possible. For example, the same balanced reaction could also be written as

$$2C_6H_{12}O_6 \quad + \quad 12O_2 \quad \rightarrow \quad 12H_2O \quad + \quad 12CO_2$$

Here, we have doubled the amounts of reactants and products. This is still a correct chemical equation. However, it is preferred and established by convention to write the coefficients as the smallest whole numbers.

The steps for balancing chemical equations

In summary, here are the steps for balancing chemical equations:

Step 1. Write down the unbalanced chemical equation.

Step 2. Identify the element that occurs in only one compound on both sides of the equation and balance it first. If more than one element satisfies this condition, you may balance them in any order.

Step 3. Continue with the rest of the elements. If a free element is present in the reaction, it is balanced last.

Step 4. Check each element to make certain that the equation is balanced.

Step 5. Make sure the coefficients are the smallest possible whole numbers.

Methane (CH_4) reacts with oxygen (O_2) to produce carbon dioxide (CO_2) and water (H_2O). Write the balanced equation for this reaction.

Given: *The unbalanced chemical equation*

$$CH_4 + O_2 \rightarrow CO_2 + H_2O$$

Solve: *We solve the problem in five steps:*

Step 1. Let's start with carbon (C). Reactants have one C atom. Products have one C atom. Carbon is balanced already.

Step 2. Let's proceed by balancing hydrogen (H). Reactants have four H atoms. Products have two H atoms. We need to add two H atoms to the products to balance H:
$$CH_4 + O_2 \rightarrow CO_2 + 2H_2O$$

Step 3. Next we balance oxygen (O). Reactants have two O atoms. Products have four O atoms. We need to add two O atoms to the reactants to balance O:
$$CH_4 + 2O_2 \rightarrow CO_2 + 2H_2O$$

Step 4. Check the number of atoms for each element on both sides of the reaction.

Reactants	Products
1 C atom	1 C atom
4 O atoms	4 O atoms
4 H atoms	4 H atoms

Step 5. The coefficients in front of the various compounds are the smallest whole numbers possible.

Answer: *The balanced equation for the chemical reaction is*
$$CH_4 + 2O_2 \rightarrow CO_2 + 2H_2O$$

10.3 Types of Chemical Reactions

Chemical equations follow certain patterns

The number of possible chemical reactions is very large. However, there are a limited number of structural patterns that every chemical reaction may fall into. By learning these patterns, we will be able to better understand these chemical reactions.

These patterns can be best seen by considering the following four classifications of chemical reactions:

1. combination reactions (synthesis reactions),
2. decomposition reactions,
3. single displacement reactions, and
4. double displacement reactions (metathesis reactions).

We will now describe the structure of each one of these types of reactions.

Comparing reaction types

| **Acid-base** |
| Double displacement reaction |
| Neutralization |

| **Precipitation** |
| Double displacement reaction |
| Insoluble product |

| **Oxidation-reduction** |
| Single displacement reaction |

Combination reactions (synthesis reactions)

A reaction in which two substances combine to form a third substance is called a combination or synthesis reaction. The general form of a combination reaction is shown here:

Synthesis reaction

Two compounds combine to make a third compound

$$A \quad + \quad B \quad \rightarrow \quad AB$$

Synthesis of compounds from elements

This symbolic form shows substances A and B combining to form a new substance AB. The substances A and B can be two compounds, two elements, or an element and a compound. The formation of water from hydrogen and oxygen is a synthesis reaction that combines two pure elements to form a compound:

$$2H_2(g) + O_2(g) \rightarrow 2H_2O(g)$$

Synthesis of compounds from other compounds

Another example of a synthesis reaction combines magnesium oxide (MgO) with water to make magnesium hydroxide, $Mg(OH)_2$, also known an *milk of magnesia*. In this example, two compounds combine to form a third compound.

$$MgO(s) \quad + \quad H_2O(l) \quad \rightarrow \quad Mg(OH)_2(s)$$

Synthesis of magnesium hydroxide from magnesium oxide and water

Milk of magnesia, a common medicine is a suspension of $Mg(OH)_2$ in water

Synthesis reactions *combine* different substances. Therefore the number of products is less than the number of reactants.

Decomposition and single displacement reactions

Decomposition is the opposite of synthesis

A decomposition reaction is the opposite of a synthesis reaction. In a decomposition reaction, a single substance breaks apart (decomposes) to form two or more new substances. The new substances may be elements or compounds.

Decomposition reaction

One compound breaks apart into two or more compounds or elements

$$AB \rightarrow A + B$$

Decomposition of limestone

Calcium oxide (CaO), also called lime, has many uses, including water treatment, glass manufacturing, food preservation, and cement manufacturing. Lime is produced from the decomposition of calcium carbonate ($CaCO_3$) in limestone. This reaction occurs when limestone is heated to 825°C:

Concrete is made with CaO

$$CaCO_3(s) \rightarrow CaO(s) + CO_2(g)$$

Another important reaction is the decomposition of water, which happens when electrical current passes through it:

$$2H_2O(l) \rightarrow 2H_2(g) + O_2(g)$$

Decomposition usually requires energy

Most decomposition reactions require the addition of some type of external energy to proceed. The energy can be in the form of heat or electrical current, as in the previous examples. Energy can also be in the form of light, as in the case of the destruction of ozone (O_3) in the upper atmosphere:

$$O_3 + light \rightarrow O_2 + O$$

Single displacement reactions

A single displacement reaction happens when an element reacts with a compound, replacing an element inside of it. The general form of a displacement reaction is shown here:

Single displacement reaction

Two compounds swap a single element or polyatomic ion

$$A + BC \rightarrow B + AC$$

Examples of displacement reactions

The element A replaces the B part of compound BD. It could also replace the D part of compound BD. A single displacement reaction occurs when zinc (Zn) or iron (Fe) is immersed in a solution of copper sulfate ($CuSO_4$):

$$Zn(s) + CuSO_4(aq) \rightarrow Cu(s) + ZnSO_4(aq)$$

$$Fe(s) + CuSO_4(aq) \rightarrow Cu(s) + FeSO_4(aq)$$

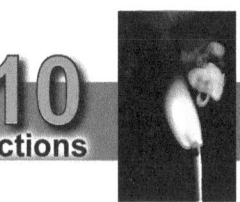

Double displacement reactions (precipitate reactions)

Ions "trade partners" in double displacement reactions

Precipitate reactions often involve the exchange of parts of the reactants. The general form of this type of reaction is shown here:

$$A\ B\ +\ D\ X\ \rightarrow\ A\ X\ +\ D\ B$$

Here we see that parts B and X, which represent the negative ions of the compounds AB and DX, exchange places. This gives us the new compounds AX and DB. Basically the positive and negative ions "trade partners."

Double displacement or precipitate reactions are one very common type of reaction that takes place in aqueous solutions. Recall that a precipitate is an insoluble solid that forms when certain aqueous solutions are mixed. The precipitate separates from the solution where it can be easily observed.

Precipitate reaction

A good example is the reaction between lead nitrate [$Pb(NO_3)_2$] and potassium iodide (KI). The pictures show a 0.1 M solution of lead nitrate and a 0.1 M solution of potassium iodide. Look carefully at their colors. Notice that the solutions are both essentially clear and colorless. When $Pb(NO_3)_2$ is added, notice the brilliant yellow color! The yellow comes from an insoluble precipitate (PbI_2), which is a product of the reaction.

Before
$Pb(NO_3)_2$ + KI
clear solutions

Adding
$Pb(NO_3)_2$

After
$PbI_2(s)$ yellow

The chemical equation for the reaction

The chemical reaction shows that the lead ion displaces the potassium ion in KI. The potassium ion in turn displaces the lead ion in $Pb(NO_3)_2$.

$$Pb(NO_3)_2(aq)\ +\ 2KI(aq)\ \rightarrow\ PbI_2(s)\ +\ 2KNO_3(aq)$$

Precipitates and solubility

The nitrate anion

Before we find out why a precipitate forms, consider the polyatomic nitrate ion (NO_3^-). The nitrate ion acts as a unit, so the nitrogen atom and three oxygen atoms remain covalently bonded together. The negative charge is the charge of the whole nitrate ion. A helpful comparison is to treat nitrate ions as if they were monatomic Cl^- ions.

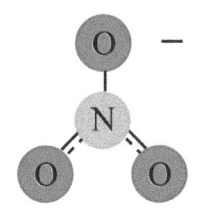

When a precipitate forms

A precipitate forms when one of the products of a reaction is *insoluble* in water. To be able to predict which ionic compound will be the precipitate, we need to refer to a set of *solubility rules*. The rules summarize which compounds are soluble and which are not.

TABLE 10.1. Solubility rules for common ionic compounds in water

Soluble compounds	Insoluble compounds (except when with group 1 metal ions and NH_4^+)
Group 1 metal ions: Li^+, Na^+, K^+, Rb^+, Cs^+ Ammonium (NH_4^+) Acetate ($C_2H_3O_2^-$) Nitrate (NO_3^-) Sulfate (SO_4^{2-}) Chlorides, bromides, and iodides, except with Cu, Pb, Ag, and Hg	Carbonates (CO_3^{2-}) Hydroxides (OH^-) (except for Ba^{2+}) Chlorides of Cu, Pb, Ag and Hg Bromides of Cu, Pb, Ag and Hg Iodides of Cu, Pb, Ag, and Hg Sulfides (S^{2-}) Phosphates (PO_4^{3-})

Using the solubility table

The balanced chemical equation for the reaction between lead nitrate and potassium iodide is given below.

$$Pb(NO_3)_2(aq) \ + \ 2KI(aq) \ \rightarrow \ PbI_2(s) \ + \ 2KNO_3(aq)$$

Solid (precipitate)

K^+ K^+ NO_3^-
Dissolved ions

Note from the table that *nitrates* are typically soluble. Therefore we expect potassium nitrate to be soluble, and it is. The table also says that iodides are generally soluble except for compounds with copper (Cu), lead (Pb), silver (Ag), and mercury (Hg). Potassium iodide is soluble. Lead iodide is insoluble and forms a precipitate.

Precipitate reaction uses and analysis

"Hard water"

Precipitate reactions are important to our environment and our drinking water supply. Minerals such as Mg^{2+} and Ca^{2+} leach into our water supply and cause a phenomenon known as "water hardness." You have experienced water hardness if you ever been in the shower and the soap did not lather well. "Hard" water leaves your skin feeling sort of sticky and filmy, because soaps and oils do not come off as easily. Iron (Fe^{2+}) and manganese (Mn^{2+}) also cause some other problems, such as staining clothes and increased bacterial growth.

Water soft-ening

To condition (or soften) the water in areas where there are large amounts of dissolved minerals, water treatment plants add special ions that precipitate out some of the Mg^{2+} and Ca^{2+} ions. Hydroxides (OH^-) and carbonates (CO_3^{2-}) are added to the water supply to precipitate out large amounts of these contaminating ions. For example, Mg^{2+} and OH^- form $Mg(OH)_2(s)$, and this solid settles to the bottom where it is easily removed.

Na_2CO_3 added

Mg²⁺ and Ca²⁺ ions in solution — CaCO₃ and MgCO₃ precipitates

Gas-forming reactions

Some double displacement reactions involve the production of a gas. For example, here is what happens when magnesium carbonate ($MgCO_3$) and hydrochloric acid (HCl) mix:

$$MgCO_3(s) + 2HCl(aq) \rightarrow MgCl_2(aq) + H_2O(l) + CO_2(g)$$

In this reaction, Mg^{2+} and H^+ ions exchange places, resulting in magnesium chloride ($MgCl_2$) and H_2O. Carbon dioxide (CO_2) is also evolved.

Solved problem

Predict what happens when silver nitrate ($AgNO_3$) is mixed with sodium chloride (NaCl). Follow the steps and write the complete balanced reaction.

Asked: *The reaction that represents the mixing of $AgNO_3$ and NaCl*

Given: *Formulas for both reactant solutions*

Relationships: *Solubility rules tell us that group 1 metal ions (here Na^+) and nitrates are soluble, but chlorides of silver are insoluble.*

Solve: *$AgNO_3(aq) + NaCl(aq) \rightarrow AgCl(s) + NaNO_3(aq)$*
According to the solubility table, sodium nitrate is soluble and dissociates into $Na^+(aq)$ and $NO_3^-(aq)$.
Silver chloride is insoluble and forms a precipitate.

Discussion: *We know the precipitate is AgCl because it does not have a group 1 metal ion or nitrate. All ions are balanced.*

Polymerization reactions

Polymers are long chains of repeated units

Many important molecules in both technology and biology are *polymers*. The word provides a clue as to how a polymer is made. The prefix "poly" means "many," and the Greek word "polymeres" means "of many parts." A **polymer** is a molecule made of many identical parts called *monomers*. A good example of a naturally occurring polymer is *starch*. Starch is a long-chain molecule, built from the repeated addition of sugar molecules.

Glucose
$C_6H_{12}O_6$

Starch
$\left[C_6H_{10}O_5\right]_n$

Polymerization

Photosynthesis in plants produces glucose. However, glucose is also rapidly used to release energy, even by plants. To save chemical energy for long-term use, plants convert glucose into starch by *polymerization*. **Polymerization** is a repeated addition reaction that assembles a polymer from smaller molecules. Anyone who likes fresh corn has tasted the difference between sugar and starch. Fresh-picked ripe corn has a high sugar content. Over a period of a day or two, enzyme reactions in the corn convert the sugar to starch. Starch does not taste sweet, and the polymerization reaction is responsible for the "old corn" taste.

Dehydration synthesis

The polymerization reaction that produces starch is called *dehydration synthesis*. Look carefully and notice that glucose has the chemical formula $C_6H_{12}O_6$ but the monomer for starch is $C_6H_{10}O_5$. The difference is one water molecule. To *dehydrate* means to "take away water" and to synthesize means "to put together." Dehydration synthesis builds up the starch molecule by removing an oxygen and two hydrogens from each glucose molecule that gets added to the chain. The bond between adjacent monomers is made through the oxygen.

Starch is a staple food

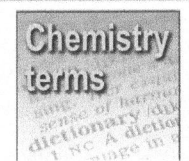

Bread is mostly starch

Starch is the staple carbohydrate of many animal diets, including humans! Bread, pasta, and all grains are mostly starches. The body reverses the synthesis process and digests starch back into glucose.

Chemistry terms

polymer: a molecule built from many repeating units of a smaller molecular fragment.

polymerization: a reaction that assembles a polymer through repeated additions of smaller molecular fragments.

310

10.4 Chemical Reactions and Energy

Chemical bonds and energy

Every chemical reaction involves the breaking and the formation of chemical bonds. These bonds store **chemical energy**. Energy must be provided to break chemical bonds, and energy is released when chemical bonds are formed. Therefore, every chemical reaction either releases or absorbs energy. The amount of energy involved depends on the particular reaction. From the burning of fossil fuels to the melting of ice on the street, we rely on the energy released or absorbed by chemical reactions.

Hot packs release energy and cold packs absorb energy

Cold and hot packs have become the best tools for athletic trainers. When an athlete is injured, the trainer reaches into the first-aid kit, grabs a small plastic bag, punches it, and applies it to the injured muscle. Within seconds the bag is ice cold. How does this happen? At another time the trainer may reach into the first-aid kit and get a small bag that in an instant becomes very hot and can be used to treat an injury. Where does this heat come from? Both the hot and the cold packs rely on chemical reactions to do their jobs. A chemical reaction inside the hot pack releases energy, and another chemical reaction inside the cold pack absorbs energy.

Exothermic: release of energy

When a chemical reaction releases energy it is called an **exothermic reaction**. When a chemical reaction absorbs energy it is called an **endothermic reaction**.

Endothermic: absorption of energy

The amount of energy that is released or absorbed is denoted by the symbol ΔH, which denotes the change in **enthalpy** of the reaction. Enthalpy, which means to put heat into, is another word for energy, and it has the units of joules. A chemical reaction is presented completely by writing the enthalpy information on the right of the chemical equation.

$$\text{Reactants} \rightarrow \text{Products}, \quad \Delta H = \text{some number}$$

$\Delta H < 0$: exothermic

For exothermic reactions ΔH is a negative number, indicating that energy is released by the reaction.

$\Delta H > 0$: endothermic

For endothermic reactions ΔH is a positive number, indicating that energy is absorbed by the reaction.

Chemistry terms

chemical energy: energy stored in chemical bonds that can be released during a reaction

exothermic reaction: a reaction that releases energy ($\Delta H < 0$).

endothermic reaction: a reaction that absorbs energy ($\Delta H > 0$).

enthalpy: the energy potential of a chemical reaction.

Thermochemical equations

Enthalpy is a measured quantity

When carbon is burned with oxygen, it produces carbon dioxide, releasing energy in the form of heat and light. It is an exothermic reaction because the reaction releases energy.

For this reaction the enthalpy change is measured to be –393.5 kJ, where a kJ (kilojoule) is 1,000 joules. The complete reaction is written as follows:

$$C(s) + O_2(g) \rightarrow CO_2(g), \quad \Delta H = -393.5 \text{ kJ}$$

This is called a **thermochemical equation**. It includes the chemical equation and the information about the enthalpy change on the right. The negative sign for ΔH means that the reaction is exothermic. As expected, the enthalpy change is related to the amount of material involved in the reaction. For example, the more carbon we burn, the more CO_2 is produced and the more energy is released. The enthalpy change refers to a certain amount of a substance involved in the reaction. In our case the denoted enthalpy change refers to the formation of 1 mole of CO_2. If we burn 2 moles of C, then the enthalpy change will be twice as great:

$$2C(s) + 2O_2(g) \rightarrow 2CO_2(g) \quad \Delta H = -787 \text{ kJ}$$

Enthalpy of formation is used to calculate reaction enthalpy

The enthalpy change is a measured quantity. It is obtained experimentally for the various reactions. Since there are millions of possible reactions, it is impossible to list all of them with their enthalpy values. Chemists have measured and cataloged the standard **enthalpy of formation** for many common substances. The enthalpy of formation corresponds to the enthalpy change during the formation of one mole of a substance. These values are given at standard conditions (25°C and 1 atm of pressure). Using these values one can then calculate the enthalpy of most reactions. Some enthalpy values for the formation of some common substances are shown in Table 10.2.

TABLE 10.2. Enthalpies of formation of some common substances

Substance	ΔH_f (kJ/mole)	Substance	ΔH_f (kJ/mole)
CO_2	–393.5	NO_2	33.2
CO	–110.5	O_3	142.7
$CuSO_4$	–771.4	C (diamond)	1.9
$H_2O(l)$	–285.5	C_6H_6	49.0
Fe_2O_3	–824.2	O_2	0

thermochemical equation: the equation that gives the chemical reaction and the energy information of the reaction.

enthalpy of formation: change in energy when one mole of a compound is assembled from pure elements.

Exothermic and endothermic reactions

Reverse reactions

The enthalpy change of the reverse reaction is the negative of the enthalpy change of the forward process. For our CO_2 example reaction we have

$$CO_2(g) \rightarrow C(s) + O_2(g), \quad \Delta H = 393.5 \text{ kJ}$$

The enthalpy of formation for each substance involved in a reaction (ΔH_f) is related to the reaction enthalpy (ΔH) by the following equation:

$$\Delta H = \Delta H_f \text{ (products)} - \Delta H_f \text{ (reactants)}$$

This is a mathematical expression of energy conservation, and it may be applied to calculate an unknown reaction enthalpy or an unknown enthalpy of formation.

Our bodies are powered by exothermic reactions

A chemical reaction that takes place continuously inside our bodies results from the combination of glucose ($C_6H_{12}O_6$) with oxygen. This is an exothermic reaction and it is given by the following thermochemical equation:

$$C_6H_{12}O_6(s) + 6O_2(g) \rightarrow 6CO_2(g) + 6H_2O(g), \quad \Delta H = -2,808 \text{ kJ}$$

The negative sign for ΔH indicates that the reaction releases energy, and thus it is exothermic. This reaction tells us that when one mole of glucose ($C_6H_{12}O_6$, 180 g) is combined with six moles of oxygen, it releases 2,808 kJ of energy. This energy is used by our bodies to help us grow and move. It is the energy that makes our lives possible.

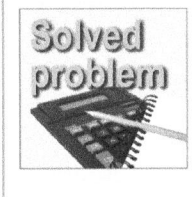
Solved problem

The complete combustion of glucose ($C_6H_{12}O_6$) releases 2,808 kJ of energy per mole of glucose. Calculate the enthalpy of formation of glucose.

Given: *The enthalpy of combustion of one mole of glucose is 2,808 kJ. The combustion reaction is*
$C_6H_{12}O_6(s) + 6O_2(g) \rightarrow 6CO_2(g) + 6H_2O(g) \quad \Delta H = -2,808 \text{ kJ}$
From Table 10.2 we read that the enthalpy of formation of O_2 is 0. The enthalpy of formation of CO_2 [$\Delta H_f(CO_2)$] is –393.5 kJ. The enthalpy of formation of H_2O [$\Delta H_f(H_2O)$] is –285.5 kJ.

Relationships: $\Delta H = \Delta H_f \text{ (products)} - \Delta H_f \text{ (reactants)}$

Solve: *We write down the reaction for the formation of glucose:*
$6CO_2(g) + 6H_2O(g) \rightarrow C_6H_{12}O_6(s) + 6O_2(g) \quad \Delta H = +2,808 \text{ kJ}$
From the enthalpy relation equation we have
$\Delta H = \Delta H_f(glucose) + 6\Delta H_f(O_2) - 6\Delta H_f(CO_2) - 6\Delta H_f(H_2O)$
$2,808 = \Delta H_f(glucose) + 0 - 6(-393.5) - 6(-285.5)$, *which gives*
$\Delta H_f(glucose) = -1,266 \text{ kJ}$

Answer: *The enthalpy of formation for glucose is –1,266 kJ per mole, or –7.0 kJ per gram since glucose has 180 g/mole.*

Calculating the enthalpy change of a reaction

Iron rusting releases energy

The rusting of iron, as we saw in the experiment at the beginning of this chapter, results from a chemical reaction that is exothermic. When iron (Fe) reacts with oxygen (O_2), it produces iron oxide (Fe_2O_3, rust) and it generates heat. For each mole of iron oxide the enthalpy change is –824.2 kJ. This reaction is written as

$$2Fe + 3/2O_2 \rightarrow Fe_2O_3, \; \Delta H = -824.2 \text{ kJ}$$

Coefficients multiply enthalpies of formation

We have written the above thermochemical equation for the formation of one mole of Fe_2O_3. This is the reason we use a fractional coefficient in front of O_2. If we were to write the coefficients using the smallest whole numbers possible, the thermochemical reaction would be

$$4Fe + 3O_2 \rightarrow 2Fe_2O_3, \; \Delta H = -1,648.4 \text{ kJ}$$

The energy released per mole of Fe_2O_3 is still the same (–824.2 kJ) but now since the chemical equation has a coefficient of 2 in front of iron oxide, we must multiply the enthalpy change by 2.

Endothermic reactions

Have you noticed that when you chew certain types of gum your mouth feels cooler? You actually feel the result of an endothermic reaction taking place in your mouth. Ingredients in gum called polyols dissolve in our saliva, resulting in an endothermic reaction. The reaction absorbs energy from your mouth, which feels cooler as a result. A common gum ingredient is xylitol ($C_5H_{10}O_4$), which when dissolved in water or saliva absorbs about 22.3 kJ/mole or about 167 J/g. This is considerable energy, resulting in a cool and refreshing feeling in your mouth.

Photosynthesis stores energy

The glucose that our bodies burn was generated by plants during **photosynthesis**. The photosynthesis reaction captures the energy of the Sun. It is the fundamental energy storage reaction. The photosynthesis reaction takes place inside plants and combines water and carbon dioxide to make glucose and oxygen. The thermochemical reaction of photosynthesis is

$$6CO_2(g) + 6H_2O(g) \rightarrow C_6H_{12}O_6(s) + 6O_2(g), \; \Delta H = +2,808 \text{ kJ}$$

Photosynthesis is an endothermic reaction

Photosynthesis is an endothermic chemical reaction as indicated by the positive sign for ΔH. The energy required to make this reaction happen is provided by sunlight. Photosynthesis is thus the ultimate energy storage reaction. It stores the energy from the Sun, producing oxygen, which in turn is used for sustaining life on Earth. Photosynthesis captures sunlight and stores it in compounds that contain carbon and hydrogen, known as hydrocarbons.

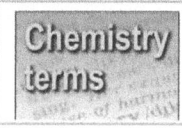
Chemistry terms

photosynthesis: the endothermic chemical reaction that is driven by sunlight and that combines CO_2 and H_2O to form glucose ($C_6H_{12}O_6$) and oxygen.

Energy profile of chemical reactions

Why
exothermic
reactions
do not start
spontaneously

The synthesis reaction of carbon dioxide is an exothermic reaction releasing a substantial amount of energy:

$$C(s) + O_2(g) \rightarrow CO_2(g), \quad \Delta H = -393.5 \text{ kJ}$$

However, carbon does not spontaneously catch fire! Burning a piece of carbon requires energy to *start* the process. It is not enough that we simply put carbon and oxygen together. Some initial energy is needed to break the bonds between oxygen atoms in O_2 before they can re-form with carbon atoms to make CO_2.

A spontaneous
reaction

Another exothermic reaction that releases considerable energy is the reaction of sodium (Na) with water (H_2O):

$$Na(s) + H_2O(l) \rightarrow NaOH(aq) + 1/2H_2(g), \quad \Delta H = -140.9 \text{ kJ}$$

This reaction *is* spontaneous. When we drop a piece of sodium metal in water, the reaction starts immediately with an impressive release of energy.

Both the carbon–oxygen and sodium–water reactions are exothermic, but one of them happens spontaneously whereas the other needs to be initiated.

The reason for
the difference

The answer has to do with chemical bonds and the energy that is required to break them and to form them. This is best shown with an energy diagram of the reaction. In an energy diagram we show the bond energies of the products and the reactants as well as the energy path that they follow during the reaction. This presentation gives us an energy profile for the reaction. On the vertical axis of the energy diagram, we give the total bond energy of reactants and products. The horizontal axis is used to show the time progression of the reaction

from reactants to products. The energy profile may have a barrier, represented as a "hump" in the diagram. This energy barrier corresponds to the energy input needed for the reaction to proceed. Once the reaction happens, the net energy of the reaction is the difference between the initial and the final energy levels. For an exothermic reaction, the energy level of the products is less than the energy level of the reactants. The difference in the energy is the amount that is released from the reaction.

The energy barrier

Some reactions need external energy to proceed

The presence of an energy barrier in the carbon–oxygen reaction means that we must provide external energy for the reaction to proceed.

Energy barrier

The external energy is needed to overcome the energy barrier. Only the molecules that have enough energy to go over the **energy barrier** can react. The energy of a reaction is stored in chemical bonds.

Without getting into the fine details of molecular bonds, we can say that all the energy information about this reaction is included in the bonds of molecular oxygen and carbon dioxide.

For the reaction to proceed, the first thing that has to happen is the breaking of the bonds of molecular oxygen. This requires a certain amount of energy input, indicated by the barrier in the energy profile of the reaction.

The energy content in the bonds of C and O_2 together is higher than the energy content of CO_2. The difference in the two energy levels corresponds to the enthalpy of the reaction.

Some reactions happen spontaneously

The sodium–water reaction has an energy profile that has a very small barrier, and all the energy that is needed to overcome it is provided by the reactants. In this case the reaction proceeds without requiring any external energy input. This type of reaction is called **spontaneous**, which means that it can happen spontaneously by simply bringing the two reactants together.

Entropy and spontaneity

Systems have a natural tendency to favor processes that increase their degree of disorder, or entropy (*S*). Physical and chemical processes that increase the entropy of a system are more likely to be spontaneous than processes that decrease entropy.

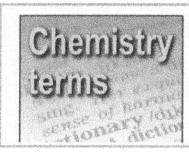

energy barrier: the energy needed to initiate a chemical reaction.

spontaneous reaction: a chemical reaction that occurs without the need for external energy input.

Hess's law: a method for calculating enthalpy change

Enthalpy does not depend on the path taken

Enthalpy is a state function

Enthalpy, like energy, is conserved and it depends only on the initial and the final states of the process that generates it. In chemistry we say that enthalpy is a state function to denote this property. Since the enthalpy depends only on the initial and the final states, the value of the enthalpy change depends only on the initial and the final states. In a chemical reaction, the initial state is related to the reactants and the final state is related to the products. As a reaction proceeds from reactants to products, the actual path that we take in calculating the enthalpy change does not matter. If we go directly from reactants to products following path 1 as indicated in the schematic, the enthalpy change is ΔH. The change is also ΔH even if we follow path 2, going from reactants to A then to B and finally to products. Note that the enthalpy going from reactants to A is negative, whereas the enthalpy going from A to B is positive. This is a general rule called Hess's law.

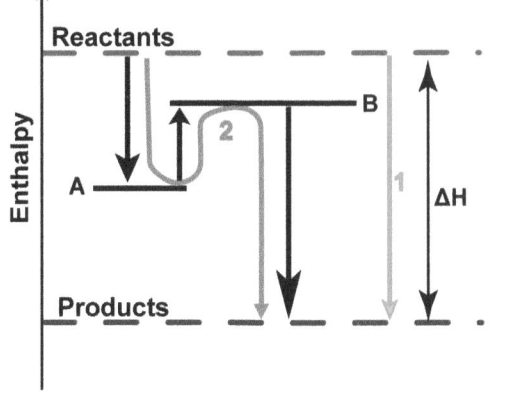

Hess's law

The overall enthalpy of a reaction is the sum of the reaction enthalpies of the various steps into which a reaction can be divided

Given that the enthalpy of combustion for graphite (C_{gr}) and diamond (C_d) are –393.5 kJ/mole and –395.4 kJ/mole, respectively, calculate the formation enthalpy of diamond from graphite.

Asked: *The enthalpy, ΔH, of the reaction*
$$C_{gr}(s) \rightarrow C_d(s)$$

Given: *The enthalpies of combustion and the compounds of interest*

Relationships: *The basic relationship is Hess's law and the combustion reactions:*
$$C_{gr}(s) + O_2(g) \rightarrow CO_2(g) \quad \Delta H_1 = -393.5 \text{ kJ/mole}$$
$$C_d(s) + O_2(g) \rightarrow CO_2(g) \quad \Delta H_2 = -395.4 \text{ kJ/mole}$$

Solve: *We will apply Hess's law by considering a path that will start with $C_{gr}(s)$ and give $C_d(s)$. We can create such a path by considering the two reactions*
$$C_{gr}(s) + O_2(g) \rightarrow CO_2(g), \quad \Delta H_1 = -393.5 \text{ kJ/mole}$$
$$CO_2(g) \rightarrow C_d(s) + O_2(g), \quad \Delta H_2 = +395.4 \text{ kJ/mole}$$
Note the change of sign for ΔH_2.
The first reaction produces CO_2 and uses O_2, and the second does the exact opposite. The sum of the two reactions gives
$$C_{gr}(s) \rightarrow C_d(s), \quad \Delta H = (395.4 - 393.5) \text{ kJ/mole} = +1.9 \text{ kJ/mole}$$

Green chemistry

Much of the technological world is created through *chemical engineering*. **Chemical engineering** is the profession of using chemistry to solve human problems. For example, plastics and medicines are produced by chemical engineers. So are fabrics, paints, dyes, metals, food additives, soaps, make-up, fuels, and thousands of products you use every day.

The goal of *green* chemistry, also known as *sustainable chemistry*, is to reduce or eliminate any harmful impact of human chemical technology on our environment and our bodies. Green chemistry is a very important idea because human civilization cannot simply give up using substances such as plastic and metal. What we can do is this:

1. Redesign the chemistry of products so they are biodegradable, nontoxic, based on renewable or recycled resources, or oth-er-wise have minimal environmental or health impact.

2. Redesign manufacturing processes so harmful chemicals and excess waste are reduced or eliminated and overall energy input is reduced.

Goals of green chemistry

1. **Products** with lower environmental and health impact

2. **Processes** with lower environmental and health impact

Have your ever owned clothes that say "dry clean only"? What is "dry cleaning" and why is it necessary for some clothes? The answer is that some fabrics such as certain wools are damaged by washing with water and soap. In the mid 1800s a French dye-maker noticed that his tablecloth looked cleaner after spilling kerosene on it. He came up with the idea of washing garments in organic solvents such as kerosene instead of water—even gasoline was used! Today, the process is called "dry cleaning" and by 1990 the United States was using 140 million kg of tetrachloroethylene, or "PERC," to wash clothing. Long-term exposure to PERC has been

Cl_4C_2

Tetrachloroethylene
$\left(\begin{array}{c}\text{or perchloroethylene}\\ \text{PERC}\end{array}\right)$

linked to kidney and liver damage and other health problems. PERC is a major contaminant in groundwater and many states have asked for it to be banned.

Is there a better way? In 1997 a green chemistry researcher named Joseph DeSimone won a presidential award for developing special soaps that work with liquid carbon dioxide instead of PERC. With the special soaps, liquid CO_2 works as a cleaning fluid and does not damage either clothes or groundwater. Washing machines that use liquid CO_2 instead of PERC are a *product innovation* that reduces harmful chemical impacts on our world. You can participate in this innovation by using alternatives to dry cleaning or buying clothes that can be washed in water.

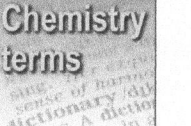

chemical engineering: field involving the application of chemistry to solving human problems, such as creating materials, fuels, medicines, or processes.

green chemistry: the practice of chemical science in a manner that is safe, is sustainable, and produces minimal waste.

Biodegradable plastics

Between 2000 and 2010, the worldwide production of plastics totaled more than 300 million tons per year. Less than 8% of that total was recycled. A significant part of the remainder becomes garbage every year. Plastic is predominantly hydrogen and carbon, which can be re-used by plants and animals. However, some plastic garbage lasts hundreds or even thousands of years before breaking down into substances that can be reused by the environment. How can this problem be solved?

Plastics are a special kind of polymer. Like all polymers, plastic molecules are long chains of identical monomers. A good example is *polyethylene*. A single polyethylene molecule might include 1,000 or more repeated ethylene monomers. The chemical formula for polyethylene is C_nH_{2n} where n can be any number from a few thousand to ten thousand or more. Individual chain lengths vary from a few thousand to ten thousand or more carbon atoms! This relatively soft plastic is used in sandwich bags, milk containers, toys, and a wide range of other consumer products.

Polyethylene plastic

C_2H_4
Ethylene
(monomer)

Polyethylene
(polymer)

Although polyethylene can be recycled, more than 90% ends up in landfills instead. Polyethylene takes hundreds of years in a landfill to break down into short fragments that can be digested by microorganisms.

Biodegradable plastics can decompose quickly in the natural environment. Microorganisms in soil extract the carbon to make biologically useful molecules such as glucose. However, a long chain of 1,000 carbon atoms cannot be "eaten" by microorganisms because the molecule is simply too large.

A biodegradable polyethylene includes a special chemical called a *catalyst*. The catalyst is like a chemical "self-destruct" system that slowly breaks the carbon–carbon bonds in the polyethylene backbone after weeks or months. This breaks up single molecules into fragments a few hundred carbon atoms long. These shorter chains can be digested by soil microbes. The final products of the process are carbon dioxide and water.

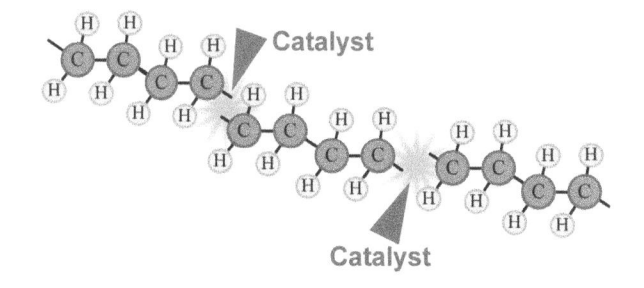

Catalyst

Catalyst

Chemical manufacturing

What does it mean to *manufacture* chemical products, such as plastics, fertilizers, dyes, and medicines? We cannot make atoms or elements. Instead, chemical manufacturing typically starts with reactants that are available raw materials, such as air, water, and natural minerals or hydrocarbons. A sequence of chemical reactions converts the reactants into the desired products. Unfortunately, many of the steps create waste products that are not used and must be disposed of.

A good example of traditional chemical manufacturing is the LeBlanc process for making soda ash (Na_2CO_3). Soda ash is used in dying fabrics and in making glass.

In the first step, salt and sulfuric acid react to produce sodium sulfate and hydrochloric acid. The second step combines the sodium sulfate with carbon from coal and calcium carbonate from limestone to produce sodium carbonate, the desired product. Notice that the reaction produces calcium sulfide and carbon monoxide as waste products.

When you analyze the process, you see that it produces 1 mole (84 g) of soda ash for every 2 moles of hydrochloric acid (73 g), 1 mole of calcium sulfide (72.1 g), and 4 moles of carbon monoxide (112 g). Overall, only 24.6% of the mass of the products is soda ash! The rest of the "products" of the reaction are waste and were once dumped into the environment.

One way to make a chemical process more environmentally friendly is to recycle or reuse the "waste products" in other processes. Early on, chemical companies realized that the hydrochloric acid given off by the LeBlanc process was a valuable resource in itself, so this "by-product" was sold for other uses. Counting HCl as another useful product raises the overall efficiency of the Leblanc process to 46%.

Atom economy

A major goal of green chemistry is to reduce waste by designing chemical manufacturing processes to be more efficient. In an ideal chemical process, all the atoms in the reactants become useful products and none are wasted. Applying the law of mass conservation to this goal provides a useful measure of how well a chemical process uses materials. This is called the *percent atom economy*, and it is given by the ratio of the mass of *useful* products divided by the total mass of products:

$$\text{atom economy} = \frac{\text{mass of desired product}}{\text{total mass of product}} \times 100$$

An ideal process would have 100% atom economy, meaning that all the mass of the reactants was converted into useful products.

The Solvay process (invented by Ernest Solvay) is a far more efficient way to produce soda ash. The Solvay process starts with salt ($NaCl$), water, ammonia (NH_3), and limestone ($CaCO_3$). There are four reactions that eventually produce one mole of sodium carbonate for every mole of calcium carbonate and salt used. The process also produces one mole of calcium chloride, which is used to melt snow on roads.

The Solvay process for producing Na_2CO_3

Notice how perfectly engineered the Solvay process is! Every product feeds back into the reaction as a reactant in another step *except* the two desired end products! For example, the ammonia used in Reaction 2 is produced in Reaction 3. The carbon dioxide used in Reaction 2 is produced by Reactions 1 and 4. The atom economy of the Solvay process is 100%, and this has become a model for other chemical manufacturing processes.

Chapter 10 Review

Vocabulary

Match each word to the sentence where it best fits.

Section 10.1

chemical reaction	mass conservation
reactants	balanced equation
chemical equation	unbalanced equation
products	

1. The process that converts one or more substances into new ones is called a/an _____.

2. The starting materials of a reaction are called the _____.

3. A/An _____ is an expression that describes the changes that happen in a chemical reaction.

4. We call the _____ the materials or substances that result from a chemical reaction.

5. _____ states that the mass of the reactants is equal to the mass of the products.

6. A chemical equation that obeys mass conservation is called a/an _____.

7. A chemical equation that does not obey mass conservation it is called a/an _____.

Section 10.3

combination reaction	displacement reaction
synthesis reaction	precipitate reaction
decomposition	polymer
	polymerization

8. A combination reaction is also called a/an _____.

9. The reaction AB + DX → AX + DB is called a/an _____.

10. In a/an _____ a single substance decomposes to form two or more new substances.

11. The reaction A + BD → B + AD is called a single _____.

12. The reaction in which two substances combine to form a new one is called a/an _____.

13. The reactions that form an insoluble solid when various aqueous solutions are mixed are called _____.

14. A molecule that is built up from many repeating units of a smaller molecule is called a/an _____.

15. The reaction that assembles a polymer is called _____.

Section 10.4

enthalpy of reaction	enthalpy of formation
chemical energy	thermochemical
exothermic	photosynthesis
endothermic	spontaneous reaction
energy barrier	

16. The amount of energy that a chemical reaction releases or absorbs is called the _____.

17. A reaction that releases energy is _____.

18. A reaction that absorbs energy is _____.

19. The equation that gives the chemical reaction and the energy information of the reaction is called a/an _____ equation.

20. The change in enthalpy during the formation of one mole of a substance is called the _____.

21. The reaction that takes place in plants and combines carbon dioxide and water to give glucose and oxygen is called _____.

22. A chemical reaction that happens without the need for external energy input is called a/an _____.

23. The energy needed to initiate a chemical reaction is called the _____.

24. Spontaneous reactions have a very small
_____.

25. During a reaction, bonds can be broken to release
the _____ stored in them.

Chemistry Connections

green chemistry	sustainable chemistry
atom economy	hazardous substances
chemical engineering	

26. _____ minimizes or eliminates the
generation of hazardous substances.

27. _____ are compounds that are
harmful to the environment.

28. Green chemistry is also called _____.

29. _____ gives us a way to calculate the
fraction of reactants that become the final product.

30. _____ is the application of chemistry
to solve human problems.

Conceptual Questions

Section 10.1

31. What a chemical reaction? Give three examples.

32. What is a chemical equation? Give an example
and identify all the relevant parts.

33. What is the difference between a chemical
equation and a chemical reaction?

34. Which of the following chemical equations
conserve mass?
   a. $N_2(g) + H_2(g) \rightarrow NH_3(g)$
   b. $H_2(g) + Cl_2(g) \rightarrow 2HCl(g)$
   c. $2N_2H_4(g) + N_2O_4(g) \rightarrow 3N_2(g) + 4H_2O(g)$

35. Describe the various components of the language
of chemistry in your own words.

36. Explain what is meant by this statement. "The
grammar of the chemical language is given by the
science that describes the chemical processes."

37. Describe why water is the most important
compound in our life and the environment.

38. Which of the following chemical equations are
balanced and why?
   a. $Fe(s) + Cl_2(g) \rightarrow FeCl_3(s)$
   b. $2NaN_3(s) \rightarrow 2Na(s) + 3N_2(g)$
   c. $NaOH(g) \rightarrow Na^+(aq) + OH^-(aq)$
   d. $NO(g) + CO(g) \rightarrow N_2(g) + CO_2(g)$

39. Explain what is missing from the chemical
equation that describes the burning of carbon:
$C + O_2 \rightarrow CO_2$

Section 10.2

40. Describe the procedure for balancing chemical
equations. What is the fundamental law that a
balanced reaction must satisfy?

Section 10.3

41. Classify the following chemical reactions as:
combination, decomposition, single displacement
or double displacement reactions. Also
differentiate as acid-base, precipitation,
oxidation-reduction.
   a. $Pb(s) + 2AgNO_3(aq)$
      $\rightarrow Pb(NO_3)_2(aq) + 2Ag(s)$
   b. $NH_4NO_3(s) \rightarrow N_2O(g) + 2H_2O(l)$
   c. $2NaOH(aq) + CuCl(aq)$
      $\rightarrow 2NaCl(aq) + Cu(OH)_2(s)$
   d. $2Fe(s) + 3Cl_2(g) \rightarrow 2FeCl_3(s)$
   e. $2NaOH + H_2SO_4 \rightarrow Na_2SO_4 + 2H_2O$

42. Determine which of the following compounds are
soluble and which are insoluble.
   a. $CaCl_2$
   b. $CaSO_4$
   c. $PbSO_4$
   d. $Pb(NO_3)_2$
   e. CuI_2
   f. K_2SO_4
   g. Na_3PO_4
   h. $CuCO_3$

43. Describe the polymerization process that produces
starch.

Chapter 10 Review

Section 10.4

44. Explain the meaning of ΔH and the significance of the positive or negative sign that it may have.

45. Explain why it is important to know the enthalpy of a chemical reaction.

46. What is the relationship between ΔH and exothermic or endothermic reactions?

47. How is the enthalpy of formation (ΔH_f) related to the reaction enthalpy (ΔH)?

48. Oil and natural gas are chemical compounds assembled from carbon, oxygen, and hydrogen. These compounds were formed millions of years ago and have since been stored in the earth.
    a. Was the reaction that created these compounds an exothermic or an endothermic reaction?
    b. What is the significance of that reaction in the current state of our world?

Chemistry Connections

49. How might each of the following careers use chemistry or products of chemistry: an auto mechanic, an actor/actress, a farmer, and a doctor?

50. What are the main goals of green chemistry?

51. Green Chemistry and your laundry machine:
    a. A dry cleaning facility claims that their service is less harmful to the environment than washing your clothes at home. Do you believe their claim?
    b. Using two examples, describe how research and chemical engineering have benefitted the environment

52. Give two examples of products that you use that are produced by green chemistry methods.

53. Why is atom economy important when we make chemical compounds?

54. Organic farming is becoming very important as people realize the harmful effects of fertilizers and pesticides. How do you think green chemistry is related to organic farming? Can you give a specific example of organic farming that affects or may have affected your life?

Quantitative Problems

Section 10.1

55. When sugar ($C_{12}H_{22}O_{11}$) ferments, it reacts with water to form aqueous ethyl alcohol (C_2H_5OH) and carbon dioxide. Write the general chemical equation for this reaction.

Section 10.2

56. When solid sodium in dropped into liquid water it reacts and produces aqueous sodium hydroxide [$NaOH(aq)$] and hydrogen gas [$H_2(g)$]. Write the balanced equation for this reaction.

57. When propane (C_3H_8) reacts with oxygen it produces carbon dioxide and water vapor.
    a. Write the chemical equation.
    b. Balance this chemical equation.

58. Acid rain is a major environmental pollutant. Acid rain is water that contains aqueous sulfuric acid [$H_2SO_4(aq)$]. Acid rain is generated when sulfur dioxide [$SO_2(g)$, which mainly comes from the combustion of coal, reacts with oxygen and liquid water.
    a. Write the general chemical equation that describes this reaction.
    b. Balance the chemical equation.

59. The process of treating iron ore for the production of iron metal is given by the following unbalanced equation:
    $Fe_2O_3(s) + CO(g) \rightarrow Fe(s) + CO_2(g)$
    Balance this equation.

60. The artificial sweetener aspartame ($C_{14}H_{18}N_2O_5$) combusts to produce carbon dioxide, nitrogen, and liquid water. Write the balanced chemical equation for this reaction.

61. The catalytic converter in the exhaust system of a car removes nitrogen oxides and carbon monoxide. The unbalanced equation for the reaction is $NO(g) + CO(g) \rightarrow N_2(g) + CO_2(g)$
    Balance this chemical equation.

62. Balance the following chemical equation using mass conservation:

    $NH_3(g) + CO_2(g) \rightarrow CO(NH_2)_2(s) + H_2O(g)$

63. The production of iron metal from iron oxide ore can be considered to take place in two steps:

    1. $Fe_2O_3(s) + CO(g) \rightarrow Fe_3O_4(s) + CO_2(g)$
    2. $Fe_3O_4(s) + CO(g) \rightarrow Fe(s) + CO_2(g)$

    Write the balanced equation for each step.

64. When ultraviolet radiation interacts with ozone (O_3) in the upper atmosphere it is absorbed by the ozone molecule*. In the process, ozone decomposes into molecular oxygen. What other element or atom results from this reaction? Write the balanced chemical equation of this important reaction. (*When ozone diminishes it creates the so called ozone hole in the upper atmosphere. The ultraviolet radiation thus can't be absorbed, and the radiation reaches the earth where it is very damaging to living organisms.)

65. Balance the following chemical equations:

    a. $O_2 + PCl_3 \rightarrow POCl_3$
    b. $C_4H_{10} + O_2 \rightarrow CO_2 + H_2O$
    c. $Ca + H_2O \rightarrow Ca(OH)_2 + H_2$
    d. $SiCl_4 + H_2O \rightarrow SiO_2 + HCl$

66. Balance the following chemical equations using mass conservation:

    a. $NO_2 + H_2O \rightarrow HNO_3 + NO$
    b. $CaCl_2 + Na_2CO_3 \rightarrow CaCO_3 + NaCl$
    c. $N_2O_5 \rightarrow NO_2 + O_2$
    d. $CH_3OH + O_2 \rightarrow CO_2 + H_2O$

Section 10.3

67. Classify each of the following reactions as a synthesis, decomposition, single displacement or double displacement reaction:

    a. $2Pb(s) + 2AgNO_3(aq) \rightarrow$ $2PbNO_3(aq) + 2Ag(s)$
    b. $2Na(s) + O_2(g) \rightarrow Na_2O_2(s)$

68. Aqueous solutions of Na_2CO_3 and $MgSO_4$ are mixed.
    a. What type of reaction occurs?
    b. Write a balanced equation for this reaction.
    c. Which product(s) is/are insoluble, if any?

Section 10.4

69. When glucose $(C_6H_{12}O_6)$ ferments it forms ethanol and carbon dioxide according to the following reaction:

    $C_6H_{12}O_6(l) \rightarrow 2C_2H_5OH(l) + 2CO_2(g)$

    This is an exothermic reaction releasing 75 kJ per mole of glucose. Use the data from pages 312 and 313 of your book to calculate the enthalpy of formation of 1 mole of liquid ethanol (C_2H_5OH).

70. Let's assume that coal is made only of carbon (you know it is not really true but it is a very good approximation). When carbon burns the thermochemical reaction is:

    $C(s) + O_2(g) \rightarrow CO_2(g), \quad \Delta H = -394$ kJ

    If we burn 1 kg of coal, how many grams of water can we heat from 10°C to 40°C?

71. The thermochemical equation for the combustion of ethanol is:

    $C_2H_5OH(l) + 3O_2(g) \rightarrow 2CO_2(g) + 3H_2O(l)$,
    $\Delta H = -1,368$ kJ

    How much energy is generated when we burn 1.00 kg of ethanol?

72. From the thermochemical equation

    $C_3H_8(g) + 5O_2(g) \rightarrow 3CO_2(g) + 4H_2O(l)$,
    $\Delta H = -2,220$ kJ

    and the data for the enthalpy of formation for $O_2(g)$, $H_2O(l)$, and $CO_2(g)$, calculate the enthalpy of formation for the compound $C_3H_8(g)$.

73. The tank of a home barbecue grill contains 10.0 kg of propane $[C_3H_8(g)]$. The propane burns with the following exothermic reaction:

    $C_3H_8(g) + O_2(g) \rightarrow 3CO_2(g) + 4H_2O(g)$,
    $\Delta H = -2,043$ kJ

    How much energy in kilojoules is contained in the tank?

74. From the information given in the previous problem and from other reactions covered in this chapter of the book, calculate the enthalpy of the following reaction: $3C(s) + 4H_2(g) \rightarrow C_3H_8(g)$

75. Research careers in green chemistry. Write a short report on one.

CHAPTER 11
Stoichiometry

How can we calculate the amounts of each chemical needed for a reaction?

How much of each chemical will be produced?

Why is it important to know the amounts of reactants and products?

Do chemists follow a recipe when mixing chemicals?

Many interesting substances such as Gore-Tex®, Claritin®, Nutrasweet® and Polarfleece® were initially developed in the chemistry lab. To make these substances, a chemist needed to decide which chemicals to mix together and in what amounts. This is similar to cooking a special dish. In cooking, the chef first needs to know how many people will be eating the meal. They then need to decide how much of each ingredient is required to make the correct amount of food. With chemicals and with food we want to make a close estimate of how much of each ingredient is required. Predicting the necessary amount allows us to decrease the waste of unused chemicals, or food, and it helps to keep the cost of production low.

Suppose you worked as a chef for a large restaurant. How would you figure out how to make enough food to serve all of your customers? Do you need to allow for a certain amount of waste or unused food to be efficient? Things do not always come out like you would expect when you bake, right? Are there any surprises? When you cook a particular type of food over and over, it becomes easier to flavor it and adjust the recipe to your particular taste. Chemists adjust ingredients to enhance certain chemical properties and to increase production. In the this chapter you will see how chemists are able to predict amounts of chemicals. Industrial chemists work hard to make sure the correct amount of a chemical such as aspirin is produced, and that it costs the company and the environment as little as possible.

Splitting water

In this experiment we will actually "see" the relative amounts of products formed in a chemical reaction. Although we cannot "see" chemical changes taking place at the molecular level with our eyes, we can observe the end result. In this experiment where hydrogen and oxygen gases are collected, we can witness the relative mole amounts as given by the balanced equation. Some molecules can be separated by using an electrical current. This process is known as electrolysis. Here we use the process of electrolysis to separate water into its constituent elements—hydrogen and oxygen.

Why are the amounts of the gases produced not the same?

In this experiment, you will see that as water decomposes into its constituent elements, there are two hydrogens for every one oxygen. This makes sense when we look at the composition of the water molecule.

In the presence of oxygen a glowing splint ignites

In the presence of hydrogen a glowing splint pops

Did you notice that the volume of hydrogen produced is twice as much as the volume of oxygen?

$$2H_2O(l) \rightarrow 2H_2(g) + O_2(g)$$

From looking at the balanced equation we see that the products are hydrogen and oxygen gas. The coefficient of 2 in front of the hydrogen gas (H_2) indicates that there is twice as much hydrogen produced as oxygen. Molecules are too small for us to see, but because of the volume of water in each test tube, we are provided with concrete evidence that twice the volume of hydrogen is produced for every volume of oxygen. This evidence supports the coefficient values shown in the balanced equation.

11.1 Analyzing a Chemical Reaction

Interpreting the chemical equation

Stoichiometry is all about counting amounts! The word stoichiometry actualy means element counting. How much reactant is needed, and how much is used up? How much product can be formed? Stoichiometry allows us to answer these questions. To use stoichiometry we need to be able to correctly interpret a balanced chemical equation. A chemical equation tells us what substances are added together as reactants and what substances are produced as products. As you learned earlier, we must always balance chemical reactions because atoms cannot be created or destroyed, just rearranged. To balance a chemical reaction we select the smallest coefficients that provide us with the same number of each type of atom on both sides of the equation. Here is the reaction for water decomposing to its elements:

$$2H_2O(l) \rightarrow 2H_2(g) + O_2(g)$$

We can interpret the information from this equation in two ways.

Coefficients tell us how much of each chemical is involved

1. Two molecules of $H_2O(l)$ yields one molecule of $O_2(g)$ and two molecules of $H_2(g)$.
2. Two moles of $H_2O(l)$ yields one mole of $O_2(g)$ and two moles of $H_2(g)$.

Using the mole relationship of reactants and products from the balanced equation is the key to understanding stoichiometry

TABLE 11.1. Information from a balanced equation

2CO(g) +	$O_2(g)$ $\rightarrow$	$2CO_2(g)$
2 molecules of CO	1 molecule of O_2	2 molecules of CO_2
2 dozen CO molecules	1 dozen O_2 molecules	2 dozen CO_2 molecules
2 moles of CO molecules	1 mole of O_2 molecules	2 moles of CO_2 molecules
$2 \times (6.022 \times 10^{23})$ CO molecules	6.022×10^{23} O_2 molecules	$2 \times (6.022 \times 10^{23})$ CO_2 molecules

Why is the mole so important? It is impossible to weigh out an individual molecule, or even 12 molecules! For this reason a chemist rarely carries out a reaction using individual molecules. Instead the larger unit of the mole is chosen. The mole is the unit commonly used to determine the relative amounts of reactants and products. Since the mole represents a quantity of atoms, it is often referred to as the "chemists dozen." Do you remember how chemists measure out a quantity in moles? They convert the amount of moles to grams using the molar mass of the substance. The amount in grams can then be weighed on a balance. This is very easy to do, and very useful too!

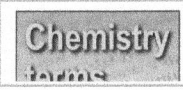

stoichiometry: the study of the amounts of substances involved in a chemical reaction.

Practice relating moles to molecules

Explaining the meaning of a chemical equation in words often helps us to understand what it represents. Here we are going to practice interpreting balanced chemical equations and looking at what information the coefficients give us.

Propane is a fuel commonly used for gas grills and for heating homes. The equation for the combustion of propane is

$$C_3H_8(g) + 5O_2(g) \rightarrow 3CO_2(g) + 4H_2O(g)$$

There are two ways to explain the meaning of the equation in terms of the number of moles and molecules:

1. 1 molecule of C_3H_8 reacts with 5 molecules of O_2 to yield 3 molecules of CO_2 and 4 molecules of H_2O or

2. 1 mole of C_3H_8 reacts with 5 moles of O_2 to yield 3 moles of CO_2 and 4 moles of H_2O.

Moles and molecules are not conserved

It is important to notice that the total number of moles of reactants (1 mole C_3H_8 plus 5 moles of O_2) do not add up to the total number of moles of products (3 moles CO_2 plus 4 moles H_2O). Six does not equal seven! It is fine that the number of moles is not conserved.

Why is it OK that the total number of moles is not conserved on both sides of the chemical equation?

But the number of atoms is conserved! The atoms were rearranged, and they now make up new compounds. The atoms are the building blocks of molecules and they are still present in the same amounts.

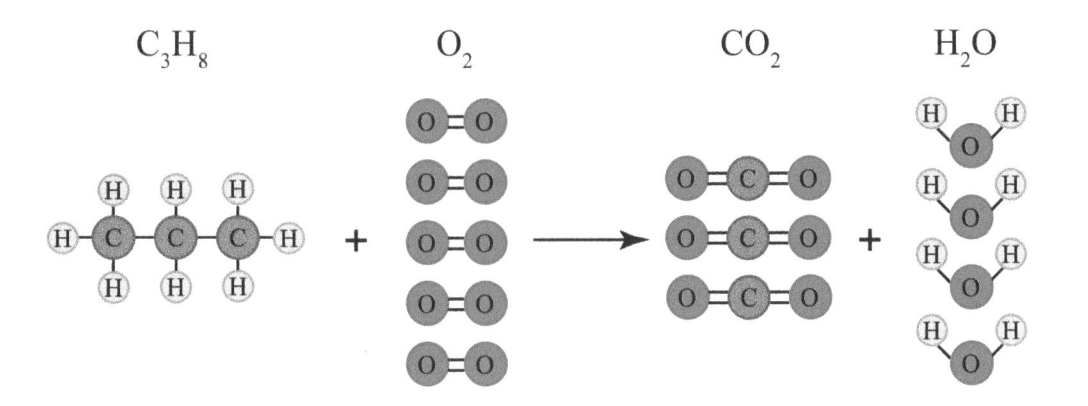

Mole-to-mole relationships

Comparing amounts of ingredients

The balanced equation gives us important information about how much of each reactant is required to form products. This is helpful because we need to know the relative amounts of chemicals to make the "chemical recipe."

Here is an example:

INGREDIENTS   PRODUCT

Cake mix + 3 eggs + ⅓ cup oil + 1 cup water yields 1 batch cupcakes

This information tells us what the ingredients are, how much you need of each ingredient, and how much product will be formed using the required ingredients.

Only compare chemicals in moles

When we use the balanced equation to determine amounts of chemicals, we compare amounts in moles. This method allows us to understand how elements combine. For example,

$$1 \text{ mole of } CO(g) + 2 \text{ moles of } H_2(g) \text{ yields } 1 \text{ mole of } CH_3OH(l)$$

You can only compare the amounts of chemicals in moles

This is because chemicals combine in simple molar proportions. When we work in the unit of the mole, all substances' relative amounts are equivalent.

Atoms have different masses, so we can never compare amounts in grams because grams are never equivalent for different molecules

We cannot compare in grams

For example, we can compare 12 apples to 12 oranges, and we see the amounts are equivalent, but we know the apple and the orange are different fruits and have different masses. So we compare the amounts of each fruit, and we can say 12 apples is equivalent to 12 oranges. Using the chemical example above, carbon monoxide (CO) and hydrogen gas (H_2) are different chemicals, so their masses are different. We can determine what amounts combine using the mole, because the amounts in moles represent the same quantity.

Mole-to-mole relationships

Let's consider the following chemical reaction:

$$CO(g) + 2H_2(g) \longrightarrow CH_3OH(l)$$

1 mole   2 moles   1 mole

The mole amounts given by the balanced equation are called **stoichiometric equivalent** amounts. The mole amounts of each substance are proportionate (~) to one another in a balanced equation. This means they combine in the amounts given by the coefficients of the balanced equation. As shown above,

$$1 \text{ mole } CO(g) \sim 2 \text{ moles } H_2(g) \sim 1 \text{ mole } CH_3OH(l)$$

Based on this equation the recipe calls for 1 mole of CO and 2 moles of H_2 to make methanol (CH_3OH).

The only way to know how to mix chemicals together is to use the balanced chemical reaction equation

Equivalent amounts are also used in cooking

The concept of relative amounts is also used in cooking. For example, if you are baking cupcakes and the recipe calls for 1 package of mix, 1/3 cup of oil, and 3 eggs to make one batch of cupcakes, then you could say that 1 package of mix is stoichiometrically equivalent to 1/3 cup of oil and 3 eggs. The fact that they are "equivalent" means for this particular recipe they are in a proportionate amounts. You get one batch when you mix all the ingredients. For some other recipe it is likely that the ratio of mix to oil and eggs is quite different.

Different chemical reactions require different amounts of chemicals

The concept of proportionate amounts in chemistry is very important because we need to know how to mix our ingredients and how much will be formed when we do mix them.

Chemistry terms

stoichiometric equivalent: case in which the mole amounts of each substance in a balanced chemical equation are proportionate.

Determining mole relationships

Finding mole amounts

Glucose ($C_6H_{12}O_6$) is the primary sugar used by our bodies for energy. In yeast, glucose undergoes a process called fermentation. This process produces ethanol, the common form of alcohol. When making blackberry wine, the sugar in the berries ferments according to the following chemical equation:

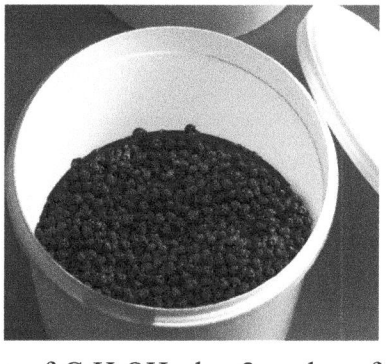

$$C_6H_{12}O_6(aq) \rightarrow 2C_2H_5OH(aq) + 2CO_2(g)$$

This equation says that 1 mole of $C_6H_{12}O_6$ yields 2 moles of C_2H_5OH plus 2 moles of CO_2. What if we have 3 moles of glucose? If 3 moles of $C_6H_{12}O_6$ decomposes, how many moles of products do we obtain?

Rebalance the chemical equation

One way to approach this is to multiply the entire equation by 3.

$$3[C_6H_{12}O_6(aq) \rightarrow 2C_6H_5OH(aq) + 2CO_2(g)]$$

$$3C_6H_{12}O_6(aq) \rightarrow 6C_6H_5OH(aq) + 6CO_2(g)$$

This gives us the following equation: 3 moles of $C_6H_{12}O_6$ yields 6 moles of C_2H_5OH plus 6 moles of CO_2. This tells us we get six moles of ethanol and carbon dioxide as products, which answers our question.

Noninteger amounts of moles

What if we have 7.5 moles of glucose ($C_6H_{12}O_6$) decomposing? How many moles of products will be formed? Here we can multiply the equation by 7.5 to obtain the answer.

$$7.5[C_6H_{12}O_6(aq) \rightarrow 2C_6H_5OH(aq) + 2CO_2(g)]$$

$$7.5C_6H_{12}O_6(aq) \rightarrow 15C_6H_5OH(aq) + 15CO_2(g)$$

This gives us the following equation: 7.5 moles of $C_6H_{12}O_6$ yields 15 moles of C_2H_5OH plus 15 moles of CO_2.

This process of rebalancing the chemical equation to obtain the number of moles always works, but it can get tedious. If we want to know the amount of only one product, there is no need to calculate each of them. In the next section we will work with a more convenient method that uses mole ratios. This method allows us to calculate the amount of one substance relative to another. These ratios are used as conversion factors that help us to determine the amounts of chemicals needed as ingredients or produced as products.

The mole ratio

Finding the mole ratio

The **mole ratio** comes from the coefficients in front of the reactants and products in the balanced chemical equation. Let's look at the following reaction:

$$CO(g) + 2H_2(g) \longrightarrow CH_3OH(l)$$
$$1\ mole \quad 2\ moles \qquad\qquad 1\ mole$$

We can set up mole ratios that allow us to compare reactants or compare reactants and products. Comparing the reactants, we see that 1 mole of CO is proportionate to 2 moles of H_2. We can show this as a ratio:

$$\frac{1\ mole\ CO}{2\ moles\ H_2} \sim \frac{2\ moles\ H_2}{1\ mole\ CO} \quad \text{just like} \quad \frac{1\ dozen}{12\ eggs} \sim \frac{12\ eggs}{1\ dozen}$$

Mole ratios of reactants

In these ratios the quantities are the same, but the comparison is reversed

Suppose you want to know how much hydrogen gas (H_2) you need to react with 4 moles of carbon monoxide (CO). To answer this question we can multiply by the mole ratio. We select the ratio that allows the proper units to cancel, leaving the desired unit in the numerator (top).

$$4\ moles\ CO \times \frac{2\ moles\ H_2}{1\ mole\ CO} = 8\ moles\ of\ H_2\ are\ needed \quad \text{Top}$$

If we want to know how much CO will react with 3.5 mole of H_2, we select the ratio with CO in the numerator (top).

$$3.5\ moles\ H_2 \times \frac{1\ mole\ CO}{2\ moles\ H_2} = 1.75\ moles\ of\ CO\ are\ needed \quad \text{Top}$$

The important point is that the mole ratio is consistent. No matter what the starting amounts are, these chemicals will always combine in the same ratio. We can use this ratio to determine how much of each chemical is consumed or produced.

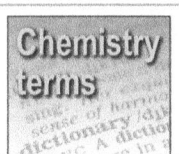
Chemistry terms

mole ratio: a ratio comparison between substances in a balanced equation., obtained from the coefficients in the balanced equation.

Using the mole ratio

Comparing reactant to product

We can compare both reactants to reactants and reactants to products. For instance, by using the balanced equation $CO(g) + 2H_2(g) \rightarrow CH_3OH(l)$, we find that the ratio between $CO(g)$ and $CH_3OH(l)$ is 1:1, the ratio of $H_2(g)$ to $CH_3OH(l)$ is 2:1, and the ratio between $CO(g)$ and $H_2(g)$ is 1:2.

Let's compare the reactant carbon monoxide (CO) to the product methanol (CH_3OH):

$$\frac{1 \text{ mole CO}}{1 \text{ mole } CH_3OH} \sim \frac{1 \text{ mole } CH_3OH}{1 \text{ mole CO}}$$

Starting with product to find reactant

Here's another question: If the reaction produces 5 moles of methanol (CH_3OH) how many moles of H_2 were consumed? Here we start with the amount of product and work backward to the reactant.

We select the mole ratio with H_2 in the numerator, because we are being asked how many moles of H_2 there are:

$$5 \text{ moles } CH_3OH \times \frac{2 \text{ moles } H_2}{1 \text{ mole } CH_3OH} = 10 \text{ moles of } H_2 \text{ are consumed}$$

Mole ratios are used as conversion factors that allow us to convert from one substance to another in a balanced chemical reaction. The important part is to select the ratio that allows the proper units to cancel each other out.

Let's try another example to practice selecting the correct mole ratio.

A mixture of aluminum metal and chlorine gas reacts to form aluminum chloride ($AlCl_3$): $2Al(s) + 3Cl_2(g) \rightarrow 2AlCl_3(s)$. How many moles of aluminum chloride will form when you react 5 moles of chlorine gas with excess aluminum metal?

Asked: Moles of $AlCl_3$ produced

Given: 5 moles of Cl_2 reacting

Relationships: Mole ratio: 3 moles Cl_2 = 2 moles $AlCl_3$

Solve: Set up the mole ratios as proportions and select the one with $AlCl_3$ on the top:

$$5 \text{ moles } Cl_2 \times \frac{2 \text{ moles } AlCl_3}{3 \text{ moles } Cl_2} = 3.3 \text{ moles } AlCl_3$$

Answer: 3.3 moles of $AlCl_3$ is produced.

Practicing with mole ratios

Notice the molar coefficients in the balanced equation:

$$CH_4(g) + 2O_2(g) \rightarrow CO_2(g) + 2H_2O(l)$$

Practice example

Using the steps outlined below, we will determine how many moles of oxygen (O_2) are required to react with 4 moles of methane (CH_4).

Steps for determining the amount of moles		
Step 1	**Step 2**	**Step 3**
Determine which mole ratio between O_2 and CH_4 to use: $\dfrac{1 \text{ mole } CH_4}{2 \text{ moles } O_2} \sim \dfrac{2 \text{ moles } O_2}{1 \text{ mole } CH_4}$	Multiply by the appropriate mole ratio: $4 \text{ moles } CH_4 \times \dfrac{2 \text{ moles } O_2}{1 \text{ mole } CH_4}$ $= 8 \text{ moles } O_2$	Clearly state your answer. It requires 8 moles of O_2 to react with 4 moles of CH_4.

Our second example involves ammonia, which is the principal chemical used to fertilize crops with nitrogen. It is prepared by the reaction between hydrogen and nitrogen:

$$3H_2(g) + N_2(g) \rightarrow 2NH_3(g)$$

Practice example

How many moles of ammonia (NH_3) can be prepared using 6.5 moles of H_2? Assume that there is excess nitrogen.

Steps for determining the amount of moles		
Step 1	**Step 2**	**Step 3**
Determine which mole ratio between H_2 and NH_3 to use: $\dfrac{2 \text{ moles } NH_3}{3 \text{ moles } H_2} \sim \dfrac{3 \text{ moles } H_2}{2 \text{ moles } NH_3}$	Multiply by the appropriate mole ratio: $6.5 \text{ moles } H_2 \times \dfrac{2 \text{ moles } NH_3}{3 \text{ moles } H_2}$ $= 4.33 \text{ moles } NH_3$	Clearly state your answer. 4.33 moles of NH_3 is formed from 6.5 moles of H_2.

Mole ratios are incredibly useful to chemists. A chemist who wants to know how much of each reactant to use or how much product will be left over simply has to look at a mole ratio to know what to use.

Gram-to-gram conversions

Our balances measure in grams

As nice as it would be, there is no scale that measures in moles! Students, chemists and people who work in the laboratory measure in grams, but substances combine in mole proportions. We must convert grams to moles so we can see how the chemicals will combine. We then convert back to grams, so that we can easily measure the amounts. In the flow chart below, the mass of substance A represents the grams of reactant or product that you are starting with, and substance D represents the amount of reactant used up or product formed. This flowchart lets you start with either reactants or products and find the one that is missing.

Process for calculating grams from grams given

This flowchart shows us that you cannot get from
grams of substance A directly to grams of substance D!
You must go through the unit of the mole

Here are the steps for using the flowchart to calculate grams from grams given:

1. First convert to moles of substance A by dividing by the molar mass of substance A (found by using the periodic table).

2. Use the mole ratio from the balanced equation to convert from moles of substance A to moles of substance D.

3. Convert moles of substance D back to grams by multiplying by the molar mass of substance D (from the periodic table).

Why is it important to know how much product is formed?

Chemists need to know how much product will be formed by a particular reaction for many reasons. Sometimes the products formed are dangerous, and not planing ahead could be harmful to the people and to the environment. Chemical companies have to know how much of a chemical to produce to fill an order.

Gram-to-gram calculations (part 1)

To understand how the flowchart works, we will consider the decomposition of calcium carbonate $CaCO_3(s)$, also known as limestone:

$$CaCO_3(s) \rightarrow CaO(s) + CO_2(g)$$

Calcium carbonate is present in rocks found all over the world. It is also found in nature as the primary component of eggshells and most seashells. Calcium carbonate decomposes, or breaks apart, when it is heated. How much carbon dioxide will be released when $CaCO_3(s)$ is heated? Let's find out.

Mass
substance
A

÷
Use molar
mass of A

Moles
substance
A

Find coefficients
for A & D

from balanced
equation

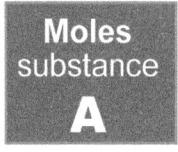
Moles
substance
D

×
Use molar
mass of D

Mass
substance
D

Solved problem

If 45.0 g of calcium carbonate ($CaCO_3$) decomposes in the reaction $CaCO_3(s) \rightarrow CaO(s) + CO_2(g)$, how many grams of CO_2 are produced?

Asked: Grams of CO_2 produced

Given: 45.0 g of $CaCO_3$ reacting

Relationships: Molar mass of $CaCO_3$: $40.078 + 12.011 + (15.999 \times 3)$
= 100.0 g/mole. Mole ratio: 1 mole $CaCO_3$ ~ 1 mole CO_2
Molar mass of CO_2 : $12.011 + (15.999 \times 2) = 44.01$ g/mole

Solve: Refer to flowchart and follow steps 1–3.

Step 1: $45 \text{ g } CaCO_3 \times \dfrac{1 \text{mole } CaCO_3}{100.09 \text{ g } CaCO_3} = 0.45 \text{ moles } CaCO_3$

Step 2: $0.450 \text{ moles } CaCO_3 \times \dfrac{1 \text{ mole } CO_2}{1 \text{ mole } CaCO_3} = 0.45 \text{ moles } CO_2$

Step 3: $0.45 \text{ mole } CO_2 \times \dfrac{44.01 \text{ g } CO_2}{1 \text{ mole } CO_2} = 19.8 \text{ g } CO_2$

Answer: 19.8 g of CO_2 is produced.

Gram to gram calculations (part 2)

Astronauts use lithium hydroxide (LiOH) canisters to absorb exhaled carbon dioxide during their space missions. These canisters are critical for keeping carbon dioxide levels low enough for the astronauts to breathe.

During the Apollo 13 space mission that began on April 11, 1970, there was an electrical explosion that caused a decrease in the oxygen supply. Astronauts had to move to a different cabin where the LiOH canisters were fresh and could support the crew members. LiOH canisters are changed roughly every 12 hours. To know when to replace them, someone calculated the amount of CO_2 they can absorb. Let's see how this was done.

Photo courtesy of NASA images.

Astronaut Christopher Ferguson changes a lithium hydroxide canister in Space Shuttle Atlantis.

Solid lithium hydroxide (LiOH) is used in space vehicles to remove exhaled carbon dioxide from the air inside the cabin. Lithium hydroxide reacts with the carbon dioxide to form solid lithium carbonate and water:

$$2LiOH(s) + CO_2(g) \rightarrow Li_2CO_3(s) + H_2O(l).$$

How many grams of CO_2 can be absorbed by 100.0 g of LiOH?

Asked: Grams of CO_2 absorbed

Given: 100.0 g of LiOH reacting

Relationships: Molar mass of LiOH: $6.941 + 15.999 + 1.0079 = 23.95$ g/mole
Mole ratio: 2 moles LiOH = 1 mole CO_2
Molar mass of CO_2: $12.011 + (15.999 \times 2) = 44.01$ g/mole

Solve:

$$100.00 \ \cancel{g \ LiOH} \times \frac{1 mole \ LiOH}{23.95 \ \cancel{g \ LiOH}} = 4.18 \ moles \ LiOH$$

$$4.18 \ \cancel{moles \ LiOH} \times \frac{1 mole \ CO_2}{2 \ \cancel{moles \ LiOH}} = 2.09 \ moles \ CO_2$$

$$2.09 \ \cancel{moles \ CO_2} \times \frac{44.01 \ g \ CO_2}{1 \ \cancel{mole \ CO_2}} = 91.98 \ g \ CO_2$$

Answer: 91.98 g of CO_2 is absorbed.

A NATURAL APPROACH TO CHEMISTRY

11.2 Percent Yield and Concentration

What is percent yield?

When you pop a bag of popcorn you expect the bag to fill up as the corn expands, but you know that there will be unpopped kernels. In other words, we know that potentially all of the kernels could pop or open up, but we know from experience that this is not what actually happens. Although the popping of popcorn is not a chemical reaction, it is a good analogy for the **percentage yield** of a chemical reaction.

amount you get to eat!

$$\text{percent yield} = \frac{\text{amount of corn popped}}{\text{amount of kernels in the bag}} \times 100$$

100 kernels   82 popped   18 unpopped

Calculation

$$\frac{82}{100} \times 100 = 82\%$$

Often with chemical reactions you do not obtain the exact amount of product you predicted with your stoichiometric calculation. This is not because you did the calculation wrong! It is simply because in real life things are often not perfect for a variety of reasons. In the laboratory when we perform an experiment, it is rare that we obtain 100% of the desired product(s). The percent yield tells us how close we get to the ideal "theoretical" yield.

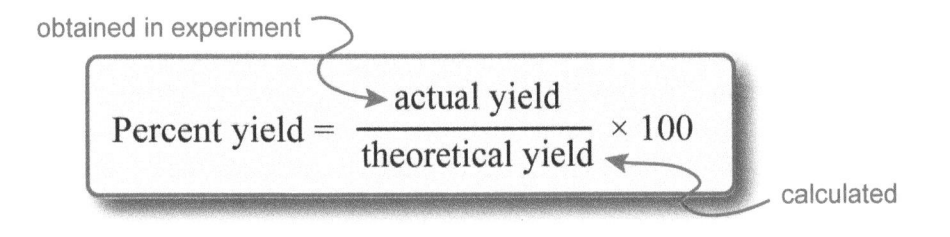

obtained in experiment

$$\text{Percent yield} = \frac{\text{actual yield}}{\text{theoretical yield}} \times 100$$

calculated

Chemistry terms

percent yield: the ratio of the amount of product actually obtained by experiment (actual yield) divided the amount of product calculated theoretically (theoretical yield) multiplied by 100.

actual yield: the amount obtained in the lab in an actual experiment.

theoretical yield: the expected amount produced if everything reacted completely.

A NATURAL APPROACH TO CHEMISTRY

Percent yield

Finding
percent yield
in the lab

As an example of how percent yield can be obtained in the laboratory, let's investigate a common reaction. When baking soda is heated it decomposes according to the following equation: $2NaHCO_3(s) \rightarrow Na_2CO_3(s) + H_2O(l) + CO_2(g)$. We can weigh the baking soda before heating and the solid product Na_2CO_3 after heating. Stoichiometry allows us to calculate the amount of product we should obtain from our initial mass of baking soda ($NaHCO_3$). We can then compare our actual mass of the solid product Na_2CO_3 with the calculated mass and see how successful we were with our experiment.

TABLE 11.2. Data for $2NaHCO_3(s) \rightarrow Na_2CO_3(s) + H_2O(l) + CO_2(g)$

Initial mass of NaHCO₃ (g)	Final mass of Na₂CO₃ (g)
10.0	4.87

Can you think of reasons why the final mass of the remaining solid Na_2CO_3 may not be accurate?

Reaction yields
are often not
100%

When we weigh the solid at the end of the experiment, we generally obtain less than the full amount of product. There are several reasons for this: 1. Generally there is some human error involved in experiments, such as not measuring exact amounts carefully; 2. maybe the heating time was not long enough for the reaction to be fully complete, so not all of the $NaHCO_3$ decomposes; 3. perhaps the product was not completely dry; or 4. maybe the product not weighed before it was cool.

Chemicals do not always fully react to form product owing to impurities in the samples, small surface area, or insufficient reaction time. Chemical reactions can also produce side reactions that can cause the desired product to turn into something else. Chemists are often faced with the challenge of "stopping" a chemical reaction so that it ends with the desired product. Lastly, some product is often lost during the isolation and purification steps.

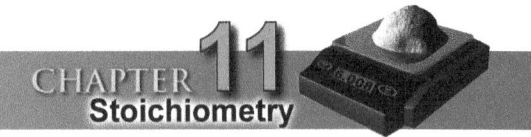

Calculating percent yield

Applying the formula for percent yield

Let's use the data obtained from heating 10.0 g of baking soda (on the previous page) to calculate the percentage yield.

First we need to calculate the theoretical yield using our flowchart according the balanced equation:

$$2NaHCO_3(s) \rightarrow Na_2CO_3(s) + H_2O(l) + CO_2(g)$$

Step 1: Convert 10.0 g of $NaHCO_3$ to moles.

molar mass of $NaHCO_3$ = 22.99 + 1.0079 + 12.011 + 3(15.999) = 84.01 g/mole

$$10.0 \ \text{g NaHCO}_3 \times \frac{1 \ mole \ NaHCO_3}{84.01 \ g \ NaHCO_3} = 0.119 \ \text{moles NaHCO}_3$$

Step 2: Convert moles of $NaHCO_3$ to moles of Na_2CO_3.

$$0.119 \ \text{moles NaHCO}_3 \times \frac{1 \ mole \ NaHCO_3}{2 \ mole \ NaHCO_3} = 0.0595 \ \text{moles}$$

Theoretical yield is the calculated yield

Step 3: Convert moles of Na_2CO_3 to grams.

molar mass of Na_2CO_3 = (22.99 × 2) + 12.011 + (15.999 × 3) = 105.99 g/mole

$$0.0595 \ \text{moles Na}_2\text{CO}_3 \times \frac{105.99 \ g \ Na_2CO_3}{1 \ mole \ Na_2CO_3} = 6.31 \ \text{g Na}_2\text{CO}_3$$

We just determined our theoretical yield to be 6.31 g of Na_2CO_3. A mass of 4.87 g was obtained from the experiment. Now we can calculate the percentage yield:

Actual yield is obtained by experiment

$$\text{percent yield} = \frac{4.87 \ g \ (actual \ yield)}{6.31 \ g \ (theoretical \ yield)} \times 100 = 77.2\%$$

Practice calculating percent yield

Another example of percent yield

To calculate the percent yield you need to know the theoretical yield and the actual yield. Recall that the theoretical yield is calculated based on the amounts of reactants used and the mole relationship obtained from the balanced equation. The actual yield can only be obtained by experiment, so it will either be given to you in the problem or you must determine it in the lab.

Solved problem

Part 1. Calcium carbonate, which is often found in seashells, decomposes when heated according to: $CaCO_3(s) \rightarrow CaO(s) + CO_2(g)$. If 30.5 g of $CaCO_3$ is heated, calculate the theoretical yield of CaO.

Asked: Amount of CaO produced (theoretical yield)

Given: 30.5 g of $CaCO_3$ reacts.

Relationships: Mole ratio: 1 mole $CaCO_3$ ~ 1 mole CaO

Molar mass of $CaCO_3$ = 40.078 + 12.011 + (15.999 × 3)
= 100.09 g/mole
Molar mass of CaO = 40.078 + 15.999 = 56.08 g/mole

Solve:

$$30.5 \; g \; \cancel{CaCO_3} \times \frac{1 \; mole \; CaCO_3}{100.\,09 \; g \; \cancel{CaCO_3}} = 0.305 \; moles \; CaCO$$

$$0.305 \; \cancel{moles \; CaCO_3} \times \frac{1 \; mole \; CaO}{1 \; \cancel{mole \; CaCO_3}} = 0.305 \; moles \; CaO$$

$$0.305 \; \cancel{moles \; CaO} \times \frac{56.08 \; g \; CaO}{1 \; \cancel{mole \; CaO}} = 17.10 \; g \; CaO$$

Answer: The theoretical yield is 17.10 g of CaO.

Now we use the theoretical yield to calculate the percentage yield.

Part 2. Calculate the percentage yield if 12.5 g of CaO is actually obtained.

Asked: Percentage yield of CaO

Given: The actual yield of 12.5 g CaO and the answer in Part 1

Relationships: The formula for percent yield

Solve:

$$percent \; yield = \frac{12.5 \; g \; (actual)}{17.10 \; g \; (theoretical)} \times 100 = 73.1\%$$

Answer: The percent yield is 73.1%.

Discussion: This tells the experimentalist the quality of the technique.

Stoichiometry with solutions (part 1)

Calculating amounts from reactions in solution

Chemical reactions often take place between solids and liquids or between two liquids. Here we will look at solid zinc metal reacting with hydrochloric acid according to this equation:

$$Zn(s) + 2HCl(aq) \rightarrow H_2(g) + ZnCl_2(aq)$$

To be able to calculate the amount of a substance that reacts in an aqueous solution, it is helpful to review our units of concentration. Recall that our concentration unit is molarity (M), which tells us the number of moles in one liter of solution: M = moles/liters.

Solved problem

A sample of zinc metal (Zn) reacts with 50.0 mL of a 3.0 M solution of hydrochloric acid (HCl) according to: $Zn(s) + 2HCl(aq) \rightarrow ZnCl_2(s) + H_2(g)$. How many grams of hydrogen gas (H_2) will be produced? Assume zinc metal is present in excess.

Asked: Grams of H_2 produced

Given: 50.0 mL of 3.0 M HCl is reacting with excess zinc.

Relationships: $M = \dfrac{moles}{L}$, so moles of HCl = 3.0 M × 0.050 L = 0.150 moles HCl

Excess Zn means more than enough, so the exact amount is not important.
Mole ratio: 2 moles HCl ~ 1 mole H_2
Molar mass of H_2 = 1.0079 × 2 = 2.02 g/mole

Solve: $$0.150 \; moles \; HCl \times \frac{1 \; mole \; H_2}{2 \; moles \; HCl} = 0.075 \; moles \; H_2$$

$$0.075 \; moles \; H \times \frac{2.02 \; g \; H_2}{1 \; mole \; H_2} = 0.15 \; g \; H_2$$

Answer: 0.15 g of H_2 is produced.

As you can see, you must always find the moles of the reactant. If the substance is a solid, you calculate moles by dividing by the molar mass. If the substance is dissolved in an aqueous solution, you must find moles using the molarity equation. In this case molarity (M) × volume (L) will give you the amount of moles. So when determining moles you need to be aware of the physical states of the chemicals you are using.

Stoichiometry with solutions (part 2)

Mass
percentage

One of the most common ways to express the concentration of a solution is to use percent by mass of the compound in solution. For instance, vinegar contains about 5% acetic acid by mass. Acetic acid comes from apples, and it is responsible for the sour taste of vinegar. So if vinegar is 5% acetic acid by mass, that means it contains about 5 g of acetic acid for every 100 g of solution. You can use the following formula:

$$\text{mass \% of compound} = \frac{\text{mass of compound}}{\text{total mass of solution}} \times 100$$

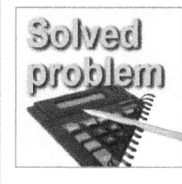
Solved problem

A solution is made by dissolving 15.6 g of glucose ($C_6H_{12}O_6$) in 0.100 kg of water. Calculate the mass percent of glucose in the solution.

Asked: Mass percent of the solute, glucose ($C_6H_{12}O_6$)

Given: 15.6 g of $C_6H_{12}O_6$ in 0.100 kg of water

Relationships: Mass % = (mass of glucose/mass of solution) × 100

Solve: $\text{Mass \% } C_6H_{12}O_6 = \dfrac{15.6 \text{ g } C_6H_{12}O_6}{(15.6 \text{ g} + 100 \text{ g})} \times 100 = 13.5\%$

Answer: 13.5% glucose by mass

Here is another example where you determine the amount of solute by mass percent:

Solved problem

Commercial vinegar is reported to be 5% acetic acid by mass. How many grams of acetic acid are in 120 mL of commercial vinegar? (Assume the density of vinegar is the same as pure water, 1.0 g/mL.)

Asked: Grams of acetic acid ($C_2H_4O_2$) in 120 mL of vinegar

Given: 120 ml of vinegar and 5% acetic acid by mass

Relationships: 120 ml = 120 g given a density of 1.0 g/mL
Mass % = (mass of acetic acid/mass of solution) × 100

Solve: 5% $C_2H_4O_2$ /100 = 0.05
0.05 × 120 g of vinegar = 6.0 g of acetic acid ($C_2H_4O_2$) in 120 mL of vinegar

Answer: 6.0 g of acetic acid

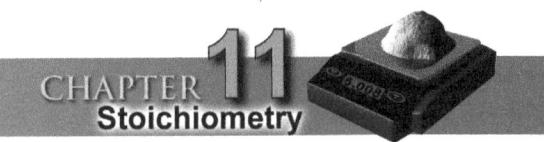

11.3 Limiting Reactants

What is a
"limiting"
reactant?

When carrying out reactions in the laboratory, it is common to have one reactant that is used up completely and another that has some "left over." The reactant that is used up completely is called the **limiting reactant**. Its name is appropriate because it "limits" the amount of product that can be formed. The concept is simple: When you run out of an ingredient (or reactant) you can no longer continue to make product. The reactant that is left over is called your **excess reactant**.

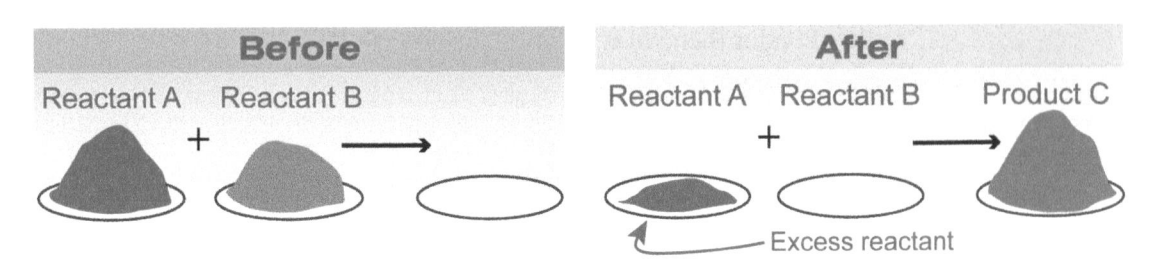

How do you
recognize
a limiting
reactant?

Let's use an analogy of making sandwiches as an example of a limiting reactant. Suppose you need to make three ham and cheese sandwiches.

First we need our recipe! For each sandwich you will need the following:

2 slices of bread + 2 slices of ham + 1 slice of cheese = 1 ham and cheese sandwich

For three sandwiches you need three times these amounts. You then go to the refrigerator and the cupboard, and you find a loaf of bread, a package of ham, and some cheese. You begin to make sandwiches and discover there are only 2 slices of cheese left. In this case the cheese is your limiting reactant, so you can only make 2 sandwiches.

The chemical that runs out first limits a chemical reaction in the same way.

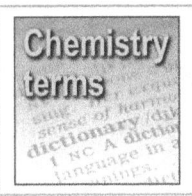
Chemistry terms

limiting reactant: the reactant that "runs out" first in a chemical reaction.

excess reactant: the reactant that is remaining after the reaction is complete.

Limiting reactants and chemical equations

A chemical example of limiting reactants

For a chemical example, we will use the following equation:

$$CH_4(g) + H_2O(l) \rightarrow 3H_2(g) + CO(g)$$

Reacting methane (CH_4) with water (H_2O) produces hydrogen gas (H_2), which is then used to make fertilizer. Carbon monoxide (CO) is also formed as a product of the reaction. By looking at the balanced equation, we can see that if we react 1 mole of methane and 1 mole of water then we will (in theory) use up each reactant completely.

Molecular representation of the limiting reactant

Suppose we have a mixture of four CH_4 molecules with six H_2O molecules.

When looking at the reactants, can you tell which one is limiting? You can if you compare the molecules shown in the picture with the mole ratio from the balanced equation! When this is done we find that methane (CH_4) is limiting because there are only four molecules of methane. The reactants are in a one-to-one mole ratio, so equal amounts are needed and there is more water! Notice in the final picture that there are no CH_4 molecules remaining.

Can you tell which reactant is in excess?

Can you tell how much excess reactant is left over? Again it's a one-to-one relationship, and there are two molecules of water still remaining with the products after the reaction.

How many molecules of H_2 form? You can find this out by counting molecules. Look at the mole ratio between the limiting reactant (CH_4) and the products H_2 and CO. Does it make sense that 12 H_2 molecules and 4 CO molecules are formed? If you are not sure, compare these amounts carefully to the balanced equation above and you will see that 4 CH_4 molecules indeed yields 12 H_2 molecules and 4 CO molecules. Remember that you must use your limiting reactant to determine how many molecules of product will form.

Determining the limiting reactant

When we are given a problem in which both reactants are available in specified amounts, we must first determine which one is limiting in order to calculate the amount of product that can be formed. As an example, let's use

$$Fe_2O_3(s) + 2Al(s) \rightarrow 2Fe(s) + Al_2O_3(s)$$

Here we will use the strategy of comparing what we have (the amounts given) to what we need (the amounts required to fully react each reactant). What we have is just like what's available in the kitchen for us to make sandwiches. What we need is what we "wish" we had available.

Never assume the smaller mass is limiting!

If we react 150 g of Fe_2O_3 and 60 g of Al, which one will be used up first?

Step 1: Convert our masses to moles.

molar mass of Fe_2O_3 = 159.7 g/mole; molar mass of Al = 26.98 g/mole

$$150 \text{ g } Fe_2O_3 \times \frac{1 \text{ mole } Fe_2O_3}{159.7 \text{ g } Fe_2O_3} = 0.94 \text{ moles } Fe_2O_3 \text{ (have)}$$

$$60.0 \text{ g } Al \times \frac{1 \text{ mole } Al}{26.98 \text{ g } Al} = 2.22 \text{ moles } Al \text{ (have)}$$

Notice that the smaller mass gave us a larger number of moles
We can never compare amounts in grams!

Step 2: Use mole ratios to see which reactant will limit the reaction.

Finding the limiting reactant

$$0.94 \text{ moles } Fe_2O_3 \times \frac{2 \text{ moles } Al}{1 \text{ mole } Fe_2O_3} = 1.88 \text{ moles } Al \text{ (need) to react with all } Fe_2O_3$$

$$2.22 \text{ moles } Al \times \frac{1 \text{ mole } Fe_2O_3}{2 \text{ moles } Al} = 1.11 \text{ moles } Fe_2O_3 \text{ (need) to react with all the } Al$$

From these calculations we can see that Fe_2O_3 is our limiting reactant because we need more of it than we have available. We also see that Al is present in excess.

Using the limiting reactant

Typically we want to know how much product can be formed in a particular reaction. We carry out reactions for the purpose of making a desired product. To take this calculation a bit further, let's determine how much iron (Fe) can be produced. To do this we add two final steps.

Use the limiting reactant to determine the amount produced

Step 3: Use the limiting reactant to calculate the amount of product formed. Use the mole ratio between the limiting reactant and the desired product (where the product is Fe).

$$0.94 \text{ moles Fe}_2O_3 \text{ (Have)} \times \frac{2 \text{ moles Fe}}{1 \text{ mole Fe}_2O_3} = 1.88 \text{ moles Fe}$$

Step 4: Convert the moles of product to grams using the molar mass.

$$1.88 \text{ moles Fe} \times \frac{55.85 \text{ g Fe}}{1 \text{ mole Fe}} = 105 \text{ g Fe formed}$$

In the end, 105 g of Fe is formed by reacting 150 g of Fe_2O_3 and 60 g of Al. At the end of the reaction some Al solid is left over.

$$150 \text{ g Fe}_2O_3 \ + \ 60 \text{ g Al} \longrightarrow 105 \text{ g Fe} \ + \ Al_2O_3 \qquad Al$$

An alternative method

Another method for determining the amount produced based on the limiting reactant involves doing two calculations, one for each reactant that forms products. In this case the amount of iron (Fe) formed for each reactant amount is calculated.

$$150 \text{ g Fe}_2O_3 \times \frac{1 \text{ mole Fe}_2O_3}{159.7 \text{ g Fe}_2O_3} = 0.94 \text{ moles Fe}_2O_3 \times \frac{2 \text{ moles Fe}}{1 \text{ mole Fe}_2O_3} = 1.88 \text{ moles Fe}$$

$$1.88 \text{ moles Fe} \times \frac{55.85 \text{ g Fe}}{1 \text{ mole Fe}} = 105 \text{ g Fe formed}$$

The mass produced is smaller because it is based on the limiting reactant.

$$60 \text{ g Al} \times \frac{1 \text{ mole Al}}{26.98 \text{ g Al}} = 2.22 \text{ moles Al} \times \frac{2 \text{ moles Fe}}{2 \text{ moles Al}} \times 2.22 \text{ moles Fe} \times \frac{55.85 \text{ g Fe}}{1 \text{ mole Fe}} = 124 \text{ g Fe formed}$$

The mass produced is larger because it was based on the excess reactant.

Once you have the amounts of product formed from each reactant, you can select the reactant that made the least product. Here the least amount was made using Fe_2O_3.

Summary of the process

In this section we will outline and emphasize the steps you need to follow when doing a limiting reactant calculation. Sometimes organizing the steps in a table is useful.

Steps for determining the limiting reactant		
Step 1	**Step 2**	**Step 3**
Convert both reactant masses to moles.	Multiply by the mole ratio from the balanced equation to find how much reactant is needed to use up all of the other reactant.	Compare the amounts of reactants. Compare what you have available to what you need.
This gives you the amount you have available to use.	This gives you the amount you need to consume all of the reactant.	If what you need is more than what you have, then this is the limiting reactant.

Essentially you have to convert your given amounts to moles. Then, to see which one will get used up first, you need to look at the mole ratio between your reactants.

Almost all chemical reactions are carried out with one reactant in excess. The one that is consumed needs to be identified.

At other times a flowchart that clearly lays out the sequence is helpful as a guide.

It may be helpful for you to sketch out this flowchart as you approach and try to solve a limiting reactant problem. Write out your information in each box and follow the steps as you go.

Practice determining the limiting reactant

Making
ammonia (NH_3)

The Haber–Bosch process allowed for the production of ammonia on a large industrial scale. Before this process was developed, ammonia could not be produced in large quantities. The production of ammonia was very important during World War I because ammonium nitrate was used to make explosives. Now it is important in the manufacture of fertilizer. Today, ammonia fertilizers are responsible for sustaining approximately one third of the world's population. We will use this reaction to practice calculations with limiting reactants.

The Haber–Bosch process for the synthesis of ammonia uses the following chemical reaction:

$$N_2(g) + 3H_2(g) \rightarrow 2NH_3(g)$$

In one reaction 100 g of nitrogen gas (N_2) reacts with 10 g of hydrogen gas (H_2). Which reactant will limit the amount of ammonia that can be produced?

First we will use our flowchart method.

Step 1
Convert grams to moles

$$100.0 \text{ g N}_2 \times \frac{1 \text{ mole N}_2}{28.02 \text{ g N}_2} = 3.57 \text{ moles N}_2 \text{ (have)}$$

$$10.0 \text{ g H}_2 \times \frac{1 \text{ mole H}_2}{2.02 \text{ g H}_2} = 4.95 \text{ moles H}_2 \text{ (have)}$$

Step 2
Use mole ratio to determine amount of moles needed to react

$$3.57 \text{ moles N}_2 \times \frac{3 \text{ moles H}_2}{1 \text{ mole N}_2} = 10.71 \text{ moles of H}_2 \text{ is needed}$$

Step 3
Identify the limiting reactant

Comparing 4.95 mole H_2 (have) < 10.71 mole (need) we see that H_2 is our limiting reactant!

Step 4
Multiply by mole ratio

$$4.95 \text{ moles H}_2 \times \frac{2 \text{ moles NH}_3}{3 \text{ moles H}_2} = 3.30 \text{ moles of NH}_3 \text{ produced}$$

Step 5
Multiply by the molar mass

$$3.30 \text{ moles NH}_3 \times \frac{17.03 \text{ g NH}_3}{1 \text{ mole}} = 56.2 \text{ g NH}_3 \text{ produced}$$

Using the Haber–Bosch process (part 1)

Now let's try this calculation using our steps as a formal solved problem. Both methods work equally well.

Solved problem

1. The Haber–Bosch process for the synthesis of ammonia uses the chemical reaction: $N_2(g) + 3H_2(g) \rightarrow 2NH_3(g)$. In one reaction, 100 g of nitrogen gas (N_2) reacts with 10 g of hydrogen gas (H_2). Which reactant will limit the amount of ammonia that can be produced?

Asked: The limiting reactant

Given: 100 g of N_2 and 10 g of H_2

Relationships: Write down the molar mass for each element.
Molar mass of N_2: 14.007 g/mole × 2 = 28.01 g/mole
Molar mass of H_2: 1.0079 g/mole × 2 = 2.02 g/mole
Mole ratio: 1 mole N_2 ~ 3 moles H_2

Solve: Step 1: Convert grams to moles.

$$100.0 \ g \ N_2 \times \frac{1 \ mole \ N_2}{28.01 \ g \ N_2} = 3.57 \ moles \ N_2 \ (have)$$

$$10.0 \ g \ H_2 \times \frac{1 \ mole \ H_2}{2.02 \ g \ N_2} = 4.95 \ moles \ H_2 \ (have)$$

Step 2: Use mole ratio to determine the amount of moles needed to react.

$$3.57 \ mole \ N_2 \times \frac{3 \ moles \ H_2}{1 \ mole \ N_2} = 10.71 \ moles \ H_2 \ needed$$

Step 3: Comparing this to what we have (4.95 moles H_2) we see that H_2 is our limiting reactant!
Or, using the other reactant, we would get

$$4.95 \ mole \ H_2 \times \frac{1 \ mole \ N_2}{3 \ moles \ H_2} = 1.65 \ moles \ N_2 \ is \ needed$$

Using this reactant and comparing this to what we have (3.57 moles of N_2) we can see that N_2 is present in excess.

Discussion: You can determine the limiting reactant using either reactant once it is converted to moles.
There is no need to do both calculations in step 3 as shown in this example. Either one gives you the correct answer!

Keep in mind that the reason we solve for the limiting reactant is to see how much product can be formed. On the next page we will use the limiting reactant to determine the amount of product (NH_3) formed.

Using the Haber–Bosch process (part 2)

Here we will use the limiting reactant to determine the amount of product formed.

Solved problem

2. Now we can calculate the amount of product based on the correct limiting reactant. How much ammonia (NH$_3$) can be produced from this reaction?

Asked: Amount of product (NH$_3$) produced

Given: H$_2$ is the limiting reactant.

Relationships: 10.0 g H$_2$ × (1 mole H$_2$ / 2.02 g H$_2$) = 4.95 moles H$_2$

Molar mass of NH$_3$: 14.007 g/mole + (1.0079 g/mole × 3) = 17.03 g/mole

Mole ratio: 3 moles H$_2$ ~ 2 moles NH$_3$

Solve: Use moles of limiting reactant to calculate moles of NH$_3$ produced.

Step 4: Multiply by mole ratio.

$$4.95 \; \text{moles } H_2 \times \frac{2 \; moles \; NH_3}{3 \; moles \; H_2} = 3.30 \; moles \; NH_3$$

Step 5: Multiply by the molar mass.

$$3.30 \; \text{moles } NH_3 \times \frac{17.03 \; g \; NH_3}{1 \; mole \; NH_3} = 56.2 \; g \; NH_3$$

Answer: 56.2 g of NH$_3$ is produced.

As mentioned earlier, ammonia is used to make fertilizer. Because of this it indirectly provides us with some of our nutritional needs. It is estimated that 150 million tons of fertilizer was produced globally in 2006. That is a lot of fertilizer! The production of ammonia using the Haber–Bosch process requires a significant amount of energy and can be expensive. Underdeveloped countries often do not have the advantage of using commercial fertilizer to grow their crops.

11.4 Solving Stoichiometric Problems

Why is it important to master this skill?

Stoichiometry gives us a sense of how chemical recipes work. For example: how do companies produce enough aspirin to have enough in every drug store? In much the same way, they produce enough chocolate chip cookies for all the grocery stores! Learning about how much of a chemical is produced helps us to be more informed citizens. When we watch the news, read the paper, and talk with our friends and family, discussions about pollution and the environment inevitably arise. If we understand how to calculate amounts of chemicals, we have a better understanding about what these amounts represent. This also helps us to understand the significance of pollution amounts and the impact of contamination by industrial products.

Key ideas

Chemicals combine in stoichiometric proportions
These proportions come from the balanced chemical equation
The mole allows us to compare between chemicals

Let's continue to practice how to calculate amounts from a balanced chemical equation.

Here are some helpful tips that will make it easier for you to master these types of calculations:

1. Copy the flowchart for each question. Write down the chemical reaction and the amounts so that you can visually see what you are starting with and what steps are required in the calculation.

2. Write out in words what you are doing next to each step.

3. Notice that you repeat the same sequence of steps each time.

4. Explain the meaning of your answer. What did you find? Try not to think of your answer as just a number, but as a quantity that represents something meaningful.

5. Remember to practice one or two examples without your notes or the text. The process always looks easier when you are reading through an example.

Refer to the flowchart for the steps involved in the following calculations.

Calculating the limiting reactant

Here we will practice using a limiting reactant to calculate the amount of product formed. Refer back to the steps in the flowchart to guide you through determining the limiting reactant as needed.

Solved problem

Part 1. Lithium metal (Li) reacts directly with nitrogen gas (N_2) to produce lithium nitride (Li_3N) according to the reaction:

$$6Li(s) + N_2(g) \rightarrow 2Li_3N(s).$$

When 48.0 g of lithium (Li) reacts with 46.5 g of nitrogen gas (N_2), which reactant is the limiting reactant? Lithium is the only group 1 metal that is capable of reacting directly with nitrogen gas.

Asked: Limiting reactant

Given: 48.0 g Li reacting with 46.5 g of N_2

Relationships: Molar mass of Li = 6.941 g/mole
Molar mass of N_2 = 14.007 g/mole × 2 = 28.01 g/mole
Mole ratio: 6 moles Li ~ 1 mole N_2

Solve: Step 1: $48.0 \, \text{g Li} \times \dfrac{1 \, moleLi}{6.941 \, g \, Li} = 6.92 \, moles \, Li \, (have)$

$46.5 \, \text{g} \, N_2 \times \dfrac{1 \, mole \, Li}{28.01 \, g \, N_2} = 1.66 \, moles \, N_2 \, (have)$

Step 2: Use the mole ratio to determine the amount of moles needed to react.

$6.92 \, mole \, Li \times \dfrac{1 \, mole \, N_2}{6 \, moles \, Li} = 1.15 \, moles \, N_2 \, (needed)$

Step 3: Comparing 1.15 moles N_2 (need) < 1.66 mole N_2 (have), we see that N_2 is our excess reactant!
Or, alternatively, calculate

$1.66 \, mole \, N_2 \times \dfrac{6 \, moles \, Li}{1 \, mole \, N_2} = 9.96 \, moles \, Li \, (needed)$

Comparing 9.96 moles Li (need) > 6.92 moles Li (have), we can see that Li is our limiting reactant.

Discussion: Again you can determine the limiting reactant using either reactant once it is converted to moles.
There is no need to do both calculations in step 3 as shown. Either one gives you the correct answer!

As you can see, finding the limiting is a methodical process. Just follow either of the two methods shown and you will always get the correct answer.

Calculating theoretical yield and percent yield

Now in Part 2 of the solved problem below, we will calculate the mass of lithium nitride that can form using our limiting reactant. Remember that this is also called the theoretical yield of lithium nitride. The following two calculations also apply to the same balanced equation as used on the previous page:

$$6Li(s) + N_2(g) \rightarrow 2Li_3N(s)$$

Solved problem

Part 2. How much lithium nitride (Li_3N) can be produced from this reaction?

Asked: Amount of product (Li_3N) produced

Given: Li is the limiting reactant (from Part 1 on previous page).

Relationships: Molar mass of Li_3N = $(6.941 \times 3) + 14.007 = 34.83$ g/mole

Mole ratio: 6 moles Li ~ 2 moles Li_3N

Solve: Step 1: Use moles of limiting reactant to calculate moles of LiN_3 produced.

$$6.92 \ \overline{moles \ Li} \times \frac{2 \ moles \ Li_3N}{6 \ moles \ Li} = 2.31 \ moles \ Li_3N$$

Step 2: Convert moles to grams using the molar mass.

$$2.31 \ \overline{moles \ Li_3N} \times \frac{34.83 \ g \ Li_3N}{1 \ mole \ Li_3N} = 80.46 \ g \ Li_3N \ produced$$

Answer: 80.46 g of Li_3N is produced.

Now we will use the theoretical yield obtained above to calculate the percent yield of the reaction. Remember the reason that the "theoretical yield" is theoretical is that it is what you would get in a perfect reaction. Chemical reactions are not perfect. We calculate percentage yield because we are given the actual amount produced. The actual yield can only be obtained in the laboratory.

Solved problem

3. Calculate the percentage yield of an experiment that actually produced 62.5 g of Li_3N.

Asked: Percentage yield of Li_3N

Given: The actual yield of 62.5 g Li_3N and the theoretical yield of 80.46 g of Li_3N as calculated above

Relationships: Formula for percent yield

Solve: $percent \ yield = \dfrac{62.5 \ g \ (actual)}{80.46 \ g \ (theoretical)} \times 100 = 77.7\%$

Answer: The percent yield is 77.7%.

Calculating the amount of excess reactant remaining

Often when a limiting reactant calculation is required, it is necessary to calculate the amount of excess reactant that is not consumed in the chemical reaction. Calculating the amount of excess reactant adds one simple step to our calculation. We subtract the amount we have from the amount we need of the excess reactant, and then convert to grams by multiplying by the molar mass.

Solved problem

In an experiment, 3.50 g of ammonia (NH_3) reacts with 3.85 g of oxygen (O_2):

$$4NH_3(g) + 5O_2(g) \rightarrow 4NO(g) + 6H_2O(g)$$

(a) Which reactant is the limiting reactant? (b) How much of the excess reactant remains after the limiting reactant is completely consumed?

Asked: Limiting reactant and amount of excess reactant

Relationships: Molar mass of NH_3 = (14.007 g/mole + (1.0079 g/mole × 3)
= 17.03 g/mole
Molar mass of O_2 = 15.999 g/mole × 2 = 32.0 g/mole
Mole ratio: 4 moles NH_3 = 5 moles O_2

Solve: a) Step 1: $3.50 \text{ g } NH_3 \times \dfrac{1 \text{ mole } NH_3}{17.03 \text{ g } NH_3} = 0.206 \text{ moles } NH_3$ *(have)*

$3.85 \text{ g } O_2 \times \dfrac{1 \text{ mole } O_2}{32.0 \text{ g } O_2} = 0.120 \text{ moles } O_2$ *(have)*

Step 2: $0.206 \text{ moles } NH_3 \times \dfrac{5 \text{ moles } O_2}{4 \text{ moles } NH_3} = 0.26 \text{ moles } O_2$ *(needed)*

$0.120 \text{ moles } O_2 \times \dfrac{4 \text{ moles } NH_3}{5 \text{ moles } O_2} = 0.096 \text{ moles } NH_3$ *(needed)*

Step 3: Compare have and need amounts for each reactant For NH_3, have (0.206 moles) > need (0.096 mole)
For O_2, have (0.102 moles) < need (0.26 mole)
Here we can see that O_2 is our limiting reactant
(b) To find excess reactant simply perform the subtraction (have – need) for NH_3.
0.206 moles NH_3 (have) – 0.096 moles NH_3 (need) = 0.110 moles
0.110 moles NH_3 remaining × 17.03 g/mole = 1.87 g NH_3 in excess

Answer: O_2 is the limiting reactant and there is 1.87 g of NH_3 in excess.

Determining the amounts of solid formed from solutions

Stoichiometry
with solutions

One of the reaction types you learned about in Chapter 10 was a precipitate reaction. Chemists use precipitate reactions to test for pollutants in water supplies.

Here you can see two solutions that form a dark brown solid precipitate when mixed. The reaction is:

$$CuSO_4(aq) + Na_2S(aq) \rightarrow CuS(s) + Na_2SO_4(aq)$$

You can probably guess that if the solutions are more concentrated, they will form a larger amount of solid. This simply means the higher the molarities are, the more moles react!

The Environmental Protection Agency (EPA) tests for certain ions by taking advantage of the fact that they form solids when mixed in the right solution. The following example involves testing for the Cu^{2+} ion in water.

Solved problem

The concentration of Cu^{2+} ions [found as $CuSO_4(aq)$] in the water discharged from an industrial plant is found by adding an excess of sodium sulfide (Na_2S) solution to 1.0 L of the contaminated water. What is the concentration of $CuSO_4$ in the water if 0.021 g of CuS is formed? The reaction is

$$CuSO_4(aq) + Na_2S(aq) \rightarrow Na_2SO_4(aq) + CuS(s)$$

Asked: Concentration of the Cu^{2+} ion [from $CuSO_4(aq)$]

Given: 1.0 L of solution tested, 0.021 g of CuS solid formed

Relationships: Molar mass of CuS = 63.55 + 32.06 = 95.61 g/mole
Mole ratio: 1 mole CuS(s) = 1 mole $CuSO_4(aq)$

Solve: $0.021 \; g \; \cancel{CuS} \times \dfrac{1 \; mole \; CuS}{95.61 \; g \; \cancel{CuS}} = 2.20 \times 10^{-4} \; moles \; CuS$

$2.20 \times 10^{-4} \; moles \; \cancel{CuS} \times \dfrac{1 \; mole \; CuSO_4}{1 \; \cancel{mole \; CuS}} = 2.20 \times 10^{-4} \; moles \; CuSO_4$

$\dfrac{2.20 \times 10^{-4} \; moles \; CuSO_4}{1.0 \; L \; solution} = 2.20 \times 10^{-4} \; M$

Answer: The concentration of $CuSO_4$ is 2.20×10^{-4} M.

Discussion: If the legal limit is 5.0×10^{-4} M of Cu^{2+}, is the industrial plant following the environmental guidelines?
Yes, because 2.20×10^{-4} M is less than the legal limit.

Stoichiometry and nature

The primary elements here on Earth are recycled over time throughout the different regions of the planet. For example, carbon is available in different molecules in the atmosphere, land, and ocean. It is important for the balance of elements to be sustainable and able to support the living systems here on Earth now and in the future. Today we hear about sustainability in many different contexts. Stoichiometry has quite a lot to do with how chemicals in the form of molecules and elements achieve a balance in our environment. We have established that chemicals make up our food, the air we breathe, the water we drink, and the buildings we work and live in. These are the essential things humans need to survive. What would happen if we did not have enough chemicals to make all of the things we need to live? Stoichiometry looks at amounts of chemicals required for a chemical reaction, and chemical reactions make actual substances. Knowing how much of a chemical is used or released is very important if we want to understand the overall picture.

To be "sustainable," humans need to consume Earth's resources at a rate that can be replaced by nature. There is much evidence to indicate that we are living in a manner that is unsustainable. Let's take the burning of fossil fuels as an example. As we burn fossil fuels, there are specific stoichiometric ratios involved. Coal is made up of carbon, sulfur, hydrogen, oxygen, and nitrogen. There are many different types of coal; however, they are all primarily composed of carbon (C). Consider the following unbalanced combustion reaction for coal:

Coal ($C_xS_yH_z$)

$$(C_xS_yH_z) (s) + O_2 (g) \rightarrow CO_2 (g) + H_2O (l) + SO_2 (g)$$

coal + oxygen → carbon dioxide + water + sulfur dioxide

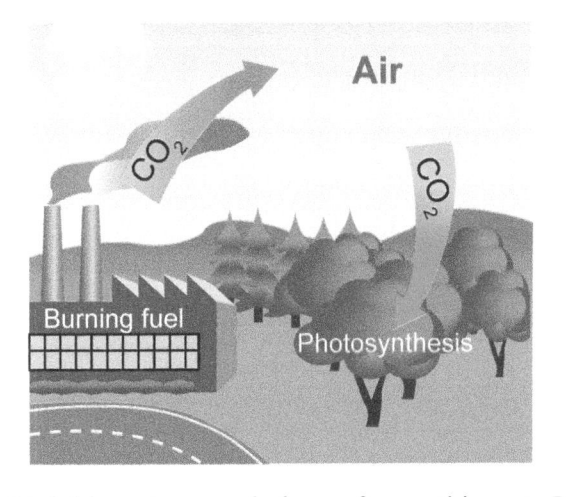
Air

CO₂

CO₂

Burning fuel

Photosynthesis

In this reaction, the mole ratio between the carbon and the carbon dioxide is one to one. If we consider the fact that the carbon and other elements in the coal itself came from the ancient remains of plants, we can begin to think about how elements cycle through Earth processes. We can use stoichiometry to roughly calculate how much carbon is released into the air when we burn coal. We can also determine how much of this carbon will be returned to the Earth when the plants use it for photosynthesis. Maybe in another million years, the carbon in the glucose molecules of plants today will be in the form of coal again!

Stoichiometry can help us figure this out. Let's say that a coal-powered electrical plant burns 1,000 kg (1 tonne) of coal, and the coal itself is approximately 60% carbon. We can calculate the mass of carbon that will enter the atmosphere. 1,000 kg × 0.60 = 600 kg.

This carbon will enter the atmosphere as CO_2, because one mole of CO_2 forms for every mole of carbon in the coal. Since one mole of CO_2 is about 3 times as heavy as one mole of carbon, burning 1 tonne of coal releases approximately 1,800 kg of CO_2 into the atmosphere. Here we are simplifying the process a little by assuming that there is complete combustion of the coal.

The amount of carbon entering the atmosphere as carbon dioxide gas worsens the greenhouse effect, which in turn affects the global climate. One method that is being used to remove some of the carbon dioxide is to capture the gas, concentrate it, and send it back below Earth's surface. This is called carbon sequestering. In this way, some of the carbon will be removed from our atmosphere and stored underground once again.

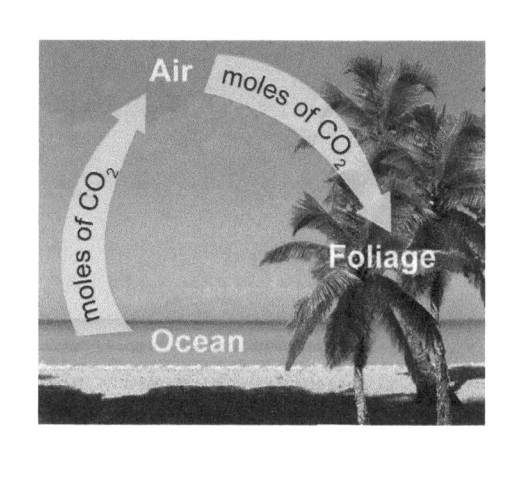

Of course, some of the carbon dioxide is recycled naturally! How does this happen? There are two primary ways this is accomplished: through the chemical reaction called photo-synthesis and through the dissolving of CO_2 by ocean water. Both of these chemical processes involve chemical reactions to which stoichiometry can be applied. Nature uses stoichiometry because life processes such as photosynthesis and respiration are balanced chemical equations!

First, plants use approximately one quarter of the CO_2 available in the air. So of the 600 kg of carbon released by burning 1 tonne of coal, approximately 600 kg × 0.25 = 150 kg of CO_2 are cycled through photosynthesis:

$$6CO_2(g) + 6H_2O(l) \rightarrow C_6H_{12}O_6(s) + 6O_2(g)$$

Here 6 moles of CO_2 are used to make 1 mole of $C_6H_{12}O_6$, giving off 6 moles of O_2 as a by-product.

Once photosynthesis is carried out, carbon is now in the form of glucose. Glucose can enter the food chain when plants are consumed by animals. The animals metabolize the glucose and release CO_2 into the air once again, through the process of respiration.

Second, another quarter of our atmospheric carbon dioxide dissolves in the ocean by direct air and water exchange. This process is represented by the following equation:

$$CO_2(g) + H_2O(l) \rightarrow H^+(aq) + HCO_3^-(aq)$$

According to this equation, for every 1 mole of CO_2 dissolved, 1 mole of HCO_3^- is formed.

In essence we use stoichiometry to help us determine how much carbon enters the atmosphere, and we take into account how much can be absorbed by natural processes. To do this we need an accurate understanding of the chemical reactions involved in these changes.

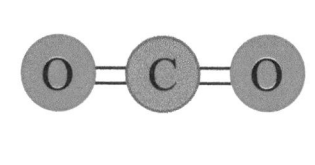

Scientists have been trying to discover more accurate methods for determining how much CO_2 is absorbed by photosynthesis. In November of 2008, a professor at the University of California was able to measure the amount of CO_2 absorbed much more accurately, because he discovered that carbonyl sulfide (COS) used in a process that runs parallel (at the same time) as photosynthesis is absorbed at the same rate as CO_2. Notice how similar molecular structure for COS is to CO_2. It is easier to measure COS because plants do not release it the way they release CO_2. We can apply stoichi-ometry more accurately with these better methods of measurement. Because of this research we will now be able to include more accurate information about how photosynthesis will be able to help us battle climate change.

Chapter 11 Review

Vocabulary

Match each word to the sentence where it best fits.

Section 11.1

stoichiometry	stoichiometric equivalent
mole ratio	

1. When analyzing a chemical equation, we can say that the mole amounts given in the balanced equation are _____ amounts.

2. To study the amounts of substances used in chemical reactions we use _____.

3. Using the coefficients from the balanced equation to make a/an _____ allows us to compare the amounts of chemicals required to those produced in a chemical reaction.

Section 11.2

actual yield	percent yield
theoretical yield	

4. The _____ is based on a calculation that assumes the reaction yields 100% of the product.

5. When we experiment in the laboratory we obtain the _____, which is generally less than the theoretical yield.

6. Calculating the _____ tells us how much of the product was obtained from our experiment.

Section 11.3

limiting reactant	excess reactant

7. The substance that limits the amount of product that can form is called the _____.

8. The _____ is left over after the chemical reaction has formed products.

Conceptual Questions

Section 11.1

9. Interpret the following equation in terms of molecules and moles:
$$C_3H_8(g) + 5O_2(g) \rightarrow 3CO_2(g) + 4H_2O(g)$$

10. Are moles conserved in a chemical reaction? Explain.

11. Explain what the unit of the mole represents in your own words.

12. Give an example from your everyday life where you use a recipe to make something.

13. Use the example you gave above and explain how this is similar to using a balanced equation to see how chemicals combine.

14. Write out the meaning of the following chemical equation in words:
$$2NaN_3(s) \rightarrow 2Na(s) + 3N_2(g)$$

15. Show the mole ratios for comparing the reactants in the following equation:
$$CH_4(g) + 2O_2(g) \rightarrow CO_2(g) + 2H_2O(l)$$

16. Using the following balanced equation:
$$Ca(s) + 2H_2O(l) \rightarrow Ca(OH)_2(aq) + H_2(g)$$

    a. Give an example of a stoichiometric equivalent amount of each chemical.

    b. What mole ratio would you use to calculate how many moles of hydrogen (H_2) could form from a given number of moles of calcium (Ca)?

17. When using the flowchart to calculate grams produced from grams given, explain why we need to:

    a. convert to moles in step 1, and

    b. use the mole ratio in step 2.

18. Why do chemists need to calculate the amount of products produced in a chemical reaction?

19. Consider the following balanced equation:
$S + O_2 \rightarrow SO_2$
Explain why 1.0 g of S will not react exactly with 1.0 g of O_2.

20. Since we weigh and measure amounts of chemicals in grams, why can't we compare chemicals in grams?

21. If 4 moles of Ca(s) react with water according to the following balanced equation:
$Ca(s) + 2H_2O(l) \rightarrow Ca(OH)_2(aq) + H_2(g)$
How many moles of hydrogen gas (H_2) are produced? Explain.

Section 11.2

22. Why don't we get 100% of the product formed in a chemical reaction? Give a couple of reasons.

23. Explain how making popcorn helps us to understand the percent yield of a chemical reaction.

24. How does a chemist determine the actual yield of a chemical reaction?

25. Give an everyday-life example of percentage yield (not popcorn!).If you have not seen an example of this in your everyday life, ask some friends.

26. Would you expect the actual yield to be larger or smaller than the theoretical yield? Explain.

27. When performing the experiment where baking soda ($NaHCO_3$) is heated to cause it to decompose into $Na_2CO_3(s) + H_2O(l) + CO_2(g)$, your final mass is close to the theoretical yield. List a couple of likely sources of error.

28. What is an example of a unit of concentration?

29. Describe how the process of calculating moles of a solute dissolved in a solution is different than calculating moles of a solid.

Section 11.3

30. Give one new (or original) real-life example of a limiting reactant.

31. Look at the picture below and refer to the following equation:
$CH_4(g) + H_2O(l) \rightarrow 3H_2(g) + CO(g)$

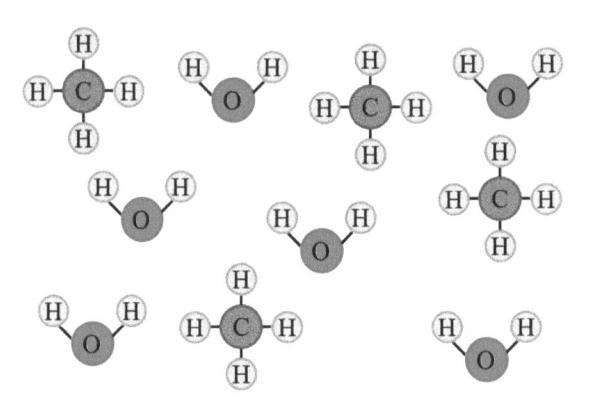

a. Which reactant is limiting? Explain.

b. Make a sketch of the molecules after the reaction.

32. Is is safe to assume the reactant present in the larger amount is always the excess reactant?

33. Explain why knowing the limiting reactant is useful.

34. Consider the following chemical reaction:
$6Li(s) + N_2(g) \rightarrow 2Li_3N(s)$
If you have 6 moles of Li and 2 moles of N_2, which reactant is limiting? Explain.

35. Consider the following chemical reaction:
$2Al(s) + 3Cl_2(g) \rightarrow 2AlCl_3(s)$
If you have 6 moles of each reactant, which one is limiting? Explain.

36. Why can't we use the excess reactant to determine the amount of product produced?

37. Sketch out the flowchart for determining the grams of product produced when a limiting reactant is involved in your calculation.

Chapter 11 Review

Quantitative Problems

Section 11.1

38. Use the equation
$$4NH_3(g) + 3O_2(g) \rightarrow 2N_2(g) + 6H_2O(g)$$
to answer the following questions. Clearly show your work.

    a. How many moles of water form when 8 moles of ammonia (NH_3) reacts with excess oxygen?

    b. How many moles of nitrogen gas (N_2) form when 7 moles of oxygen (O_2) reacts with excess ammonia?

    c. If you start with 3.5 moles of ammonia (NH_3), how many moles of oxygen will be consumed?

    d. If 10 moles of water is formed, how many moles of oxygen gas were required?

    e. If we need to produce 20 moles of water, how many moles of both ammonia and oxygen are required to produce it?

39. Nitrogen (N_2) reacts with iodine (I_2) according to the following equation:
$$N_2(g) + 3I_2(s) \rightarrow 2NI_3(s)$$

    a. Explain what information this equation gives.

    b. How many moles of NI_3 can form when 127.0 g of I_2 reacts with excess nitrogen gas?

    c. If you wish to prepare 2.0 g of NI_3, how many moles of nitrogen are required?

    d. When 28.0 g of nitrogen (N_2) reacts with excess iodine, how many moles of nitrogen triiodide (NI_3) form?

40. For each of the following equations listed below, calculate the moles of product that would be produced by reacting 4.0 moles of oxygen (O_2) with the reactant. Be sure to clearly show the mole ratio in each calculation.

    a. $4Fe(s) + 3O_2(g) \rightarrow 2Fe_2O_3(s)$

    b. $2Mg(s) + O_2(g) \rightarrow 2MgO(s)$

    c. $2Cu(s) + O_2(g) \rightarrow 2CuO(s)$

    d. $4Ag(s) + O_2(g) \rightarrow 2Ag_2O(s)$

41. Calculate the number of moles of each substance from each of the following masses given:

    a. 15.0 g of carbon dioxide (CO_2)

    b. 30.0 g of copper (Cu)

    c. 10.0 g of neon (Ne)

    d. 20.0 g of HCl

    e. 32.00 g of $Cu(OH)_2$

    f. 50.0 g of $Al_2(SO_4)_3$

42. Given the following reaction:
$$N_2(g) + O_2(g) \rightarrow 2NO(g)$$

    a. How many moles of NO can form when 40.0 g of N_2 reacts with excess oxygen?

    b. How many grams of NO can form using the amounts in part a?

43. Using the unbalanced equation
$$S(s) + H_2SO_4(aq) \rightarrow SO_2(g) + H_2O(l),$$
answer the following questions:

    a. Balance the equation.

    b. Explain in words what the balanced coefficients tell us.

    c. Calculate the number of moles of SO_2 that can be formed from 100.0 g of sulfur (S) and excess sulfuric acid (H_2SO_4).

    d. How many grams of SO_2 form given the amounts in part c?

    e. How many grams of water form when 100.0 g of sulfur (S) reacts with excess sulfuric acid (H_2SO_4)?

    f. If 64.0 g of sulfur dioxide (SO_2) forms, how many grams of sulfuric acid were required?

44. Silver tarnishes and turns a dull gray color when exposed to the oxygen in the air. The reaction for the tarnishing of silver is
$$Ag(s) + O_2(g) \rightarrow Ag_2O(s)$$

    a. Balance the equation.

    b. If you react 8.0 g of silver with excess oxygen, how many grams of silver oxide can form?

45. Iron oxide, or rust (Fe_2O_3), reacts with aluminum metal (Al) to form iron (Fe) and aluminum oxide (Al_2O_3) according to the reaction
$$Fe_2O_3(s) + Al(s) \rightarrow Fe(s) + Al_2O_3(s)$$

    a. Balance the equation.

    b. When 25.0 g of aluminum reacts with excess iron oxide, how many grams of iron will be produced?

Section 11.2

46. Two students performed a precipitate experiment based on the following equation:
$$Ba(NO_3)_2(aq) + Na_2SO_4(aq)$$
$$\rightarrow BaSO_4(s) + 2NaNO_3(aq)$$
    Before the experiment, they calculated the theoretical yield of barium sulfate ($BaSO_4$) to be 2.58 g. After the experiment when they filtered and dried their precipitate, they obtained 1.98 g of $BaSO_4$. Calculate the students' percent yield.

47. Based on your prelaboratory calculations, your experiment should yield 4.36 g of magnesium oxide. However, when you perform the experiment and weigh the MgO produced, you find that you obtain only 3.98 g MgO. What is your percent yield?

48. When phosphorous reacts with chlorine it forms phosphorus trichloride (PCl_3) via the equation
$$P_4(s) + 6Cl_2(g) \rightarrow 4PCl_3(l)$$

    a. How much PCl_3 can be formed by reacting 6.00 g of P_4 with excess chlorine?

    b. If a 19.50 g sample of PCl_3 was obtained from the reaction, calculate the percent yield.

    c. In another experiment, the theoretical yield was calculated to be 35.20 g PCl_3. What was the actual yield for this experiment if it produced a 75.20% yield?

49. Limestone decomposes with heat in the following equation:
$$CaCO_3(s) \rightarrow CaO(s) + CO_2(g)$$
    If 8.80 g of CO_2 is produced by heating 28.0 g of $CaCO_3$, what is the percent yield of this reaction?

50. For each of the following, calculate the number of moles of solute present in the solution:

    a. 50.0 mL of 1.33 M NaOH

    b. 25.0 mL of 6.0 M NaCl

    c. 10 mL of 0.10 M $AgNO_3$

    d. 10.0 g of NaCl in 250 mL of distilled water

51. A sample of magnesium metal (Mg) reacts with 45.0 mL of 3.0 M solution of hydrochloric acid (HCl) via the following reaction:
$$Mg(s) + 2HCl(aq) \rightarrow MgCl_2(aq) + H_2(g)$$

    a. How many moles of HCl are reacting?

    b. Assume the Mg is in excess. How many moles of H_2 gas are produced?

    c. How many grams of H_2 gas are produced?

52. A student performed a precipitate experiment based on the following equation:
$$Cu(NO_3)_2(aq) + Na_2CO_3(aq)$$
$$\rightarrow CuCO_3(s) + 2NaNO_3(aq)$$
    In the experiment 25.0 mL of 1.0 M $Cu(NO_3)_2$ is mixed with excess sodium carbonate (Na_2CO_3).

    a. How many moles of $Cu(NO_3)_2$ are reacting?

    b. How many grams of copper carbonate ($CuCO_3$) will form?

53. Two students carried out a precipitate experiment based on the following equation:
$$AgNO_3(aq) + NaCl(aq) \rightarrow AgCl(s) + NaNO_3(aq)$$
    They mix 10.0 mL of 3.0 M $AgNO_3$ with excess sodium chloride (NaCl).

    a. How many moles of $AgNO_3$ are reacting?

    b. How many grams of AgCl will form?

54. A solution is made by dissolving 20.0 g of glucose ($C_6H_{12}O_6$) in 200.0 g of water. Calculate the mass percent of glucose in the solution.

55. Commercial hydrogen peroxide (H_2O_2) is advertised as 3% by mass. How many grams of hydrogen peroxide are in 200 mL of commercial solution? (Assume the density of hydrogen peroxide is the same as for pure water, 1.0 g/mL.)

56. A certain brand name mouthwash contains 0.50% ethanol by mass. How many grams of ethanol (CH_3OH) are in 100.0 mL of mouthwash?

57. Commercial vinegar is 5% acetic acid by mass. How many grams of acetic acid (CH_3COOH) are in 25.00 mL of commercial vinegar?

Section 11.3

58. Iron (Fe) can be produced by the thermite reaction according to the following equation:

$$Fe_2O_3(s) + 2Al(s) \rightarrow 2Fe(s) + Al_2O_3(s)$$

   a. If 100.0 g of Fe_2O_3 reacts with 30.0 g of Al, which one will be used up first?

   b. Explain your answer to part a.

   c. How much iron (Fe) can be produced in grams?

   d. Calculate the grams of excess reactant remaining after the reaction.

59. Lithium metal reacts with nitrogen gas to produce lithium nitride according to the following equation:

$$6Li(s) + N_2(g) \rightarrow 2Li_3N(s)$$

   Use your flowchart to answer the following questions:

   a. If you have 20.0 g of Li and 15.0 g of N_2, which reactant will be used up first?

   b. Explain your answer to part a.

   c. How many grams of Li_3N can be produced?

   d. Calculate the amount of excess reactant remaining after the experiment.

60. Zinc metal reacts with copper(II) nitrate to produce solid copper according to the following equation:

$$Zn(s) + Cu(NO_3)_2(aq) \rightarrow Zn(NO_3)_2(aq) + Cu(s)$$

   Use your flowchart to answer the following questions:

   a. If you have 5.00 g of Zn and 25.0 mL of 1.00 M $Cu(NO_3)_2$, which reactant will be used up first?

   b. Explain your answer to part a.

   c. How many grams of solid Cu can be produced?

   d. Calculate the moles of excess reactant remaining.

61. Small bottles of propane gas are sold at hardware stores for propane torches. The combustion of propane is used for small campfires, heating ski wax, and soldering, and follows the equation

$$C_3H_8(g) + 5O_2(g) \rightarrow 3CO_2(g) + 4H_2O(l)$$

   Use your flowchart to answer the following questions:

   a. If you have 1.0 L of propane gas, how much oxygen will be required to burn it all? (Assume propane has a density of 0.82 g/L)

   b. Explain your answer to part a.

   c. How many grams of H_2O can be produced?

62. For each of the following equations listed below, determine the liming reactant when 10.0 g of each reactant is used. Be sure to clearly support your answer with a calculation.

   a. $4Fe(s) + 3O_2(g) \rightarrow 2Fe_2O_3(s)$

   b. $2Mg(s) + O_2(g) \rightarrow 2MgO(s)$

   c. $2Cu(s) + O_2(g) \rightarrow 2CuO(s)$

   d. $4Ag(s) + O_2(g) \rightarrow 2Ag_2O(s)$

63. Using the reactions in the previous question, calculate the mass of product formed in each reaction.

Section 11.4

64. Aluminium metal reacts with oxygen in the air to form a layer of aluminum oxide (Al_2O_3) according to the equation
$$4Al(s) + 3O_2(g) \rightarrow 2Al_2O_3(s)$$

    This layer protects the aluminum atoms underneath from further corrosion.

    a. If 28.0 g of Al reacts with excess oxygen in the air, what mass of aluminum oxide is formed?

    b. How many moles of oxygen are consumed during this reaction?

    c. If 250 g of Al_2O_3 is formed, how much Al reacted?

65. When gasoline or octane (C_8H_{18}) combusts, the products are water and carbon dioxide gas:
$$2C_8H_{18}(g) + 25O_2(g) \rightarrow 16CO_2(g) + 18H_2O(l)$$

    a. Calculate the mass of water formed from the combustion of 5.0 L of gasoline. (The density of gasoline is 0.79 g/mL.)

    b. What mass of carbon dioxide will be released into the air when the 5.0 L of octane is combusted?

66. Wine can spoil or become "vinegary" when ethanol (C_2H_5OH) is converted to acetic acid (CH_3COOH) by oxidation:
$$C_2H_5OH(aq) + O_2(g)$$
$$\rightarrow CH_3COOH(aq) + H_2O(l)$$

    a. Determine the limiting reactant when 5.00 g of ethanol and 2.0 g of oxygen are sealed in a wine bottle.

    b. Calculate how much acetic acid will form in grams.

    c. Calculate the amount of excess reactant remaining in grams.

67. Make a sketch of what this chemical reaction looks like after the reaction takes place:
$$N_2(g) + 3H_2(g) \rightarrow 2NH_3(g)$$

The blue molecules represent nitrogen and the white ones represent hydrogen. Put them together appropriately to make NH_3 as your product. Be sure to include any unreacted molecules as well as the products formed in your sketch.

68. One step in the synthesis of rocket fuel is to make nitrogen dioxide (NO_2) from NO and O_2:
$$2NO(g) + O_2(g) \rightarrow 2NO_2(g)$$

    a. If 20.0 g of NO reacts with 10.0 g of O_2, which reactant will limit the amount of NO_2 that can be formed?

    b. How many grams of NO_2 will form?

    c. Calculate the amount, in grams, of the excess reactant remaining.

69. Consider the following reaction:
$$Pb(s) + KNO_3(s) \rightarrow PbO(s) + KNO_2(s)$$

    In the laboratory a yield of 20.2 g of potassium nitrite (KNO_2) was obtained when 35.0 g of potassium nitrate (KNO_3) reacted with excess lead (Pb). Calculate the percentage yield of potassium nitrite (KNO_2).

CHAPTER 12
Reaction Rates and Equilibrium

What determines how rapidly chemicals will react?

Do chemical reactions "stop" after a period of time?

Can chemical reactions go "backward"? Are they reversible?

Why are some chemical reactions fast, whereas others are slow? Let's think about a few everyday chemical reactions that are familiar to us. What determines how quickly food spoils? This is a very important question for many developing countries! Chemistry has improved methods of food preservation, and it has helped reduce the number of people suffering from starvation. We know from our own life experience that warmer temperatures speed up the spoiling of food. We keep milk in the refrigerator, and we freeze our meat to make it last longer. In developing areas of the world refrigeration is scarce, and it is much too expensive to use. Therefore people must rely on chemical preservatives. These chemical preservatives slow down or

Can you spot the chemical reactions?

interfere with the chemical reactions that cause food to spoil. In this chapter you will learn about the factors that affect the speed of a chemical reaction.

The human body is an excellent example of chemical equilibrium. The chemical systems in our bodies are in a delicate balance, called homeostasis, that is constantly maintained. One example of this is breathing. As you breathe, you continuously exchange carbon dioxide and oxygen gases with the surrounding air. We exhale carbon dioxide and inhale oxygen. During heavy exercise our breathing rate increases, which allows us to get rid of the excess carbon dioxide produced from our increased metabolic rate. This excess carbon dioxide needs to be eliminated to restore your body's proper chemical balance.

Observing reactions over time

To study reaction rates, or the speed at which a chemical process is happening, it is helpful to have something that you can see or directly observe. Here we will use color change to determine how fast a chemical reaction is occurring. Many of us know that bleach removes stains from clothing. Grass stains for instance are very difficult to remove without bleach! Many fabrics have natural and synthetic dyes that can be removed with bleach.

Reaction rates are determined by measuring the change in concentration over a period of time. In the images here, the first blue solution is the most concentrated, as you can tell from the deeper shade of blue. The initial solution was made using 100 mL of water and three drops of food coloring; its concentration is about 3 drops per 100 mL. As the chemical reaction between the dye and the bleach occurs, we will see the solution become lighter.

In the first picture, at time zero, the bleach is just being added to the cuvette containing the dye. You can see that the dye has not yet begun to fade. Two minutes after the bleach is added, the color is much lighter, indicating that a chemical reaction between the bleach and the dye has taken place. After a longer period of time (4 minutes), or twice as long, we can see the solution in the cuvette is almost clear!

Bleach removes stains by breaking double bonds in the dye molecules. This alteration affects the dye's ability to absorb visible light. Once this is done, no color can be seen and the stain is removed. The speed of this chemical process can be determined by noting the change in color and the change in time. Over a longer time period we can see that more of the color fades or disappears.

What affects how quickly the color fades?

The chemical formula for bleach is NaOCl, and the formula for Blue dye #1 is $C_{37}H_{34}N_2Na_2O_9S_3$. A representation of Blue dye #1 is shown here at right.

12.1 Reaction Rates

Some reactions are fast and others are slow

Chemical reactions are the essence of chemistry. We know that reactions reorganize atoms into different molecules and compounds. In this section we are going to look at how fast these changes occur. Some reactions are fast, like a match burning. Some are slower, like milk spoiling when it is left out. The process of rusting occurs slowly over time when a metal object, such as a bicycle, is left out in the rain.

Mg(s) strip in HCl(aq)

Factors influencing reaction speed

The speeds of chemical reactions are affected by several factors:

1. The concentrations of the reacting chemicals: Many chemical reactions happen more rapidly if the reactant concentrations are increased. The more reactants that are present, the faster the reaction occurs.

2. The temperature at which the reaction is carried out: The higher the temperature, the faster the reaction proceeds. For example, the process of cooking speeds up the chemical reactions that take place in food.

3. The surface area or size of the reacting particles: This is particularly important if the reactants are in solid form. The larger the surface area, the faster the reaction will take place. The more atoms that come in contact with each other, the more likely they are to react. A medicine will be absorbed more quickly by our bodies if we ingest it in the form of a powder (held in a dissolvable capsule), rather than in the form of a solid pill. This is because our stomach can dissolve a powder more quickly than a pill.

4. The addition of a catalyst: A catalyst is a substance that facilitates a chemical reaction without being used up itself. It helps the chemicals to react, but it does not break down or become chemically changed. In a catalytic converter, a transition metal such as rhodium acts as a catalyst by providing a surface for molecules to attach to, which allows them to come into contact more easily. The rhodium metal itself does not par-ticipate in the chemical reaction, but it reduces the polluting gases that would be oth-erwise emitted in the exhaust.

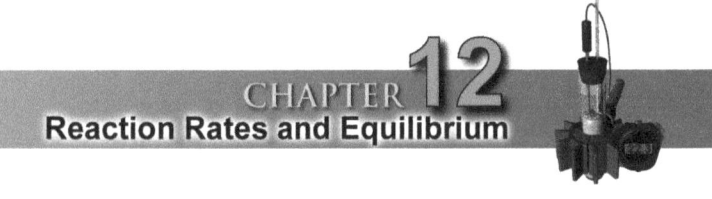
The idea of rate

The concept of speed is similar to rate

When we drive in our cars, we measure our speed by reading the speedometer. The speedometer tells us our speed in miles per hour (mph). If we are traveling at a speed of 45 mph, that means we will cover a distance of 45 miles in one hour. A thoroughbred race horse can maintain a speed of 45 mph for over a mile! In the Kentucky Derby, which is 1.25 miles long, the average race horse covers this distance in approximately 2.00 minutes. The race time is measured with a stopwatch.

Let's find the average speed traveled by a typical race horse:

$$\text{speed (rate)} = \frac{\text{distance}}{\text{time}} = \frac{1.25 \text{ miles}}{2.00 \text{ minutes}}$$

The speed of the horse varies during the race. Most race horses finish at a faster speed than they start at. Imagine as the horses begin the race that they need a burst of energy to get started. The horses then maintain their speed until the home stretch, the final piece of the race. Here the horses slowly accelerate as they approach the finish.

This example shows that the rate or speed can change during a horse race. The rate of a chemical reaction changes over time as well. The difference is that chemical reactions have a faster rate at the beginning and a slower rate at the end. Chemical reactions tend to slow down over time. We measure the rate of a chemical reaction by measuring a change in the amount of reactant or product per unit time:

$$\text{rate} = \frac{\text{change in concentration}}{\text{change in time}}$$

Rate in chemistry

Reaction rate

Chemists measure the change in concentration of a reactant or a product per unit time. The **reaction rate** is used to describe how reactions evolve over time.

For example, given a generic reaction where A → C, we can measure the rate at which the reaction proceeds by measuring the decrease in the concentration of reactant A over time, or by measuring the increase in concentration of product C over time. As the reaction proceeds the amount of reactant A decreases as it is converted to product C.

Observing reaction progress

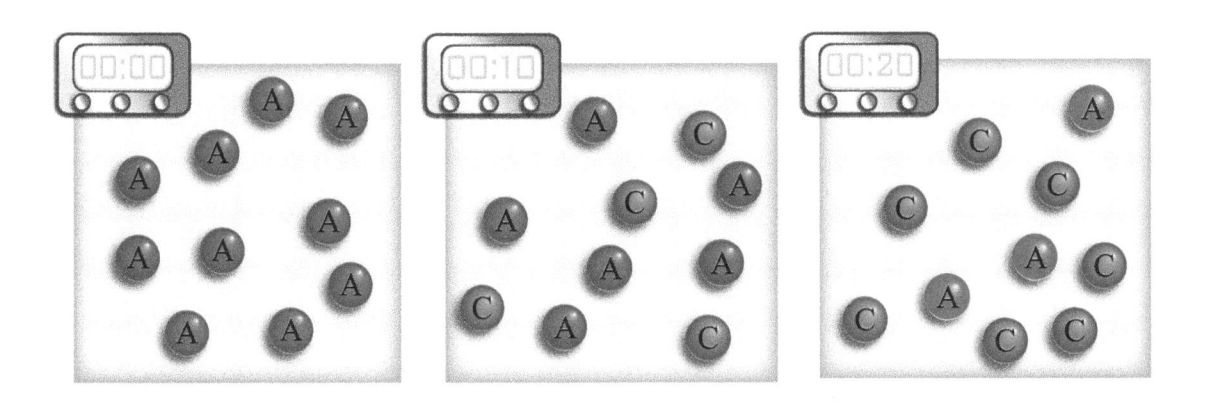

What do you notice about the reaction rate when you compare the three pictures?

Notice that the time interval between each picture is constant, at 10 s, but the rate decreases. Why? Because fewer molecules of A are converting to C over time.

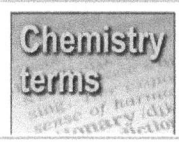

reaction rate: the speed at which a chemical reaction occurs, measured by the change in concentration of a reactant or product per unit time.

Calculating average rate of reaction

Average rate equation

The simplest way to calculate a reaction rate is to use the average rate equation:

$$\text{average rate} = \frac{\text{change in concentration}}{\text{change in time}} = \frac{\Delta M \text{ (moles/L)}}{\Delta t \text{ (s)}}$$

Delta means "change in"

The average rate can be calculated between any two times during the chemical reaction.

TABLE 12.1. Data for reaction A → C in a 1 L container

Time (min)	Time (s)	Moles of A	Moles of C
0	0	1.00	0.00
10	600	0.74	0.26
20	1,200	0.54	0.46
30	1,800	0.40	0.60
40	2,400	0.30	0.70

The average rate of appearance for product C can be found as follows:

$$\text{average rate of C} = \frac{[\text{moles/L of C (at t = 20 min)} - \text{moles/L of C (at t = 10 min)}]}{20 \text{ min} - 10 \text{ min}}$$

$$= \frac{(0.46 \text{ moles/L of C} - 0.26 \text{ moles/L of C})}{20 \text{ min} - 10 \text{ min}} = 0.02 \text{ moles/L} \cdot \text{min}$$

Using the information for reactant A, we could calculate the average rate of disappearance for A. We would account for the disappearance by using a negative sign in front of the calculated rate, to indicate a decrease:

$$\text{average rate of A} = \frac{(0.54 \text{ moles/L of A}) - (0.74 \text{ moles/L of A})}{20 \text{ min} - 10 \text{ min}} = -0.02 \text{ moles/L} \cdot \text{min}$$

Here the rate of appearance of C is equal to the rate of disappearance of A because they are in a one-to-one mole relationship in the equation A → C.

The rate of reaction is not constant

If you calculate the rate between later time periods, you will see that the rate decreases. This indicates that the reaction goes slower and slower until there is no longer any measurable change in the concentration. This is because there is less and less reactant remaining, and therefore less product will be formed per unit time.

Stoichiometry and rate

When using a balanced equation such as $2A \rightarrow B + C$, we use stoichiometry when the mole ratios are not one to one. You can correctly assume that the rates of appearance of B and C would be the same because they are present in the same one-to-one molar proportions. The rate of disappearance of A will be twice as much, because the balanced equation has a 2 in front of A.

Mole ratios and rate

The mole ratios from the balanced equation show us the relationship between the rates of reactants and products. For example,

$$2HI(g) \longrightarrow H_2(g) + I_2(g)$$

Rate: $-2(6.0 \times 10^{-3}\text{moles/L·s})$ $(6.0 \times 10^{-3}\text{moles/L·s})$ $(6.0 \times 10^{-3}\text{moles/L·s})$

If the rates of formation for I_2 and H_2 are 6.0×10^{-3} moles/L-s, then the rate of formation for HI will be $2 \times (6.0 \times 10^{-3}$ moles/L-s). We add a minus sign in front of HI's rate because it is disappearing.

The decomposition of N_2O_5 follows the reaction

$$2N_2O_5(g) \rightarrow 4NO_2(g) + O_2(g)$$

The rate of decomposition of N_2O_5 was measured after 25 s and was found to be 5.60×10^{-6} M/s. What is the rate of appearance of NO_2?

Asked: *The rate of NO_2 production*

Given: *Rate of decomposition of N_2O_5 : 5.6×10^{-6} moles/L·s*

Relationships: *Mole ratio: 2 moles N_2O_5 ~ 4 moles of NO_2*

Solve: $5.60 \times 10^{-6} \times \dfrac{4 \text{ moles NO}_2}{2 \text{ moles N}_2O_5} = 1.12 \times 10^{-5}$

Answer: *The rate of appearance of NO_2 is 1.12×10^{-5} moles/L·s.*

Discussion: *The mole ratio tells us that the rate of appearance of NO_2 is twice the rate of N_2O_5 decomposition.*

How fast products are formed

Using stoichiometry to calculate the rates of product formation can help us to predict how fast the product will form before we carry out the chemical reaction. This is often very helpful information. Sometimes reactions are so fast that they become explosive. For instance, when too much hydrogen gas is produced it can become an explosion hazard. Other times we want to use a reaction that occurs rapidly, producing combustible gases for thrust, such as during a rocket launch. Knowing the reaction rate can mean the difference between a controlled burn and a dangerous explosion.

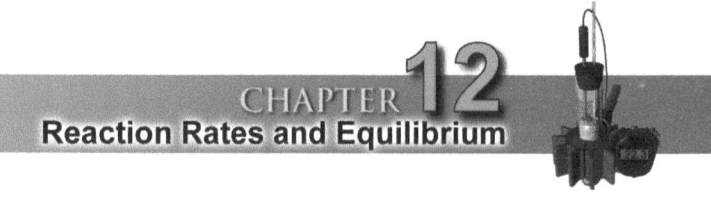
Collision theory

Molecules must hit each other to react

Chemical reactions take place at the molecular level, where molecules of reactant are colliding with each other. We cannot directly observe this aspect of chemical change. As experimenters, we can only observe the macroscopic changes. It makes sense that molecules need to hit one another to react. If they never collided, how would atoms be exchanged? Chemists believe that there are certain criteria that must be met in order for a molecular collision to be successful and form products. The game of pool makes a good analogy to help us understand these criteria or conditions.

First, if you wish to hit a pool ball into a pocket, you need to line up the cue ball with the one you are attempting to hit. If the cue ball is lined up properly, the angle at which it hits will cause the ball to roll in the direction of the pocket. What do you think some of the other factors are? One could be how hard you hit the cue ball. If you do not hit it hard enough, the other ball will not make it to the pocket. You must hit the cue ball hard enough to get the other ball into the pocket, or else the two balls will just collide and roll away from each other.

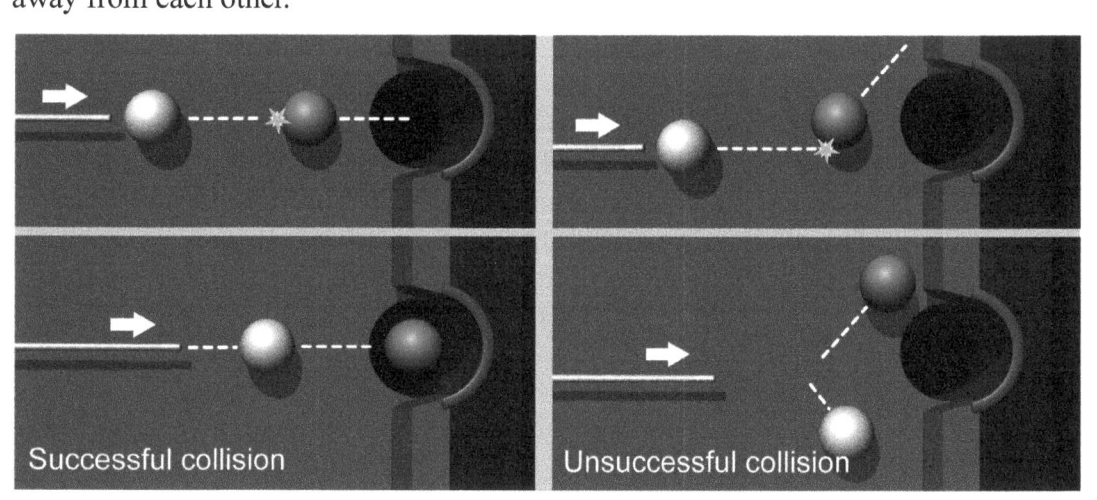

Successful collision   Unsuccessful collision

Activation energy

If we use the pool ball analogy as a comparison, we see that molecules have to hit each other properly to react. Bonds can be broken only if the molecules hit each other with enough energy at the proper angle. This allows bonds to be re-formed. For atoms to be rearranged, bonds need to be broken and re-formed. The formation of a new compound would be analogous to the pool ball going into the pocket. The minimum amount of energy required for molecules to react is called the **activation energy (E$_a$)**. When two molecules collide with sufficient activation energy, a new high-energy state can be achieved, called the **transition state**.

Transition state

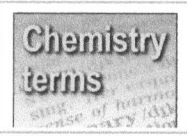
Chemistry terms

activation energy: the minimum amount of energy required for molecules to react.
transition state: a high-energy state where bonds are being broken and reformed, also referred to as the activated complex.

Energy changes in a chemical reaction

A reaction profile

Reaction: A + B $\longrightarrow$ C + D

Energy changes always accompany chemical reactions. Here we use a graph called a **reaction profile** to describe what happens when molecules or particles collide.

The reaction profile helps us to visualize what happens when the reactant molecules collide with each other. The graph shows us that the reactants must have enough energy to get up the "hill." This is represented by the **activation energy (E_a)** labeled on the graph. Recall that this is the minimum amount of energy required for the molecules to react. At the top of the hill is the highest energy, and

Activated complex

this is place where the **activated complex (Ac)** forms. The activated complex lasts for only a fraction of a second. Once the activated complex is formed, the colliding particles may form products or they may go back and re-form reactants. The activated complex is extremely unstable because it forms at such a high energy. For this reason it cannot be isolated in the laboratory. From the high point on the graph where the activated complex exists, there is an equal chance (probability) that products will be formed or that reactants will be re-formed.

Even if the activated complex forms, it may not lead to the formation of products!

This graph shows that the products are lower in energy than the reactants. In this case energy is released and the reaction is exothermic, with a negative ΔH. If we subtract the final energy of the products C and D (approximately 12 kJ) from the reactants A and B (approximately 23 kJ), we can see that the products are 11 kJ lower in energy. The fact that the products are lower in energy makes them more stable than the reactants.

Chemistry terms

reaction profile: a graph showing the progress of a reaction with respect to the energy changes that occur during a collision.

activated complex: a high-energy state where bonds are being broken and reformed; also referred to as the transition state.

Analyzing the reaction profile

Now let's look at the same reaction profile, but for the reverse chemical reaction.

Reaction: C + D ⟶ A + B

Here we see that the reactants (C and D) are at a lower energy than the products (A and B). What does this tell us? Let's assess ΔH carefully here. The reactants are at about 12 kJ and the products are at about 23 kJ, so this means the products absorbed about 11 kJ of energy. This reaction profile shows us that the reaction is endothermic, with a positive ΔH of 11 kJ.

We need to consider how this affects the energetics of the overall reaction! Look carefully at the hill. Is the hill higher now that we are looking at the reverse reaction?

Measuring the activation energy

To measure the activation energy (E_a) we start at the reactants and measure the energy required to get to the top of the hill. Here we see that we start at 12 kJ for the reactants and end at about 68 kJ at the top of the hill. The measured E_a here is approximately 56 kJ. So the hill is indeed higher!

How can we relate this to the graph of the reverse reaction? If we take the E_a of the reverse reaction and add the ΔH value to it, we end up with the activation energy of the forward direction that we see here! Remember that all chemical reactions are reversible. They often favor one direction over another. This explains why the activation energy is smaller in one direction. When less energy is required, the reaction is more likely to proceed in that direction. So when the "hill" is lower, the reaction requires less energy to break bonds.

Exothermic reactions tend to be more common than endothermic reactions because the activation energy is lower

Exothermic reactions are more common in nature. The energy they release is often used to make endothermic reactions that require more energy to go forward. This process is referred to as coupling reactions. Coupled reactions use the energy released from an exothermic reaction to make a harder endothermic reaction proceed more easily.

Interpreting reaction profiles

Creating reaction profiles

See if you can sketch the curve shown on the left and label the parts of the reaction profile.

Specifically, label the reactants (A and B) and products (C and D) at their locations on the curve. Label the activation energy E_a and give an approximate energy value by reading from the vertical axis. Locate the place where the activated complex will form, and write A_c. Look at the relative energies of the reactants and products. Do you think this graph has a negative or positive ΔH? Explain why. Estimate the value of the ΔH. What happens if you go backward on the curve starting from products and going to reactants? Look carefully at the activation energy and compare it with the activation energy of the forward reaction.

Let's look again at a molecular collision and review the importance of molecular orientation.

Molecules are always colliding

Molecules are colliding all the time! For example, oxygen and hydrogen molecules are hitting each other constantly in the air, but it is not always raining outside! Now we know that a collision does not always mean that a chemical reaction will take place.

Very few collisions result in the actual formation of products

It's a good thing too, because our bodies would be mush if every collision between any two molecules resulted in a reaction.

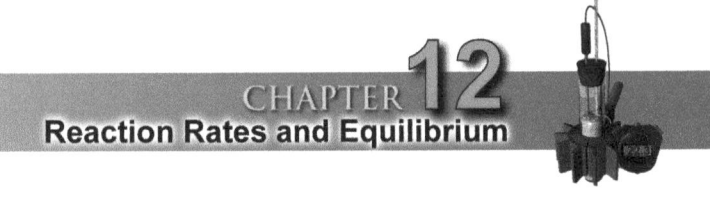

Collision theory and factors affecting rate

Higher concentration of reactant means more collisions

Collision theory explains why changing the concentration of the reactants changes the rate of a chemical reaction. Can you guess why? Look at the picture below.

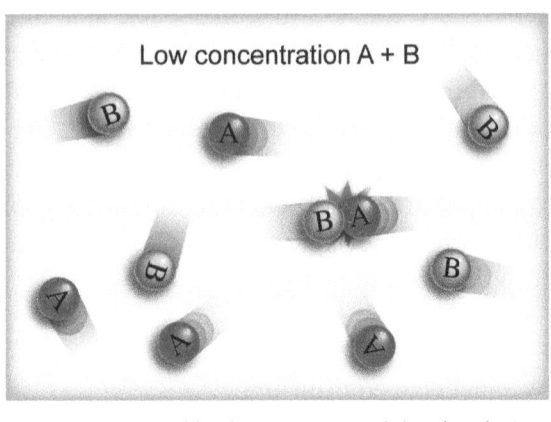

Having more particles leads to an increased number of collisions.

More collisions occur when the concentration is higher, and this speeds up the reaction rate.

Increased temperature means more collisions

Collision theory also explains why increasing the temperature of a reaction mixture generally increases the rate of the reaction. Temperature is a measure of the average kinetic energy of the reacting molecules. The higher the kinetic energy, the higher the number of molecules that can collide with enough activation energy to get up the hill. If we raise the temperature of a reaction mixture, a greater percentage of molecules will be moving faster and therefore will have the energy (E_a) necessary to get up the hill.

Increased surface area means more collisions

The effect of surface area can also be understood in terms of collision theory. The larger the surface area, the more particles there are available for collisions. For this reason solids are often ground up into a powder form, or dissolved in a solution. Both of these methods allow for a separation of particles, which allows them to react more readily.

12.2 Chemical Equilibrium

Chemical reactions are reversible

Up until now we have treated chemical reactions as though they only go in one direction, from reactants to products. In this section you will learn that chemical reactions are reversible. The fact that reactions are capable of going back and forth allows them to achieve a "balance," known as **equilibrium**. When equilibrium has been established in a chemical system, there is no overall change in the amounts of reactants and products. To understand the concept of equilibrium it is helpful to develop the idea of chemicals forming products and reactants simultaneously. As reactants are forming products, products are also forming reactants, so we can picture a chemical reaction moving forward from left to right and backward from right to left at the same time! A chemical reaction that happens in both directions is indicated with the double arrow, $\rightleftharpoons$, like this:

Equilibrium

$$\text{reactants} \rightleftharpoons \text{products}$$

Equilibrium is like a two-way bridge

To further understand this new concept of equilibrium, let's look at a bridge. In this example, a bridge with a steady traffic flow in both directions represents a chemical reaction.

When the number of cars moving into the city, traffic in, is higher than the number of cars moving out of the city, traffic out, the number of cars in the city increases. If the traffic out is higher than the traffic in, the number of cars in the city decreases.

The flow of cars represented by traffic in and traffic out determines the number of cars that are in the city and outside the city at any time.

number of cars in the city $\xrightarrow{\text{traffic out}}$ number of cars outside the city

$\xleftarrow{\text{traffic in}}$

When the number of cars moving into and out of the city across the bridge is constant, traffic in = traffic out, we can say that the system has established a balance.

The key to understanding chemical equilibrium is to realize that both the forward and the reverse reactions are happening together simultaneously. The result is that the amounts of products and reactants remain constant over time, but the molecules are continuously being exchanged just like the cars in and out of the city

---

Chemistry terms

equilibrium: a "balance" in a chemical system, at which the rate of the forward reaction is equal to the rate of the reverse reaction, and the concentrations of reactants and products remain constant over time.

378

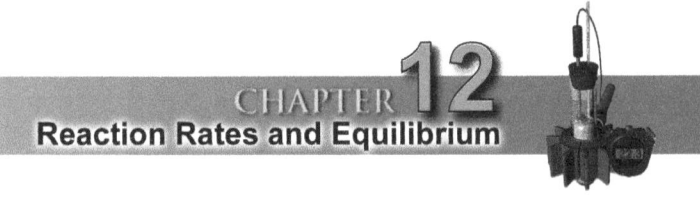

Physical equilibrium

Balance between evaporation and condensation

The evaporation of water in a closed container is a good example of physical equilibrium. It is called **physical equilibrium** because it is an equilibrium between two phases of the same substance, and the changes that take place are physical changes. Here we will carefully consider what is happening to water molecules as they move between the vapor and liquid phases. Let's take a glass jar, fill it about halfway with water, and then cover it.

What will happen after we cover the jar? Will anything change over time?

We can show this cycle of water as $H_2O(l) \rightleftharpoons H_2O(g)$

When the jar is first covered, some molecules will be trapped as they evaporate and enter the gas phase. As a result some water vapor will build up over the water liquid in the jar. After a while, some molecules in the vapor phase will begin to condense and drip back down to the liquid phase. When the number of molecules evaporating and condensing reaches a balance, a state of physical equilibrium will be achieved.

Change is always taking place at the microscopic (molecular) level

Water changes phases at equal rates

At the macroscopic level it may appear that nothing is happening. However, at the microscopic level molecules are continuously being exchanged between the liquid and the gas phase. Because the rates of the forward and reverse reactions are equal, there is not a noticeable change in the water level. Once equilibrium has been established, the water level remains the same as long as the jar remains at a constant temperature.

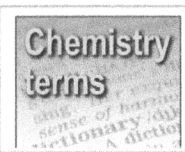

Chemistry terms

physical equilibrium: a "balance" in a physical system where there is an equilibrium between two or more phases of the same substance.

Equilibrium is dynamic

Equilibrium systems are always changing

One common misconception about equilibrium is that it is static and unchanging once it has been reached. This is because the system does not appear to change. To explain this, it is helpful to consider a simple demonstration with beakers of orange-colored water. Look at the picture of the beakers below. Notice they both have the same amount of water in them. If we remove 50 mL of water from each beaker and we simultaneously pour it into the other beaker, the water levels in both beakers will still remain the same.

It looks like nothing is happening!

So, while molecules of water moved from beaker A to beaker B, there was no noticeable change in either beaker. If you look at the beakers before and after the transfer of water you would not know that they were different. However, we know that water molecules were transferred from beaker A to beaker B. In chemical reactions, we are thinking about the rate of the forward reaction being equal to the rate of the reverse. This example mimics the equal rate by transferring equal amounts of water at the same time, so that the rate of change is equal over time. This is what fools us into thinking nothing happened. A chemical reaction has different chemicals that make up the forward and reverse reactions; however, the rates at which the forward and reverse reactions take place are constant in equilibrium, so there is no overall observable change. This chemical example is just like the beakers of water above.

It is important to emphasize that a balance is achieved between the two beakers. The amounts of water transferred are the same. In this example we started with beakers A and B having the same amounts of water. This would be similar to a chemical reaction where the amount of product and reactant are present in equal amounts. As you will see on the next page, the equilibrium starting position and balance may not be the same. However, equilibrium still occurs.

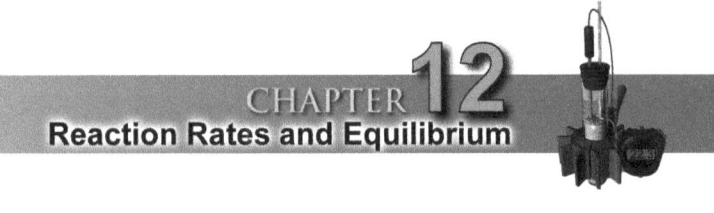

Equilibrium balance

Balance is established no matter where the equilibrium system begins.

 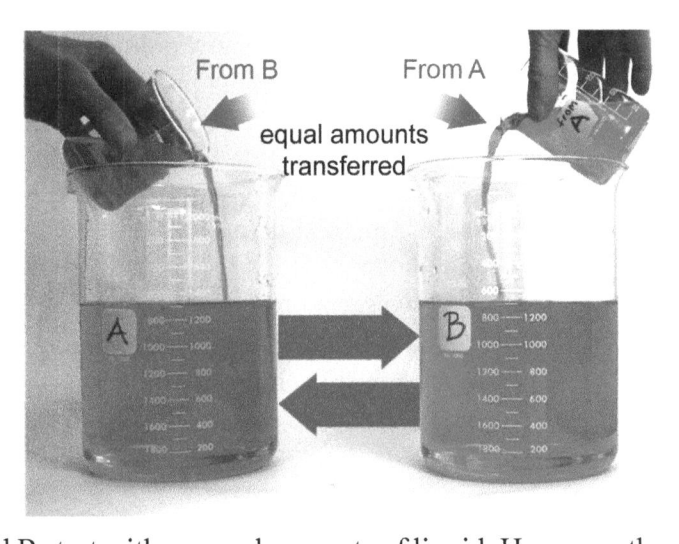

Here you can see that beakers A and B start with unequal amounts of liquid. However, the same amount of liquid is transferred between beakers A and B, which mimics the "rate" of the forward and reverse reaction being equal over time.

Equilibrium does not mean that there must be equal amounts of reactants and products

Equilibrium simply means that a balance has been established. The "balance" is often different for different chemical reactions. Even though the beakers contain different amounts of reactants and products, the water levels remain the same as long as the "rate" of transfer between the two is equal. Equal numbers of molecules are being exchanged between the two beakers. The amounts of reactants and products are not "equal," as shown by the unequal levels of liquid in the beakers.

Non-equilibrium

In a case of nonequilibrium the amounts of water transferred would be unequal, and over time you would see a net change in the water levels. The water levels would continue to become more unbalanced as "unequal" amounts of liquid are transferred. What would happen over time? We would notice that the water levels would noticeably change over time. One beaker would overflow and one would become empty. In this case, there would be no balance achieved, because the rate of transfer is not equal between the beakers. Of course it is often impossible for us to see the molecules being exchanged back and forth, so to our eyes it appears as though nothing is happening. In the lab we rely on color changes and sampling amounts as they change over time. To measure the change over time requires some sensitive equipment, such as a spectrophotometer.

Chemical equilibrium (part 1)

Chemicals establish equilibrium

In a **closed system** many chemical reactions do not just form products but tend to have a mixture of reactants and products present. Recall that when a chemical reaction is in equilibrium we show a double arrow, which indicates that both the forward and reverse reactions are taking place.

How can we observe the reversibility of a chemical reaction?

One method is to look for a color change inside the closed system. In this example the reactant $N_2O_4(g)$ is a clear and colorless gas, and the product $NO_2(g)$ is a red-brown gas. If we see a change in color, then it must be due to the change in amounts of the reactant and product. This is an example of **chemical equilibrium**, because the reaction shows a chemical change from reactant to product, not just a change in phase of the same substance.

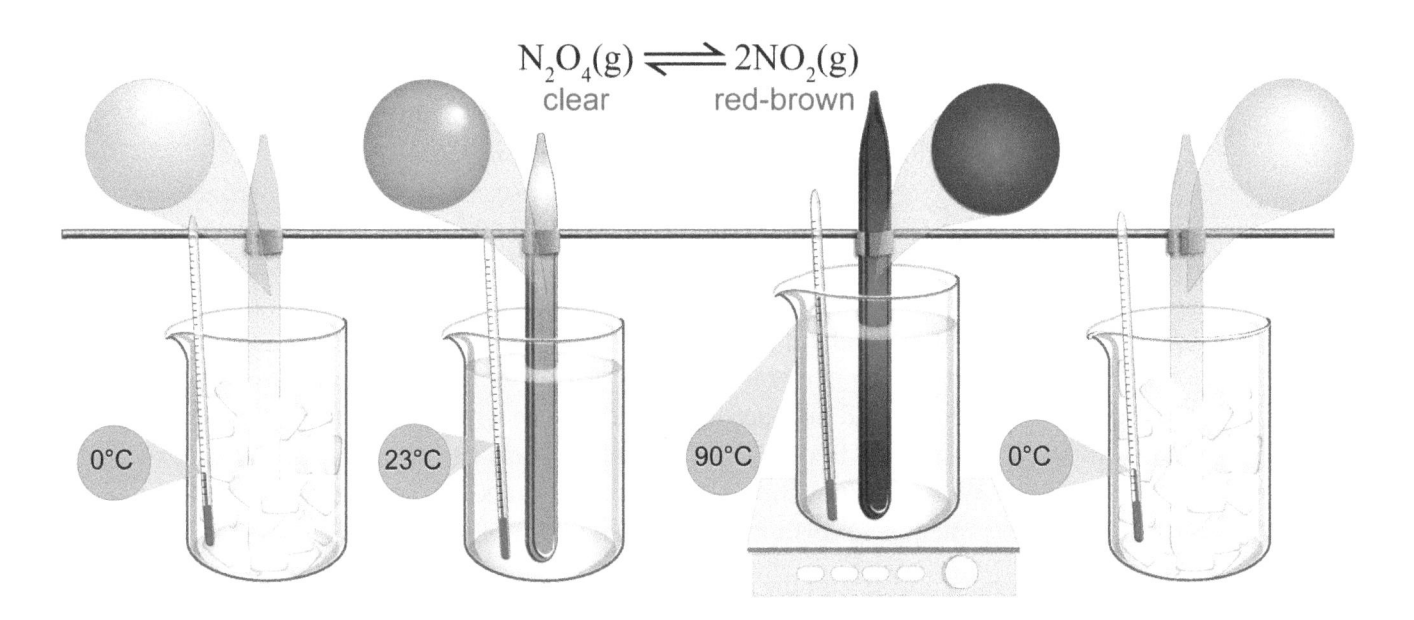

$$N_2O_4(g) \rightleftharpoons 2NO_2(g)$$
clear   red-brown

0°C   23°C   90°C   0°C

In each picture equilibrium has been established inside the tube, but the amount of product relative to reactant is different at different temperatures. Why the temperature causes the equilibrium balance to shift will be covered later in the chapter.

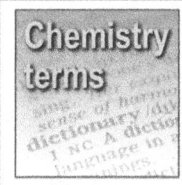

Chemistry terms

closed system: a system that is not allowed to exchange matter with its surroundings, often the products and reactants in a chemical reaction, or a mixture of chemicals in a closed container.

chemical equilibrium: a "balance" in a system where there is an equilibrium between two or more chemicals.

A NATURAL APPROACH TO CHEMISTRY

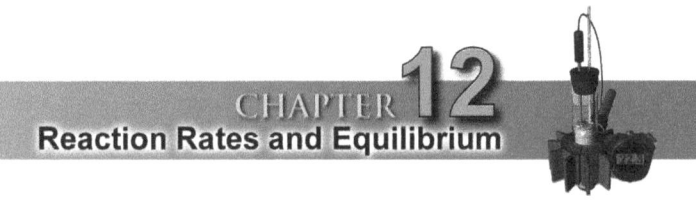

Chemical equilibrium (part 2)

Equilibrium in the air

This equilibrium of $N_2O_4(g) \rightleftharpoons 2NO_2(g)$ is present in the air around us. Nitrogen dioxide (NO_2) is produced in automobile exhaust emissions. Depending upon where you live, you are exposed to different amounts of the gases. Areas with high populations tend to have more people commuting to work and therefore higher levels of NO_2 in the air. The NO_2 present in the air sets up a natural equilibrium balance with N_2O_4.

$NO_2(g)$ is a very dangerous air pollutant

Nitrogen dioxide (NO_2) is a poisonous gas that can cause serious trouble for people with breathing disorders, such as asthma or emphysema. When air quality is tested and the pollutant levels are high, people are often warned to say indoors if they have any breathing difficulties. More NO_2 is present at higher temperature, and the air has more of the visible red-brown gas in it. Interestingly, NO_2's brown orange color makes for lovely sunsets!

The smoggy skyline of Los Angeles

Equilibrium can be established from either direction

Equilibrium can be established by starting with only reactants or only products. If we start with pure N_2O_4 that is frozen in a closed flask, and we warm it to room temperature, the forward reaction will create some NO_2 and establish an equilibrium. There doesn't need to be any NO_2 present initially for equilibrium to be established. In reverse, if we begin with just NO_2 in the flask, the reaction will form reactant (N_2O_4) to establish equilibrium. In each case no matter what we start with, equilibrium will be established.

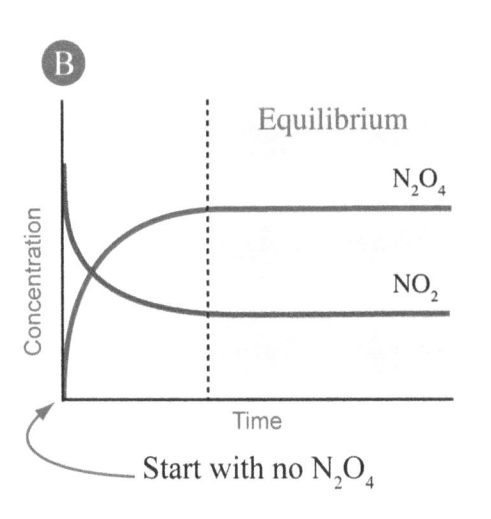

Equilibrium position

The balance that is achieved is different for different chemical reactions. Reversible chemical reactions can "favor" the direction of the products or the reactants. It is quite rare for a reaction in equilibrium to have similar amounts of reactants and products.

Equilibrium does not mean equal amounts!

Equilibrium is achieved when the rate of the forward reaction is equal to the rate of the reverse reaction. However, this does not mean that the actual amounts of reactants and products are "equal" or the same. For any given chemical reaction, we can determine the **equilibrium position** by measuring the amount of reactants and products present once equilibrium has been established.

In the N_2O_4/NO_2 system the reactant is "favored"

If you look carefully at the figure on the preceding page, you will see that in each graph of the equilibrium system $N_2O_4(g) \rightleftharpoons 2NO_2(g)$, the concentration of reactant (N_2O_4) is higher than the concentration of product (NO_2). What does this tell us? Basically, the reactant side of this equilibrium is "favored" under the conditions of 25°C and 1 atm. The fact that the N_2O_4 concentration is always greater indicates that there is more of it present at equilibrium.

The relative equilibrium amounts of reactants and products present for a given reaction are dictated by the initial starting concentrations, and the temperature and the pressure of the system. For any given reaction, it is possible that one direction of the reaction is favored over the other. Data must collected in the laboratory to fully understand this behavior.

Below are two graphs of concentration versus time of the $2SO_2(g) + O_2(g) \rightleftharpoons 2SO_3(g)$ equilibrium system. The first starts with all reactants; the second starts with just product. In each case, equilibrium is established over time.

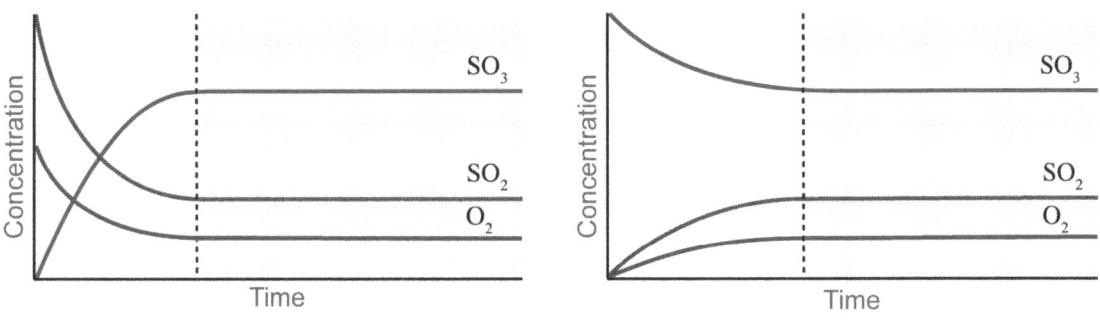

Analyzing graphs

Look carefully at these graphs. Can you tell which side of the reaction is favored? What does this tell you about the equilibrium position?

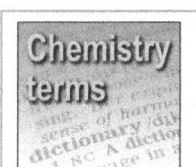

equilibrium position: the favored direction of a reversible reaction, determined by each set of concentrations for the reactant(s) and product(s) at equilibrium.

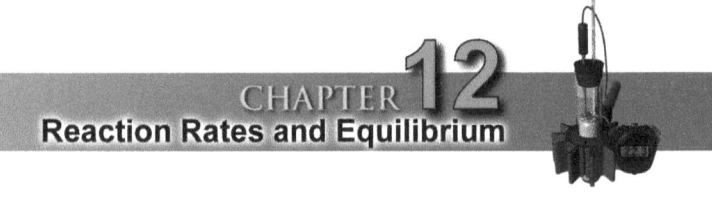

Le Châtelier's principle

Chemists carefully study ways to influence equilibrium positions. In industry and in the environment it can be important to understand how to make a chemical reaction move more in one direction. What factors affect the direction an equilibrium reaction "favors"? How can we influence the reaction and make it go in the direction we desire? Four variables affect the direction of equilibrium: concentration, temperature, pressure, and volume. In this section we will study how changes in conditions affect the equilibrium position.

Systems shift to "partially" offset the stress

A French chemist, Henri Le Châtelier, proposed a good general rule that allows us to predict how an equilibrium reaction will respond to changes. **Le Châtelier's principle** states that when a "change" is placed on a system at equilibrium, the system will shift in a direction that partially offsets the "change." The change placed on an equilibrium system refers to changes in concentration, pressure, volume, or temperature.

The "change" causes the equilibrium balance to be disturbed

We avoid stress too!

Le Châtelier's principle is very applicable to our everyday lives! Just think about it—most of us tend to avoid or move away from things that cause us stress. Changes in our environment cause us to adjust our behavior. Chemical reactions behave the same way! Remember that equilibrium is a "balance," so anything that changes the balance would cause an adjustment.

$$N_2 + 3H_2 \rightleftharpoons 2NH_3$$

 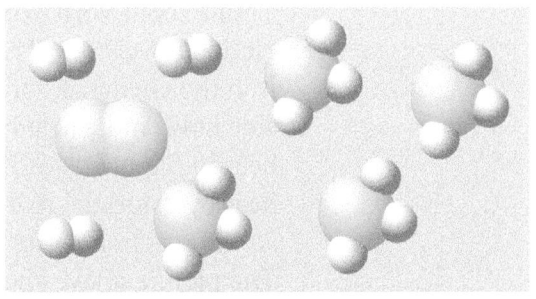

Two NH_3 molecules are removed so the reaction shifts to the right

Some reactants are used to make more NH_3 to compensate for the removal

Chemistry terms

Le Châtelier's principle: principle that states that when a "change" is made to a system at equilibrium, the system will shift in a direction that partially offsets the "change"; the change can be defined as a change in temperature, concentration, volume, or pressure.

The effect of a change in temperature

Reversible
reactions shift
to absorb or
release heat

The familiar equilibrium system for the $N_2O_4 - NO_2$ system is

$$N_2O_4(g) + 58.0 \text{ kJ/mole} \rightleftharpoons 2NO_2(g)$$
clear   red-brown

Here the reaction is absorbing heat in the forward direction.

How does this system react to changes in temperature?

1. An increase in temperature will cause the system to shift to decrease the temperature. Think about what you do if you are hot. You might remove your jacket or a layer of clothing. A chemical reaction "cools off" by taking in some of the added heat and holding it in the chemical bonds, thereby absorbing some of the added heat. The endothermic side holds more heat in the bonds of the chemicals, while the exothermic side holds less heat in the bonds of its chemicals. A chemical reaction gets rid of some of the added heat by "storing" it. The $N_2O_4 - NO_2$ system is endothermic in the forward direction, so the reaction shifts toward products to partially offset the increase in temperature. The picture above shows us that the system becomes a darker red-brown when placed in hot water.

2. A decrease in temperature will cause the system to want to release some heat to counteract the change. If the system is cooled down, then it wants to compensate by heating up a little. How does the system release heat? It shifts to the exothermic side and releases some of the "stored" heat from the chemical bonds. Here the exothermic side is the reactants side: $N_2O_4(g) + 58.0 \text{ kJ/mole} \rightleftharpoons 2NO_2(g)$ When going from right to left using this chemical reaction, heat is released and this partially compensates for the decrease in temperature. This reaction tells us that as 2 moles of $NO_2(g)$ form from 1 mole of the reactant, $N_2O_4(g)$, 58.0 kJ of heat is released.

The effect of a change in concentration

Equilibrium shifts to counteract changes in concentration

Increasing or decreasing the concentration of the reactants or products changes the amounts available for the overall reaction. If the amounts decrease, the reaction will shift to increase them. If the amounts increase, the reaction will shift to decrease them.

1. If the amount of SO_2 increases, the system will shift to the right (the products side) to consume some of the added reactant:

$$2SO_2(g) + O_2(g) \rightleftharpoons 2SO_3(g)$$
reactants   product

Shifts right

In a reversible equilibrium reaction, forming product means "using up" or consuming reactants

2. If the amount of SO_2 is decreased, the system will shift to the left (the reactants side) to produce some of the lost reactant:

$$2SO_2(g) + O_2(g) \rightleftharpoons 2SO_3(g)$$
reactants   product

Shifts left

Forming reactants means consuming some of the products

Just remember that if there is an increase in concentration, Le Châtelier's principle says that the system will shift to decrease some of the concentration. The reverse is also true.

Solved problem

Using the equilibrium system
$$PCl_5(g) \rightleftharpoons PCl_3(g) + Cl_2(g)$$
predict the direction in which the system will shift as a result of an increase in the concentration of Cl_2.

Asked:	Direction that the system will shift
Given:	Increase in Cl_2
Relationships:	Note that Cl_2 is a product on the right side of the equation.
Solve:	The system will shift toward the reactant to consume some of the added Cl_2.
Answer:	Shifts left to produce some PCl_5
Discussion:	The shift in direction partially offsets the increase in Cl_2.

The effect of a change in pressure or volume

Changes in pressure or volume only affect gaseous equilibrium systems. To understand how a change in pressure or volume can influence an equilibrium system, we will first look at how pressure and volume are related. In this example, we will assume we have a container of fixed volume with rigid walls that cannot expand or contract.

Gas particles can compress or expand when inside a piston

The picture below shows a piston with a gas trapped inside. In Figure a, when the pressure on the gas is increased, the volume of the gas decreases. However, in Figure b, when the pressure on the gas decreases, the volume of the gas increases and the gas expands. We can study the effects of pressure changes on the following equilibrium system:

$$2SO_2(g) + O_2(g) \rightleftharpoons 2SO_3(g)$$

2 moles   1 mole   2 moles

Consider the system to be in a container that has a movable piston, like the one shown above.

What happens when pressure changes?

1. If there is increased pressure on the system, then Le Châtelier's principle predicts that the system will adjust to partially decrease the pressure. Chemical reactions do this by shifting to the side of the reaction with fewer moles. In this case that would be the products side. Two moles of SO_3 gas exerts less pressure than 3 moles of the reactant gases [2 moles SO_2 plus 1 mole $O_2(g)$]. The fewer the gas particles, the lower the pressure. Think of each individual gas particle as a force that pushes. The more parti-cles of a gas, the higher the pressure.

2. If there is decreased pressure on the system, the reaction shifts to the side with more moles to try to raise the pressure. The side with more moles in this case would be the left side (the reactants).

3. If the total moles of gas are equal on both sides of the gaseous equilibrium equation, then there would be no shift because neither direction would partially offset the change.

The equilibrium expression

ADVANCED AP

To gain a better understanding of equilibrium, we must study experimental data that allow us to look at the relationship between the forward and the reverse reactions. How can we tell whether a chemical reaction prefers to go one way or another? How can we attempt to find out?

Which direction is favored?

Let's pretend that there is a path that goes off in two directions. How could we tell whether one direction is favored over the other? The easiest way would be to sit by the path and see which direction people go. We would then have some data to predict the favored direction. If several of our friends help and they record observations a few more times, the data could then be "pooled" and we could see if one direction is favored over the other. The problem with this analogy is that people have a choice, and they might make a different choice from day to day. However, chemicals have no choice; the direction they "favor" depends on reaction conditions such as temperature. However, we determine the favored direction in the same way. We observe and collect data.

Experimental observations led to the equilibrium expression

After many experiments, two Norwegian chemists proposed an expression based on their observations called the **law of mass action**. It is a general description of equilibrium for any equilibrium reaction, $aA + bB \rightleftharpoons cC + dD$. In other words, a moles of reactant A and b moles of reactant B react to yield c moles of product C and d moles of product D.

Using this generic reaction we can learn how to set up the **equilibrium expression**:

molarity of D
molarity of C
molarity of A
molarity of B

$$K = \frac{[C]^c [D]^d}{[A]^a [B]^b} = \frac{[\text{Products}]}{[\text{Reactants}]}$$

Equilibrium expression

Here our reactant and product amounts will be measured in units of concentration, usually molarity (M). The use of brackets around our reactants and products indicates that they are concentrations. Each concentration is raised to the power of the corresponding coefficient in the balanced equation. K is the **equilibrium constant** that represents the numeric value of the ratio. The equilibrium constant always has the same value at a specified temperature for a specified chemical reaction. Most importantly, equilibrium data repeatedly support this special ratio.

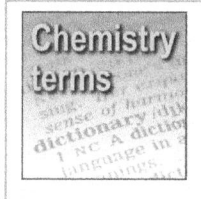

Chemistry terms

equilibrium expression: a special ratio of product concentrations to the reactant concentrations. Each concentration is raised to the power of the corresponding coefficient in the balanced equation.

equilibrium constant: the numeric value of the equilibrium expression.

law of mass action: a general description of any equilibrium reaction.

The equilibrium constant

The constant K is temperature dependent

The equilibrium constant K is only affected by changes in temperature. Otherwise it remains the same for a given reaction.

Let's write an equilibrium expression for the following reaction:

$$N_2O_4(g) \rightleftharpoons 2NO_2(g)$$

reactants   product

$$K = \frac{[NO_2]^2}{[N_2O_4]}$$

$$N_2O_4(g) \rightleftharpoons 2NO_2(g)$$

We can predict equilibrium concentrations using K

The importance of the equilibrium expression is that we can substitute known concentration values for reactants and products and calculate the constant K. If we know the value of K, we can predict equilibrium concentrations before doing the experiment!

Let's practice writing equilibrium expressions.

To write the expression for $H_2(g) + I_2(g) \rightleftharpoons 2HI(g)$, we would get

$$K = \frac{[HI]^2}{[HI][I_2]}$$

For $CH_4(g) + 2H_2S(g) \rightleftharpoons CS_2(g) + 4H_2(g)$, the equilibrium expression would be

$$K = \frac{[CS_2][H_2]^4}{[CH_4][H_2S]^2}$$

Always remember that the products are raised to the power of their molar coefficients in the numerator, and the reactants are raised to the power of their molar coefficients in the denominator. The number of moles of the reactants and products that appear after the equation is balanced make the equilibrium expression simple or more complex depending upon the number of moles of each substance.

Calculating equilibrium constants

For a specific reaction at a given temperature, the equilibrium constant K will always be the same, or constant. Using data from many experiments, we find that when we solve for K it is always the same.

Experimental data

TABLE 12.2. Results of 3 experiments for:
$N_2(g) + 3H_2(g) \rightleftharpoons 2NH_3(g)$ at 500°C

Experiment	Equilibrium concentrations			$K = \dfrac{[NH_3]^2}{[N_2][H_2]^3}$
	$[N_2]$	$[H_2]$	$[NH_3]$	
1	0.921	0.763	0.157	0.0603
2	0.399	1.197	0.203	0.0602
3	2.59	2.77	1.82	0.0602

Let's calculate K using the above data and see whether it agrees with the last column's value of 0.0602.

Solving for K

Applying our equilibrium expression to the data from experiment 1, we have

$$K = \frac{[NH_3]^2}{[N_2][H_2]^3} = \frac{[0.157]^2}{[0.921][0.763]^3} = 0.0603$$

Applying our equilibrium expression to the data from experiment 2 gives

$$K = \frac{[NH_3]^2}{[N_2][H_2]^3} = \frac{[0.203]^2}{[0.399][1.197]^3} = 0.0602$$

We can apply the same calculation to experiment 3, and once again we get the same value for K. This supports the fact that K is constant at the same temperature.

Although the equilibrium constant is the same for each experiment, the equilibrium concentrations are all very different!

However, when applied to our equilibrium expression, we get the same value for K. Equilibrium concentrations may be different for each experiment, but this special ratio is the same in each case!

Using the equilibrium constant

As we have just seen in the previous section, the equilibrium expression is used to determine a numeric value for the equilibrium constant. Chemists use the equilibrium constant to tell them how much a particular direction is favored by the system at equilibrium and to solve for equilibrium concentrations of reactant(s) or product(s).

The size of K predicts the favored direction

The numeric size of K, whether large or small, tells us to what extent the reaction goes to products. Using the simple reaction $A(g) \rightleftharpoons B(g)$, we can set up the expression as

$$K = \frac{[B]}{[A]}$$

If K is very large ($K > 10^4$), then [B] must be much larger than [A] and the products are favored for this reaction.

If K is very small ($K < 10^{-4}$), then [A] must be much larger than [B] and the reactants are favored for this reaction.

Sometimes K is neither very large nor very small, but somewhere in between. This indicates that there are appreciable amounts of both reactants [A] and products [B].

Here are some equilibrium constants for some common reactions:

$$2H_2(g) + O_2(g) \rightleftharpoons 2H_2O(l), \quad K = 1.4 \times 10^{83} \text{ at } 25°C \quad \text{Large } K \text{ favors product}$$

$$CaCO_3(s) \rightleftharpoons CaO(s) + CO_2(g), \quad K = 1.9 \times 10^{-23} \text{ at } 25°C \quad \text{Small } K \text{ favors reactant}$$

Let's look at a problem to solve for an unknown equilibrium concentration.

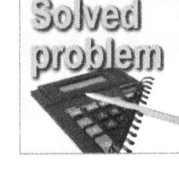

Calculate the equilibrium concentration of [HI] given the following information:

$H_2(g) + I_2(g) \rightleftharpoons 2HI(g)$, K = 50 at 450°C, [$H_2$] = 0.22 M, and [$I_2$] = 0.22 M

Asked: Calculate the concentration of HI at equilibrium

Given: K = 50 at 450°C, [H_2] = [I_2] = 0.22 M

Relationships: Equilibrium expression: $K = \dfrac{[HI]^2}{[H_2][I_2]}$

Solve: $K = 50 = \dfrac{[HI]^2}{[0.22][0.22]} = \dfrac{[HI]^2}{0.0484}$

$50 \times 0.0484 = 2.42 = [HI]^2$

The square root of 2.42 = 1.56 M = [HI]

Answer: The equilibrium concentration of [HI] = 1.56 M

Discussion: Here we used a known equilibrium constant (K) to solve for the unknown equilibrium concentration of the product.

12.3 Chemical Pathways

Chemical reactions take place through a series of steps

So far we have always treated chemical reactions as though they go from reactants to products all in one step. Atoms in the reactants are rearranged to form products seemingly all at once. This is actually a large simplification! Now we will consider the fact that each reaction occurs in a series of **elementary steps**. These elementary steps combine to form a "pathway" for a chemical reaction. The term "pathway" helps us to visualize the series of paths or steps that take place when reactants are converted to products. The series of steps is referred to as a **reaction mechanism.** A reaction mechanism is proposed based on experimental evidence, and it must be supported by what is observed in the laboratory. Sometimes there is more than one proposed reaction mechanism for a chemical reaction. Chemists cannot know for certain which mechanism, or pathway, is correct because as you learned in Section 12.1, the high-energy molecules formed during the reaction cannot be isolated, because they exist for a such a small fraction of time.

A good analogy for a reaction mechanism is following a map on a trip. You follow a series of roads that take you to your destination. The series of roads represents the reaction mechanism. An overall chemical reaction only shows the start of the trip and the end of the trip, but it is impossible to go directly to your destination. You have to follow the roads! The reaction mechanism shows the roads you take on your trip, as well as the start and finish.

 Chemistry terms

elementary steps: a series of simple reactions that represent the overall progress of the chemical reaction at the molecular level.

reaction mechanism: a proposed sequence of elementary steps that leads to product formation and must be determined using experimental evidence.

Two-step reaction mechanism

Let's look at an example of a reaction mechanism with two elementary steps. Here we will use the reaction between hydrogen (H_2) and iodine monochloride (ICl). The overall reaction is

$$H_2(g) + 2ICl(g) \rightarrow I_2(g) + 2HCl(g)$$

The proposed reaction mechanism that is supported by experimental evidence is:

The elementary steps must add up to the overall reaction

1. elementary step: $H_2 + ICl \rightarrow HI + HCl$

2. elementary step: $HI + ICl \rightarrow I_2 + HCl$

    overall reaction: $H_2 + HI + 2ICl \rightarrow I_2 + HI + 2HCl$

The sum of the elementary steps must yield the overall balanced equation. In the first elementary step, one H_2 molecule collides with one ICl molecule. This step is followed by the collision between HI and the second ICl molecule.

Step 1   H H + Cl I ⟶ H I + H Cl

Step 2   H I + Cl I ⟶ I I + H Cl

Note that it is much more likely that two molecules would collide favorably in each step than three molecules all at once, as proposed by the overall reaction. HI is referred to as a reaction **intermediate**. A reaction intermediate is formed in one of the early elementary steps, and it is consumed in a later elementary step. Intermediates are higher in energy than the reactants, and they become the reactant(s) for the next elementary step.

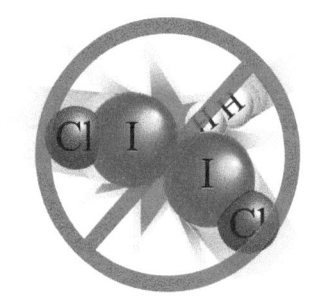

This reaction can't occur in one step! The likelihood of three molecules colliding at just the right orientation and speed is just about zero.

If you think back to collision theory, it is unlikely that all three reactant molecules collide with sufficient energy and at the proper orientation to form products!

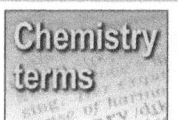

Chemistry terms

intermediate: a chemical species that is formed during the elementary steps, but is not present in the overall balanced equation.

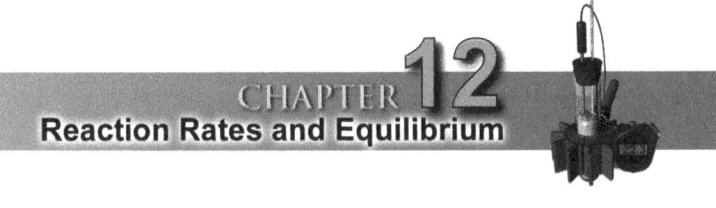

Reaction progress curves

Most reactions have more than one elementary step

The way that reactions proceed can be graphed in the form of a reaction profile. The simple reaction profile that you learned about earlier is only for one elementary step. Here we will look at the reaction profile for a reaction with two elementary steps leading to products.

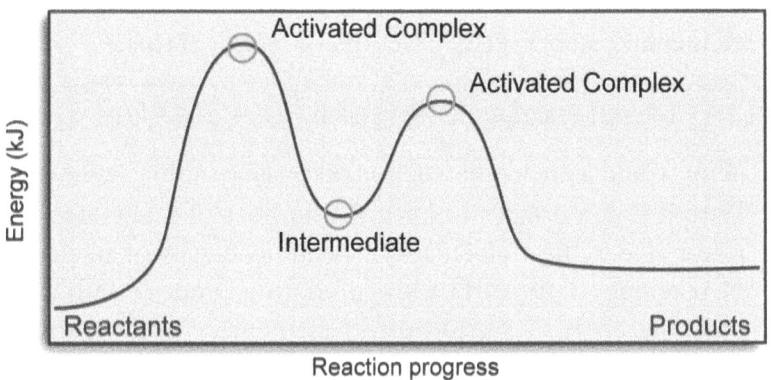

This graph shows the formation of a reaction intermediate. You can pinpoint the place on the curve where the intermediate is present by looking for a dip (or valley) in the curve that is higher in energy than the reactants. The reaction intermediate becomes a reactant in the following step. The overall graph has two peaks, which refer to the energies of the two activated complexes, one for each elementary step.

Analyzing graphs

Look at the graph below to help you answer the following questions.

How many elementary steps are there in this overall reaction?
How many intermediates are formed?

Reaction mechanisms

More complex mechanisms involve three steps

As you just saw in the graph, some reactions have more than just two elementary steps. Here is an example of a proposed mechanism with three steps:

elementary step 1: $NO_2(g) + F_2(g) \rightleftharpoons NO_2F_2(g)$ (fast)

elementary step 2: $NO_2F_2(g) \rightarrow NO_2F(g) + F(g)$ (slow)

elementary step 3: $F(g) + NO_2(g) \rightarrow NO_2F(g)$ (fast)

_____

overall reaction: $2NO_2(g) + F_2(g) \rightarrow 2NO_2F(g)$

Why would a chemical reaction take place in this series of seemingly complicated steps? Here it is important to notice the number of reactants in each elementary step. This is referred to as the molecularity. The molecularity of an elementary step tells us the number of reactants. **Unimolecular** refers to a process with a single reactant dissociating or breaking apart. A **bimolecular** elementary process involves the collision of just two molecules. Remember that an overall reaction that involves three molecules, here two NO_2s and one F_2, reacting is highly unlikely. The complicated steps actually simplify the overall process! Each step involves either one or two reactants coming together, which is more probable, based on collision theory.

Mechanisms must be determined by experiment

The other important aspect of a proposed reaction mechanism is that it must correspond to the experimentally observed rate law. The rate law is an equation that predicts the relationship between the concentration of reactants and the speed of the chemical reaction. It is possible to predict the slowest step, or the **rate determining step**, from the predicted reaction mechanism. This can be identified as the elementary process that takes the longest, and therefore it acts as a bottleneck in the overall reaction mechanism.

A good analogy for the rate determining step is a toll booth on a highway. You may be able to travel at 55 mph on the highway, but you must slow down and wait in line to get through the toll booth. Once you are through, you can once again resume your faster speed. In a chemical reaction, there is one step that has the highest activation energy and takes the longest to occur. In the three-step mechanism above, the second step is the slowest, and it will therefore be the rate determining step. Remember to consider the fact that the last step cannot occur until the second step is complete.

Chemistry terms

unimolecular: an elementary step where only one reactant is involved.

bimolecular: an elementary process involving the collision of two molecules.

rate determining step: the slowest elementary step in the reaction mechanism that determines the overall rate (or speed) of the chemical reaction.

Biological pathway

Your body carries out complex chemical reactions as a series of steps, as do many microorganisms. Most biological pathways involve many enzymes and are the subject of biochemistry. Here we will study the fermentation process as a simple example of how living organisms use a "pathway" to carry out an overall chemical reaction.

Fermentation looks like a simple chemical reaction!

Yeasts and a few other microorganisms use alcoholic fermentation to produce energy.

When starting with a six-carbon sugar such as glucose, the overall chemical process is

$$C_6H_{12}O_6 \rightarrow 2C_2H_5OH + 2CO_2 + energy\ (2\ ATP)$$

In words, we can write this as

$$glucose\ (sugar) \rightarrow ethanol + carbon\ dioxide + energy$$

During the process of fermentation, the overall sugar molecule is modified during several chemical reactions that are facilitated by specific enzymes.

Breakdown of the glucose molecule via fermentation requires 12 enzymes!

In the first step of this chemical pathway the sugar, glucose, is broken into two pyruvic acid CH_3COCO_2H, molecules:

Step 1 splits the glucose molecule

$$C_6H_{12}O_6 \rightarrow 2CH_3COCO_2H \quad \text{This step requires 10 different enzymes!}$$

This step is really a series of elementary steps during which the substrate glucose is oxidized, and the electrons are given to an electron acceptor NAD^+ to form NADH. The cells use the NADH as a form of energy for their metabolic processes.

Step 2 produces ethanol and carbon dioxide

The second step in this pathway, where pyruvic acid is broken down into ethanol and carbon dioxide, yields NAD^+, which is recycled back to the first step.

$$2CH_3COCO_2H \rightarrow 2C_2H_5OH + 2CO_2 \quad \text{This step requires only two enzymes.}$$

12.4 Catalysts

Catalysts facilitate chemical reactions

Catalysis is one of the most important areas of chemical research. A **catalyst** is a substance capable of speeding up a chemical reaction without being "used up" during the reaction. The fact that catalysts are unchanged by a chemical reaction makes it possible for them to be reused over and over. In our experiences with chemical reactions so far, reactants are consumed when they make products. But a catalyst is not a reactant. You can think of catalysts as facilitators of chemical reactions.

Catalysts work by providing a new pathway with a lower activation energy

Reaction: A + B ⟶ C + D

In the graph above, the reaction A + B → C + D has an uncatalyzed E_a (activation energy) of 250 kJ. The red line shows that the E_a of the catalyzed reaction is approximately 125 kJ. The activation energy of the catalyzed reaction is half that of the uncatalyzed reaction. This is amazing! Because the activation energy is lower, more molecules now have sufficient energy to react, causing the reaction to happen at a faster rate overall.

We are alive right now because our bodies contain thousands of catalysts, which speed up complicated reactions that would be too slow at normal body temperatures

The types of catalysts that work in our bodies are called **enzymes**.

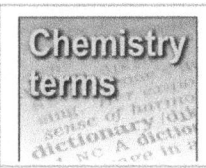

Chemistry terms

catalyst: a substance that speeds up the rate of a chemical reaction, by providing a pathway with a lower activation energy.

enzymes: biological catalysts, responsible for speeding up the chemical reactions inside our bodies.

Enzymes

One enzyme that is very important to our bodies is called carbonic anhydrase. Carbonic anhydrase is responsible for the rapid conversion of carbon dioxide and water to acid (H^+) and bicarbonate (HCO_3^-). Here is the reaction:

Carbonic anhydrase catalyzes the reaction of CO_2 with water

$$H_2O(l) + CO_2(g) \rightarrow H^+(aq) + HCO_3^-(aq)$$

Carbonic anhydrase helps to remove carbon dioxide (CO_2) from your tissues by dissolving it in the form of HCO_3^- ions, which can be carried to the lungs by our blood. Once it reaches our lungs, the CO_2 converts back to its gaseous form and is exhaled. Without carbonic anhydrase, we would not be able to effectively remove the necessary carbon dioxide from our tissues.

If you take a sip of really cold soda, you will feel a tingling on your tongue. This sensation occurs because your saliva contains carbonic anhydrase, which creates some acid (H^+). When this acid comes into contact with the nerve endings on your tongue, it makes them tingle.

Another natural enzyme, bromelain, is contained in certain fruits. Pineapple contains the bromelain enzyme, which helps to digest or "break down" proteins.

Bromelain is an enzyme found in pineapples

At the molecular level, bromelain breaks the bonds that hold the protein's structure together. We can witness the effect that the enzyme has on proteins by using a simple experiment with gelatin and pineapple. Gelatin is a protein made from collagen, which comes mainly from the bones and connective tissues of animals. The experiment is shown in the pictures below. The picture on the left shows the control (without the pineapple enzyme), which gels properly. In the picture on the right, fresh pineapple was mixed with the gelatin. Here the gelatin will not "gel" (become firm). The protein in gelatin cannot hold together in the presence of the bromelain enzyme.

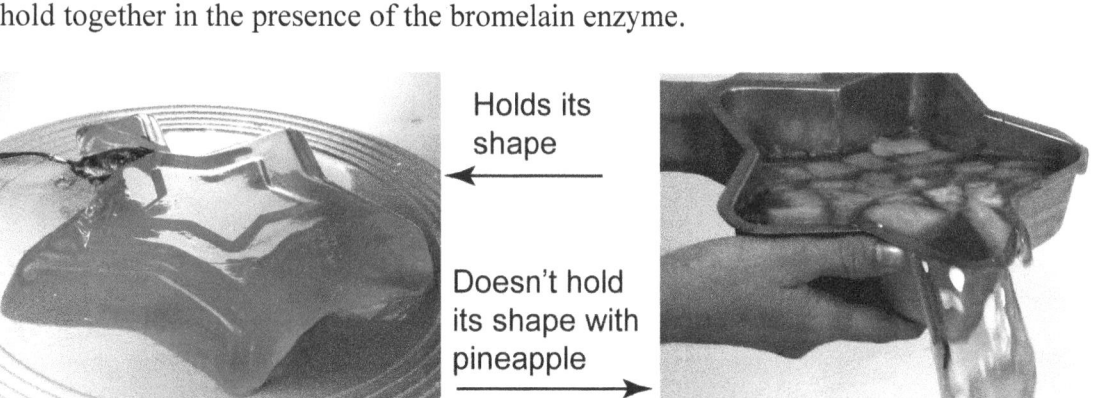

Holds its shape

Doesn't hold its shape with pineapple

Environmental effects of catalysts

Ozone (O_3) absorbs harmful UV rays

The ozone layer in the upper atmosphere protects us from the Sun's harmful ultraviolet radiation. Chemicals called chlorofluorocarbons, or CFCs, have been shown to interfere with ozone formation. Chlorofluorocarbons were widely used in air conditioning systems, as refrigerants, in aerosols, and in the manufacture of Styrofoam™ products.

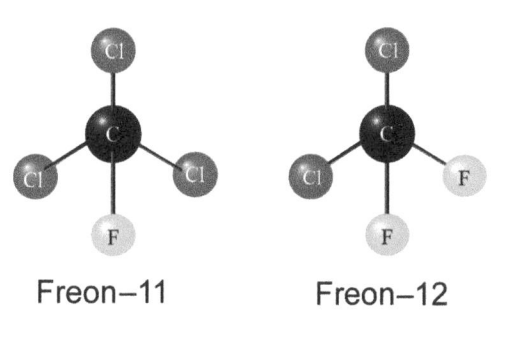

Freon–11   Freon–12

Cl atoms act as catalysts in the destruction of ozone (O_3)

These CFCs are relatively inert, or unreactive, near Earth's surface. However, as they float up into the atmosphere, the Sun's energy breaks off a chlorine atom (Cl•), which is a free chlorine radical with an unpaired electron. This chlorine atom acts as a catalyst in the depletion of ozone.

Natural ozone cycle (in the stratosphere):

$O_3(g) + UV(radiation) \rightarrow O• + O_2(g)$, followed by $O• + O_2(g) \rightarrow O_3(g)$, …

Notice the O• and O_2 recombine to form O_3 once again. This creates a cycle where ozone is regenerated after it absorbs ultraviolet radiation.

Let's compare this to what happens when in the presence of the chlorine atom.

Ozone depletion mechanism:

Step 1: $Cl(g) + O_3(g) \rightarrow ClO(g) + O_2(g)$

Step 2: $O• + ClO(g) \rightarrow Cl• + O_2(g)$

overall: $O• + O_3(g) \rightarrow 2O_2(g)$

Notice that in this case ozone cannot be regenerated, leading to ozone depletion.

What is ClO?

Here you can see that Cl is a catalyst, because it is present at the start of the reaction and at the end of the reaction in the same form. ClO is a reaction intermediate, because it is formed in the first reaction and then consumed by the second reaction. If we look at the overall reaction, we can see that two oxygen (O_2) molecules are formed. Oxygen is not capable of absorbing the dangerous UV radiation, and the natural cycle has been destroyed.

Estimates predict that one chlorine radical can catalyze the destruction of about one million ozone molecules per second!

In 1996, the manufacture of freon was banned with a 10-year grace period for developing countries. However, the effects of CFCs will linger for decades.

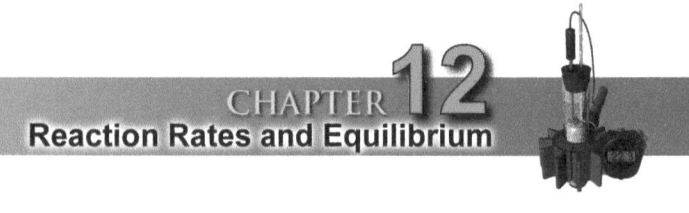
Why catalysts are important

Catalysts provide us with a safe and efficient way to speed up a reaction

First it is important to realize that without a catalyst, our only method for speeding up a chemical reaction is to raise the temperature. We know this will speed up a chemical reaction. However, sometimes it is not practical to heat a reaction up to a high temperature; this method often causes the products to undergo further reactions that decrease the yield of the reaction we are interested in. Carrying out a reaction at high temperatures can also be very costly, and even dangerous. Using a substance that can facilitate the reaction, such as a catalyst, can often be a better method.

Society benefits from catalysts

Our society depends upon the production of chemicals used for food, shelter and clothing. Industrial chemists work hard to increase the speed of production for chemicals that are in high demand. This is a very important factor in the growth of the economies of developing countries. Approximately 90% of all commercially produced chemical products use catalysts at some point in the process of their manufacture.

Catalysts can help the environment

Environmental chemists also design ways to speed up reactions that decrease the amount of high-level pollutants. Catalytic converters are a good example of this. A catalytic converter speeds up chemical reactions that decrease the amount of harmful gases emitted from the exhaust produced by our automobiles. With a large population of people driving to work, the poisonous gases released by our automobiles would accumulate in the air. Los Angeles was the first city to mandate the use of catalytic converters on cars.

Living systems use catalysts

Catalysts are very important in nature too! Remember that our bodies use enzymes that speed up important metabolic reactions. When our cells burn sugar for energy and heat, we are using enzymes that allow us to obtain the potential energy contained in the bonds of the sugar molecules. Burning sugar in the presence of oxygen requires temperatures much higher than body temperature. Enzymes allow these reactions to take place at the low temperatures found in living animals.

Cave chemistry

Have you ever visited a limestone cave? If so, then you have seen equilibrium in action. Stalagmites and stalactites are the long formations inside a cave that look like icicles. A stalagmite refers to an "icicle" that rises from the floor of a cave. The stalagmite is formed by deposition of calcium carbonate ($CaCO_3$). Stalactites form from drips on the ceiling of the cave. Sometimes the stalagmites and stalactites grow together and form a large column. There are many caves and caverns scattered across the United States. The chemistry that causes the formation of stalactites and stalagmites is a good example of the reversibility of chemical reactions. You will see that Le Châtelier's principle helps us to explain why stalagmites and stalactites form.

There is something beautiful and mysterious about a cave. Why do these interesting looking stalagmites and stalactites form?

Rain absorbs carbon dioxide gas as it moves through the atmosphere, but especially when it moves through the soil. Soil contains some carbon dioxide, which is released from decaying animals and plants.

Rainwater reacts with CO_2 to form carbonic acid:

$$H_2O(l) + CO_2(g) \rightleftharpoons H_2CO_3(aq)$$

Carbonic acid is capable of dissolving some minerals and certain types of rock, such as limestone. Limestone is formed from calcium carbonate ($CaCO_3$). Although carbonic acid is a weak acid, it is much more effective at

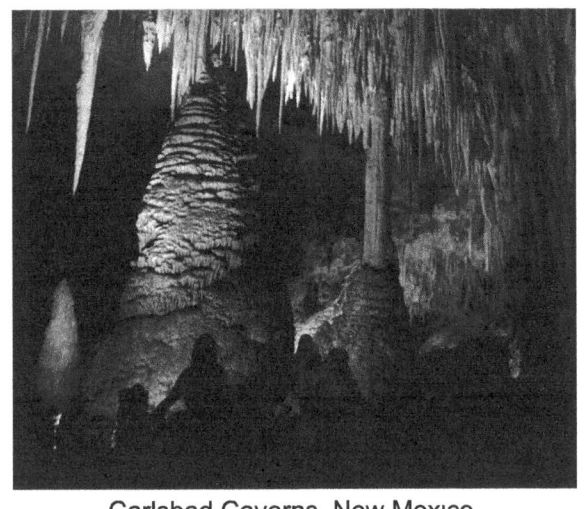

Carlsbad Caverns, New Mexico.

dissolving rock than pure rainwater. As the carbonic acid reacts with the limestone rock, it dissolves the calcium ion (Ca^{2+}) along with other minerals. Here is the reaction:

$$CaCO_3(s) + H_2CO_3(aq) \rightleftharpoons Ca^{2+}(aq) + 2HCO_3^-(aq)$$

Water seeping through rock

As this mineral-laden water seeps into the rock, it follows small cracks and fissures that allow it to go deeper into the rock. As the water moves along the openings, more rock is dissolved and it is able to get even deeper into the Earth. This cycle continues, creating larger and larger openings for the water to pass through. The dissolving of rock slowly opens up into large fissures and small caverns present inside the Earth.

There are many different types of rock that are present in caves. Each of these types—limestone, granite, sandstone, and others—have unique properties. The more colorful stalactites and stalagmites sometimes have dissolved copper ions (Cu^{2+}), which give them a beautiful shade of blue.

The formation of stalactites and stalagmites is driven by the process of equilibrium! As the water flowing through the rock reaches cavities filled with air, the water releases some of the dissolved carbon dioxide it is carrying into the air of the cave. It does this to try to equilibrate the partial pressure of carbon dioxide between the cave air and the water. Usually, the cave air has a lower partial pressure of carbon dioxide than the water does, because of this some of the dissolved carbon dioxide comes out of solution in an effort to reach equilibrium and increase the amount of CO_2 in the air. This equilibrium process balances the levels of carbon dioxide gas.

In the reaction

$$Ca^{2+}(aq) + 2HCO_3^-(aq) \rightleftharpoons CaCO_3(s) + CO_2(g) + H_2O(l)$$

the equilibrium position shifts to the right to products.

Luray Caverns, Virginia

As the carbon dioxide gas is released into the cave air, some calcium carbonate solid ($CaCO_3$) precipitates out along with it. Recall that precipitation is the formation of a solid from aqueous salt solutions. In this example, the aqueous solutions are shown on the reactants side [$Ca^{2+}(aq) + 2HCO_3^-(aq)$]. As the precipitate forms inside drops of water, gravity slowly brings it down to the lowest point. The formation is very similar to that of an icicle on the edge of a roof; the more water that drips, the larger the icicle that forms.

A section of Carlsbad Caverns called "the Doll House"

Another formation of stalactites

A drop of water slowly driping from a young stalactite

Le Châtelier's principle explains the precipitation of calcium carbonate ($CaCO_3$) to form stalagmites and stalactites. Because the partial pressure of carbon dioxide is lower in the cave air than in the water entering the cave, the carbon dioxide molecules leave the water and enter the air. They do this to try to reach equilibrium! Balance is very important in nature. If you carefully consider the equation above, you will see that carbon dioxide appears on the product side of the equilibrium reaction. If the reaction shifts to the right to release some CO_2, the precipitate of calcium carbonate ($CaCO_3$) is also formed as well as water. So in essence, the release of CO_2 forces the equilibrium position to the side that causes deposition of calcium carbonate.

Chapter 12 Review

Vocabulary

Match each word to the sentence where it best fits.

Section 12.1

reaction rate	activation energy
transition state	activated complex
reaction profile	

1. The _____ is the smallest amount of energy necessary for molecules to react.

2. The speed or _____ of a chemical reaction is measured by the change in concentration per unit time of a reactant or product.

3. A graph that shows the progress of a chemical reaction with respect to energy is called a/an _____.

4. Bonds are broken and reformed at this high-energy point, called the _____.

Section 12.2

closed system	equilibrium position
equilibrium	Le Châtelier's principle
law of mass action	equilibrium expression
equilibrium constant	

5. The _____ tells us which direction of a reversible reaction is favored.

6. During _____, the rate of the forward reaction is equal to the rate of the reverse reaction.

7. In the laboratory we sometimes observe a _____, where the chemicals are not open to the environment.

8. _____ states that when a change is experienced by a chemical system in equilibrium, the system will adjust to partially offset the change.

9. A general description of any equilibrium reaction can be explained by the _____, which shows the relationship of chemicals and their molar coefficients.

10. We use the _____ to determine unknown equilibrium concentrations. It describes the relationship of the products relative to the reactants in a chemical equilibrium system.

11. The value of the _____ only changes when the temperature changes.

Section 12.3

reaction mechanism	intermediate
bimolecular	unimolecular rate
elementary steps	determining step

12. A reaction _____ is a chemical species formed during the elementary steps and then consumed, so it is not present in the overall equation.

13. An elementary step that shows the collision of two molecules is called a/an _____ collision.

14. A series of _____ represent the overall progress of the chemical reaction.

15. A proposed pathway or _____ must be supported by experimental evidence.

16. The slow step in a reaction mechanism is called the _____.

17. An elementary step that involves only one reactant is called a/an _____ step.

Section 12.4

enzyme	catalyst

18. A substance that speeds up a chemical reaction is called a/an _____.

19. A/An _____ is a biological catalyst that speeds up chemical reactions in our bodies.

Conceptual Questions

Section 12.1

20. List the four factors that affect reaction rates.

21. Give an example of how decreasing the temperature affects the rate of a chemical reaction.

22. Explain how a catalyst such as rhodium (Rh) works in a catalytic converter.

23. When strips of magnesium metal are added to a beaker containing 1.0 M HCl and another beaker containing 6.0 M HCl, which one will have the strongest reaction? Explain.

24. How do we measure the speed of a chemical reaction?

25. During the course of a chemical reaction, the rate changes. Explain how it changes. In other words, does it speed up or slow down, and why does it do this?

26. When we measure the average rate of a chemical reaction, what formula do we use?

27. Consider the hypothetical reaction:
    A + B → 2C

    a. How does the rate of disappearance of substance A relate to the rate of disappearance of B? Explain.

    b. How does the rate of appearance of substance C relate to the rate of disappearance of substance A? Explain.

28. List the factors that are important during a molecular collision.

29. If molecules collide, will they react to form product? Explain.

30. What happens after the activated complex forms in a chemical reaction?

31. Look at the graph at the top of the next column and label the following:

    a. reactants and products

    b. activated complex (A_c)

    c. the activation energy (E_a)

    d. the overall energy change (ΔH) in the reaction

Reaction: A + B ⟶ C + D

32. For a chemical reaction where A + B → C + D, the overall energy change is endothermic. Make a sketch of the reaction profile that represents the endothermic reaction, given that ΔH is 50 kJ.

33. Explain why endothermic reactions are less likely to occur when compared to exothermic reactions. To answer this, use the information related to a reaction profile.

34. Explain what the graph below is telling us.

Section 12.2

35. Give an example of equilibrium in your daily life. Explain how this example works.

36. Explain how water inside a closed container reaches an equilibrium balance between molecules in the liquid and vapor phases.

Chapter 12 Review

37. Explain what we mean when we say "equilibrium is a dynamic process."

38. For equilibrium to be established in a system, do there have to be equal amounts of reactants and products? Why or why not?

39. Remarkably, an equilibrium balance can be established in a closed container, even when we start with only the reactants! Explain why this is true.

40. Look at the graphs below and explain which side (reactants or products) is favored in this equilibrium system:
$2SO_2(g) + O_2(g) \rightleftharpoons 2SO_3(g)$

41. Chemists working in the lab need to know which side of an equilibrium system is favored. Why would this be important?

42. Describe Le Châtelier's principle in your own words.

43. Consider the following equilibrium system:
$N_2O_4(g) \rightleftharpoons 2NO_2(g)$ $\Delta H = 58.0$ kJ Predict which direction the equilibrium will shift to under the following conditions and why.
    a. Some N_2O_4 is removed.
    b. Some NO_2 is added.
    c. The temperature is increased.

44. Given the reaction,
$PCl_5(g) \rightleftharpoons PCl_3(g) + Cl_2(g)$, $\Delta H = 87.9$ kJ
predict in which direction the equilibrium will shift with the following changes and why
    a. The pressure of the system is increased.
    b. Some Cl_2 is removed.
    c. Some PCl_5 is added.
    d. The temperature of the system is decreased.

45. Explain how each of the following changes will affect the equilibrium system shown below and why:
$2SO_2(g) + O_2(g) \rightleftharpoons 2SO_3(g)$, $\Delta H = -320$ kJ
    a. The temperature is increased.
    b. Some O_2 is removed.
    c. The pressure of the reaction mixture is decreased.
    d. Some SO_3 is removed.

46. Write the expressions for the equilibrium constants for each of the following reactions:
    a. $N_2(g) + O_2(g) \rightleftharpoons 2NO(g)$
    b. $PCl_5(g) \rightleftharpoons PCl_3(g) + Cl_2(g)$
    c. $2SO_2(g) + O_2(g) \rightleftharpoons 2SO_3(g)$
    d. $2Cl_2(g) + 2H_2O(g) \rightleftharpoons 4HCl(g) + O_2(g)$
    e. $3NO(g) \rightleftharpoons N_2O(g) + NO_2(g)$

Section 12.3

47. A reaction mechanism is a series of elementary steps that make up an overall chemical reaction. Does it make sense that chemical reactions actually happen in a series of smaller steps? Explain your thinking.

48. Consider the two elementary steps
step 1: $N_2O(g) \rightarrow N_2(g) + O$
step 2: $N_2O(g) + O \rightarrow N_2(g) + O_2(g)$
    a. Write the balanced equation for the overall chemical reaction.
    b. Identify any reaction intermediates.

49. Consider the elementary steps
step 1: $H_2(g) + ICl(g) \rightarrow HI(g) + HCl(g)$
step 2: $HI(g) + ICl(g) \rightarrow I_2(g) + HCl(g)$
    a. Write the balanced equation for the overall chemical reaction.
    b. Identify any reaction intermediates.

50. Explain why it is unlikely that the following reaction occurs all in one step:
$2SO_2(g) + O_2(g) \rightleftharpoons 2SO_3(g)$

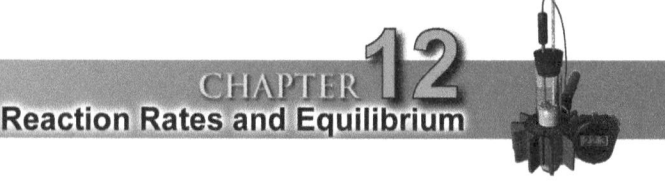
51. Give an example of a biological pathway in your body. Explain why you consider it a pathway.

Section 12.4

52. How do catalysts speed up chemical reactions?

53. Do our bodies use catalysts? If so, what are they called?

54. Make a generic sketch of a reaction profile, and label your axes. Clearly show how a catalyst would affect your graph.

55. Why will gelatin not set or gel when fresh pineapple is added?

56. Give an example of an enzyme in your body that is involved in the digestion process.

57. Explain one way that catalysts are useful in our society.

58. How do the formation of stalagmites and stalactites in caves relate to our study of equilibrium?

Quantitative Problems

Section 12.1

59. The reaction of nitrogen and oxygen to produce nitrous oxide is
$N_2(g) + O_2(g) \rightleftharpoons 2NO(g)$
The rate of disappearance of N_2 is measured to be 4.3×10^{-5} moles/L-s. What is the rate of formation of NO?

60. The decomposition of NO follows the reaction
$3NO(g) \rightleftharpoons N_2O(g) + NO_2(g)$
What is the rate of disappearance of NO if the rate of appearance of N_2O is 3.6×10^{-4} moles/L-s?

61. Use the data in the table below to answer the following questions about the reaction A → C.

Time (min)	Moles of A	Moles of C
0	1.00	0.00
5	0.85	0.15
10	0.74	0.26
15	0.62	0.38
20	0.54	0.46

a. What do you notice about the amounts of reactant relative to the product being formed?

b. Calculate the average rate of appearance of C during the time period from t = 5 min to t = 10 min.

c. Calculate the rate of disappearance of A during the first five minutes of the reaction.

d. Calculate the rate of disappearance of A during the last five minutes, between t = 15 min and t = 20 min.

e. What do you notice about the rate at the start of the reaction relative to the rate at the end of the reaction?

Section 12.2

62. For the following reactions, look at the value of the equilibrium constant to decide whether the reaction contains mainly reactants or mainly products. Explain your reasoning for each.

a. $2NO(g) + O_2(g) \rightleftharpoons 2NO_2(g)$, K = 5.0×10^{12}

b. $2SO_3(g) \rightleftharpoons 2SO_2(g) + O_2(g)$, K = 4×10^{-10}

63. Carbon monoxide and hydrogen gas are catalyzed to commercially produce methanol:
$CO(g) + 2H_2(g) \rightleftharpoons CH_3OH(g)$
Calculate the value of K at a constant temperature of 227°C, given that there are 0.041 moles of CH_3OH, 0.17 moles of CO, and 0.30 moles of H_2 present in a 2.0 L reaction vessel.

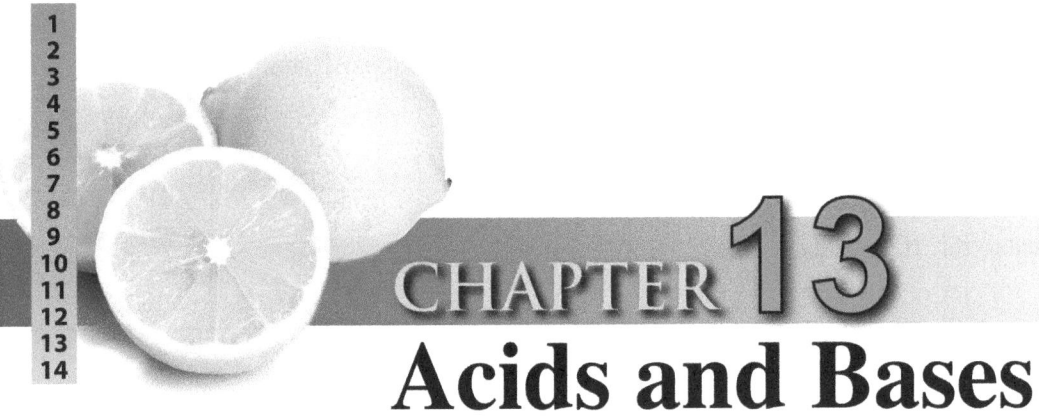

CHAPTER 13
Acids and Bases

What is an acid?

What is a base?

What kinds of chemical reactions occur with acids and bases?

Why are acids and bases important?

You might be surprised to know that your stomach contains a chemical strong enough to burn skin and dissolve metal. That chemical is *hydrochloric acid* (HCl), and it is a necessary part of your body's chemical system for digesting food. The stomach has special adaptations that prevent the strong acid from escaping and damaging other parts of your body. The acid in your stomach is converted to water by a reaction with bicarbonate (HCO_3^-) ions produced in your pancreas. Bicarbonate belongs to a group of chemicals called *bases*. You can think of a base as the chemical opposite of an acid.

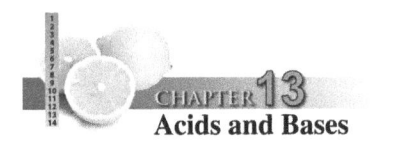

CHAPTER 13
Acids and Bases

The chemical properties we call "acid" and "base" come directly from water itself. Acids and bases are important because they play a huge role in the chemistry of aqueous solutions, including those in your body and also in the environment. In this chapter you will see how water is both an acid and a base! Some of the acids you probably eat or drink include acetic acid (found in vinegar), citric acid (found in orange juice), and malic acid (found in apples). Acids create the tart and sour flavors in foods. Bases around your household environment include soap, ammonia in cleaning solutions, and magnesium hydroxide found in some antacids. Bases create the slippery feel of soaps and the bitter taste in grapefruit, spinach, and other foods.

The chemistry of antacids

Magnesium hydroxide

$Mg(OH)_2$

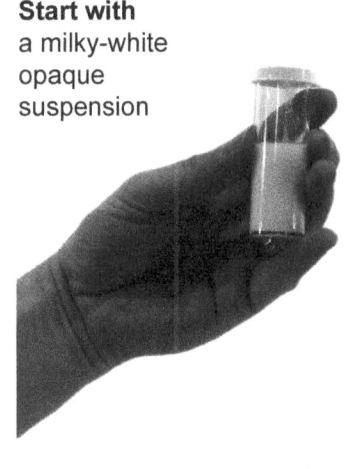

Next time you go to a drug store, look around in the "antacids" section. Try to find some milk of magnesia. This medicine is a thick, milky suspension of magnesium hydroxide [$Mg(OH)_2$] in water, usually with some sweetener to make it taste better. The medicine is a suspension because magnesium hydroxide is insoluble in water.

People use milk of magnesia to relieve acid reflux and as a laxative. The recommended dose is one teaspoon, or 5 mL. If you look at the label on the back, you see that one teaspoon (5 mL) contains 400 mg, or 0.4 g, of $Mg(OH)_2$. This information is really telling us the concentration! The formula mass for $Mg(OH)_2$ is 58.3 g. So that means one teaspoon contains 0.00686 moles of magnesium hydrox-ide molecules.

400 mg (0.4 g)   5 mL (0.005 L)

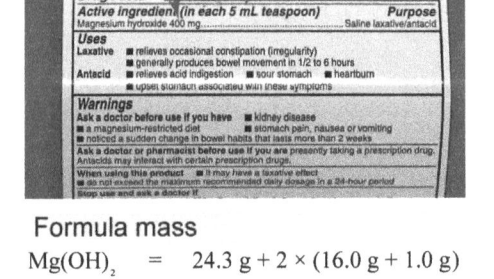

Formula mass

$$Mg(OH)_2 = 24.3\ g + 2 \times (16.0\ g + 1.0\ g)$$
$$= 58.3\ g$$

Moles of $Mg(OH)_2$ in 0.400 g

$$\frac{0.400\ g}{58.3\ g/mole} = 0.00686\ moles$$

- Why is the recommended dose 5 mL?

- How does magnesium hydroxide relieve acid reflux?

- How much acid will one teaspoon of this medicine neutralize?

Start with a milky-white opaque suspension

Add *twice* as many moles of acid as there are of Mg(OH)2

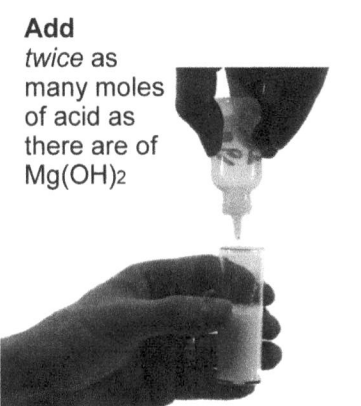

In the **reaction** the liquid turns clear!

Nothing visible happens when you add the same number of moles of stomach acid (HCl). But when you add exactly twice as many moles, the solution turns from milky to clear! This happens because of a chemical reaction between the hydrochloric acid molecules and the magnesium hydroxide molecules.

13.1 The Chemical Nature of Acids and Bases

Dissociation of water

Acids and bases are important to chemistry because almost every reaction that occurs in an aqueous solution is affected. This includes your body, the ocean, and much of the biosphere of Earth. The reason is partly because water partially *dissociates*. On average, 1 out of every 550 million water molecules is dissociated into a hydrogen (H^+) ion and a hydroxide (OH^-) ion. *The hydrogen ion is chemically powerful and quite unique.*

$$H_2O \xrightleftharpoons{\text{dissociation}} H^+ + OH^-$$

Neutral means $[H^+] = [OH^-]$

In **neutral** water, the concentrations of H^+ ions and OH^- ions are *equal*. This is evident from the balanced equation. In the context of acidity, the word "neutral" means $[H^+] = [OH^-]$.

The dissociation reaction is written with a double arrow to show that the reaction goes both ways. Some H^+ and OH^- ions are always recombining to make water molecules. In equilibrium, there is a balance between molecules dissociating into H^+ and OH^- and ions recombining to make whole molecules again.

Properties of acids

An **acid** is a compound that dissolves in water to make a solution that contains *more* H^+ ions than OH^- ions. Some properties of acids are listed below.

Properties of acids

pH < 7	Create a sour taste in foods	React with bases to make water and a salt	React with metals to release hydrogen gas	Are highly corrosive and can cause severe injury

$$HCl(aq) \rightarrow H^+(aq) + Cl^-(aq)$$

When hydrochloric acid (HCl) dissolves in water, it ionizes completely into hydrogen (H^+) and chlorine (Cl^-) ions. The fact that H^+ ions are created is what makes HCl an acid. Some other common acids are acetic acid (found in vinegar) and citric acid (found in citrus fruits).

Chemistry terms

neutral: in the context of acids and bases, a solution with pH = 7.0, which also means the concentrations of H^+ and OH^- ions are equal.

acid: a chemical that dissolves in water to create more H^+ ions than there are in neutral water.

Bases

A base is the chemical opposite of an acid

A **base** is a compound that dissolves in water to make a solution with *more* OH^- ions than H^+ ions. In many ways a base is the chemical opposite of an acid. Acids make more H^+ ions and bases make more OH^- ions. Some of the properties of bases are listed below.

Properties of bases

| Create a bitter taste in foods | React with acids to make water and a salt | Feel slippery, like wet soap | Are highly corrosive and can cause severe injury |

pH > 7

Acid or base but not both

Because H^+ and OH^- can combine to make neutral water, a solution that is not neutral must be either acidic or basic. A solution cannot be both acidic and basic at the same time. The pH scale reflects this either–or behavior. Acids have pH < 7, neutral solutions have pH = 7, and bases have pH > 7.

NaOH is a common base

A common base in both the lab and the hardware store is sodium hydroxide (NaOH). This compound is also known by two common names: *lye* and *caustic soda*. When dissolved in water, sodium hydroxide dissociates into sodium ions (Na^+) and hydroxide ions (OH^-). A 1.0 M solution of NaOH has a pH of 14 and is a *strong base*. Concentrated NaOH is a dangerous and powerfully reactive sub-stance that can burn eyes and skin.

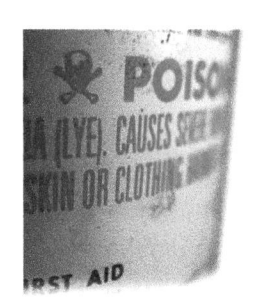

NaOH is also known as **lye** or **caustic soda**

$$NaOH(aq) \rightarrow Na^+(aq) + OH^-(aq)$$

Alkaline substances make basic solutions

An *alkaline* substance is a salt of a group 1 or group 2 metal that dissolves in water to make a base. A good example is potassium hydroxide (KOH). This ionic compound is used in alkaline batteries. When dissolved in a paste inside a battery, potassium hydroxide dissociates to make potassium ions (K^+) and hydroxide ions (OH^-).

K^+ and OH^- ions in wet paste

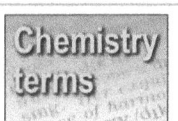
Chemistry terms

base: a chemical that dissolves in water to create fewer H^+ ions than there are in neutral water or, equivalently, more OH^- ions.

The importance of the H⁺ ion

The H⁺ ion
is unique
because it has
no electrons

The H$^+$ ion is powerful because *it has no electrons*! No other element participates in chemistry as a bare nucleus, or a single proton stripped of its electrons. We learned that chemistry is due to interactions between electrons in atoms. Although this is true, it is ultimately the electrical *energy* linking electrons and protons that drives chemical behavior. Electrons have negative charge. The H$^+$ ion is a tiny, concentrated *positive* charge with no negative electrons to shield it. The whole subject of acids and bases has to do with the extraordinary chemical power of the H$^+$ ion, the "naked proton."

The Arrhenius
definition of
acid and base

The properties of acids, such as reacting with metals, were known a thousand years before anyone knew *why* they had such properties. "Acids" were solutions that tasted sour and dissolved metals. Likewise, bases were identified as solutions that had a bitter taste, were slippery, and neutralized acids. Around 1880, Svante Arrhenius, a Swedish chemist, realized that the properties of acids resulted from an excess of H$^+$ ions in aqueous solutions. He also noticed that the properties of bases were associated with an excess of OH$^-$ ions. Arrhenius proposed the first definition of acids and bases.

> **Arrhenius theory**
>
> Acids are chemicals that produce H$^+$ ions in aqueous solutions
>
> Bases are chemicals that produce OH$^-$ ions in aqueous solutions

H⁺ and the
hydronium
ion (H₃O⁺)

The H$^+$ ion is so chemically attractive that it instantly pairs up with a water molecule to make H$_3$O$^+$. This is called the **hydronium ion**. Hydronium is sometimes called a *hydrated proton*, since H$^+$ is a proton and it becomes "hydrated" by bonding to water molecules. When we talk about the H$^+$ ion in water, we are really talking about H$_3$O$^+$ since H$^+$ really does not exist by itself for very long.

Solitary H$^+$ ions immediately bond to polar water molecules to form H$_3$O$^+$

H⁺ is shorthand
for H₃O⁺

In this chapter (and keeping with history) we will refer to the hydronium ion as just H$^+$ and not H$_3$O$^+$. This is really just because H$^+$ is easier to write and more convenient. However, keep in mind that the hydrated form (H$_3$O$^+$) is closer to reality.

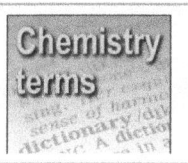

Chemistry terms

Arrhenius theory: definition of acids and bases in which acids form H$^+$ and bases form OH$^-$ in solution

hydronium ion: H$_3$O$^+$ ion forms when an H$^+$ bonds to a complete water molecule, giving acids their unique properties.

Brønsted–Lowry acids and bases

How is NH₃ a base?

Ammonia (NH₃) is a weak base, even though the ammonia molecule does not contain the OH⁻ ion. When ammonia dissolves in water, the ammonia molecule strips a proton from a water molecule, leaving an OH⁻ ion. This makes NH₃ a base because it dissolves to create OH⁻ ions, but does it by taking protons (H⁺) from water molecules. Ammonia is a *weak* base because only a fraction of the ammonia molecules form NH₄⁺ and OH⁻.

Brønsted–Lowry definition

Acids are chemicals that **donate** protons (H⁺ ions)

Bases are chemicals that **accept** protons

$$NH_3 + H_2O \xrightleftharpoons{(aq)} NH_4^+ + OH^-$$

The Brønsted–Lowry theory

Ammonia acts as a *proton acceptor* when dissolved in water. This give us another, more powerful way to define a base. *A base is a compound that accepts protons.* Ammonia is a base because it accepts a proton from a water molecule, leaving an OH⁻ ion. This idea is known as the **Brønsted–Lowry definition** of acids and bases.

A better way to define acids and bases

According to the Brønsted–Lowry definition, an acid is a compound that donates a proton. A base is a compound that accepts a proton. In many ways the Brønsted-Lowry perspective is a better way to think about acids and bases because it explicitly recognizes the relationship between acids (proton donors) and bases (proton acceptors).

All acids are Brønsted–Lowry acids

All acids and bases can be thought of in the Brønsted–Lowry sense. Nitric acid (HNO₃) dissociates in water to make H⁺ ions and NO₃⁻ ions. The nitric acid molecule donates the proton (H⁺), which is why it is an acid.

$$HNO_3(aq) \rightarrow H^+(aq) + NO_3^-(aq)$$

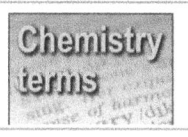
Chemistry terms

Brønsted–Lowry definition: a different way to look at what defines acids and bases, in which acids are compounds that donate protons (H⁺) and bases are compounds that accept protons.

Acids and bases are always paired

Acids and bases act in pairs

The Brønsted–Lowry definition brings up an important idea: For a molecule or ion to act like an acid by donating a proton, another molecule or ion must act like a base by accepting the proton! The opposite is also true. You cannot have something acting like an acid without something else acting like a base and vice versa.

Water can act like an acid

Going back to ammonia, we can see that the NH_3 molecule acts like a base by accepting a proton to become NH_4^+. Water acts like an acid by donating a proton to become OH^-.

NH₃ acts like a base because it accepts a proton to become NH₄⁺   H₂O acts like an acid because it donates a proton to become OH⁻

$$NH_3 \ + \ H_2O \ \underset{}{\overset{(aq)}{\rightleftharpoons}} \ NH_4^+ \ + \ OH^-$$

Water can also act like a base

Now consider a strong acid. When dissolved in water, hydrochloric acid (HCl) is a proton donor, dissociating to make H^+ ions. Water acts basic by accepting a proton and becoming H_3O^+.

HCl acts like an acid because it donates a proton to become Cl⁻   H₂O acts like a base because it accepts a proton to become H₃O⁺

$$HCl \ + \ H_2O \ \underset{}{\overset{(aq)}{\rightleftharpoons}} \ H_3O^+ \ + \ Cl^-$$

Water is amphoteric

One of the most important properties of water is its ability to act as both an acid and a base. In the presence of an acid, water acts as a base. In the presence of a base, water acts as an acid. A substance that can be either an acid or a base is known as **amphoteric**. Water is amphoteric because H_2O can both donate protons ($H_2O \rightarrow H^+ + OH^-$) or accept protons ($H_2O + H^+ \rightarrow H_3O^+$).

Chemistry terms

amphoteric: a substance that can act as either an acid or a base under different circumstances; water is amphoteric.

A NATURAL APPROACH TO CHEMISTRY

Identifying and naming acids and bases

The chemical formula for an acid starts with an "H"

The chemical formula for an acid is always written with an "H" first (if the acid contains hydrogen). For example, acetic acid is written $HC_2H_3O_2$ instead of $C_2H_4O_2$. Both formulas give the correct molecule, but the first is quickly recognized as an acid because of the leading "H." If the acid dissolves to make two H^+ ions, its chemical formula begins with H_2. One example is ascorbic acid (vitamin C), which is written $H_2C_6H_6O_6$.

TABLE 13.1. Common acids

Name	Formula	Strength	Name	Formula	Strength
Hydrochloric	HCl	strong	Ascorbic	$H_2C_6H_6O_6$	weak
Nitric	HNO_3	strong	Citric	$H_3C_6H_5O_7$	weak
Sulfuric	H_2SO_4	strong	Carbonic	H_2CO_3	weak
Phosphoric	H_3PO_4	weak	Acetic	$HC_2H_3O_2$	weak

The chemical formula of a base

The chemical formula for a strong base is written with the "OH" last. A good example is sodium hydroxide, written NaOH. Most weak bases such as ammonia (NH_3) do not contain "OH," so you have to learn other ways to recognize them as bases.

TABLE 13.2. Common bases

Name	Formula	Strength	Name	Formula	Strength
Sodium hydroxide	NaOH	strong	Carbonate ion	HCO_3^-	weak
Potassium hydroxide	KOH	strong	Hypochlorite ion	ClO^-	weak
Calcium hydroxide	$Ca(OH)_2$	strong	Caffeine	$C_8H_{10}N_4O_2$	weak
Ammonia	NH_3	weak	Ephedrine	$C_{10}H_{15}ON$	weak

Strong acids and bases

A **strong** acid or base dissociates completely in water so that each molecule contributes one H^+ ion (acids) or one OH^- ion (bases). Nitric acid (HNO_3) is an example of a strong acid. Every molecule of HNO_3 dissociates into a hydrogen ion (H^+) and a nitrate ion (NO_3^-). Sodium hydroxide (NaOH) is a strong base; every mole of NaOH that dissolves yields one mole of OH^- ions and one mole of Na^+ ions. Solutions of strong acids and bases are strong electrolytes because the free, dissociated ions can conduct electricity.

Weak acids and bases

A **weak** acid or base only dissociates partially or produces relatively few H^+ or OH^- ions in solution. For example a 1 M solution of acetic acid produces less than 1% as many H^+ ions as the same concentration of hydrochloric acid. Because fewer free ions are present, solutions of weak acids and bases are considered weak electrolytes.

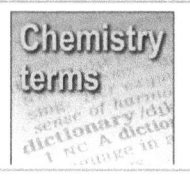

Chemistry terms

strong acid (base): acid (base) that dissociates completely or almost completely, usually yielding 1 mole of H^+ (OH^-) ions for every mole of acid (base) dissolved. **weak acid (base):** acid (base) that only partially dissociates in solution, typically with only a few percent (or less) of molecules dissociating to yield H^+ (OH^-) ions.

13.2 The pH Scale

Why pH is important

Ask anyone who keeps an aquarium about pH. They will tell you pH is *important*. If the pH of the aquarium water is wrong, the fish will die. Ask serious gardeners or a farmers and they will also tell you pH is important. Each kind of plant has a preferred range of soil pH. That's why a good gardener would not plant blueberries next to vegetables. Blueberry bushes need soil with a pH between 4 and 5. Vegetables (such as broccoli) need a pH between 6 and 7.

What pH measures

What exactly is pH? The simple answer is that pH tells you whether a solution is acid, base, or neutral. Familiar acids and bases have a pH between 0 to 14. Pure water has a pH of 7 and is neutral. The farther away from 7 you get, the stronger the acid or base.

Acids have pH less than 7

Acids have a pH of less than 7. Natural rainwater has a pH of between 5.5 and 6, which is very slightly acidic. A weak acid like tomato juice has a pH of 4. A 0.1 M hydrochloric acid solution (a strong acid) has a pH of 1. Anything with a pH of less than about 2 is dangerous and should be handled with care.

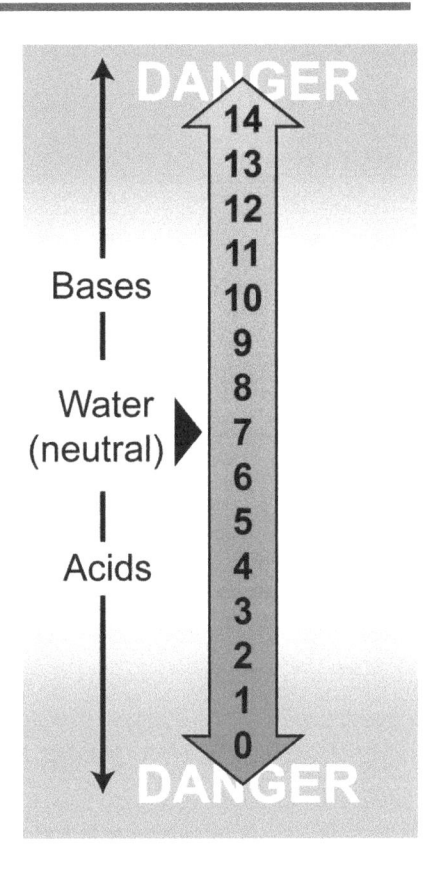

Bases have pH greater than 7

A base has a pH that is greater than 7. Weak bases such as milk of magnesia [$Mg(OH)_2$] and baking soda ($NaHCO_3$) have pH between 8 and 10. A concentrated solution of a strong base such as a 1 M sodium hydroxide solution has a pH close to 14. Anything with a pH greater than about 12 is dangerous and should be handled carefully.

Some common acids and bases

Table 13.3 lists the pH of some common substances. Many foods are acidic. Many household cleaning products are bases.

TABLE 13.3. The pH of some common acids and bases

Household chemical	Acid or base	pH
lemon juice	acid	2
vinegar	acid	3
soda water	acid	4
baking soda	base	8.5
bar soap	base	10
ammonia	base	11

Concentration, pH, and scientific notation

The meaning of pH

The pH tells us much more than just whether a solution is an acid or a base. The pH also tells how *strong* the acid or base is. In this sense, "strong" means concentrated and "weak" means dilute. In fact, *pH is a special way of describing the molarity of the H⁺ ion* in a solution. If you know the pH, then you also know the concentration of H⁺ ions, and vice versa. If you know the molarity of H⁺ ions, then you can calculate the pH.

The pH scale is based on scientific notation

Earlier we noted that about 1 in 556 million H_2O molecules in ordinary water dissociates into H^+ and OH^- ions. There are 55.6 moles of H_2O in one liter. If you work out the math, the concentration of H^+ in neutral water is 0.0000001 M, or 1×10^{-7} M. The pH of neutral water is 7 because the concentration of H^+ is 10^{-7} M.

Numbers greater than 1 in scientific notation

In scientific notation, a number is written as a value multiplied by a power of 10. The power of 10 is given by the **exponent**. For example, we can write 500 as 5×100.

The number 100 is a power of 10 because $100 = 10 \times 10 = 10^2$. The number 500 can be written $500 = 5 \times 10^2$. The value is 5 and the exponent is 2. Exponents are positive when numbers are greater than one.

$$\underset{\text{Number}}{500} = \underset{}{5.00} \times \underset{\text{Power of 10}}{100}$$

$$= 5.00 \times 10^{2}$$

Exponent

Numbers less than 1 in scientific notation

This gets tricky when numbers are less than one. Consider the number 0.05. This is the same as 5/100. The number 100 is a power of 10, but now it is the denominator instead of the numerator. That means we divide by 100 instead of multiply.

The number $0.05 = 5 \times 1/100 = 5 \times 1/10^2 = 5 \times 10^{-2}$. A negative exponent means you divide by the power of 10 rather than multiply. *All values less than 1 have negative exponents.*

$$\underset{\text{Number}}{0.05} = \underset{}{5} \times \underset{\text{Power of 10}}{\frac{1}{100}}$$

$$= 5 \times 10^{-2}$$

Exponent

A negative exponent means the number is less than 1

Chemistry terms

exponent: the power of 10 for a number written in scientific notation, such as 2 in $500 = 5 \times 10^2$.

Logarithms and pH

Mathematical meaning of pH

On the previous page we said the concentration of H^+ was 10^{-7} M in neutral water. Neutral water has a pH of 7. Do you see the connection? *The pH value is −1 times the H^+ molarity expressed as a power of 10.* This is the true meaning of pH. Let's explore how it works.

pH = 0 means the H^+ concentration is 1 M

A strong acid like HCl dissociates completely in water to H^+ and Cl^-. That means a 1 M solution of HCl also has a 1 M concentration of H^+ ions. In scientific notation, $1 = 10^0$. That means the pH of a 1 M solution of HCl is zero (pH = 0). A solution with a pH of 0 is a very strong acid.

Calculating pH with logarithms

When the number is a perfect power of 10, the pH is the exponent multiplied by −1. How about numbers that are not perfect powers of 10? Suppose the H^+ molarity is 0.05 M. The rule still applies, but the exponent is no longer an integer. Instead we ask the question, is there a number N such that $10^N = 0.05$? The answer is yes, and the number is −1.301. If you raise 10 to the power −1.301 you get 0.05:

$$10^{(-1.301)} = 0.05$$

The definition of pH

The number −1.301 is the **logarithm** of 0.05. The logarithm of a number is the power of 10 that gives you the same number back. *The pH of the solution is 1.301* because pH is the logarithm multiplied by −1. We can now give a precise definition for pH.

pH is −1 × logarithm of H^+ molarity

> **Definition of pH**
>
> $$pH = -\log[H^+]$$
>
> pH is −1 times the logarithm of the H^+ molarity

Logarithms are easiest to see when numbers are perfect powers of 10. The logarithm of 100 is 2. We write this as $2 = \log(100)$:

$$\log(100) = 2 \text{ because } 10^2 = 100$$

Why ordinary pH is between 0 and 14

Almost all the acids and bases you come across in ordinary life have an H^+ molarity between 1 and 10^{-14}. The logarithm of 1 is zero, so when the molarity of H^+ is 1, the pH is zero (strong acid). The logarithm of 10^{-14} is 14. If a solution has an H^+ concentration of 10^{-14} M, then pH is 14 (strong base). However, *pH can be negative* for stronger acids and greater than 14 for exceptionally strong bases.

Chemistry terms

logarithm: in base 10, a number A derived from another number B such that $10^B = A$.

Calculating pH

Why we use logarithms for pH	We use logarithms for pH because the range from 0 to 14 is a lot easier to think about than the range from 1 (or 10^0) to 0.00000000000001 (or 10^{-14}). This is the range of H^+ molarity in ordinary acids and bases. However, the pH scale does not stop at 0 or 14. A concentrated 6M solution of hydrochloric acid has a pH of –0.78.
Calculating pH	To calculate pH, you must do the following:

1. Determine the molarity of H^+ ions.
2. $pH = -1 \times log(\text{molarity of } H^+)$

If you know the pH, you can also determine the concentration of H^+ ions. Use the fact that pH is the power of 10 of the H^+ molarity. If the pH is 3, then the molarity of H^+ ions is 10^{-3} or 0.001 M.

Solved problem

A solution of acetic acid ($HC_2H_3O_2$) has an H^+ concentration of 5×10^{-5} M. What is the pH of the solution?

Asked: *pH of a solution*

Given: *Molarity of H^+ is 5×10^{-5}.*

Relationships: *$pH = -1 \times log(H^+ \text{ molarity})$*

Solve: *$pH = - log(5 \times 10^{-5}) = 4.3$, a relatively weak acid*

You may have noticed a very important rule: Changing the pH by 1 changes the concentration by a factor of 10. That means a change of 2 pH units is really a change of 100 in concentration! The converse is also true. If you dilute a solution by 10 to 1, you reduce the H^+ concentration by a factor of 10 and *the pH increases by 1*.

Each pH change of 1 changes the H^+ concentration by 10

Dilution by 10:1 raises the pH by 1 unit

Solved problem

A solution of nitric acid (HNO_3) has a pH of 3. What will the pH be if you add 10 mL of the solution to 90 mL of pure water?

Asked: *pH of the new solution*

Given: *The old solution had a pH of 3. The new solution has 10 ml of the old solution out of 100 mL of total solution.*

Relationships: *Dilution by 10:1 raises the pH by 1.*

Solve: *The new solution has a pH of 4.*

Calculating pH for bases

H+ and OH– are linked by the dissociation of water

The pH scale works for bases as well as acids. This is because of the one-to-one relationship between the H^+ ion and the OH^- ion, or between proton donors (acids) and proton acceptors (bases). In any aqueous solution, H^+ and OH^- can always recombine to produce neutral water (H_2O). Any change that increases the concentration of OH^- decreases the concentration of H^+ because it forces some H^+ to recombine and form water. Conversely, any change that increases H^+, will decrease OH^- for the same reason.

For this reason the concentrations of H^+ and OH^- satisfy the following three equations:

$$[\text{concentration of } H^+] \times [\text{concentration of } OH^-] = 10^{-14}$$

$$\log[H^+] + \log[OH^-] = -14$$

$$pH = 14 + \log[OH^-]$$

Mathematically, each of these equations says the exact same thing! But, the third one is easiest to use because logarithms are numbers you can add and subtract easily.

Calculating pH from OH– concentration

If you know the concentration of OH^- you can use any of these equations to quickly find the pH. The diagram below shows how to do it.

Suppose the concentration of OH⁻ is 0.005 M, what is the pH?

Step 1: Calculate the log of [OH⁻] $\log[0.005] = -2.3$

Step 2: Apply the rule pH = 14 + log[OH⁻] $pH = 14 - 2.3 = 11.7$

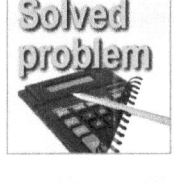

Solved problem

Find the pH of a 0.012 M sodium hydroxide (NaOH) solution.

Asked: *pH of the solution*

Given: *NaOH is a strong base that dissociates 100% in aqueous solution.*

Relationships: *pH = 14 + log[OH ⁻]*

Solve: *[OH⁻] = 0.012 M*
pH = 14 + log [0.012] = 14.0 – 1.92 = 12.1 The solution has a pH of 12.1 and is a strong base.

pH indicators

Measuring pH

You usually can't determine pH by just looking at a solution or measuring its density or its temperature. However, there are three common *indirect* techniques chemists use.

- Perform a chemical reaction with a solution of known pH.
- Use a chemical that changes color at different pH values.
- Measure the electrical properties of the solution.

Indicators are chemicals that turn colors at different pH

Certain chemicals turn different colors at different pH. These chemicals are called pH **indicators**. The juice of boiled red cabbage contains chemicals called *anthocyanins*. These chemicals change color at different pH. Red cabbage juice is normally deep purple, but it becomes deep pink or red in a strong acid and green or yellow in a strong base.

The color of red cabbage juice at different pH

Litmus paper is an indicator

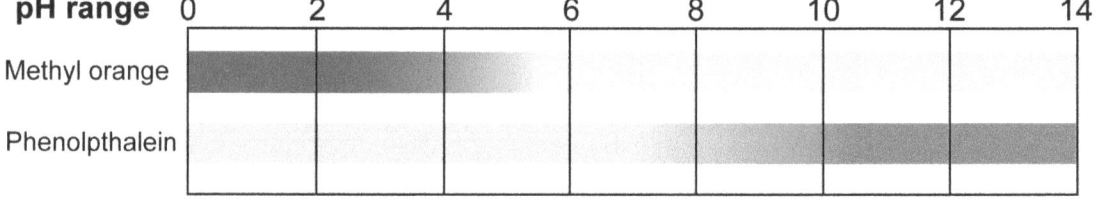

Red litmus turns blue in bases   Blue litmus turns red in acids

Litmus paper is another pH indicator that changes color. Litmus paper is made from a dye extracted from certain lichens, plants that grow on rocky places. Blue litmus paper turns red in acid. Blue litmus paper stays blue in a basic solution. Red litmus paper turns blue in a base, but it stays red in an acid.

Methyl orange and phenolphthalein indicators

In the lab you may use methyl orange and phenolphthalein, two common pH indicators. The chart below shows the color changes of each one for different ranges of pH. Methyl orange is best for measuring the pH of acids because its color changes between a pH of 3 and a pH of 5. Phenolphthalein is best for measuring the pH of bases.

pH range	0	2	4	6	8	10	12	14
Methyl orange								
Phenolphthalein								

pH meters

There are instruments called *pH meters* that are also used to measure pH. These instruments work because solutions that are acids or bases conduct electricity. The ease at which electricity flows through the solution (its *conductivity*) depends on the pH. A pH meter senses the pH by sending a tiny electrical signal through the solution.

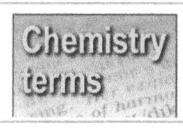

Chemistry terms

indicator: a chemical that turns different colors at different values of pH, used to determine pH directly or in reactions with solutions of known pH.

13.3 Acid–Base Equilibria

The relation between H^+ and OH^-

When the concentration of OH^- ions increases, the concentration of H^+ ions decreases and vice versa. This is because excess OH^- ions combine with the H^+ ions normally present in water to make neutral water molecules.

The ion product constant

Because recombination and dissociation are always going on, the concentration of H^+ and OH^- ions in dilute aqueous solutions obeys an equilibrium rule. For the reaction:

$$H_2O \xrightleftharpoons{\text{dissociation}} H^+ + OH^-$$

$$[H^+] \times [OH^-] = 1.0 \; 10^{-14}$$

The **ion product constant** for water (K_w) is 1.0×10^{-14} at 25°C. When either the H^+ or OH^- concentration is changed (by adding acids or bases) the equilibrium rule is still obeyed. This is why you can calculate the pH of a base from the concentration of OH^-. The pH depends only on the H^+ concentration; however, $[H^+]$ and $[OH^-]$ are related by the ion product constant (K_w).

Solved problem

A certain solution has a concentration of H^+ ions of 0.0005 M. What is the concentration of OH^- ions? Is the solution acidic or basic?

Asked: *$[OH^-]$ and pH of the new solution*

Given: *$[H^+] = 0.0005$*

Relationships: *$[H^+] \times [OH^-] = 1.0 \times 10^{-14}$*

$pH = -1 \times logarithm \, [H^+]$

Solve: *$[OH^-] = \dfrac{1.0 \times 10^{-14}}{[H^+]} = \dfrac{1.0 \times 10^{-14}}{0.0005} = 2 \times 10^{-11} \, M$*

$pH = -1 \times log[0.0005] = 3.3$

Answer: *The concentration of OH^- ions is $2 \times 10^{-11} \, M$.*
The solution has a pH of 3.3 and is a moderately strong acid.

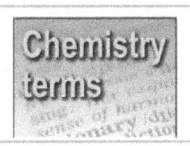

Chemistry terms

ion product constant: in dilute aqueous solutions, $[H^+] \times [OH^-] = 1.0 \times 10^{-14} = K_w$ at 25°C.

Weak acids

ADVANCED AP

Comparing strong and weak acids

In a weak acid or base, only some of the molecules actively increase or decrease the concentration of H^+ ions. Acetic acid ($HC_2O_3H_2$), found in vinegar, is a good example. If you mix a 0.1 M solution of acetic acid, you get a pH of 2.87. That immediately tells us that not all the acetic acid molecules dissociated to H^+ ions. By comparison, the same molarity of hydrochloric acid has a pH of 1.0, which is much more acidic.

1 M hydrochloric acid

1.0 M
0.1 M   *Strong*
0.01 M
0.001 M

HCl   Cl⁻   H⁺

Water

Complete dissociation

1 M acetic acid

1.0 M
0.1 M   *Weak*
0.01 M
0.001 M

$HC_2H_3O_2$ $C_2H_3O_2^-$ H⁺

Water

Partial dissociation and recombination

Equilibrium relationship and K_a

The concentration of H^+ in a weak acid (or base) obeys an equilibrium relationship. For acids and bases the equilibrium constant is called the acid–base dissociation constant (K_a). Strong acids like HCl dissociate completely and have large K_a values ([products]>>[reactants]). Weak acids have small K_a values ([products]<[reactants]). For example, acetic acid has $K_a = 1.8 \times 10^{-5}$. Like all chemical equilibria, acetic acid molecules are *constantly* dissociating and coming back together again.

Calculating the pH of a weak acid

Let's calculate the pH of a 0.1 M acetic acid solution. This is a good example for how to solve similar problems. The calculation has four major steps:

1. Write down the balanced net ionic equation.

2. Use the net ionic equation to set up the equilibrium relationship.

3. Use the RICE table to solve the relationship for the H^+ ion concentration.

4. Calculate the pH from the H^+ concentration ($pH = -\log[H^+]$).

Start with the balanced net ionic equation

The balanced net ionic equation shows that we need to consider three different species: H^+ ions, acetate ions ($C_2O_3H_2^-$), and whole acetic acid molecules. The concentrations of the three species obey the equilibrium relationship. Remember, brackets indicate molarity, so read [H^+] as "the molarity of H^+."

Balanced net ionic equation

$$HC_2H_3O_2 \xrightleftharpoons{(aq)} H^+ + C_2H_3O_2^-$$

acetic acid   hydrogen   acetate
                  ion   ion

Equilibrium relationship

$$K = \frac{\text{molarity of products}}{\text{molarity of reactants}}$$

$$K_a = \frac{[H^+][C_2H_3O_2^-]}{[HC_2H_3O_2]}$$

Using the RICE table

ADVANCED AP

Setting up variables

Acetic acid is a simple dissociation because one acid molecule dissociates into only two ions of equal concentration. If we let x be the concentration of H^+ ($x = [H^+]$) then the RICE table looks like this.

RICE table

Reaction	$HC_2H_3O_2$ $\rightleftharpoons$	H^+	+	$C_2H_3O_2^-$
Initial	0.1 M	0.0 M		0.0 M
Change	-x	+x		+x
Equilibrium	0.1 - x	x		x

The concentration of $HC_2H_3O_2$ decreases by x and the concentration of H^+ and $C_2H_3O_2^-$ increase by x. Writing down the equilibrium relationship yields a quadratic equation.

$$K_a = \frac{[H^+][C_2H_3O_2^-]}{[HC_2H_3O_2]} \qquad K_a = \frac{x^2}{0.1 - x} \qquad x^2 + K_a x - 0.1K_a = 0$$

Quadratic equation

Solving the equation by approximation

This is a weak acid by definition, and therefore the H^+ concentration (x) will always be much less than the initial molarity of acetic acid (0.1 M). Mathematically, that means the term $K_a x$ is always *much* less than $0.1K_a$, typically a thousand times less or even smaller. That means $K_a x$ can be neglected without causing much error in the solution of the equation. This makes the equation easier to solve and we get a value of $x = [H^+] = 0.00133$ M.

$$K_a x \ll 0.1K_a$$

$$x^2 + \boxed{K_a x} - 0.1K_a = 0$$
neglect this term

$$x^2 - 0.1K_a = 0$$

$$x = \sqrt{0.1K_a}$$

Weak acid–base equilibria

For weak acid or base equilibria of the form HA $\rightleftharpoons$ H^+ + A^- the H^+ concentration is given by the formula below where K_a is the dissociation constant and M is the initial molarity of the solution.

$$= \sqrt{(0.1)(1.8 \times 10^{-5})}$$

$$= 1.33 \times 10^{-3}$$

Dissociation of weak acids or bases	If HA is an acid with a net ionic equation of the form

$$HA \rightleftharpoons H^+ + A^-$$

and the ratio M/K_a is greater than 100, then

$$[H^+] = \sqrt{MK_a}$$

the initial molarity [HA] ——— dissociation constant

Solving equilibrium problems

When the approximation is OK to use

Note that the formula $[H^+] = \sqrt{MK_a}$ is an *approximation*. That means it only gives the right answer if certain conditions are met. The conditions are that the ratio M/K_a must be greater than 100. For the acetic acid problem, $M/K_a = 5,555$, which is much greater than 100! We can therefore be confident the formula gives us an accurate value for $[H^+]$. If the value of M/K_a were less than 100, the approximate formula would *not* give us an accurate answer and we would need to solve the quadratic equation.

Carbonic acid is polyprotic

An acid is *polyprotic* if each molecule dissociates to provide multiple H^+ ions. Carbonic acid is a good example. Carbonic acid (H_2CO_3) is an Arrhenius acid because it creates H^+ ions in solution. Carbonic acid dissolves in two steps, creating more than one H^+ ion per acid molecule:

$$H_2CO_3 \rightleftharpoons H^+(aq) + HCO_3^-(aq)$$

$$HCO_3^- \rightleftharpoons H^+(aq) + CO_3^{2-}(aq)$$

Step 1 - provides 1 H+ ion

H_2CO_3 HCO_3^- H^+

Step 2 - provides another H+ ion

HCO_3^- CO_3^{2-} H^+

Weak polyprotic acids

Weak polyprotic acids typically dissociate in several steps, with each step weaker than the last. In a 1 M solution of carbonic acid, 0.07% of the acid molecules dissociate to make H^+ and bicarbonate (HCO_3^-) ions. Only about 0.005% of the bicarbonate ions dissociate further into a second H^+ ion and a carbonate (CO_3^-) ion. For most purposes it is reasonable to assume that the pH of a carbonic acid solution is determined solely by the first dissociation, so in fact, carbonic acid acts like a *monoprotic* acid.

Solved problem

Calculate the pH of a 1.0 M solution of carbonic acid (H_2CO_3). Assume that only the first dissociation affects the pH ($H_2CO_3 \rightleftharpoons H^+ + HCO_3^-$). The value of K_a for this dissociation is $K_a = 4.3 \times 10^{-7}$.

Asked: *pH of a carbonic acid solution*

Given: *$M = 1.0$ M, $K_a = 4.3 \times 10^{-7}$, simple dissociation*

Relationships: $[H^+] = \sqrt{K_a M}$ *if $M/K_a > 100$, pH $= -1 \times log[H^+]$*

Solve: *$M/K_a = (1.0)/(4.3 \times 10^{-7}) = 2,300,000$, so the formula is OK*

$$[H^+] = \sqrt{(4.3 \times 10^{-7})(1.0)} = 6.6 \times 10^{-4} M$$

$$pH = -log(6.6 \times 10^{-4}) = 3.2$$

Answer: *The pH is 3.2. Since the pH is less than 7, the solution is an acid.*

Weak bases

Weak bases such as ammonia

A **weak base** is one that produces relatively few OH⁻ ions per molecule of base. Many important chemicals are weak bases. Ammonia is produced in living organisms as a waste product. You probably have smelled ammonia near a cat litter box, or around a chicken coop. Ammonia is also a cleaning product.

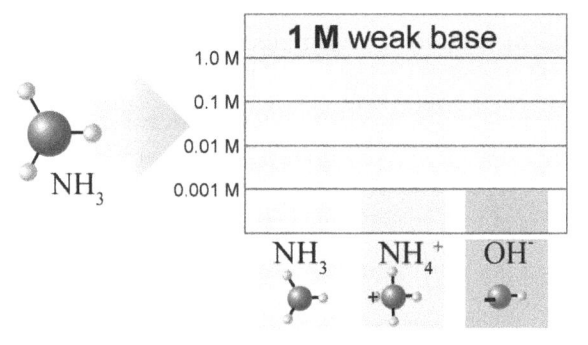

Why ammonia is a base

The basic property of an ammonia solution comes from the ammonia stripping a hydrogen from water to form an ammonium ion (NH_4^+) and a hydroxide ion (OH^-):

$$NH_3 + H_2O \rightleftharpoons NH_4^+ + OH^- \qquad K_b = 1.8 \times 10^{-5}$$

Using the base equilibrium constant

There is a base equilibrium constant (K_b) for bases just as there is a K_a for acids. Weak bases like ammonia also have much smaller K_b values than strong bases due to less dissociation. To determine the pH of 1.0 M NH_3 we need the concentration of OH^-, which we get from an equilibrium calculation with K_b. The RICE table looks like this:

RICE table

Reaction	NH_3	+	H_2O	$\rightleftharpoons$	NH_4^+	+	OH^-
Initial	1.0 M				0.0 M		0.0 M
Change	-x				+x		+x
Equilibrium	1.0 - x				x		x

Equilibrium expression

$$K_b = \frac{[NH_4^+][OH^-]}{[NH_3][H_2O]} \implies \frac{[x][x]}{[1.0 - x][1]} \implies \frac{x^2}{1.0 - x} = 1.8 \times 10^{-5}$$

Approximate solution for $[OH^-]$

$$x = [OH^-] = \sqrt{1.0 K_b} = 4.24 \times 10^{-3} \qquad \log(4.24 \times 10^{-3}) = -2.4$$

Calculate pH

$$pH = 14 + \log[OH^-] = 14 - 2.4 = 11.6$$

Calculating the pH of a base

Since the molarity of water is 1 in an equilibrium relationship, the equation has the same form as the weak acid equilibrium. The approximate solution gives the concentration of OH^- as 4.24×10^{-3} M. We know that the pH is 14 + log[OH^-], so we get a pH of 11.6.

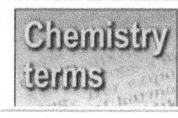

weak base: a base that only partially dissociates in solution, typically with only a few percent (or less) of the molecules dissociating to produce OH⁻ ions.

13.4 Acid–Base Reactions

Types of acid–base reactions

Long before people understood the chemistry of acids and bases, they were classified by their reactions with each other and with metals. For example, magnesium hydroxide [$Mg(OH)_2$] is a base. When 1 mole of magnesium hydroxide is added to 2 moles of hydrochloric acid, the resulting solution has a pH of 7 and is neutral. This is an example of a *neutralization* reaction. Acids and bases neutralize each other though chemical reactions.

Neutralization reaction

$$Mg(OH)_2 + HCl$$
base   *acid*

$$MgCl_2 + H_2O$$
a salt   *water*

Corrosion and etching

Acids react with metals to produce hydrogen gas. The reaction is an example of corrosion, because the metal is chemically eaten away from its solid form and put into solution. For example, copper reacts with nitric acid (HNO_3). This reaction eats away copper metal and is used to produce fine jewelry and printed circuit boards. A printed circuit board starts out covered in a uniform thin layer of copper. Areas that are not to be etched are covered with an acid-resistant material (called *resist*). The board is then dipped in nitric acid. The copper is etched away wherever the acid touches it. Areas that were covered with resist are untouched and become the electrical paths for the circuit.

Step 1
Thin copper layer

Step 2
Print resist on areas that are to be copper

Step 3
Etch away areas not painted with resist, leaving copper circuit trace

Printed circuit board

Nitric acid creates H⁺ ions $HNO_3(aq) \rightarrow H^+(aq) + NO_3^-(aq)$

Copper metal reacts with H⁺ to produce dissolved Cu²⁺ and hydrogen gas $Cu(s) + 2H^+(aq) \rightarrow Cu^{2+}(aq) + H_2(g)$

Electrolysis

Many people believe that hydrogen is the best transportation fuel for the future. Hydrogen burns clean and the product of the reaction is water. In one favorite scenario, solar energy is used to split sea water into hydrogen and oxygen. The hydrogen is then liquefied, bottled, and used for fuel. The chemical process is called electrolysis and it requires an electric current to flow through water. Acids and bases make excellent electrolytes and one established hydrogen production technique uses potassium hydroxide (KOH) as the electrolyte.

Sunlight

$$2H_2O \rightarrow 2H_2 + O_2$$

Hydrogen fuel

$$2H_2 + O_2 \rightarrow 2H_2O$$

Neutralization reactions

Neutralization

In general, adding acid lowers pH and adding base raises pH. Complete **neutralization** occurs when the H^+ ions from the acid combine with the OH^- ions from the base to produce neutral water.

Adding acid lowers pH and adding base raises pH

Example neutralization of NaOH

Sodium hydroxide is a strong base. When it is combined with acetic acid ($HC_2O_3H_2$), a neutralization reaction occurs:

$$NaOH(aq) + HC_2O_3H_2(aq) \rightarrow H_2O(l) + Na^+(aq) + C_2O_3H_2^-(aq)$$

Baking soda can partially neutralize strong acids

At a pH of 7.0, we say the solution has been *neutralized*. All strong acids should be neutralized before being disposed of. A simple way to neutralize a strong acid is with baking soda ($NaHCO_3$). When baking soda is added to hydrochloric acid, the H^+ ions from the acid combine with bicarbonate ions to make carbonic acid (H_2CO_3). Carbonic acid is a weak acid. A 1 M solution of HCl has a pH of 0 (strong), whereas a 1 M solution of carbonic acid has a pH of 3.2 (weak), and it is much less dangerous. Over time carbonic acid decomposes into CO_2 and water.

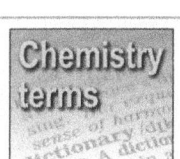

Hydrochloric acid

Baking soda

$$NaHCO_3 + HCl \rightarrow CO_2 + H_2O + NaCl$$
Neutralization reaction

Carbon dioxide + Water + Salt

Neutralization in your body

This process also goes on in your body. As food and digestive fluids leave the stomach, the pancreas and liver produce bicarbonate (a base) to neutralize stomach acid (HCl). Antacids such as magnesium hydroxide (milk of magnesia) have the same effect.

Adjusting soil pH

Neutralization reactions are important in gardening and farming. For example, about 25% of the yards in the United States have soil that is too acidic for grass (pH less than 5.5). Many people add lime, a base, to their yard every spring to raise the soil pH. A common form of lime is ground-up calcium carbonate ($CaCO_3$) made from limestone. For example, sulfuric acid (H_2SO_4) in soil reacts with the calcium carbonate to form water and calcium sulfate ($CaSO_4$), also known as gypsum. Sulfuric acid is created in the atmosphere from pollutants in the air. Many of the walls of buildings and homes are made with "plaster board," which is a sheet of gypsum (plaster) covered with paper on both sides.

Chemistry terms

neutralization: a reaction in which the pH of an acid is raised by combining with a base, or the pH of a base is lowered by combining with an acid; complete neutralization results in a pH of 7, the same as neutral water.

Titration

Titrations are precise neutralization reactions

A **titration** is a special kind of neutralization reaction often used to accurately determine the pH of a solution. Titrations are done with known concentrations of acids or bases. Indicators are used to detect when the pH changes through the neutral region. Titrations can be *much* more accurate than pH papers or indicators used alone.

The equivalence point

For example, suppose you have an acid and you slowly add base to it one drop at a time. Each drop of base raises the pH a proportionally small amount. However, close to the **equivalence point** even a single drop of base can change the pH dramatically. The equivalence point occurs when the number of moles of H^+ from the acid are exactly balanced by equivalent moles of base. Near the equivalence point, the pH is very close to neutral, and that's when pH changes very quickly.

Burette

Base (or acid) of *known* concentration

The burette allows precise metering of liquids

Valve

Acid (or base) of *unknown* concentration

Why titration is accurate

Notice that methyl orange and phenolphthalein both go through their entire color change on the steep part of the curve. That makes it easy to tell that equivalence occurs when 5 mL of base has been added.

The results of a titration

The volume of the added base gives a precise measure of the number of moles of base added. In the example, $5 \text{ mL} \times 1.0 \text{ M} = 0.005$ moles. If sodium hydroxide (NaOH) is the base, each mole of NaOH neutralizes one mole of H^+. That means there were 0.005 moles of H^+ in the original solution. The original solution had a volume of 50 mL; therefore its original H^+ concentration was 0.1 M. This means the original pH must have been 1.0.

pH

Phenolphthalein

Equivalence point

Methyl orange

Volume of added NaOH (mL)

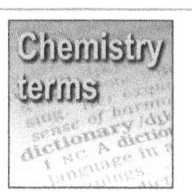

titration: a laboratory process to determine the precise volume of acid or base of known concentration that exactly neutralizes a solution of unknown pH.

equivalence point: in a titration, the point at which the moles of H^+ from the acid and OH^- from the base are exactly equal.

Salts

Acid–base reactions form salts

What types of chemicals are formed when you react an acid and a base? Consider the neutralization reaction between hydrochloric acid (HCl) and sodium hydroxide (NaOH). The product of the reaction is salt (NaCl):

$$NaOH + HCl \rightarrow NaCl + H_2O$$

Salt is an ionic compound that is highly soluble in water. Since the whole reaction takes place in solution, the products are dissolved sodium ions (Na^+) and chloride ions (Cl^-).

base + acid = a salt + water

NaOH + HCl = NaCl + H₂O

Sodium hydroxide | Hydrochloric acid | Table salt | Water

The chemical meaning of "salt"

Chemically, the term "**salt**" means *any* ionic compound in which the positive ion comes from a base and the negative ion comes from an acid. Ordinary table salt (NaCl) is just one example of a whole category of ionic chemicals that form in acid–base reactions.

TABLE 13.4. Common salts

Name	Formula
Sodium chloride (table salt)	NaCl
Sodium acetate	$NaC_2H_3O_2$
Potassium chloride	KCl
Sodium bicarbonate	$NaHCO_3$

Name	Formula
Sodium sulfate	Na_2SO_4
Ammonium chloride	NH_4Cl
Ammonium nitrate	NH_4NO_3
Potassium nitrate	KNO_3

Salts dissociate in water

An important property of salts is that they dissociate completely in water. For example, potassium chloride (KCl) dissociates into potassium ions (K^+) and chloride ions (Cl^-). Ammonium nitrate (NH_4NO_3) dissociates into ammonium ions (NH_4^+) and nitrate ions (NO_3^-). Because salts dissociate into ions, aqueous salt solutions are *electrolytes*, so they conduct electricity.

$$KCl(aq) \rightarrow K^+(aq) + Cl^-(aq)$$

$$NH_4NO_3(aq) \rightarrow NH_4^+(aq) + NO_3^-(aq)$$

Chemistry terms

salt: an ionic compound in which the positive ion comes from a base and the negative ion comes from an acid.

A NATURAL APPROACH TO CHEMISTRY

Salts of weak acids

Some salts have acid or base properties in solution

Salts form from acids and bases, and it should come as no surprise that some salts can affect the pH of solutions. This is because some salts react with water and change the equilibrium of H^+ and OH^- ions. This effect is strongest when the negative ion of the salt forms a weak acid.

The acetate ion comes from a weak acid (acetic acid)

For example, sodium acetate ($NaC_2O_2H_3$) is a salt that dissociates into a sodium ion (Na^+) and an acetate ion ($C_2O_2H_3^-$). The acetate ion also forms acetic acid ($HC_2H_3O_2$). Since acetic acid is a weak acid, its equilibrium has only a few dissociated acetate ions and mostly whole acetic acid molecules. When sodium acetate is dissolved in water, the acetate ions seek equilibrium by combining with H^+ ions from water to form whole acetic acid.

Why a sodium acetate solution is basic

During the formation of acetic acid, OH^- ions are created and H^+ ions are removed; as a result the pH goes up. A solution of sodium acetate in water will be basic, even though sodium acetate is a *salt*!

Some salts act like acids or bases when in solution

Sodium acetate is the ion from a weak acid (acetic acid)

Some of the acetate ions capture H^+ from water and become acetic acid molecules. Some OH^- ions are released from water so the solution is a base!

A salt whose negative ion is from a weak acid raises the pH of a solution (makes it more basic)

Why salts of strong acids do not affect pH

Sodium chloride is also a salt, but it has no effect on pH. In solution, NaCl creates positive sodium ions (Na^+) and negative chloride (Cl^-) ions. The acid formed by the chloride ion is hydrochloric acid (HCl), which is a *strong* acid. NaCl has no effect on pH; any Cl^- ions that combine with H^+ ions immediately dissociate again because HCl is a strong acid. When the ions in the salt come from *strong* acids and bases, there is no effect on pH when the salt is dissolved.

A salt whose negative ion is from a strong acid has no effect on pH

The Cl^- ion comes from a strong acid (HCl) so it does not combine with H^+ from water and *therefore has no effect on pH*

$$Na^+ Cl^- \qquad Na^+ \qquad Cl^-$$

$$NaCl(aq) \rightarrow Na^+(aq) + Cl^-(aq)$$

Buffers

Common ions

Solutions of weak acids and their associated salts have a very important application. Consider a solution containing both acetic acid and sodium acetate (a salt). These two compounds share a **common ion**: acetate ($C_2O_3H_2^-$). A common ion is one that is produced by two different chemicals in the same solution, such as an acid and a salt.

Conjugate acids and bases

On the previous page you learned that sodium acetate is a weak base because solutions of sodium acetate have a pH greater than 7. In fact, sodium acetate is a *conjugate base* to acetic acid. Recall that, according to the Brønsted–Lowry definition, an acid is a proton donor. Acetic acid contributes protons (H^+ ions) by dissociation. Every proton donor has a proton acceptor, which is called its conjugate base.

$$HC_2H_3O_2 \rightarrow H^+ + C_2H_3O_2^-$$

Acetic acid donates a proton
(Brønsted–Lowry acid)

$$C_2H_3O_2^- + H^+ \rightarrow HC_2H_3O_2$$

Acetate accepts a proton
(Brønsted–Lowry base)

Buffer solutions

A mixture of a weak acid and its conjugate base is an example of a **buffer**. A buffer is a solution that resists small changes in pH by chemical action. Suppose a small amount of acid is added. Acid increases H^+ and would normally lower the pH. However, acetic acid is a *weak* acid, so the ratio of H^+ to whole $HC_2O_3H_2$ molecules is small and constant. Because the solution contains an overabundance of acetate ions from the salt, excess H^+ combines with those ions to form acetic acid! *The pH stays about the same.* The excess of common ions allows any additional H^+ to be absorbed.

Acid

Excess H^+ from added acid combine with the common ion to make whole acetic acid

Buffer

The pH stays the same!

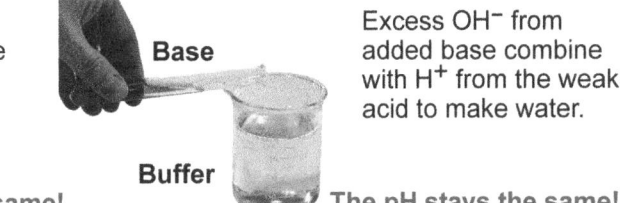

Base

Excess OH^- from added base combine with H^+ from the weak acid to make water.

Buffer

The pH stays the same!

When a base is added the pH also stays constant because of neutralization by the weak acid. Excess OH^- ions from the base combine with H^+ from the acid to make water.

Chemistry terms

common ion: an ion produced by two or more different chemicals in the same solution.

buffer: a solution that resists changes in pH by chemical action.

432

Buffer capacity

A buffer can only absorb a limited pH change

A buffer resists changes in pH because a dissolved ion from weak acid or base supplies a reservoir of ions that can absorb both excess H^+ and OH^-. The process works very well for small changes in acidity. For example, the graph shows a buffer when increasing amounts of 0.1 M HCl are added. Notice that the color, and hence the pH, does not change until about 45 mL are added. from 40 to 50 mL of added acid, the color change is dramatic, showing that the pH changed substantially.

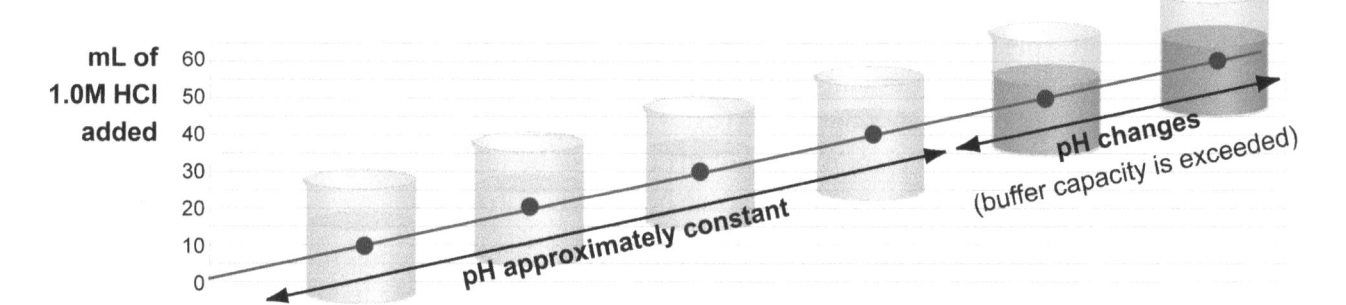

mL of 1.0M HCl added

pH approximately constant

pH changes (buffer capacity is exceeded)

Buffer capacity

Eventually, all the common ions from the salt are combined until there is no longer a reservoir to absorb excess H^+ or OH^- ions. Once this point is reached, adding additional acid changes the pH just as it would with a nonbuffered solution. The **buffer capacity** describes how much acid or base a buffer can absorb without changing the solution pH.

Sea water is a buffer

Since living things are sensitive to pH changes, buffers are vital to our planet. For example, the ocean maintains a pH of about 8.3 and sea water acts as a giant buffer, resisting pH changes from rain (typically acidic) and weathering of substances such as limestone (typically basic). The major components of the ocean's buffer are calcium carbonate from shells of marine animals and carbonic acid from dissolved atmospheric CO_2.

Sea water is a buffer at a pH of 8.3

Blood plasma is a buffer

Your blood is also a buffer, maintaining your body's internal pH at a very stable and slightly basic pH between 7.35 and 7.45. The weak acid is carbonic acid, which forms in water from CO_2 generated by respiration. The conjugate base is bicarbonate, which is produced in your pancreas. Acidosis can result when excess carbonic acid builds up beyond the blood's buffer capacity. Breathing difficulties can cause acidosis, because CO_2 builds up in blood if it cannot be exhaled adequately.

Blood is a buffer with a pH of 7.35 - 7.45

Chemistry terms

buffer capacity: the amount of excess acid or base a buffer can neutralize without significantly changing the pH of the solution.

pH in the environment

Blueberries prefer highly acidic soil with a pH below 5.5

Plants draw trace minerals, such as magnesium and phosphorus, from dissolved salts in moist soil. The pH of the soil affects the form and concentration of these nutrients for plants. Most plants prefer a slightly acidic soil with a pH between 6.5 and 7.0. Azaleas, blueberries, and conifers grow best in more acid soils with a pH of 4.5 to 5.5. Vegetables, grasses, and most other shrubs do best in less acidic soils with a pH range of 6.5 to 7.0.

In highly acidic soils (pH below 4.5) too much aluminum, manganese, and other elements leach out of solid soil particles. This happens because acids react with metals to produce soluble ions. Metal ion concentrations above a certain threshold are toxic to plants. Also, at strongly acidic pH values, calcium, phosphorus, and magnesium are less available to plant roots. Soil pH can also be too high for average plants. At pH values of 6.5 and above (more basic), iron and manganese become less available.

Every good gardener or farmer pays attention to soil pH. Soil pH depends greatly on average rainfall. Soils in wet or temperate areas with more than 20 inches of rain per year tend to be acidic. Soils in dry climates with less than 20 inches of rain per year tend to be alkaline (basic). Desert soils tend to be alkaline; gardeners in Phoenix, Arizona, often have to grow plants in soils with a pH between 7 and 8. A standard remedy for alkaline soil is to add *sulfur*. Over time, sulfur reacts slowly with rainwater to produce a small amount of sulfuric acid to neutralize the alkalinity.

The pH of water directly affects aquatic life. Most freshwater lakes, streams, and ponds have a natural pH in the range of 6 to 8. Most freshwater fish can tolerate a pH between 5 and 9, although some negative effects appear below a pH of 6. Trout (such as the California Golden) are among the most pH-tolerant fish and can live in water with a pH ranging from 4 to 9.5.

Frog life cycle

Adult

Eggs

Tadpole

Frogs and other amphibians are even more sensitive to pH than fish. Most frogs prefer pH close to neutral and don't survive below a pH of 5.0. Frog eggs develop and hatch in water with no protection from environmental dangers. Research shows that even a pH below 6 has a negative effect on frog-egg hatching rates.

Some plants change dramatically with pH. The *hydrangea* flower is a probably the best known example. Hydrangeas have different colored blossoms depending upon whether the soil they are growing in is acidic or basic. The blossoms are blue when in acidic soils and pink in basic soils. Hydrangea growers adjust the soil pH to create the color flower they want.

| Basic soil makes hydrangea flowers pink | Acid soil makes hydrangea flowers blue |

Hydrangea color is affected by the element aluminum! Acidic conditions convert the aluminum in the soil to a form that the shrub can absorb (when it drinks); this turns the flower blue. In basic soil, the aluminum in the soil is insoluble and therefore cannot be absorbed by the hydrangea. Without the aluminum the flower color is pink.

To make a soil more basic (increase pH) gardeners add lime. Lime is calcium carbonate ($CaCO_3$). Calcium carbonate neutralizes some of the acid in the soil by first dissociating into calcium ions and carbonate ions. Carbonic acid is a weak acid, so most of the carbonate ions bond with H^+ ions in the soil to form whole carbonic acid molecules. This reduces the H^+ concentration and makes the soil more basic. The result is pink flowers!

Calcium carbonate (lime) dissociates into calcium and carbonate ions

Step 1 $$CaCO_3 \rightarrow Ca^{2+} + CO_3^{2-}$$

Carbonate ions combine with H^+ to make bicarbonate ions

Step 2 $$H^+ + CO_3^{2-} \rightleftharpoons HCO_3^-$$

Bicarbonate ions combine with H^+ to make carbonic acid

Step 3 $$H^+ + HCO_3^- \rightleftharpoons H_2CO_3$$

To make aluminum available to the plant and get blue flowers, the pH of the soil needs to be between 5.2 and 5.5. Hydrangea growers often add aluminum sulfate [$Al_2(SO_4)_3$] to make their soil more acidic. Adding aluminum sulfate both increases the acidity of the soil and provides a source of aluminum. When dissolved in water, $Al_2(SO_4)_3$ ionizes according to the reaction

$$Al_2(SO_4)_3(s) + H_2O(l) \rightarrow 2Al^{3+}(aq) + 3SO_4^{2-}$$

The Al^{3+} ion has a very small size, with a radius of 53 pm. The fact that the aluminum ion is small and highly charged means it acts almost like H^+ in water, giving it the ability to act as an acid in aqueous solutions. Al^{3+} is able to draw the electron density of a water molecule away from the OH bond, favoring the release of the H^+ ion. The release of the H^+ ion causes the soil to become more acidic.

Chapter 13 Review

Vocabulary

Match each word to the sentence where it best fits.

Section 13.1

acid	base
hydronium ion	Arrhenius
neutral	Brønsted–Lowry
strong acid	amphoteric
weak acid	weak base
	strong base

1. HCl is an example of a strong _____ because it releases hydrogen ions.

2. A solution that is _____ contains more hydroxide ions than hydrogen ions.

3. A solution that has a pH of seven is considered to be _____.

4. Water can accept an H^+ ion or donate an H^+ ion and this makes it _____.

5. A/An _____ only ionizes partially in water and yields fewer hydrogen ions than a/an _____, which fully ionizes in water.

6. Ammonia (NH_3) is an example of a/an _____.

7. The _____ definition of an acid and a base explains which substance is a hydrogen ion acceptor and which is a hydrogen ion donor.

8. When water bonds to a hydrogen ion in an aqueous solution the _____ is formed in solution.

9. Sodium hydroxide (NaOH) is an example of a/an _____.

10. The _____ definition of acids and bases says that acids form H^+ in aqueous solution and bases form OH^- in aqueous solution.

Sections 13.2 and 13.3

exponent	logarithm
indicator	ion product constant

11. The _____ of 10,000 is 4.

12. Phenolphthalein is an example of a/an _____, which is a substance that turns a different color as the pH changes.

13. In the number 2.3×10^{-5}, the -5 represents a/an _____. It is negative because the number represents a value less than one.

14. The equilibrium constant for water at 25°C and 1 atm is called the _____, which represents a value called K_w.

Section 13.4

neutralization	equivalence point
titration	salt
common ion	buffer
buffer capacity	

15. A/An _____ is an important laboratory method used to determine the concentration of a solution of an acid or base.

16. During a/an _____ reaction, the acid and the base react until the number of H^+ ions equals the number of OH^- ions.

17. At the _____ we can make the important assumption that the number of moles of base equals the number of moles of acid.

18. A solution that is able to resist small changes in pH is called a/an _____.

19. Potassium chloride (KCl) is a/an _____ that is formed from the positive ion of a base and the negative ion of an acid.

20. Buffers work based on the _____ principle, which recognizes that an ion is produced by two or more chemicals in the same solution.

21. The _____ tells us how much acid or base a solution can neutralize before changing pH.

Conceptual Questions

Section 13.1

22. Compare and contrast an acid and a base. Clearly explain their chemical differences and give an example of each.

23. Give two examples (each) of acidic and basic substances that you use in your daily life.

24. Explain what a neutral solution means in terms of the chemical ions present.

25. Using the chemical formulas of common bases and acids, write a chemical equation that represents:
    a. how a strong base ionizes in water
    b. how a strong acid ionizes in water

26. What type of solution is formed when group I and II metals dissolve in water? Explain and support your answer using a chemical equation.

27. The hydrogen ion can be thought of as a naked proton. Explain why this is important in terms of chemical reactions.

28. Explain the main difference between the early Arrhenius theory of acids and bases and the Brønsted–Lowry theory of acids and bases.

29. Explain how ammonia (NH_3) acts as a Brønsted–Lowry base when dissolved in water. Show the chemical equation that represents this process.

30. What ion is formed when an acid is dissolved in water? Show the Lewis structure for this ion.

31. In each of the following chemical reactions, identify the substance acting as the acid and the substance acting as the base. Label them as (A) acid or (B) base.
    a. $HF + H_2O \rightleftharpoons F^- + H_3O^+$
    b. $HNO_2 + H_2O \rightleftharpoons NO_2^- + H_3O^+$
    c. $NH_3 + H_2O \rightleftharpoons NH_4^+ + OH^-$
    d. $HC_2H_3O_2 + NH_3 \rightleftharpoons C_2H_3O_2^- + NH_4^+$

32. For question 31(b), clearly explain the reason for the answer.

33. Look at questions 31(b) and (c) and explain water's role in each equation.

34. Name the following substances and identify them as strong acids or strong bases:
    a. KOH
    b. HNO_3
    c. $Ba(OH)_2$
    d. H_2SO_4
    e. HCl

35. Write a chemical equation that shows how nitric acid (HNO_3) ionizes in an aqueous solution.

Section 13.2

36. Briefly explain what pH measures in an aqueous solution.

37. Make a sketch of the pH scale and label the numbers zero to 14. Label where on the scale these substances would be located:
    a. lemon juice
    b. baking soda
    c. dish soap
    d. soda water
    e. blood
    f. milk

38. The pH of a solution is 6.8. From this information, can you conclude that the solution is acidic? Explain.

39. Write the equation that relates pH to pOH.

40. If you have a strong acid, does that mean the pH of the solution of this acid will be low? Explain.

41. Based on the pH scale, substances that are acidic have a pH less than 7. What does this tell you about the amount of [H^+] relative to [OH^-] in the solution? Explain.

42. Explain how an aqueous solution can have a pH of 7. What would have to be true?

43. If the pH changes by 2 units, by what factor does the [H^+] change?

44. Name two different types of indicators.

45. How are indicators used to help determine the pH of a solution? Explain.

46. Sometimes the pH of an acidic solution can be zero or negative. Explain how.

Chapter 13 Review

Section 13.3

47. Autoionization occurs when water ionizes on its own into H^+ and OH^- ions to a very small degree.

    a. Write the chemical equation for this process.

    b. The equilibrium constant (K_w) for this reaction is 1.0×10^{-14}. This means that when water dissociates the relative concentration of H^+ and OH^- remains constant. Explain what the magnitude of K_w tells us about the reaction in the forward direction.

48. Although all acids release H^+ ions, strong and weak acids will dissociate to different amounts in water.

    a. Write the chemical reaction for the strong acid hydrochloric acid ionizing in water.

    b. Write the chemical reaction for the weak acid acetic acid ionizing in water.

    c. Compare the weak and strong acid's behavior (degree of dissociation) in water.

49. Similarly, bases will dissociate to give OH^- ions in water, but to different extents.

    a. Write the chemical reaction for the strong base sodium hydroxide ionizing in water.

    b. Write the chemical reaction for the weak base ammonia ionizing in water.

    c. Compare the behavior (degree of dissociation) of the strong and weak bases in water.

50. Give an example of a weak base and a weak acid.

51. Calculate the number of moles of NaOH in 8.50 mL of a 0.450 M solution.

52. Predict the products for the following weak acid and base ionizations:
    a. $HF + H_2O \rightleftharpoons$
    b. $CH_3NH_2 + H_2O \rightleftharpoons$
    c. $HNO_2 + H_2O$

53. Suppose you have a 1.0 M solution of HCl and a 1.0 M solution of $HC_2H_3O_2$. List some things that would be different in each of these solutions. If you did not know which was which, how could you determine which one was HCl?

Section 13.4

54. Give an example of the following acid–base reactions (include reactants and products):
    a. neutralization
    b. metal and acid

55. What are the products of a neutralization reaction between HCl and NaOH?

56. Do you think neutralization reactions always have a pH of 7? Why or why not?

57. In the laboratory baking soda is often kept handy to neutralize any strong acid spills. How does baking soda neutralize strong acids?

58. Answer the following:
    a. Show the chemical reaction for the addition of the salt potassium nitrate (KNO_3) to water.
    b. Will this solution conduct electricity? Explain.

59. List two common salts formed during the neutralization of a strong acid and strong base.

60. Explain how adding 4.0 g of the salt sodium acetate ($NaC_2H_3O_2$) to an acidic solution would affect the pH.

61. Predict how the overall pH would be affected if solid sodium chloride (NaCl) were added to a neutral solution with a pH of 7.

62. Buffers are used to control the pH of a solution.
    a. What is unique about a buffer?
    b. Can a mixture of sodium acetate and acetic acid act as a buffer? Explain.

Quantitative Problems

Section 13.2

63. If a solution has $[H^+]$ of 3.5×10^{-4}, what its pH?

64. A solution is measured to have a pH of 5.60. Calculate the $[H^+]$ concentration of the solution.

65. Calculate the pH of the following solutions:
    a. a glass of lemonade with a 4.30×10^{-5} M H^+ concentration
    b. salad dressing, $[H^+] = 2.51 \times 10^{-6}$
    c. a glass of tomato juice, $[H^+] = 6.40 \times 10^{-5}$
    d. a glass of milk, $[H^+] = 7.94 \times 10^{-9}$

66. Calculate the pH for each of the following hydrogen ion concentrations. State whether the pH is acidic, basic, or neutral.
    a. $[H^+] = 2.45 \times 10^{-4}$
    b. $[H^+] = 2.11 \times 10^{-11}$
    c. $[H^+] = 4.96 \times 10^{-7}$
    d. $[H^+] = 1.00 \times 10^{-7}$
    e. $[H^+] = 3.51 \times 10^{-14}$

67. Calculate the pH for each of the following hydroxide ion concentrations. State whether the pH is acidic, basic, or neutral.
    a. $[OH^-] = 4.03 \times 10^{-2}$
    b. $[OH^-] = 9.55 \times 10^{-9}$
    c. $[OH^-] = 5.20 \times 10^{-5}$
    d. $[OH^-] = 7.26 \times 10^{-12}$

Section 13.3

68. Calculate the $[OH^-]$ concentration for each of the following $[H^+]$ concentrations. State whether the pH is acidic, basic, or neutral.
    a. $[H^+] = 3.15 \times 10^{-4}$
    b. $[H^+] = 2.11 \times 10^{-10}$
    c. $[H^+] = 5.96 \times 10^{-7}$

69. Calculate the $[H^+]$ concentration for each of the following $[OH^-]$ concentrations. State whether the pH is acidic, basic, or neutral.
    a. $[OH^-] = 3.23 \times 10^{-2}$
    b. $[OH^-] = 8.65 \times 10^{-8}$
    c. $[OH^-] = 5.41 \times 10^{-6}$

70. Calculate the $[H^+]$ concentration and the pH of each of the following solutions of strong acids:
    a. 2.4×10^{-5} M HCl
    b. 0.0045 M H_2SO_4
    c. 5.51×10^{-4} HNO_3
    d. 6.41×10^{-4} HCl

71. Determine the pH of a 0.50 M solution of acetic acid ($HC_2H_3O_2$). Use a RICE table to do your calculation. K_a for acetic acid is 1.8×10^{-5}.

72. Calculate the pH of a 0.10 M solution of lactic acid. Lactic acid ($HC_3H_5O_3$) is a weak monoprotic acid and it is the acid that sometimes makes your muscles sore after you exercise. K_a for lactic acid is 1.4×10^{-4}.

73. Calculate the pH of a 0.25 M solution of ammonia (NH_3), a weak base. Use a RICE table to do your calculation. K_b for ammonia is 1.8×10^{-5}.

74. Calculate the pH of a 0.085 M solution of ethylamine ($C_2H_5NH_2$), whose K_b is 6.4×10^{-4}.

75. Calculate the percent ionization for the acetic acid in question 69. Show your work.

76. Codeine ($C_{18}H_{21}NO_3$) is a weak organic base. Calculate the K_b of a codeine solution with an initial molarity of 4.80×10^{-3} M, given that this codeine solution has a pH of 9.90.

Section 13.4

77. Calculate the molarity of an NaOH solution, if 26.0 mL of the solution is needed to neutralize 16.8 mL of a 0.298 M HCl solution. Remember that "neutralize" means that $[H^+] = [OH^-]$.

78. Calculate the volume in mL of a 1.26 M NaOH solution required to titrate the following solutions:
    a. 25.00 mL of 2.35 M HCl solution.
    b. 25.00 mL of 4.30 M HNO_3 solution
    c. 30.00 mL of 3.35 M HCl solution

79. Calculate the volume of 0.80 M HCl solution needed to neutralize:
    a. 12.00 mL of a 0.400 M NaOH solution.
    b. 12.00 mL of a 0.200 M $Ba(OH)_2$ solution.

80. A 2.653 g sample of a solid monoprotic acid was dissolved in 25.0 mL of distilled water. The solution required 18.30 mL of a 0.160 M NaOH solution to titrate. Calculate the acid's molar mass.

81. Acetic acid (CH_3COOH) is the acid present in apple cider vinegar. A sample of 25.00 mL of vinegar is titrated using a 1.10 M solution of NaOH. This sample required 2.35 mL of NaOH to neutralize it. Determine the concentration of the acetic acid in the vinegar.

82. What volume of 0.152 M HCl is required to neutralize 3.40 g of $Mg(OH)_2$? Write out the balanced chemical reaction that occurs to help with this calculation.

83. How many milliliters of 0.120 M HCl are needed to neutralize completely 31.00 mL of 0.150 M $Ba(OH)_2$ solution? Write out the balanced chemical reaction that occurs as part of your answer.

CHAPTER 14
Gases

Why do my tires get flat on a very cold day?

Why do high-altitude mountain climbers need to bring oxygen tanks when summiting peaks like Mt. Everest?

Why won't my vacuum cleaner work on the Moon?

We live at the bottom of an ocean of air. Gases surround us and press down on us constantly. We breathe in one mixture of gases and exhale a different one. The oxygen in the air helps us to burn our fuel (food), and we keep the pH in our blood balanced by exhaling carbon dioxide. In chemistry, gases were some of the first substances about which careful research was done

Gases provided humans with the first chance to fly. In 1783, a balloon made by the Montgolfier brothers lifted off from Paris, France. The balloon flew for 22 minutes and landed 500 ft away. Today the record for the longest balloon flight was set in 1991 with a flight of 4,767 miles from Japan to Canada, and the longest duration was set in 1997, lasting 50 hours and 38 minutes.

First human balloon flight, 1783

Other types of ballooning using hydrogen or helium instead of hot air for lift extended the ranges for extreme height, distance, and duration. In 2002, the first solo flight around the world was completed by Steve Fosset in approximately 15 days, and in 1960 Captain Joe Kittinger parachuted from a helium balloon after it reached an astounding altitude of 102,000 ft! He was so high at the time of his jump that he was surrounded by the blackness of space, instead of a blue sky.

A NATURAL APPROACH TO CHEMISTRY

Shrinking air

When a gas is cooled it contracts, and when it is heated it expands again. You can see it for yourself if you take a helium balloon outside on a cold day. The balloon gets noticeably smaller as it cools, just like when it deflates. Bring it back into a warm house and it returns to its original size and firmness.

An extreme way to clearly see how temperature affects the volume of a gas is to cool a balloon with liquid nitrogen. Liquid nitrogen boils at –196°C! This means for nitrogen to be in the liquid phase, it must be at a temperature below –196°C. The pictures below show what happens when liquid nitrogen is poured over a latex balloon at normal room temperature.

1 The balloon is fully inflated at room temperature

2 Liquid nitrogen is poured on the balloon to cool it down

The balloon begins to collapse.

4 The balloon expands back to its original size again as it warms up

3 The balloon continues to collapse as it cools

Why does the balloon shrink when liquid nitrogen is poured on it? Why does it expand when it warms back up? At first, you might think the larger (warmer) balloon has more matter inside. More matter should take up more space, shouldn't it? However, the balloon is sealed so no matter can get in or out. There is the same amount of air in the balloon whether it is warm or cold. If you could measure it, the balloon would have the same mass warm or cold.

The real explanation is more subtle. Molecules in a gas are like trillions of tiny bumper cars whizzing about, colliding with each other and with the walls of the balloon. When the balloon is cold, the molecules inside slow down. The molecules in the room are still warm and moving fast. The pressure of molecules from outside air is temporarily higher than the chilled molecules inside the balloon, and the imbalance of pressure pushes the sides of the balloon inward. As the air inside warms back up, the molecules regain their vigor and push back as strongly as before, reinflating the balloon.

14.1 Pressure and Kinetic Theory

Physical properties of gases

Gases have a unique set of physical properties:

1. Gases are translucent or transparent.
2. Gases have very low densities when compared to liquids or solids.
3. Gases are highly compressible compared to liquids and solids.
4. Gases can expand or contract to fill any container.

Kinetic molecular theory

These properties stem directly from the atomic nature of matter. A gas is made from many tiny atoms or molecules with a lot of space between them. These particles are in continuous, frantic motion as they collide with each other and the walls of their container. This idea is the basis of **kinetic molecular theory**. Kinetic theory provides an explanation for all four of the properties of gases listed above.

Gases consist of atoms or molecules in constant motion

Experimental demonstration of the kinetic theory

In a gas, the molecules are widely separated from each other. This is the explanation for properties 1 and 2. Gases are transparent because they are mostly empty space with a large distance between molecules. This also explains their low densities. Molecules (mass) are thinly distributed in a gas. The empty space also explains the compressibility and container-filling properties. Compression is reducing the space between molecules, while expansion is letting them get farther apart. Simple experiments like the one in the diagram below support the idea that gas is made of molecules that are far apart and in constant motion.

Evidence for the Atomic/Molecular Nature of Matter

molecules of liquid water

water boiling

molecules of gaseous water

As a liquid the water molecules are packed very close together, so water appears to be a continuous substance, not made of individual particles (molecules).

After being heated the water seems to disappear, but it is still there as a gas. If the liquid and gas are both made from the same molecules, you can explain the "disappearance" by assuming that the molecules are now spread out in the gas phase.

> **Chemistry terms**
>
> **kinetic molecular theory:** the theory that explains the observed thermal and physical properties of matter in terms of the average behavior of a collection of atoms and molecules.

Brownian motion

Brownian motion

In 1827, botanist Robert Brown made an extraordinary discovery while observing tiny pollen particles suspended in water. The smallest particles seemed to jiggle and move without anything apparently causing the motion. Initially, it was thought that Brown might have stumbled upon the "essence of life." Additional experiments were done with tiny particles of ground glass and other nonliving matter. If the particles were small enough, they all showed the same strange jiggling motion. This came to be known as **Brownian motion**. With common skepticism of the existence of atoms and a minimal understanding of heat, the true nature of Brownian motion would remain a mystery for over 70 years.

Brownian motion can be seen by magnifying diluted milk and observing tiny fat globules getting knocked around by the surrounding water molecules

What Brownian motion tells us

Brownian motion is a result of two fundamental truths about matter:

1. Matter consists of discrete particle (molecules or atoms).

2. Molecules (or atoms) are in constant, vigorous motion as a result of temperature.

Why Brownian motion occurs

Brownian motion is observed under a microscope with particles smaller than about 10 microns in size (1 micron is equal to 10^{-6} m). The irregular jerky movements are the result of impacts with individual water molecules, which are 1,000 times smaller still. To get a feeling for why Brownian motion occurs, consider people throwing pebbles at two balls floating in a quiet pool. One ball is very large, and it moves smoothly under the average impact of lots of pebbles. The other ball is small, and it moves in a jerky way when struck by individual pebbles. The motion of the big ball is smooth because its mass is much greater than the mass of a single pebble. The smaller ball moves irregularly because its mass is not so much larger than the mass of a single pebble.

Many small impacts lead to no discernable motion

Many small impacts cause irregular jerky motion

Thermal motion is normally hidden

A ping-pong ball floating in a perfectly still pool does not move at all. There is no indication that water molecules are in constant, agitated motion. Brownian motion is like a peek into the microscopic world of atoms to see details that are normally hidden by the law of averages and the enormous number of incredibly small atoms.

| Chemistry terms | **Brownian motion:** the erratic, jerky motion of tiny particles suspended in a fluid, caused by individual collisions with the fluid molecules in thermal motion. |

Pressure

Force in a gas

Think about what happens when you push down on an inflated balloon. The downward force you apply creates forces that act in other directions as well as down. For example, sideways forces push the sides of the balloon outward. This is very different from what happens when you push down on a solid ball. A solid ball transmits the force directly down. Because a gas can easily change shape, forces applied to a gas do not act in simple ways as they do on solids.

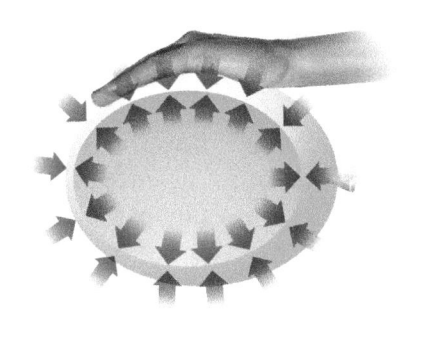

Units of pressure

Gases exert *pressure*. **Pressure** is the force per unit area that the gas exerts on any surface in contact with the gas. The units of pressure are units of force divided by units of area. The SI unit of force is the *newton*. A pressure of 1 N/m^2 means a force of one newton acts on each square meter. The unit combination N/m^2 is also named the *pascal* (Pa). One **pascal** is equal to a pressure of one newton of force per square meter of area (1 Pa = 1 N/m^2). The English unit of pressure is pounds per square inch (psi). One psi is equal to one pound of force per square inch of area (lb/in^2). One psi is a much larger unit of pressure than one pascal (1 psi = 6,895 Pa).

Pressure

$$\text{pressure} \atop (\text{Pa})\ \ P = \frac{F}{A}\ {\text{force (N)} \atop \text{area (m}^2)}$$

$$1\,Pa = \frac{1\,N}{m^2}$$

Solved problem

Two jars contain air at a pressure of 35 psi. One jar is 3 inches in diameter and the other is 1 inch in diameter. The larger jar blows its lid off but the smaller one does not. Calculate the force on each lid resulting from pressure. (Hint: A = πr^2)

Asked: *Force on the lid from pressure*

Given: *P = 35 psi*

Relationships: *P = F ÷ A, so F = P × A*

Solve: *For the 3 inch diameter jar,*
F = (7.07 in^2)(35 lb/in^2) = 247 lb
For the 1 inch diameter jar,
F = (0.79 in^2)(35 lb/in^2) = 27.5 lb

Area = 7.07 in^2 Area = 0.79 in^2

Answer: *The lid of the 3 inch jar feels a force of 247 lb, the lid of the 1 inch jar only feels a force of 27.5 lb.*

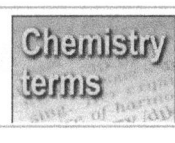
Chemistry terms

pressure: force per unit area.
pascal (Pa): the SI unit of pressure, equal to 1 N/m^2.

A NATURAL APPROACH TO CHEMISTRY

Atmospheric pressure

Air forms a layer around the Earth

On top of you is a column of air that is about 100 km (60 miles) high being pulled down by gravity. If you could get in a rocket and fly straight up, as you go higher and higher in the atmosphere there is less air on top of you. The pressure decreases and the air gets "thinner," because the molecules are not packed together as closely. The pressure we feel from the air around us is called *atmospheric pressure*.

Earth is covered with a thin layer of air

Image Credit: NASA (photo from Apollo 7 spacecraft)

Standard air pressure at sea level is 14.69 lb/in²

We don't normally feel the pressure from the air around us, because we are used to constantly feeling it. However, this pressure is significant! Using the units we have used so far, normal atmospheric pressure is 14.69 psi. Let's assume the palm of your hand is approximately 6 × 3 in, so it has a surface area of 18 in². If each square inch feels a force of 14.69 lb from the air, the total force on your hand is about 260 lb. That is the same pressure you would feel if a 260 lb person stood on one of your hands!

The pressure you feel from the surrounding air on just the palm of your hand is equivalent to the pressure you would feel if a 260 lb person were standing on it

6 in

3 in

Standard Air Pressure = $14.69 \dfrac{lb}{in^2}$

$A = 6 \text{ in} \times 3 \text{ in} = 18 \text{ in}^2$

$P = \dfrac{F}{A} \longrightarrow 14.69 \dfrac{lbs}{in^2} = \dfrac{F}{18 \text{ in}^2}$

$F = \dfrac{14.69 \text{ lb} \times 18 \text{ in}^2}{in^2} = \boxed{260 \text{ lb}}$

Pressure is measured in using many different units

$$\text{Standard Pressure} = 14.69 \dfrac{lb}{in^2} = 14.69 \text{ psi} = 1.000 \text{ atm} = 760.0 \text{ mmHg} = 101305 \text{ Pa}$$

Solved problem

Convert 60,000 lb/in² of pressure to atmospheres (atm).

Relationships: *Standard pressure = 14.69 lb/in² = 1 atm*

Solve:

$$60,000 \dfrac{lb}{in^2} \times \dfrac{1 \text{ atm}}{14.69 \dfrac{lb}{in^2}} = 60,000 \dfrac{\cancel{lb}}{in^2} \times \dfrac{1 \text{ atm} \times in^2}{14.69 \cancel{lb}} = 4,084 \text{ atm}$$

Measuring pressure

Atmospheric pressure drops with altitude

Standard pressure is defined to be 101,325 Pa. This is the average pressure you would measure from the air if you were standing at sea level. But altitude affects air pressure. The higher you go, the less air there is above you, so the weight of the air column decreases. This causes the air pressure around you to decrease as well. The air pressure at the top of Mt. Everest, the world's highest mountain, is only about one third the pressure we typically experience at sea level.

The air pressure at the top of Mt. Everest is only one third the air pressure at sea level

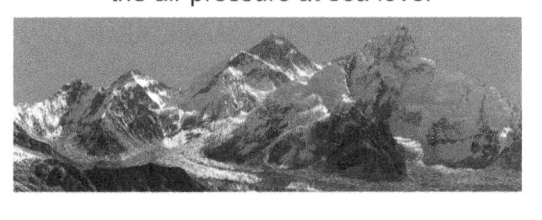

The barometer

One of the first instruments used to measure atmospheric pressure was the **barometer**, invented by Italian scientist Evangelista Torricelli in 1643. To understand his invention, consider what happens when you place your finger over the top of a straw and then lift the straw out of a glass of water. The liquid stays in the straw, because the pressure exerted by the water in the straw is less than the air pressure outside of the straw. If you had a straw that was over 32 feet tall, then the water would exert a greater pressure than the surrounding air and some water would come out. Torricelli used mercury, which is 14 times denser than water, causing the column of liquid needed to balance air pressure to be much shorter. It turns out that standard air pressure can support a column of mercury 760 mm tall, and that is where the pressure unit "mmHg" comes from. As the air pressure changed, so did the height of the mercury column.

A barometer

As air pressure changes, the height of the mercury column it can support also changes

← Empty space

Gravity pulls mercury down the tube

Air pressure pushes mercury up the tube

Variations in atmospheric pressure affects the weather

Most weather maps today show areas of high and low atmospheric pressure. Large areas of slightly varying pressure caused by temperature variations and associated changes in air density have a significant effect on weather patterns.

Weather Maps Show Areas of High and Low Pressure

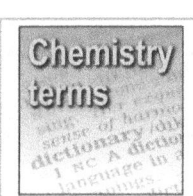

barometer: an instrument that measures atmospheric pressure.

The kinetic theory of pressure

The microscopic view of pressure

On the microscopic level, pressure comes from collisions between atoms or molecules. Think about the air in a balloon. The air exerts pressure against the inside of the balloon. On a microscopic level, molecules are moving around, bouncing off the walls of the balloon. It takes force to make a molecule reverse its direction and bounce the other way. The bouncing force is applied to the molecule by the inside surface of the balloon. According to Newton's third law, an equal and opposite reaction force is exerted by the molecule on the balloon. The reaction force is what creates the pressure acting on the inside surface of the balloon. Trillions of molecules per second are constantly bouncing against every square millimeter of the surface of the balloon. Pressure comes from the collisions of those many, many atoms inside *and outside* the balloon.

Why gases fill any size container

Bernoulli imagined the molecules of a gas to be like tiny rubber balls, continually bouncing off each other and the walls of any container. Each ball was treated as if it followed Newton's laws of motion, moving in a straight line until it collided with another gas molecule or the wall of its container. This would explain why a gas will fill any size container. If you put the gas into a larger container, then the molecules just keep flying straight until they hit the sides of the new container.

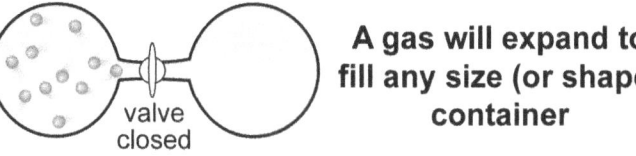

A gas will expand to fill any size (or shape) container

How molecular impacts affect pressure

The average force from molecular impacts depends on two things, and both affect the pressure:

1. Faster (hotter) molecules mean more force per impact and higher pressure.

2. More molecules per cubic centimeter (higher density) mean more impacts and therefore higher pressure.

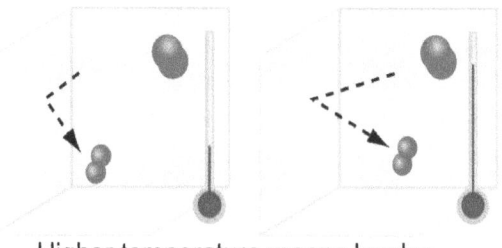

Higher temperature means harder collisions and higher pressure

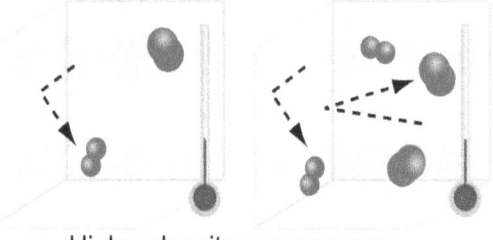

Higher density means more collisions and higher pressure

Diffusion and the speed of molecules in a gas

Molecules move quite fast

The molecules in a gas are moving quite fast! The average speed of a nitrogen molecule in air is 417 meters per second (m/s), which is 933 miles per hour (mph)! Oxygen molecules move a little slower (390 m/s, or 873 mph).

Random motion

Non-random motion

The idea of random motion

A balloon on a table can still be motionless because molecular motion is *random*. Random means there is no preferred direction, and molecules are moving in all directions. The average *direction* is zero even though the average speed is not zero.

The effect of frequent collisions

Molecules move in the same direction until they collide with the walls of a container or with other molecules. To get a sense of it, consider that air at normal pressure contains 3×10^{19} atoms/cm^3. On average, a nitrogen molecule in air has 140,000 collisions with other molecules *in one centimeter*. Each collision changes the direction of both molecules so the frequent collisions completely scramble, or randomize, the directions of molecular motion.

A typical air molecule has 140,000 collisions in a centimeter

Thermal energy depends only on temperature

Kinetic theory tells us that the energy of molecules in a gas depends *only* on temperature. Molecules at higher temperature have more energy of motion, and molecules with lower temperature have less. Since kinetic energy depends on both mass and speed, this means that lighter molecules move faster and heavier molecules move slower—even at the same temperature.

Molecule or atom	He (helium)	N_2 (nitrogen)	O_2 (oxygen)	CO_2 (carbon dioxide)	$C_8H_8O_3$ (vanillin)	$C_{15}H_{26}O$ sandalwood
Formula mass (g/mole)	4	28	32	44	152	222
Average speed (m/s)	**1,104**	**417**	**390**	**333**	**179**	**148**

Diffusion

The difference in speeds has a large effect on *diffusion*. **Diffusion** is the rate at which a gas (or other substance) spreads out and mixes with its surroundings. Helium diffuses rapidly in air because helium molecules move faster. Heavier molecules diffuse more slowly. If you put beakers of alcohol, vanilla, and sandalwood scent across the room, you would smell the alcohol first, the vanilla next, and the sandalwood last because of the sizes of the molecules.

Diffusion is the slow spread of one type of molecules within another type

---

Chemistry terms

diffusion: the spreading of molecules through their surroundings through constant collisions with neighboring molecules.

Boltzmann's constant

ADVANCED AP

Average
molecular
speed

The energy of molecular motion in a gas is given by Boltzmann's constant (k). **Boltzmann's constant** relates the average energy in joules of a single molecule to the temperature of a collection of molecules and has the value k = 1.381 $\times$ 10^{-23} J/K. The average molecular speed is derived by assuming all the energy is kinetic energy of motion.

There is a range
of molecular
speeds

The formula above gives that average speed of a gas molecule, but in real gases there is a wide spread of speeds and energies. Some molecules are going much faster than average, and some are going much slower. The graph shows the distribution of speeds for a sample of 1,000 nitrogen molecules at two different temperatures.

Interpreting
the graph

Notice two important properties of this graph:

1. As temperature increases, the average speed of molecules increases. At 25°C the largest number of molecules (370) had speeds between 200 and 400 m/s. At 1,000°C, the largest number of molecules (191) had speeds between 800 and 1,000 m/s.

2. As temperature increases, the *spread* of molecular speeds increases. At 25°C, all 1,000 molecules had speeds between 1 and 1,400 m/s. At 1,000°C, the range of speeds went from 0 to 2,600 m/s.

The graph is known as a *Maxwellian distribution*, and it is the basis for the kinetic theory of matter. The average molecular speed is calculated from the Maxwellian distribution.

Chemistry
terms

Boltzmann's constant (k): a constant relating the kinetic energy in molecular motion to temperature, k = 1.381 $\times$ 10^{-23} J/K.

14.2 The Gas Laws

Increased frequency or strength of molecular impacts increases gas pressure

The pressure exerted by a gas is due to the average of many molecular impacts, so anything that affects either how frequently the molecules collide or how hard they collide will affect the pressure.

Gas pressure is increased by more frequent and/or harder collisions

less frequent impacts
lower pressure

more frequent impacts
higher pressure

weaker impacts
lower pressure

harder impacts
higher pressure

Changes in the amount of gas, the size of the container, and the gas temperature all change the pressure

You can have more impacts by doing several things:

Lower pressure   **Higher pressure**

fewer impacts   more impacts

fewer impacts   more impacts

fewer impacts   more impacts
harder impacts

- **Put more molecules into the same size container.** For example, when you pump up a tire, the size of the tire doesn't change very much. The increased number of molecules in the tire does cause increased molecular collisions, which causes an increase in gas pressure.

- **Keep the number of molecules the same, but reduce the volume of the container.** By giving each molecule less space to move around in, there is an increase in molecular collisions, causing an increase in gas pressure. Every time you exhale, your lungs decrease their volume to increase the pressure inside. Higher pressure inside forces air out.

- **Heat the gas up.** An increase in temperature causes the kinetic energy of the molecules to increase. This means they move faster. If they are moving faster, then they hit the walls more often *and* they hit harder. Both effects increase pressure. The increase of pressure with heat is the reason most aerosol cans have a warning to keep the cans away from heat and fire. If the temperature caused too much of a pressure increase, the can could explode!

Boyle's law: volume versus pressure

P vs. V at constant T and moles

Robert Boyle explored the relationship between the pressure of a gas and its volume. Using Torricelli's ideas, he constructed a device that would allow him to measure the pressure of an enclosed gas by observing the height of a column of mercury supported by that gas. He poured mercury into the open end of a tube shaped like the letter "J" and sealed on one side. He could determine the pressure by measuring the height of the mercury, and by taking measurements of the tube and amount of space taken up by the gas he could determine the volume. Because no gas could get in or out, the number of gas molecules was kept constant. Boyle made sure to keep the temperature constant while taking measurements.

J-tube apparatus to measure P and V

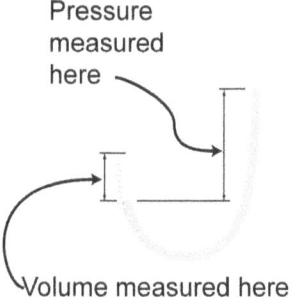

Pressure measured here

Volume measured here

Below are some typical data that could be collected in such a constant temperature experiment as well as a graph of the data.

TABLE 15.1. Pressure versus volume at constant temperature and moles

Pressure (atm)	Volume (mL)	P × V (atm · mL)
0.25	200	50
0.50	100	50
1.00	50	50
2.00	25	50
5.00	10	50
10.00	5	50

Pressure is inversely proportional to volume

In 1643, Boyle discovered that doubling the pressure caused the volume to be cut in half, and doubling the volume caused the pressure to be cut in half. This means that pressure is inversely proportional to volume and can be expressed as PV = some constant. The "constant" could change from one experiment to another if the temperature or amount of initial gas used was different, but as long as the temperature and moles of gas remained the same, the PV = constant relationship would remain true.

Boyle's law

P = pressure
V = volume
k = a constant
(depends on temperature and moles of gas)

$$P V = k \quad \text{or} \quad P_1 V_1 = P_2 V_2$$

Only true for constant temperature and constant number of gas molecules (moles)

Applications of Boyle's law

Weather balloons expand as they reach high altitudes

Every day, twice a day at about 1,000 stations worldwide, weather balloons are released into the air carrying special instruments to measure wind speed, humidity, and several other properties of the atmosphere. These balloons are filled with hydrogen or helium and soar high into the sky, reaching an altitude of about 100,000 ft (30 km) before bursting and releasing their parachuting instruments to the ground. As these balloons climb higher and higher, the pressure gets lower and lower. Boyle's Law predicts that the balloon should get bigger and bigger; that is why it eventually bursts. The pictures here show a high-altitude research balloon being launched. Notice that the balloon looks mostly empty on the ground, but the gas inside has expanded enormously once it reaches high altitude.

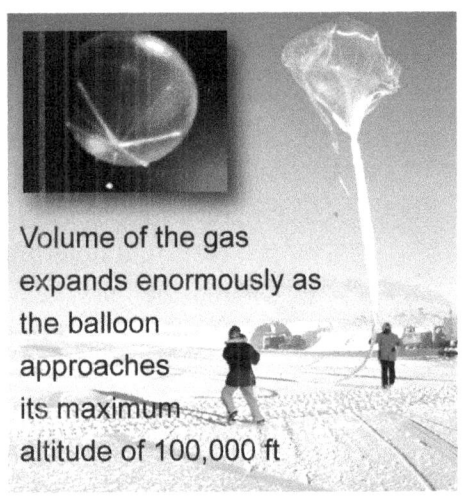

Volume of the gas expands enormously as the balloon approaches its maximum altitude of 100,000 ft

Changes in V change the space between molecules and the frequency of molecular impacts

From a molecular standpoint, the inverse relationship between pressure and volume makes sense. If the volume of the gas expands, then there will be more space between the molecules, so there will be fewer impacts per second on the walls of its container, lowering the pressure.

Larger volume = fewer Impacts = lower pressure

$$P_1V_1 = P_2V_2$$

$$1.00 \text{ atm} \times 3.0 \text{ L} = 0.50 \text{ atm} \times 6.0 \text{ L}$$

$$3.0 \text{ atm} \cdot \text{L} = 3.0 \text{ atm} \cdot \text{L}$$

$P_1 = 1.00$ atm
$V_1 = 3.0$ L

$P_2 = 0.50$ atm
$V_2 = 6.0$ L

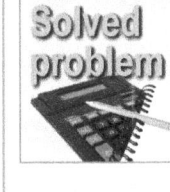
Solved problem

If a weather balloon is released on the ground with a volume of 3.0 m³ and a pressure of 1.00 atm, how large will it get when it reaches an altitude of 100,000 ft, where the pressure is 0.0100 atm?

Asked: *Volume of the balloon when it reaches 100,000 ft*

Given: $P_1 = 1.00 \text{ atm}, V_1 = 3.0 \text{ m}^3, P_2 = 0.0100 \text{ atm}$

Relationships: $P_1V_1 = P_2V_2$

Solve:

$$1.00 \text{ atm} \times 3.0 \text{ m}^3 = 0.0100 \text{ atm} \times P_2$$

$$P_2 = \frac{1.00 \text{ atm} \times 3.0 \text{ m}^3}{0.00100 \text{ atm}} = 300 \text{ m}^3$$

There is no such thing as suction

Gases can only push

It may seem strange to say that there is no such thing as suction. Of course something happens when you suck air into your lungs. However, it is not the pulling force that you might expect. In almost every case, suction can be explained by an imbalance of gas pressures. Gas exerts a pressure by having its molecules *push* on something, so there is no way for a gas to pull on anything.

Pressures tend to equalize, so we often forget we are surrounded by gases

Remember, we live at the bottom of an ocean of air whose pressure is quite strong, typically 14.69 psi. The reason we don't see things getting pushed around by this air pressure is that it is nearly the same everywhere. Take a balloon for example. Once you blow it up and seal it with a knot, it appears as if nothing is happening. However, at the molecular level there is a huge amount of activity with molecules colliding into the balloon both outside and inside. It doesn't get any bigger or smaller because the pressures inside and outside are equal.

Pressure inside balloon is equal to the pressure outside

Breathing is possible because air pushes its way into your lungs

When you inhale, its feels like you are pulling air into your lungs. However, what is really happening is that you are lowering the pressure inside your lungs, so the air outside which is at higher pressure pushes its way in. This is just another application of Boyle's law. When you breathe in, you use muscles to expand the volume of your lungs. If your lungs get bigger then there is more space for the air molecules inside, spreading them out and reducing their impacts. The air outside your lungs is then pushing and colliding with greater frequency, and those molecules push their way into the lower pressure region you created inside of your lungs.

Three stages of inhalation

Stage 1: Before inhaling, the pressure inside and outside of your lungs is the same

Stage 2: Lung volume is expanded, so molecules spread out, and pressure decreases inside lung

air pushes into low pressure lung

Stage 3: Inhalation is finished when pressure inside and outside of the lung is equal

Straws and vacuum cleaners

The same thing happens with a straw, a vacuum cleaner, or anything else that seems to pull something in by suction. When using a straw, you typically expand the volume inside of your mouth, lowering the pressure and allowing the liquid in the straw to be pushed into your mouth by the larger outside air pressure. Vacuum cleaners work by creating a region of low pressure near the mouth of the vacuum. The higher air pressure outside of the vacuum pushes air (and dirt carried by the air) into the machine.

Volume, temperature, and the Kelvin temperature scale

Amontons discovered that heating a gas caused it to expand

In 1702, Guillaume Amontons demonstrated that a change in temperature caused a change in gas volume. He realized that heating a gas caused it to expand, meaning that an increase in temperature caused an increase in volume. However, at the time, there was no well-defined temperature scale, so he was unable to determine the exact relationship between temperature and volume of a gas.

The exact relationship between V and T

In 1787, Jacques Charles, with the benefit of the Celsius temperature scale, was able to determine a mathematically precise relationship. In his experiments, Charles used a sealed container that could change size easily. By using a container that could change size, the pressure was kept constant, so in his experiments a constant number of molecules (or moles) and a constant pressure can be assumed. Only the temperature and volume were allowed to change. Below is an example of data for such an experiment.

TABLE 15.2. Volume versus temperature at constant pressure and moles

Volume (mL)	Temp. (°C)	V/(T+273) (mL/°C)
91.6	0	0.335
106.7	45	0.335
125.2	100	0.335
167.1	225	0.335
323.0	200	0.335

Volume and temperature are directly proportional

Lord Kelvin discovered absolute zero

One thing that becomes apparent when you look at the graph is that as temperature decreases, so does volume. Lord Kelvin realized that if you extended the line to the point where the volume of the gas would be zero, the smallest possible volume, you would also reach the lowest possible temperature. On the graph above, the lowest temperature is − 273°C. This lowest temperature came to be known as absolute zero, and a new temper-ature scale named after Kelvin was invented. It was identical to the Celsius scale, except that it started at 0 instead of −273. To convert from Celsius to Kelvin you just add 273 to the Celsius temperature.

Kelvin temperatures simplify the V versus T relationship

Doubling the Kelvin temperature will double the volume of a gas

A NATURAL APPROACH TO CHEMISTRY

Charles's law: volume versus temperature

Volume is directly proportional to Kelvin temperature

If the Kelvin temperature scale is used, the volume versus temperature relationship is simplified so that doubling the Kelvin temperature of gas causes a doubling of its volume. This means that volume is directly proportional to temperature, and it can be expressed as V/T = some constant. The "constant" could change from one experiment to another if the pressure or amount of initial gas used was different, but as long as the pressure and moles of gas remain the same (and the temperature is measured in kelvins), the V/T = constant relationship will be true.

> **Charles's law**
> T = temperature
> V = volume
> k = a constant
> (value depends on pressure and moles)
>
> $$\frac{V}{T} = k \quad \text{or} \quad \frac{V_1}{T_1} = \frac{V_2}{T_2}$$
>
> Only true for constant pressure and constant number of gas molecules (moles)

Changes in temperature

From a molecular standpoint, the direct relationship between pressure and volume makes sense. If the temperature of the gas is increased, then there will be more frequent and harder impacts on the walls of the container. This will cause the gas to expand until the molecules are spread far enough apart so that the pressure inside and outside of the container are now equal again.

Increased temperature → harder & more impacts
→ expanded volume to equalize pressure

$V_1 = 10\ L$
$T_1 = 200\ K$

$$\frac{V_1}{T_1} = \frac{V_2}{T_2}$$

$$\frac{10\ L}{200\ K} = \frac{20\ L}{400\ K}$$

$$0.05\ \frac{L}{K} = 0.05\ \frac{L}{K}$$

$V_2 = 20\ L$
$T_2 = 400\ K$

Solved problem

If you inflate a balloon to a size of 8.0 L inside where the temperature is 23°C, what will be the new size of the balloon when you go outside where it is 3°C? *Before going on, discuss with your classmates how to convert from °C to K.*

Asked: *Volume of the balloon when the temperature drops to 3°C*

Given: $V_1 = 8.0\ L$, $T_1 = 23°C$, $T_2 = 3°C$

Relationships: $\dfrac{V_1}{T_1} = \dfrac{V_2}{T_2}$ *and Kelvin temperature = Celsius temperature + 273*

Solve: *Convert temperature to Kelvin:* $T_1 = 23°C + 273 = 296\ K$

$$T_2 = 3°C + 273 = 276\ K$$

$$\frac{8.0\ L}{296\ K} = \frac{V_2}{276\ K} \longrightarrow V_2 = \frac{8.0\ L \times 276\ \cancel{K}}{296\ \cancel{K}} = 7.5\ L$$

The combined gas law

The combined gas law

So far we have looked at Boyle's law, which can tell us how pressure varies with volume, but only if you hold the temperature and number of molecules (or moles of molecules) constant. We have also studied Charles's law, which can tell us how volume varies with temperature as long as the pressure and moles of gas are kept constant. However, all of those things may be changing in most real-life situations. The easiest one to keep constant is the moles of gas, because all you need is a sealed container to make sure the moles of gas remain constant. We can combine Boyle's and Charles's laws to give a new formula that will allow for pressure, volume, and temperature to all vary. This relationship is derived below.

Combined gas law
P = pressure
T = temperature
V = volume
k = a constant
(depends on moles)

$$\frac{PV}{T} = k \quad \text{or} \quad \frac{P_1V_1}{T_1} = \frac{P_2V_2}{T_2}$$

Only true for constant number of gas molecules (moles)

constant T and moles **Boyle's law** $P_1V_1 = P_2V_2$

Combined gas law $\frac{P_1V_1}{T_1} = \frac{P_2V_2}{T_2}$ constant moles

constant P and moles $\frac{V_1}{T_1} = \frac{V_2}{T_2}$ **Charles's law**

Solved problem

Imagine you were to hitch a ride on a high-altitude research balloon that reaches an altitude of 100,000 ft. At sea level, where the pressure is 1.00 atm and the temperature is 20°C, you'll need 18 m³ of helium to fill the balloon. What will be the new volume of the gas when you reach altitude, where the pressure is 0.0100 atm and the temperature is –50°C?

Asked: *Volume of the balloon when it reaches 100,000 ft*

Given: $P_1 = 1.00 \text{ atm}, V_1 = 18.0 \text{ m}^3, T_1 = 20°C = 293 \text{ K},$
$P_2 = 0.0100 \text{ atm}, T_2 = -50°C = 223 \text{ K}$

Relationships: $\frac{P_1V_1}{T_1} = \frac{P_2V_2}{T_2}$ *Kelvin temperature = Celsius temperature + 273*

Solve:

$$\frac{1.00 \text{ atm} \times 18.0 \text{ m}^3}{293 \text{ K}} = \frac{0.0100 \text{ atm} \times V_2}{223 \text{ K}}$$

$$V_2 = \frac{1.00 \text{ atm} \times 18.0 \text{ m}^3 \times 223 \text{ K}}{293 \text{ K} \times 0.0100 \text{ atm}} = 1{,}370 \text{ m}^3$$

Avogadro's law: volume versus moles

Equal volumes of gas contain equal numbers of molecules

In 1811, Amedeo Avogadro studied how gases chemically combine with each other. For example, we know that hydrogen combines with oxygen in a two-to-one mole ratio by looking at the chemical equation $2H_2 + O_2 \rightarrow 2H_2O$. Avogadro found that volumes of gases would combine in the same kinds of ratios. In other words 2 L of hydrogen would combine with 1 L of oxygen to form 2 L of water vapor. This would only work if each liter of gas contained the same number of molecules regardless of the type of gas.

Two equal volumes of hydrogen react with one volume of oxygen to produce two volumes of water vapor. Gas volumes act like moles because the same size container has the same number of molecules (at the same temperature and pressure).

Below are some data that could be collected to see the relationship between volume of a gas and the number of molecules (n) in that volume.

TABLE 15.3. Volume versus moles at constant temperature and pressure

Volume (L)	Moles (mole)	V/n (L/mole)
200	10	20
300	15	20
400	20	20
500	25	20
600	30	20
800	40	20

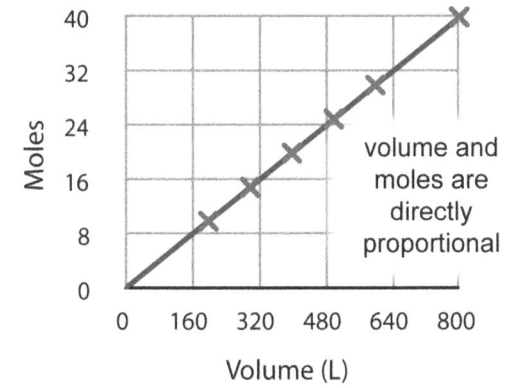

Volume is directly proportional to moles of gas

The above data show that doubling the number of moles doubles the volume. This means that volume is directly proportional to moles, and it can be expressed as V/n = some constant. The "constant" could change from one experiment to another if the temperature or pressure of the initial gas used was different, but as long as the temperature and pressure remained the same, the V/n = constant relationship would be true.

Avogadro's law
V = volume
n = moles
k = a constant
(value depends on pressure and temperature)

$$\frac{V}{n} = k \quad \text{or} \quad \frac{V_1}{n_1} = \frac{V_2}{n_2}$$

Only true for constant pressure and constant temperature

Molar volume

Doubling the number of gas molecules doubles the space they require

At a molecular level, Avogadro's law states that doubling the number of gas molecules (moles) results in doubling the amount of space they take up.

What requires a bit more explanation is why the same volume of gas should contain the same number of gas molecules regardless of the type of gas (as long as the temperature and pressure of both gases are the same).

A volume of gas that is double in size will have double the number of molecules, assuming the temperature and pressure are the same

This is only true for gases, not liquids or solids

Gas molecules are spread so far apart that the size of a molecule is not important in determining gas volume

Typically, gases are one-thousandth as dense as liquids because there is so much empty space between molecules in a gas and almost no empty space between molecules in liquids (or solids). This means that the size of an individual molecule has little to do with the amount of space the gas will take up. Instead, it is the size of the container that defines the volume of a gas.

Liquid volumes result from the size of their molecules, whereas gas volumes result from the size of the container

In a gas, the space between molecules is large enough that molecule size doesn't matter

One mole of any gas occupies a volume of 22.4 L at standard temperature and pressure

The temperature of a gas is directly related to the kinetic energy of its molecules. This means that two gases that are at the same temperature must have molecules with the same kinetic energy. If one gas has heavier molecules, then its molecules will move more slowly than the molecules of a gas with lighter molecules. The two different molecules will exert the

Each molecule here has the same kinetic energy

In gases with the same temperature, lighter molecules move faster, so the force from the impact is the same as for the slower molecules that have more mass

same force when impacting the wall of the container, so both gases will have the same pressure for the same number of molecules and occupy the same volume. At standard temperature (273 K) and standard pressure (1.00 atm), one mole of any gas will occupy 22.4 L. This is considered the molar volume.

Chemistry terms

molar volume: the amount of space occupied by a mole of gas at standard temperature and pressure.

The ideal gas law and the universal gas constant

Combining all of the individual gas laws will give you the Ideal Gas Law

All of the gas laws we have studied so far only work under certain conditions. Boyle's law only works if the temperature and moles of the gas remain constant. Charles's law only works if the pressure and volume of the gas remain constant. Avogadro's law only works if the pressure and temperature remain constant. The problem with these gas laws is that it is more realistic for pressure, temperature, volume, and sometimes moles of gas to change all at the same time. We made some progress by combining Boyle's and Charles's laws. If we also combine Avogadro's law, then we will have an equation that works for all gases under all conditions: the ideal gas law!

Ideal gas law
P = pressure
V = volume
n = moles
T = temperature
R = universal gas constant

$$\frac{PV}{nT} = R \quad \text{or} \quad \frac{P_1V_1}{n_1T_1} = \frac{P_2V_2}{n_2T_2}$$

True for all gases under all conditions!
Frequently written as $PV = nRT$

Combined gas law

constant moles
$$\frac{P_1V_1}{T_1} = \frac{P_2V_2}{T_2}$$

constant P and T
$$\frac{V_1}{n_1} = \frac{V_2}{n_2}$$

Avogadro's law

No restrictions!

$$\frac{P_1V_1}{n_1T_1} = \frac{P_2V_2}{n_2T_2} = R$$

or

$$PV = nRT$$

Ideal gas law

*The calculation of PV/nT will be the same for all gases under all conditions, so calculating the value gives us one of Nature's special numbers: **the universal gas constant, R***

The universal gas constant holds for all gases under all conditions

As with the other gas laws, a constant is calculated. However, unlike the other gas laws in which the constant depended on some starting condition of the gas, this constant is the same value for any gas under any set of initial conditions. It is therefore known as the universal gas constant, and it is given a special letter R to represent it. This is a fundamental constant of nature like pi (π). The only thing affecting the value of R is the units used to calculate it. Consider the following examples:

Calculating the universal gas constant using various units

V = liters and P = atmosphere	V = cubic meters, and P = Pascals
P = 1.00 atm n = 1.00 mole	P = 101,325 Pa n = 1.00 mole
V = 22.414 L T = 273.15 K	V = 0.022414 m^3 T = 273.15 K

$$R = \frac{PV}{nT} = \frac{1.00 \text{ atm} \times 22.414 \text{ L}}{1.00 \text{ mole} \times 273.15 \text{ K}}$$

$$\boxed{R = 0.08206 \frac{\text{atm} \cdot \text{L}}{\text{mole} \cdot \text{K}}}$$

$$R = \frac{PV}{nT} = \frac{101,325 \text{ Pa} \times 0.022414 \text{ m}^3}{1.00 \text{ mole} \times 273.15 \text{ K}}$$

$$\boxed{R = 8.3145 \frac{\text{Pa} \cdot \text{m}^3}{\text{mole} \cdot \text{K}}}$$

Using the ideal gas law under uniform conditions

Gases with low temperatures or high pressures may not closely obey the ideal gas law

There are limitations to how the ideal gas law can be applied. It is only 100% accurate if you are using an **ideal gas**, or one in which the molecules take up no space and have no interactions with each other. This is most important when the molecules are close together, which happens for gases under high pressure and/or low temperatures. If the gas is cooled down to very low temperatures, then the van der Waals attractions will also play a greater role. For gases of sufficiently high temperature and/or low pressure, the ideal gas law can be quite accurate.

Difference between a real and an ideal gas

Real gases reach a minimum volume when they get cold enough to condense into a liquid.

When calculating the state of an unchanging gas, use PV = nRT

If you are given a problem where the conditions are not changing (i.e., no changes in initial and final pressure, temperature, etc.), then use the PV = nRT version of the ideal gas law. Solving problems using this equation involves the following steps:

Steps for using PV = nRT		
Step 1	**Step 2**	**Step 3**
Select one version of R.	Convert known values to the same units as R.	Solve for unknown value using PV = nRT.

Solved problem

What would be the pressure inside of a 50.0 L tank containing 1,252 g of helium at 20°C?

Asked: *Tank pressure*

Given: $V = 50.0\ L,\ T = 20°C,\ mass = 1{,}252\ g,\ He = 4.003\ g/mole$

Relationships: $PV = nRT,\ R = 0.08206\ \frac{atm \cdot L}{mole \cdot K}$

Solve:

Convert to units of R:

$V = 50.0\ L$

$T = 20.0°C + 273 = 293\ K$

$n = 1252\ \cancel{g} \times \dfrac{1\ mole}{4.003\ \cancel{g}} = 312.8\ mole$

$P \times 50.0\ L = 312.8\ moles \times 0.08206\ \dfrac{atm \cdot L}{mole \cdot K} \times 293$

$P = \dfrac{312.8\ \cancel{moles} \times 0.08206\ atm \cdot \cancel{L} \times 293\ \cancel{K}}{50.0\ \cancel{L} \times \cancel{mole \cdot K}}$

$P = 150\ atm$

Chemistry terms

ideal gas: a gas made from molecules that have no volume or interactions with each other, obeys the various gas laws, including the ideal gas law; gases with high temperatures and low pressures are good approximations of an ideal gas.

Using the ideal gas law under changing conditions

If any property of the gas is changing then compare initial and final conditions

Because the ideal gas law contains all the other gas laws, you only need this one formula to solve any problems related to gases. You just need to choose the correct version of the formula.

If you are doing a "changing conditions" problem, then you can use any pressure and volume units you like as long at the initial and final conditions use the same units. However, you still need to convert your temperatures to the Kelvin temperature scale.

Any properties not mentioned in the problem can be assumed to be held constant, causing the ideal gas equation to be simplified into several of the more basic gas laws. So, solving problems in which one or more properties of the gas are changing involves the following steps:

$$\text{Steps for using } \quad \frac{P_1 V_1}{n_1 T_1} = \frac{P_2 V_2}{n_2 T_2}$$

Step 1	Step 2
Simplify the equation by cancelling out properties that stay constant. For example, if the temperature stays constant ($T_1 = T_2$), cancel it out.	Substitute remaining known quantities and solve for the unknown using the simplified equation.

Solved problem

What would be the new volume of a bubble in bread dough once it goes from a room temperature (20°C) volume of 0.050 cm³ to a 191°C oven?

Asked: *Find the volume of a bubble under changing temperature conditions*

Given: $V_1 = 0.050 \ cm^3, \ T_1 = 20°C = 293 \ K, \ T_2 = 191°C = 464 \ K$

Relationships: $\dfrac{P_1 V_1}{n_1 T_1} = \dfrac{P_2 V_2}{n_2 T_2}$

Solve: *Pressure and moles stay constant, so they cancel out.*

$$\frac{\cancel{P_1} V_1}{\cancel{n_1} T_1} = \frac{\cancel{P_2} V_2}{\cancel{n_2} T_2}$$

$$\downarrow$$

$$\frac{V_1}{T_1} = \frac{V_2}{T_2}$$

$$\frac{0.050 \ cm^3}{293 \ K} = \frac{V_2}{464 \ K}$$

$$V_2 = \frac{0.050 \ cm^3 \times 464 \ \cancel{K}}{293 \ \cancel{K}}$$

$$= 0.079 \ cm^3$$

14.3 Stoichiometry and Gases

Solving
stoichiometry
problems

In Chapter 11 you learned how to do stoichiometry with grams of a substance or liters of solutions. Here we will extend your ability to do stoichiometry when one or more gases are part of the equation. The pattern you previously used followed one of these patterns:

Solving grams to grams stoichiometry problems

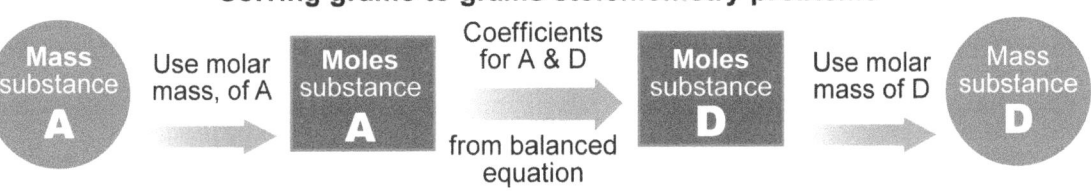

Solving solutions stoichiometry problems

The same
pattern can
be used for
stoichiometry
problems that
involve gases

We can generalize these patterns to solve any kind of stoichiometry problem in the following way, including problems that involve gases:

Solving generic stoichiometry problems

Steps for stoichiometry problems

Step 1	Step 2	Step 3
Use what you know about the first substance to convert it to moles. • If you have grams, use the molar mass. • If you have liters of solution, use the molarity. • If you have pressure, volume, and temperature of a gas, use the ideal gas law.	Use the balanced equation to determine a mole ratio between the substance you have information about and the substance you are trying to calculate. Then multiply the moles of the first substance by the mole ratio to give the moles of the second substance.	Now that you have the moles of the second substance, do whatever conversion is necessary to calculate the final answer. To convert moles • to grams, use the molar mass. • to liters of solution, use the molarity. • to volume, pressure, or temperature of gas, use the ideal gas equation.

Gas–solid stoichiometry calculations

In gas–solid calculations, use the molar mass and ideal gas law to solve the problem

In a reaction that involves both a gas and a solid, the gas is typically measured in volume at a certain temperature and pressure, while the solid is measured in grams. As with all stoichiometry reactions, the key is to get everything into moles to construct a ratio between two substances in the balanced equation. In this kind of reaction you will either be given information about the gas and asked to find the grams of the other substance or you will be given the grams of a substance and asked to find some property of the gas (temperature, pressure, or volume). Here is one example.

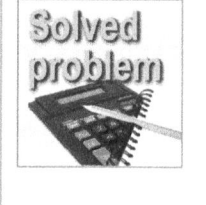

Solved problem

If you burn a 125 g candle made of paraffin wax, the peak temperature of the flame is about 1,400°C. Assuming the carbon dioxide produced is initially at that temperature, what volume of CO_2 is produced at peak temperature and a pressure of 790 mmHg? The combustion reaction is

$$2C_{20}H_{42} + 61O_2 \rightarrow 40CO_2 + 42H_2O$$

Asked: *Volume of CO_2 produced*

Given: *Paraffin: mass of 125 g*
Carbon dioxide: P = 790 mmHg, T = 1,400°C

Relationships: *Molar mass of paraffin = (12.011 × 20) + (1.0079 × 42)*
= 282.6 g/mole
Mole ratio: 2 moles $C_{20}H_{42}$ ~ 40 moles CO_2
PV = nRT

Solve: *Calculate moles of paraffin:*

$$125 \ \cancel{g \ C_{20}H_{42}} \times \frac{1 \ mole \ C_{20}H_{42}}{282.6 \ \cancel{g \ C_{20}H_{42}}} = 0.442 \ moles \ C_{20}H_{42}$$

Use mole ratio to determine moles of CO_2:

$$0.442 \ \cancel{mole \ C_{20}H_{42}} \times \frac{40 \ mole \ CO_2}{2 \ \cancel{mole \ C_{20}H_{42}}} = 8.85 \ moles \ CO_2$$

Convert gas units to the ones used by R:

$$P = 790 \ \cancel{mmHg} \times \frac{1.00 \ atm}{760 \ \cancel{mmHg}} = 1.04 \ atm$$
$$n = 8.85 \ moles$$
$$T = 1,400°C + 273 = 1,673 \ K$$

Solve ideal gas equation:
$$PV = nRT$$

$$1.04 \ atm \times V = 8.85 \ moles \times 0.08206 \frac{atm \cdot L}{mole \cdot K} \times 1,673 \ K$$

$$V = \frac{8.85 \ \cancel{mole} \times 0.08206 \ \cancel{atm} \cdot L \times 1,673 \cancel{K}}{1.04 \ \cancel{atm} \cdot \cancel{mole} \cdot \cancel{K}} = 1,170 \ L$$

Gas–Solution stoichiometry calculations

In gas–solution calculations, use the molarity and the ideal gas law to solve the problem

In a reaction that involves a gas and a solution, the gas is typically measured in volume at a certain temperature and pressure, while the solution is measured in volume and molarity. As with all stoichiometry reactions, the key is to get everything into moles to construct a ratio between two substances in the balanced equation. In this kind of reaction you will either be given information about the gas and asked to find the volume or concentration of a solution or you will be given the volume and concentration of a solution and asked to find some property of the gas (temperature, pressure, or volume). Here is one example.

Solved problem

A common reaction is when an acid reacts with a metal to produce hydrogen gas. Assume you are doing a reaction in which 0.050 L of 1.25 M hydrochloric acid reacts with excess magnesium:

$$Mg + 2HCl \rightarrow H_2 + MgCl_2$$

If the gas produced is captured in a 1.00 L container that starts out empty, what will be the pressure at the end of the reaction when the gas has cooled to 22°C?

Asked: *Pressure of hydrogen produced in a reaction*

Given: *Acid: V = 0.050 L, molarity = 1.25 M = 1.25 moles/L*
Hydrogen gas: V = 1.00 L, T = 22°C

Relationships: *Mole ratio: 2 moles HCl ~ 1 mole H_2*
PV = nRT

Solve: *Calculate moles of HCl:*

$$0.050 \; \cancel{L \; HCl} \times \frac{1.25 \; moles \; HCl}{1 \; \cancel{L \; HCl}} = 0.0625 \; moles \; HCl$$

Use mole ratio to determine moles of CO_2:

$$0.0625 \; \cancel{moles \; HCl} \times \frac{1 \; mole \; H_2}{2 \; \cancel{moles \; HCl}} = 0.0313 \; moles \; H_2$$

Convert gas units to the ones used by R:

$$V = 1.00 \; L$$
$$n = 0.0313 \; moles$$
$$T = 22°C + 273 = 295 \; K$$

Solve ideal gas equation:

$$P \times 1.00 \; L = 0.0313 \; moles \times 0.08206 \; \frac{atm \cdot L}{mole \cdot K} \times 295 \; K$$

$$P = \frac{0.0313 \; \cancel{moles} \times 0.08206 \; atm \cdot \cancel{L} \times 295 \; \cancel{K}}{1.00 \; \cancel{L} \cdot \cancel{mole} \cdot \cancel{K}} = 0.756 \; atm$$

Gas–gas stoichiometry calculations

Use the ideal gas law to solve gas-only problems

In a reaction that involves two gases, you will be given the temperature, pressure, and volume of one gas and asked to calculate the temperature, pressure, or volume of the second gas. As with all stoichiometry reactions, the key is to get everything into moles to construct a ratio between two substances in the balanced equation.

Solved problem

What volume of butane gas is needed at room temperature (23 °C) and typical pressure (0.984 atm) to produce 85.0 L of carbon dioxide at 825°C and a pressure of 1.04 atm? The reaction is

$$2C_4H_{10} + 13O_2 \rightarrow 8CO_2 + 10H_2O$$

Asked: *Volume of butane gas needed to produce a specific volume of carbon dioxide gas*

Given: *Butane: $P = 0.984$ atm, $T = 23°C$*
Carbon dioxide: $P = 1.04$ atm, $V = 85.0$ L, $T = 825°C$

Relationships: *Mole ratio: 2 moles C_4H_{10} ~ 8 moles CO_2*
$PV = nRT$

Solve: *Convert CO_2 units to the ones used by R:*
$P = 1.04$ atm
$V = 85.0$ L
$T = 825°C + 273 = 1,098$ K

Solve ideal gas equation for moles of CO_2:
$PV = nRT$

$1.04 \ atm \times 85.0 \ L = n \times 0.08206 \dfrac{atm \cdot L}{mole \cdot K} \times 1,098 \ K$

$n = \dfrac{1.04 \ \cancel{atm} \times 85.0 \ \cancel{L} \cdot moles \ \cancel{K}}{0.08206 \ \cancel{atm} \cdot \cancel{L} \times 1,098 \ \cancel{K}} = 0.981 \ moles \ CO_2$

Use mole ratio to determine moles of butane:

$0.981 \ \cancel{moles \ CO_2} \times \dfrac{2 \ moles \ C_4H_{10}}{8 \ \cancel{moles \ CO_2}} = 0.245 \ moles \ C_4H_{10}$

Convert butane units to the ones used by R:
$P = 0.984$ atm
$T = 23°C + 273 = 296$ K
$n = 0.245$ moles

Solve ideal gas equation:
$PV = nRT$

$0.984 \ atm \times V = 0.245 \ moles \times 0.08206 \dfrac{atm \cdot L}{mole \cdot K} \times 296 \ K$

$V = \dfrac{0.245 \ \cancel{moles} \times 0.08206 \ \cancel{atm} \cdot L \times 296 \ \cancel{K}}{0.984 \ \cancel{atm} \cdot \cancel{mole} \cdot \cancel{K}} = 6.05 \ L$

High-altitude training for athletes

In high endurance competitions such as the triathlon, athletes compete in a very demanding race of swimming, cycling and running at different altitudes. You may have also heard that Kenyans dominate in the sport of distance running. The first person to ever reach the top of Mt. Everest was Sir Edmund Hillary. What do all of these people have in common? And what does this have to do with chemistry?

All of these athletes have performed well at high altitudes, and this has to do with their body's ability to absorb oxygen (O_2). The body's ability to absorb oxygen is directly related to chemistry! To understand the basics of how the body absorbs oxygen at different altitudes, we must understand the concept of atmospheric pressure and how this influences the partial pressure of oxygen gas. Hemoglobin molecules present in our red blood cells also play a very important role in the body's ability to absorb oxygen.

At sea level, where atmospheric pressure is relatively high, more oxygen molecules are able to enter our lungs. At high altitudes the atmospheric pressure is lower, and this results in fewer oxygen molecules entering our lungs per breath. Fewer oxygen molecules enter our lungs because the partial pressure of oxygen is lower at high altitudes. The partial pressure is the pressure of an individual gas. It is called "partial" because it is one part of a whole group of gases that sum together. Using the atmosphere as an example, we can sum the individual partial pressures of nitrogen, oxygen, water, and argon—the primary gases in the atmosphere. This gives us the total pressure, which we refer to as the atmospheric pressure.

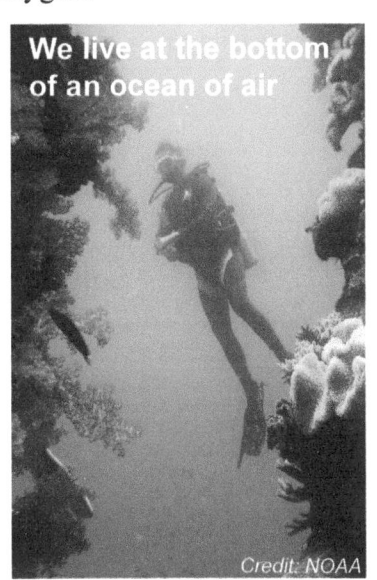

We live at the bottom of an ocean of air

Credit: NOAA

The atmospheric pressure helps push air molecules into our lungs, and because the pressure exerted by the atmosphere is lower up high, fewer gas molecules enter our lungs. At high altitude the partial pressure of each gas is decreased, and when they are added together the result is a lower atmospheric pressure.

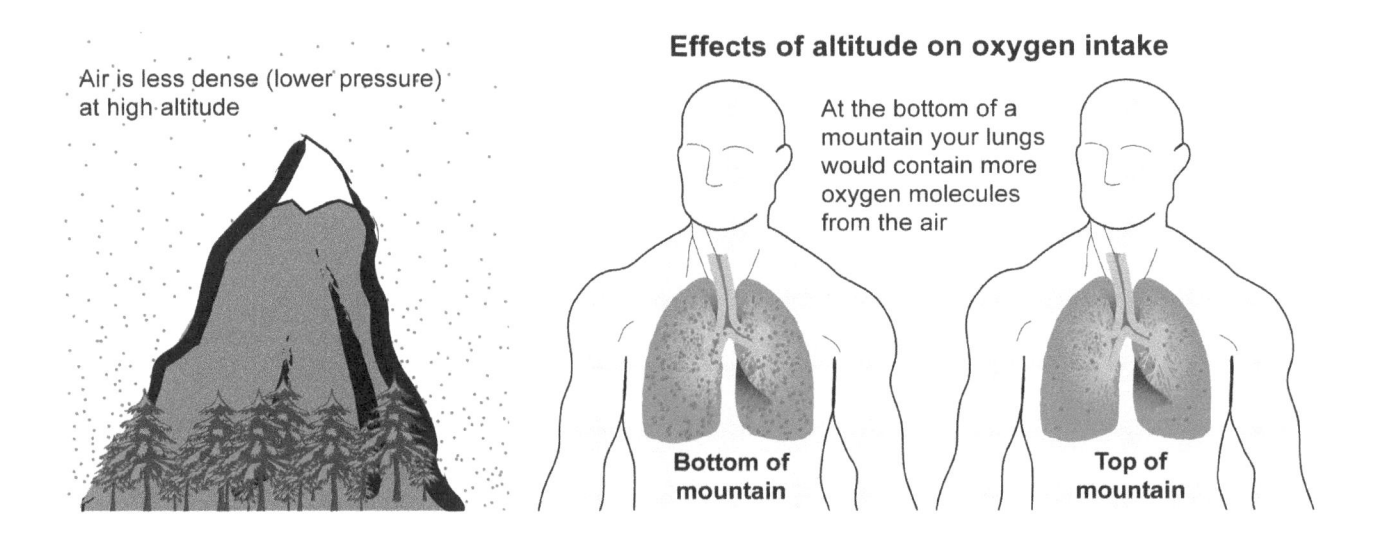

Air is less dense (lower pressure) at high altitude

Effects of altitude on oxygen intake

At the bottom of a mountain your lungs would contain more oxygen molecules from the air

Bottom of mountain

Top of mountain

Often competitive athletes such as runners, cyclists, and hikers train at high altitudes, way up in the mountains. For example, at 12,000 ft (3,658 m) the atmospheric pressure is only 0.64 atm, compared to sea level, where it is 1 atm. The atmospheric pressure is lower at altitude because there are fewer air molecules from above pushing down. At an altitude of 12,000 ft, approximately 40% fewer oxygen molecules enter your lungs! You may have heard the saying "the air is thinner" up on high mountains; this essentially means the air pressure is not as great.

When athletes first go to train at high altitudes they must allow time (generally 1–3 days) for their bodies to adjust to the lower atmospheric pressure. Why do their bodies require time to acclimate? It's because their bodies need to function with less oxygen. To make sure there is enough oxygen getting to its tissues, the body makes some changes. First the breathing rate increases, increasing the number of oxygen molecules entering the lungs. The body also makes more hemoglobin-containing red blood cells, which in turn pick up (bind to) more of the available oxygen molecules and deliver them to the tissues.

When training at high altitude your body makes more oxygen carrying red blood cells (RBCs)

Each RBC has over 250 million hemo-globin molecules

Athletes perform better when more oxygen is being delivered to their tissues. They experience less fatigue and their bodies are capable of performing better for longer periods of time. In any endurance sport there is a high dependency on oxygen, so there is a definite advantage for athletes who can improve the amount of oxygen being delivered to the working muscles. To take advantage of this, many athletes train at higher altitudes. When they return to a lower altitude to compete, they now have an increased amount of circulating oxygen molecules.

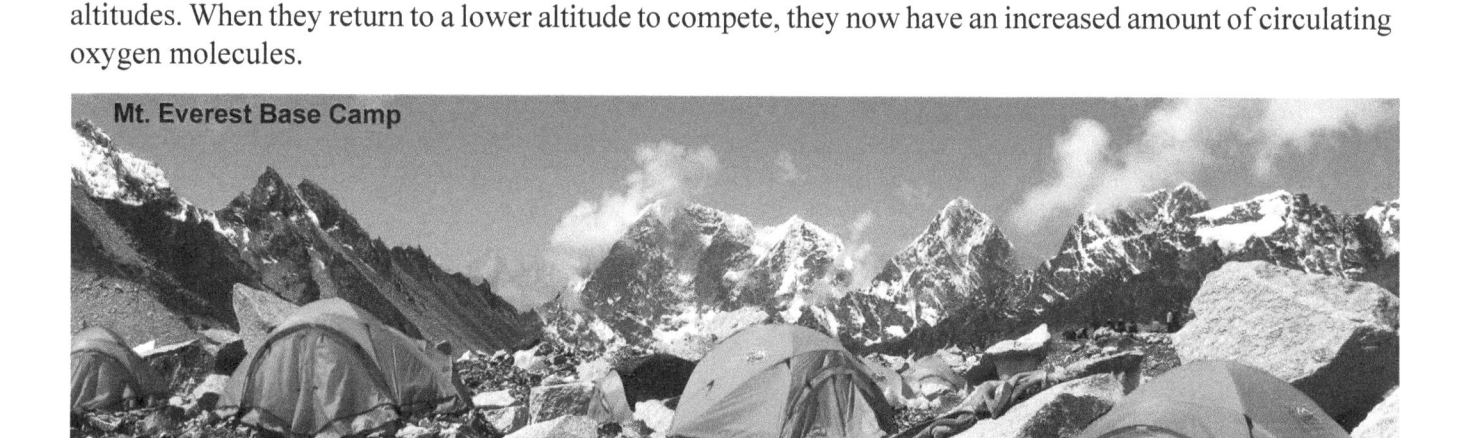
Mt. Everest Base Camp

Over time we have noticed the benefits of high-altitude training. When Kenyan runners first began to dominate the international middle- and long-distance races, it prompted significant interest in the athletic community. Much research was done, and scientists concluded that the primary factor that contributed to their repeated success was the high-altitude conditions under which they trained. Interestingly, all of these athletes are found to have unusually high levels of oxygen in their blood when tested during training. Even Sir Edmund Hillary who conquered Mt. Everest back in 1953, was also documented as having higher than normal circulating levels of oxygen in his blood! All of these amazing people appear to owe a large part of their success to the oxygen molecule! In addition to high-altitude training, it is believed that there is likely a genetic component involved that may contribute to some people having slightly higher levels of circulating oxygen.

Chapter 14 Review

Vocabulary

Match each word to the sentence where it best fits.

Section 14.1

| kinetic molecular theory | Brownian motion |
| Bernoulli principle | barometer |

1. If you view tiny particles in a liquid or gas using a microscope you can see _____.

2. You can measure atmospheric pressure using a/an _____.

3. Whenever you fly in an airplane you rely on the _____.

4. _____ describes our basic understanding of substances at the molecular level.

Section 14.2

| molar volume | ideal gas |

5. At standard temperature and pressure you will find 6.02×10^{23} molecules in a/an _____.

6. The gas laws are only 100% accurate for a/an _____.

Conceptual Questions

Section 14.1

7. Compare a gas, a liquid, and a solid on the molecular level.

8. What are some common properties of gases?

9. What is kinetic molecular theory?

10. Describe how kinetic molecular theory explains why gases have the properties you mentioned in question 8.

11. How was Brownian motion discovered, and what is it caused by?

12. What is the difference between force and pressure?

13. How does a gas exert pressure if there is lots of empty space between its molecules?

14. Why is it better to lie down on ice that is cracking beneath your feet than to remain in a standing position?

15. What causes atmospheric pressure?

16. Why is atmospheric pressure on top of a mountain less than at the base of that same mountain?

Section 14.2

17. Many aerosol cans have warning labels on the side that say to keep away from heat and fire. Why?

18. One of the first thermometers was made from sealing a gas in a container that would allow the gas to expand or contract. Explain how this could be used as a thermometer.

19. Why does it makes sense that the pressure in a sealed syringe will go up if you squeeze the air in it? Explain on a molecular level.

20. When you drive a car, the tires heat up because of friction with the road and internal friction between the molecules of the rubber. What will happen to the gas pressure in the tire as the tire heats up? Explain on a molecular level.

21. When pumping up a bicycle tire with a hand pump, it gets harder and harder to continue pumping. Explain using Avogadro's law.

22. Explain why weather balloons, which are sealed latex balloons filled with helium, eventually pop when they reach extremely high altitudes.

23. Explain why it makes sense to use a temperature scale that starts at zero, such as the Kelvin temperature scale.

24. What is the relationship between temperature and kinetic energy?

25. Guy-Lussac gave us another law that states that pressure and temperature are directly proportional to each other if volume and number of moles are constant. Using this law, what do you predict will happen to the pressure of a gas when its temperature is increased? Explain.

26. Plants breathe through the stomata on their leaves, which are small pores that can be opened or closed as needed. Plants grown in an environment with a high partial pressure of CO_2 have fewer stomata. Why does this make sense?

27. Describe everything you can about the molecules of two different gases that are at the same temperature.

28. How can the molar volume of *all* gases be the same 22.4 L volume at standard temperature and pressure? Why doesn't the size of the molecule have any effect?

29. What is meant by an ideal gas, and what laws and relationships apply to it?

30. Ideal gases have molecules that take up no space. However, real molecules do take up some space. How does this fact affect the volume predicted by Boyle's law and Charles's law? Will it be larger or smaller than the volume predicted for an ideal gas? Explain.

31. Ideal gases have molecules that don't interact with each other. However, real molecules feel the weak intermolecular attractions felt by all molecules. How does this fact affect the volume predicted by Boyle's law and Charles's law? Will it be larger or smaller than that predicted for an ideal gas? Explain.

Section 14.3

32. If you run an electric current through water it goes through a dissociation reaction, breaking back down into hydrogen and oxygen gas via this reaction: $2H_2O(l) \rightarrow 2H_2(g) + O_2(g)$.
If you measure the masses of the hydrogen and oxygen produced, you will find a mass ratio of $2H_2:16O_2$. If you measure the volume of the hydrogen and oxygen, you will get a volume ratio of $2H_2:1O_2$ —the same as the molar ratio in the balanced chemical equation. Why does the volume ratio match the molar ratio, but not the mass ratio?

Quantitative Problems

Section 14.1

33. What is the pressure exerted by an elephant weighing 8,000 lb if the total area of the bottom of its four feet equals 312 in²?

34. What is the weight of a car that has its tires inflated to 35 lb/in² and is touching the ground over an area equal to 285 in²?

35. Perform the following conversions:
    a. 3.50 psi to pascals
    b. 200,435 Pa to atmospheres
    c. 5.67 atm to millimeters of Hg
    d. 0.89 atmospheres to inches of mercury. You will need the following equalities to help: 1 in = 2.54 cm and 10 mm = 1 cm.

Section 14.2

36. Draw a graph of two variables that are directly proportional to each other.

37. Draw a graph of two variables that are inversely proportional to each other.

38. You decide to climb to the tops of some of the tallest mountains. Before you are about to leave on your epic journey, a friend gives you a balloon with a volume of 800.0 cm³ that was inflated under standard atmospheric pressure. You climbed two different mountains with this balloon: Mt. Everest (29,028 ft above sea level with an average atmospheric pressure of 221 mmHg) and Mt. McKinley (20,320 ft above sea level with an average atmospheric pressure of 345 mmHg). What was the volume of the balloon on each mountain top?

39. A 50.0 mL soap bubble is blown at standard pressure. When a thunderstorm passes later in the day, the pressure becomes 700.0 mmHg. Will the bubble get bigger or smaller? What is its new volume?

40. A balloon was inflated to a volume of 5.0 L at a pressure of 0.90 atm. It rises to an altitude where its volume becomes 25.0 L. Will the pressure around the balloon increase or decrease? What is the new pressure?

41. A scuba diver inflates a balloon to 10.0 L at the surface and takes it on a dive. At a depth of 100.0 ft the pressure is 4.0 atm. Will the volume of the balloon increase or decrease? What is the new volume of the balloon?

42. The living quarters of the space shuttle has a volume of 2.00×10^4 L and is kept at 12.0 lb/in². If all the air were lost, it would have to be replaced from a compressed air cylinder, which has a volume of 50.0 L. What is the pressure in that tank? (In other words, how much pressure would it take to compress all the air in the shuttle into a 50.0 L space?)

Chapter 14 Review

43. The space shuttle living quarters has a volume of 2.00×10^4 L at a pressure of 500.0 mmHg. The shuttle docks with a space lab that has a volume of 2.30×10^5 L and no air in it. What does the air pressure in both become when the hatch is opened between the two?

44. A fountain pen, which has a total volume of 2.4 cm³, is half full with ink at the surface, where the pressure is 780.0 mmHg. It is put in the pocket of a pilot who flies to an altitude where the pressure is 520.0 mmHg. How much ink leaks out of the pen?

45. A 50.0 mL soap bubble is blown in a 27.0°C room. It drifts out an open window and lands in a snow bank at –3.0°C. What is its new volume?

46. A balloon was inflated to a volume of 5.0 L at a temperature of 7.0°C. It landed in an oven and was heated to 147°C. What is its new volume?

47. During the day at 27°C a cylinder with a sliding top contains 20.0 L of air. At night it only holds 19 L. What is the temperature at night? Give the answer in kelvins and degrees Celsius.

48. A 113 L sample of helium at 27°C is cooled to –78°C. Calculate the new volume of the helium.

49. On all aerosol cans you see a warning that tells you to keep the can away from heat because of the danger of explosion. What is the potential volume of the gas contained in a 500.0 mL can at 25°C if it were heated to 54°C? In other words, if the can could expand to allow the gas to take up a greater volume, what would be the new volume of the gas when heated as previously described?

50. A 0.20 mL CO_2 bubble in cake batter is at 27°C. In the oven it gets heated to 177°C.
    a. What is its new volume?
    b. If the cake had 5,000 bubbles, by how many mL would the cake rise when it was cooked?
    c. What common baking ingredient was used to create the original CO_2 bubble?

51. A 500.0 mL glass filled with air is placed into water upside down while at 7.0°C. The water is then heated to 77°C. How much air bubbles out from under the glass?

52. At one point in history, people could measure temperature by looking at the volume of a sample of gas. Suppose a sample in a gas thermometer has a volume of 135 mL at 11.0°C. Indicate what temperature would correspond to each of the following volumes: 113, 142, 155, and 127 mL.

53. A balloon is filled with helium to a volume of 4.0 L when the pressure is 1.0 atm and the temperature is 27.0°C. It escapes and rises until the pressure is 0.25 atm and the temperature is 23.0°C. What is the new volume of the balloon?

54. When a bubble escapes form a sunken ship, it has a volume of 12.0 cm³ at a pressure of 400.0 atm and a temperature of –3.00 °C. It reaches the surface where the pressure is 1.10 atm and the temperature is 27.0 °C. What is its new volume?

55. A CO_2 bubble in some bread dough had an original volume of 0.30 mL when it formed at 27.0°C and 750 mmHg of pressure. While baking, its temperature rose to 177.0°C and a thunderstorm moved in, dropping the pressure to 725 mmHg. What is the new volume of the bubble?

56. If a hot air balloon holds 3.00×10^3 L of air at 17.0°C and standard pressure, how much air will escape as the balloon is heated to 67.0°C and rises to where the pressure is 13.5 lb/in²?

57. A scuba diver's tank holds 200.0 L of air at 27.0°C and 150.0 atm. How many 1.50 L breaths can the diver take where the pressure is 4.00 atm and the temperature is 7.00°C?

58. You drive to school in a hurricane where the pressure is an abnormally low 720.0 mmHg. However, when you get out of your car you notice that the volume of your tires seems to be a normal 29 L. During the day a high-pressure system moves overhead, changing the pressure to 780.0 mmHg. When you return outside you notice your tires seem a little flat. What is the new volume of your tires?

59. During the day at 25.0°C a cylinder with a sliding top contains 20.0 L of air. At night it only holds 18.0 L of air. None of the air leaked out. What is the temperature at night? Give the answer in kelvins and in degrees Celsius.

60. At what temperature would 2.10 moles of N_2 gas have a pressure of 1.25 atm in a 25.0 L tank?

61. When filling a weather balloon with gas, you have to consider that the gas will expand greatly as it rises and the pressure decreases. Let's say you put about 10.0 moles of He gas into a balloon that can inflate to hold 5,000.0 L. Currently, the balloon is not full because of the high pressure on the ground. What is the pressure when the balloon rises to a point where the temperature is –10.0°C and the balloon has completely filled with the gas?

62. What volume is occupied by 5.03 g of O_2 at 28°C and a pressure of 0.998 atm?

63. Calculate the pressure in a 212 L tank containing 23.3 kg of argon gas at 25°C.

64. Suppose you took a volleyball scuba diving with you. On your dive, you take it to a place where the pressure is 2,943 mmHg, and the temperature is 0.245°C. What would be its new volume if it started at the surface with a volume of 2.00 L under a pressure of 752.0 mmHg and a temperature of 20.0°C?

65. What is the volume of 1.00 mole of a gas at standard temperature and pressure?

66. A 113 L sample of helium at 27°C is cooled at constant pressure to –78.0°C. Calculate the new volume of the helium.

67. What volume is occupied by 2.35 moles of He at 25°C and a pressure of 0.980 atm?

68. An aerosol can contains 400.0 mL of compressed gas at a pressure of 5.2 atm. When the gas is sprayed into a large plastic bag, the bag inflates to a volume of 2.14 L. What is the pressure of gas inside the plastic bag?

69. At what temperature does 16.3 g of nitrogen gas have a pressure of 1.25 atm in a 25.0 L tank?

70. What mass of CO_2 is needed to fill an 80.0 L tank to a pressure of 150.0 atm at 27.0°C?

71. At what temperature does 5.00 g of H_2 occupy a volume of 50.0 L at a pressure of 1.01 atm?

72. How many moles of gas would you have if you had a volume of 38.0 L under a pressure of 1,432 mmHg at standard temperature?

73. According to the ideal gas law, what happens to volume if the number of moles is doubled and pressure and absolute temperature are halved?

74. A gas-phase reaction goes to completion according to $3A(g) \rightarrow 5B(g) + 2C(g)$. If we begin with 1.2 L of gas A, what *total* volume of products will be formed at the same temperature and pressure?

75. A sample of 2.5 mol gas occupies 8.0 L. With temperature and pressure constant, how much gas should we *add* for a final volume of 10.L?

Section 14.3

Use the following chemical equation to answer questions 76–79: $2C_8H_{18} + 25O_2 \rightarrow 16CO_2 + 18H_2O$

76. If 4.00 moles of gasoline are burned, what volume of oxygen is needed if the pressure is 0.953 atm, and the temperature is 35.0°C?

77. How many grams of water would be produced if 20.0 liters of oxygen were burned at a temperature of –10.0°C and a pressure of 1.3 atm?

78. If you burned one gallon of gas (approximately 4,000 grams), how many liters of carbon dioxide would be produced at a temperature of 21.0°C and a pressure of 1.00 atm?

79. How many liters of oxygen would be needed to produce 45.0 L of carbon dioxide if the temperature and pressure for both are 0.00°C and 5.02 atm?

Use the following chemical equation which shows the acetylene combustion reaction used in acetylene welding torches, to answer questions 80–82: $2C_2H_2 + 5O_2 \rightarrow 4CO_2 + 2H_2O$

80. If you had 0.564 moles of acetylene, what volume of oxygen would be needed to react with it if the pressure was 13.9 psi and the temperature was 23°C?

81. What volume of acetylene did you use if 10.5 g of water was produced, the pressure was 12.0 atm, and the temperature was 18°C?

82. What is the temperature of the reaction if 3.65 moles of oxygen is used and 500.0 L of CO_2 is produced under a pressure of 1.04 atm?

CHAPTER 15
Electrochemistry

What are antioxidants, and how do they work?

How do batteries work?

Why are some batteries rechargeable while some are not?

Why do some metals corrode (rust) while others do not?

What does electricity have to do with chemistry? Consider the abundance of life on Earth. Every plant and animal on Earth depends on energy from the Sun. Plants capture light energy from the Sun and store it as chemical energy in their roots, leaves, fruits, and branches, as well as in the oxygen that they release. In turn, animals extract the stored energy by eating the plants and breathing the oxygen.

Photosynthesis is not one reaction, but a complex sequence of many chemical reactions. Virtually all the energy in life on Earth originates with photosynthesis. Most of the energy in technology (oil and natural gas) comes from decayed living organisms that lived long ago. When we burn gasoline, we actually use "fossilized photosynthesis" that has been stored as hydrocarbon compounds in the Earth for millions of years.

Animals eat fruit and leaves, extracting the energy stored in them. This process is called *respiration*. Like photosynthesis, respiration is a complicated sequence of chemical reactions.

Now consider the details of just *how* photosynthesis and respiration work. At the very heart of these reactions is the transfer of electrons between compounds and molecules. Some molecules lose electrons and others gain them. The movement of electrons and the associated chemical change is the subject of *electrochemistry*. Nature is the ultimate electrochemical engine, and to understand it we must first understand the fundamentals of electrochemistry.

Electricity from a lemon

Electrochemistry brings electricity and chemistry together. This is the science that relates chemical reactions to the flow of electric charge. It happens in a battery, it happens in your body, and it can be made to happen with a lemon from the grocery store!

To make a lemon battery you need:

- a piece of magnesium (Mg) ribbon,
- a piece of copper (Cu) ribbon or thick wire,
- a red light emitting diode (LED),
- a lemon,
- two wires with alligator clips, and
- the Lab-Master with the voltage probe.

The experiment

The goal of the experiment is to make a lemon light up the LED. However, just poking the LED into the lemon is not going to work. You need to use the electrochemical properties of the magnesium and copper metals.

1. Knead the lemon gently to break up the juicy cells inside so the juice can flow easily within the fruit.
2. Next, make two small incisions on the lemon about 2 cm apart. Insert the pieces of magnesium and copper into the lemon.
3. Using the alligator clips, connect the leads of the LED to the copper and the magnesium.

Observations and questions

1. Seeing the LED light up implies that electricity is flowing. Where does the electricity come from?
2. Notice the gas bubbles forming at the base of the electrodes. What is that gas and where does it come from?
3. The measured voltage across the electrodes is 1.7 V.

Everything about this lemon reminds us of a battery. The lemon operates an electrical device (the LED). The lemon causes electricity to flow through wires, and it has a measured voltage like a battery. The chemical processes that generate the electricity in the lemon are very similar to those that go on inside more familiar batteries.

15.1 Electrochemistry and Electricity

Chemical defense in the body

Our health depends on a complex, self-adjusting dance among many thousands of chemical compounds. In the same way that rust damages the integrity of iron used in a bridge, a living body can be damaged by compounds that are harmful to essential molecules. Part of the chemical processing that every body does is to "deactivate" these harmful molecular compounds. Like most other chemical reactions, the process of "deactivation" is based on electrochemistry.

Rusting is oxidation

Free radicals

Iron rusts via a process called *oxidation*. We will talk more about oxidation later in this chapter. For now, let's think about oxidation as the process of losing electrons. In the same way that iron rusts by losing electrons, molecules in our bodies also "rust" or become oxidized. These electron-deficient molecules are called **free radicals**. Free radicals are highly reactive because they have a tendency to grab electrons from nearby molecules, and cause chain reactions that result in cell damage. Some free radicals are generated in the normal operation of our body. Others are produced when we are exposed to toxins, stress, and pollutants.

regular molecule loses an electron and becomes a free radical: a very reactive molecule

missing electron

donates an electron to the free radical

Antioxidant

Antioxidants

A healthy body protects itself from free radicals with molecules called *antioxidants*. **Antioxidants** are chemical compounds that prevent oxidation. Antioxidants protect the body by donating electrons to free radicals, thereby deactivating them. Despite the loss of electrons, antioxidants remain chemically stable. The production and the introduction of free radicals in our bodies is a continuous process, so the body's supply of antioxidants needs to be regularly replenished through a healthy diet.

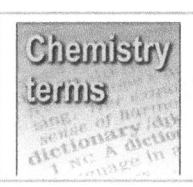
free radicals: molecules or atoms that are highly reactive owing to their having one or more unpaired valence electrons.

antioxidants: molecules that react easily with free radicals.

Electric charge and current

The basics of electricity

Being able to generate electricity from a lemon and a couple of pieces of metal is fascinating! Electrochemistry describes the detailed process by which chemical reactions in the lemon generate electricity. Electrochemistry also explains how electricity can cause chemical change. Understanding the basic principles of electricity is the first step in learning electrochemistry.

Charge is measured in coulombs

Consider the hydrogen atom, which has a single proton and an electron. The charge of the proton is equal and opposite to the charge of the electron. The unit of charge is called the **coulomb (C)**.

$$Charge\ of\ proton = +1.602 \times 10^{-19}\ C$$

$$Charge\ of\ electron = -1.602 \times 10^{-19}\ C$$

Electric charge is conserved

Electric charge, like mass, is a fundamental property of matter, and it is conserved. In this context, "conserved" means the total electric charge in a closed system remains constant.

In metals such as copper, some of the electrons that form bonds between the atoms are free to move. These "free" electrons move randomly between the fixed positive ions in a solid copper wire. Free electrons are light and fast, so they move very easily. This makes copper and other metals very good conductors of heat and electricity. Normally, the average charge of the free electrons does not move because the same number of electrons are going one way as the other way.

⊕ Fixed atom ⟵•⊙ Mobile electron

Electric current is the flow of electric charge

When a battery is attached to a wire, the motion of the electrons can change. When the free electrons move in a *collective* way (as a group), their charge also moves. This movement of charge results in the flow of **electric current**. The energy that the electrons need in order to move is provided by the battery. Current is measured in **amperes (A)**, which is a fundamental SI unit like the kilogram (kg), the meter (m), the second (s), Kelvin (K), the mole or, the candela (cd).

Chemistry terms

coulomb (C): the SI unit of electrical charge.
electric current: the directed flow of electric charge.
ampere: the SI unit of electrical current.

Electric current in solutions

Current can flow in ionic solutions

In *electrolyte* solutions, mobile ions with both positive and negative charges are present. For example, when sodium chloride salt (NaCl) is dissolved in water, the Na^+ and Cl^- ions are free to move in the solution.

Movement of either (or both) positive sodium ions (Na^+) and/or negative chlorine ions (Cl^-) may create an electric current. Any process that creates an average movement of electric charge creates an electric current.

NaCl crystal

Electro-chemistry generates electric current

In the lemon battery, electric current is created by chemical reactions at the interfaces between the lemon juice, the copper, and the magnesium metal. The atoms of magnesium interact with the citric acid ($C_6H_8O_7$) in the lemon juice and give up electrons. These electrons flow in the wire, through the light bulb, and return into the lemon via the copper metal.

The total number of charges in the entire system (lemon, copper, magnesium, and wires) does not change. The number of negative charges is equal to the number of positive charges, and the entire system is charge neutral. This property of charge balance is called **electroneutrality**.

No current can flow if there are no mobile charges

If there are no mobile electric charges, then no electric current can flow. For example, a solution of sugar in water does not conduct electric current. There *are* electrons and protons in sugar; however, there are exactly as many electrons as protons, and they cannot move separately from each other. A sugar molecule is *charge neutral*, so it cannot carry any current. Current can only be carried by particles that have a net electric charge and can move independently of each other, such as free electrons or ions.

Chemistry terms

electroneutrality: the property of charges to balance each other, resulting in a charge neutral system.

A NATURAL APPROACH TO CHEMISTRY

Voltage

Voltage is the difference in electrical potential

There are always free electrons in a copper wire, but they don't move to make current unless there is a *force* causing them to move. Think of the wire as a pipe inside which the electrons can flow like water. Water flows in a pipe driven by the difference in pressure.

No height difference; no water flows

Height difference causes water to flow

Voltage

Electrons flow in a wire because of the difference in an equivalent *electrical pressure* between two points. This difference in electrical pressure is called **voltage**. The unit for voltage is the **volt (V)**.

No voltage difference; no current flows

Voltage as potential energy

Voltage is a measure of electrical potential energy per unit of charge. One volt is one joule per coulomb.

Voltage difference causes current to flow

$$\text{volt (V)} = \frac{\text{joule (J)}}{\text{coulomb (C)}}$$

This means that if one coulomb of charge moves through a difference of one volt, it gains or loses one joule of potential energy. The charge loses energy if it goes from a higher voltage to a lower voltage, and it gains energy if it goes from a lower voltage to a higher voltage.

Resistance

When electrons flow in solid copper, they collide with the fixed copper ions. The continuous collisions absorb energy and cause *resistance*. **Resistance** limits how much current flows for any given voltage. If resistance is high, current is low. If resistance is low, current can be high. Electrical resistance is measured in units called **ohms**. A resistance of one ohm means one ampere of current flows when the voltage is one volt. The Greek letter omega (Ω) is used to represent ohms.

Ohm's law

The current (I) depends on the voltage (V) and the resistance (R). **Ohm's law** gives the formula that relates the current, the voltage, and the resistance.

$$\text{current (amperes, A)} \longrightarrow I = \frac{V \longleftarrow \text{voltage (volts, V)}}{R \longleftarrow \text{resistance (ohms, } \Omega)}$$

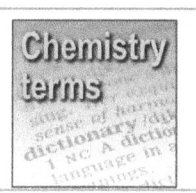

Chemistry terms

voltage: the electrical potential difference between two objects.

volt: the unit of voltage.

ohm (Ω): the unit of electrical resistance.

Ohm's law: the relationship among voltage, current, and electrical resistance.

15.2 Oxidation–Reduction (Redox) Reactions

Electro-chemistry is driven by electron transfer

In the early development of chemical knowledge, an important application was the refinement of pure metals such as iron, copper, aluminum, and tin. These elements exist naturally as mineral compounds such as aluminum oxide (Al_2O_3). Early chemists talked about "reducing" compounds into pure metals long before people understood the chemistry of what was happening. Today we know that "reducing" aluminum oxide to elemental aluminum and oxygen involves transferring electrons from oxygen to aluminum. The atoms that lose electrons are **oxidized** and the atoms that gain electrons are **reduced**. For example, Al^{3+} gains three electrons and is *reduced* to aluminum metal. Oxygen gains the electrons, and O^{2-} becomes *oxidized* to molecular oxygen.

Oxidation: Loss of electrons. The oxidized element becomes more positive.

Reduction: Gain of electrons. The reduced element becomes more negative.

***redox* is short for *red*uction–*ox*idation**

Oxidation–reduction reactions or **redox reactions** are among the most common and most important chemical reactions in everyday life. These reactions always occur in pairs. Oxidation does not occur without reduction and reduction does not occur without oxidation. The process of oxidation–reduction together with the concept of charge conservation forms the foundation of electrochemistry.

Even though we can't observe the actual transfer of electrons, we can easily see the results. If you dip a zinc (Zn) nail into a solution of copper sulfate ($CuSO_4$), the nail becomes covered with a brownish coating of copper metal.

The $CuSO_4$ solution contains Cu^{2+} and SO_4^{2-} ions. The copper ions are *reduced* to pure copper metal by electrons coming from the zinc. The zinc is *oxidized* by losing the electrons to become Zn^{2+} ions in the solution. The chemical equation that describes the complete reaction is

$$Zn(s) + CuSO_4(aq) \rightarrow ZnSO_4(aq) + Cu(s)$$

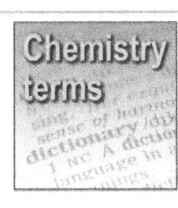
Chemistry terms

oxidized: loss of electrons resulting in increase of oxidation number
reduced: gain of electrons resulting in decrease of oxidation number
oxidation reaction: a chemical reaction that increases the charge—charge becomes more positive—of an atom or ion by giving up electrons.
reduction reaction: a chemical reaction that decreases the charge—charge becomes more negative—of an atom or ion by accepting electrons.
redox reaction: the abbreviation for an oxidation–reduction reaction.

Oxidation numbers

Familiar reactions may be redox reactions

Chemical processes such as the burning of natural gas (CH_4) and the rusting of iron (Fe) are very familiar. The chemical equations for these reactions are

$$4Fe(s) + 3O_2(g) \rightarrow 2Fe_2O_3(s) \quad \text{(rusting of iron)}$$

$$CH_4(g) + 2O_2(g) \rightarrow CO_2(g) + 2H_2O(g) \quad \text{(burning of methane)}$$

How can we determine whether these are redox reactions? Which elements are oxidized and which are reduced?

How to determine if a reaction is redox

To determine if a reaction is redox, we must find out if there is electron loss and gain that takes place among the elements involved in the reaction. If we find that there are some elements that lose electrons and some other elements that gain electrons, then we have the answer. The elements that lose electrons are oxidized, the elements that gain electrons are reduced, and the overall process is a redox reaction.

Hydrochloric acid (HCl) provides a good example that is easier to analyze. Hydrogen and chlorine combine to form HCl by sharing a pair of electrons. One of these electrons comes from H and the other from Cl, and they form a polar covalent bond.

Oxidation number

Since chlorine is more electronegative than hydrogen, the shared electrons stay closer to Cl than to H. As a result, it appears that chlorine has gained an electron and hydrogen has lost an electron. This apparent gain of an electron by the chlorine atom is indicated by an *oxidation number* of –1, which means that Cl is reduced. The **oxidation number** is the effective unit charge an atom in a compound would have if the electron were completely transferred to the more electronegative atom. In this case, chlorine is the more electronegative atom, and if it takes

Electrons spend more time closer to Cl

Cl appears to have gained electrons

H appears to have lost electrons

the electron from hydrogen, its charge is –1. Therefore its oxidation number in the compound HCl is also –1. In this reaction chlorine is *reduced* since it gains an electron and its oxidation number becomes lower (more negative).

Since HCl is neutral overall, the corresponding oxidation number of hydrogen should be +1. Hydrogen is *oxidized* since it loses an electron and its oxidation number increases (it becomes more positive).

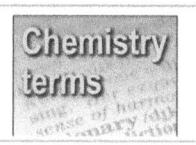
Chemistry terms

oxidation number: the number of electrons that an element has lost or gained in forming a chemical bond with another element.

Rules for assigning oxidation numbers

Oxidation number and ionic charge

The oxidation number is different from the real charge of the atom. The assignment of electrons to the atoms and the associated oxidation number is just a way to account for the electrons that are associated with the atoms.

Ionic charge is denoted $2-$
(sign follows the number)

The oxidation number is written with a sign followed with the number (e.g. –1, +1, –3, 0, etc.). This is different than the way we write the ionic charge for which the sign follows the number (e.g., 1–, 2–, 3+, etc.).

Oxidation number is denoted -2
(number follows the sign)

Rules for assigning oxidation numbers

By looking at the properties of atoms and the way that they bond with other atoms to form various compounds, scientists have come up with a set of rules to assign an oxidation number to each atom in a compound. These rules are explicit representations of the Lewis formulation and give us the number of electrons—the *oxidation number*—that is assigned to each atom in a compound.

TABLE 15.1. Rules for assigning oxidation numbers

1. The oxidation number of an atom in a pure element is 0. For example, the oxidation number of chlorine in Cl_2 or O in O_2 is 0.
2. The sum of the oxidation numbers of atoms in a neutral molecule is zero. For example, the sum of the oxidation numbers of C and O in CO_2 is 0. The oxidation number of carbon (n_C) plus two times the oxidation number of oxygen = 0: $n_C + 2n_O = 0$.
3. The sum of the oxidation numbers of all atoms in an ion is equal to the charge of the ion. For example, the oxidation number of Cu in Cu^{2+} is +2. For SO_4^{2-}, the oxidation number of S (n_S) plus four times the oxidation number of O (n_O) = –2: $n_S + 4n_O = -2$.
4. Metals have positive oxidation number according to their group: • Group 1A metals (Na, K, Li) have oxidation number +1. • Group 2A metals (Mg, Ca) have oxidation number +2.
5. The oxidation numbers of nonmetals are as follows: • Fluorine (F): –1 • Hydrogen (H): +1 except in hydrides such as LiH and NaH in which the oxidation number is –1. • Oxygen (O): –2 • Group 7A (Cl, Br, I): –1. • Group 6A (S, Se, Te): –2. • Group 5A (N, P, As): –3.

Application of oxidation number rules

Oxidation rules must be applied in order

The oxidation number rules apply in the order they appear on the list. If there is a conflict, the rule that is higher in the list has priority. For example, consider potassium peroxide (K_2O_2).

From Rule 4 we see that K has oxidation number +1 and Rule 5 tells us that oxygen has oxidation number –2. Obviously there is a conflict, since Rule 2, which keeps track of the overall charge balance, is violated. To solve this problem we must give priority to the order in which the rules appear.

Here are the steps to calculate the oxidation numbers of potassium and oxygen in K_2O_2:

TABLE 15.2. Technique for the calculation of oxidation numbers

Step 1	Step 2	Step 3
From Rule 2 we know that the sum of the oxidation numbers of all atoms in K_2O_2 must be zero. If the oxidation number for potassium is n_K and the oxidation number for oxygen is n_O then $$2(n_K) + 2(n_O) = 0$$	From Rule 4 we know that the oxidation number of potassium is +1 ($n_K = +1$). Since Rule 4 has priority over Rule 5, the oxidation number for O (n_O) is still unknown. Now we have an equation that we can use to solve for n_O: $$2(n_K) + 2(n_O) = 0$$	Solving the equation $$2(n_K) + 2(n_O) = 0$$ we obtain $n_O = -1$ and we are done. In K_2O_2, • the oxidation number of potassium (K) is +1 and • the oxidation number of oxygen (O) is –1.

The oxidation number of elements in a compound can be found by following these steps.

Solved problem

Find the oxidation number for each element in carbon monoxide (CO).

Asked: *The oxidation numbers of O and C in CO*

Relationships: *The rules for assigning oxidation numbers*

Solve: *The solution procedure is as follows:*
Since Carbon monoxide (CO) is a neutral compound, the sum of oxidation numbers of C and O must add to zero (Rule 2).
The oxidation number of oxygen = –2 (Rule 5).
The oxidation number of carbon (n_C) is found from
$n_C + (-2) = 0$, which gives $n_C = +2$.

Answer: *The oxidation number for C in carbon monoxide (CO) is +2.*
The oxidation number of O in carbon monoxide is –2.

Finding oxidation numbers

The same element can have different oxidation numbers

The oxidation number is a way to keep track of the electrons associated with each atom in a compound. *The oxidation number of the same element may be different from one compound to the other.* For example, in carbon dioxide (CO_2) the oxidation number of oxygen is –2. In potassium peroxide (K_2O_2) the oxidation number of oxygen is –1.

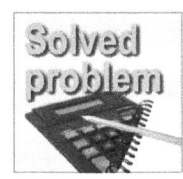

Find the oxidation number for each element in carbon dioxide (CO_2)

Asked: *Oxidation numbers of O and C in CO_2*

Relationships: *The rules for assigning oxidation numbers*

Solve: *Since carbon dioxide (CO_2) is a neutral compound the sum of the oxidation numbers of C and O_2 must add to zero (Rule 2).*
The oxidation number of O is –2 (Rule 5).
The oxidation number of O_2 is 2(–2) = –4.
The oxidation number of carbon (n_C) is found from
$n_C + 2(-2) = 0$, which gives $n_C = +4$

Answer: *The oxidation number for carbon in CO_2 is +4 and that for oxygen is –2.*

Find the oxidation number for each element in the nitrite ion (NO_2^-).

Asked: *Oxidation numbers of elements of an ion with overall charge of –1.*

Given: *The elemental arrangement of the ion*

Relationships: *The rules for assigning oxidation numbers*

Solve: *Nitrite (NO_2^-) is an ion with a charge of –1 and so the oxidation numbers of the elements must add up to –1. The sum of the oxidation numbers of N and O_2 must add to –1 (Rule 3).*
The oxidation number of oxygen is –2 (Rule 5).
The oxidation number of nitrogen (n_N) is found from
$n_N + 2(-2) = -1$, which gives $n_N = +3$.

Answer: *The oxidation number of O in NO_2^- is –2.*
The oxidation number of N in NO_2^- is +3.

Discussion: *As a check, note that $+3 + 2(-2) = -1$, which is the overall charge of the nitrite ion.*

Fractional oxidation numbers

Oxidation numbers may also be fractions

The oxidation number of an atom in a substances is usually a whole number such as +1, –1, +2, –2, etc. However, it is also possible for the oxidation number of atoms to be fractions such as +1/2, –1/2, –2/3, etc. This is often the case for the oxidation number of carbon in various compounds with hydrogen (hydrocarbons).

Let's consider methane (C_3H_8) and go through the various steps for calculating the oxidation numbers of C and H in this molecule.

TABLE 15.3. Steps for calculating oxidation numbers

Step 1	Step 2	Step 3
• From Rule 2 we know the sum of the oxidation numbers of all atoms in C_3H_8 must be zero. • If the oxidation number for carbon is n_C and the oxidation number for hydrogen is n_H then the equation that relates these oxidation numbers is $3(n_C) + 8(n_H) = 0$.	• From Rule 5 we know that the oxidation number of hydrogen is +1 ($n_H = +1$). • The oxidation number for C (n_C) is still unknown, but now we have an equation that we can solve for it: $$3(n_C) + 8(+1) = 0$$	• Solving the equation $3(n_C) + 8(+1) = 0$ we obtain $n_C = -8/3$. • So we see that the oxidation number can be a fraction. • Check the answer by verifying that the sum of oxidation numbers is zero: $3(-8/3) + 8 = 0$.

Solved problem

Find the oxidation number for each element in the compound C_3H_4.

Asked: *Oxidation number of each element in methylacetylene (C_3H_4)*

Relationships: *The rules for assigning oxidation numbers*

Solve: *C_3H_4 is a neutral compound, so the sum of the oxidation numbers of H_4 and C_3 must add to zero (Rule 2).*
The oxidation number of hydrogen (n_H) is +1 (Rule 5).
The oxidation number of carbon (n_C) is found from
$3(n_C) + 4(+1) = 0$, which gives $n_C = -4/3$.

Answer: *The oxidation number of C in C_3H_4 is –4/3.*
The oxidation number of H in C_3H_4 is +1.

Identifying redox reactions

Oxidation numbers in redox reactions

Determining the oxidation numbers is the first step in identifying a redox reaction. The next step is to see whether the oxidation numbers for any elements have *changed* in the reaction. If we find that any oxidation numbers have changed from the left side (reactants) to the right side (products) *then we know that we have a redox reaction.* If the oxidation numbers of the elements in the reactants and the products do not change, the reaction is not redox. The best way to learn this is with an example.

Solved problem

Find the element that is oxidized and the element that is reduced in the reaction of iron with oxygen resulting in rust (iron oxide, Fe_2O_3):

$$4Fe(s) + 3O_2(g) \rightarrow 2Fe_2O_3(s)$$

Asked: *The element that is oxidized and the element that is reduced*

Given: *The balanced chemical reaction of Fe and O_2 and the rules for assigning oxidation numbers*

Relationships: *The rules for assigning oxidation numbers to each element in compounds*

Solve: *We look at both the left and right sides of the reaction.*

Let's start with the reactants.

Since both Fe and O_2 are free elements the oxidation number of the Fe and O atoms on the left side of the equation is zero.

Next let's look at the product (Fe_2O_3) of the reaction.

The sum of the oxidation numbers in Fe_2O_3 must add to zero.

The oxidation number of oxygen is –2.

Now if we add the oxidation number of oxygen and the unknown oxidation number of iron (n_{Fe}) we have the equation

$2(n_{Fe}) + 3(-2) = 0$

Solving this equation for n_{Fe} we find that the oxidation number of iron in Fe_2O_3 is +3.

Answer: *The oxidation number of Fe has increased; it went from 0 to +3.*

Iron has lost electrons and so it is oxidized.

The oxidation number of oxygen has decreased, it went from 0 to –2.

Oxygen has gained electrons and it is reduced.

Analyzing a redox reaction

Oxidized: oxidation number increases (loses electrons)

Reduced: oxidation number decreases (gains electrons)

Charge balance is maintained

The number of electrons that are received by the reduced element is equal to the number of electrons that have been given up by the oxidized element. The total number of electrons does not change; overall charge neutrality must be maintained.

In the iron–oxygen reaction, we saw that the iron was oxidized and the oxygen was reduced. We can also say that "iron is oxidized by oxygen," which is another way of saying that oxygen facilitates the oxidation of iron. We may also say that "oxygen is reduced by iron"; oxygen is reduced and iron facilitates this reduction.

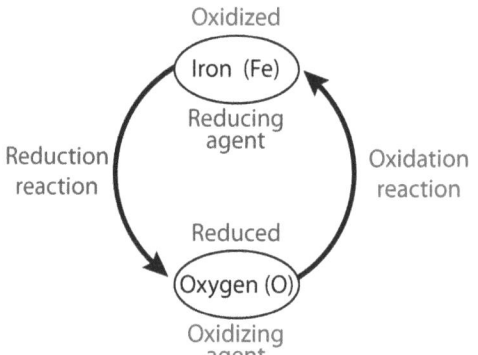

Oxidizing agent

Reducing agent

The element that oxidizes another element is called the oxidizing agent; in our example this is oxygen. The element that reduces another element is called the reducing agent. In our example iron is the reducing agent.

$$4Fe(s) + 3O_2(g) \rightarrow 2Fe_2O_3(s)$$

In the reaction $4Fe(s) + 3O_2(g) \rightarrow 2Fe_2O_3(s)$:

- Fe is oxidized.
- O is reduced.
- Fe is the reducing agent.
- O is the oxidizing agent.

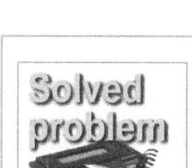

Find the reducing and the oxidizing agents in: $2Mg(s) + O_2(g) \rightarrow 2MgO(s)$.

Relationships: *The rules for assigning oxidation numbers and the chemical reaction*

Solve:

$$O_2(g) \ + \ 2Mg(s) \ \rightarrow \ 2MgO(s)$$

The oxidation number of oxygen decreases from 0 to −2, so oxygen is reduced. Therefore, oxygen is the oxidizing agent.
The oxidation number of magnesium increases from 0 to +2, so magnesium is oxidized. Therefore, magnesium is the reducing agent.

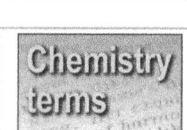

oxidizing agent: element that is reduced and thus oxidizes another element.
reducing agent: element that is oxidized and thus reduces another element.

15.3 Balancing Redox Equations

Mass conservation

For redox reactions, just like any other type of chemical reaction, mass is conserved. The number and types of atoms in the reactants must equal the number and types of atoms in the products.

Charge conservation

In addition to mass conservation we must also check to make sure that charge is conserved. We do this by keeping track of the electrons that are exchanged between various atoms and make certain that they balance. The number of electrons associated with the reactants must be equal to the number of electrons associated with the products. Also, the total increase in the oxidation number of some atoms must be equal to the total decrease of the oxidation numbers of some other atoms.

Balance mass and charge

The things that we learned in the previous section about oxidation numbers and redox reactions are now the tools that we use to balance redox reactions.

Balancing redox reactions

Step 1   Balance mass by counting atoms of each element

Step 2   Balance charge by counting electrons (oxidation numbers)

Methods for balancing redox reactions

Since balancing redox reactions requires balancing both mass and charge, the procedure is often more complicated than balancing non-redox reactions.

There are two methods for balancing redox reactions:

1. the oxidation number method and

2. the oxidation reaction and reduction reaction method combination (also called the half-reaction method).

Both of these methods are based on the same fundamental principles, and they simply represent structured applications of these procedures.

Balancing by Inspection

In some cases it is possible to balance a redox reaction by the inspection method. These "easy to balance" reactions are usually the ones that do not occur in aqueous solutions. Consider the unbalanced reaction of carbon with iron oxide. This reaction takes place in a furnace where iron oxide (Fe_2O_3) reacts with carbon, resulting in pure iron and carbon dioxide as a by-product:

$$C + Fe_2O_3 \rightarrow Fe + CO_2$$

This is a redox reaction. Carbon is oxidized and iron is reduced. The oxidation number of oxygen does not change in this reaction. By balancing the masses of the three elements that take part in this reaction, we obtain the following balanced equation:

$$3C + 2Fe_2O_3 \rightarrow 4Fe + 3CO_2$$

The oxidation number method

Most redox reactions can't be balanced with the inspection method. For such reactions we use the oxidation number method.

Balancing equations using oxidation numbers

The basic rule that drives this method is charge balance.

> ## The increase in oxidation number for the oxidized atoms
>
> ## equals
>
> ## the decrease in oxidation number for the reduced atoms

Steps for balancing a redox reaction

The basic steps for balancing a redox reaction with the oxidation number method are these:

1) Assign oxidation numbers

1. Assign oxidation numbers to all atoms.

   a. Use the rules for assigning the oxidation numbers.

   b. Write the oxidation number for each element below it.

2) Identify oxidation and reduction

2. Identify and label the atoms that are oxidized and the atoms that are reduced.

   a. An increase in oxidation number (loss of electrons) means oxidation.

   b. A decrease in oxidation number (gain of electrons) means reduction.

3) Adjust coefficients to equalize oxidation and reduction

3. Adjust the appropriate coefficients in the chemical equation so that the total increase in oxidation number (total loss of electrons) is equal to the total decrease in the oxida-tion number (total gain of electrons).

4) Check mass balance

4. Check for overall mass balance. Check to see that the number of atoms is the same on both sides of the equation. If not, make the necessary changes to the coefficients.

When we apply these steps in order, the resulting balanced equation should satisfy both mass and charge conservation.

Each step has a well-defined set of rules. However, applying all of the steps together can be challenging! Balancing redox reactions requires practice to become familiar with it.

Example: balancing a complex redox reaction

Using the oxidation number method, balance the equation

$$HNO_3(aq) + Cu_2O(s) \rightarrow Cu(NO_3)_2(aq) + NO(g) + H_2O(l)$$

Solve: *Follow the steps for balancing redox equations.*

Step 1. Assign the oxidation numbers to each element:

Step 2. Identify the atoms that are reduced and oxidized:

The oxidation number of N decreases in NO, so N is reduced.
The oxidation number of Cu increases, so Cu is oxidized.
The oxidation numbers of the other atoms do not change.

Step 3. First we balance all atoms whose oxidation numbers have changed:

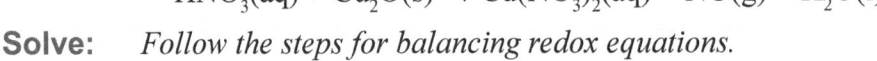

N atoms whose oxidation number changes are already balanced
To balance Cu atoms we adjust the coefficients; multiply by 2.
The total increase in oxidation number is 2: Cu loses two electrons.
The decrease in oxidation number of N is 3: N gains three electrons.
Balance the number of electrons lost and gained. Multiply the species
that contain Cu by +3 and the species that contain N by +2:

$$2HNO_3 + 3Cu_2O \rightarrow 6Cu(NO_3)_2 + 2NO + H_2O$$

Step 4. Balance mass.
  Add 12HNO_3 to the left side to balance N.
  Add 6O and 12H to the right side to balance oxygen and hydrogen.
  This is done by adding 6H_2O to the right side to balance H and O.

$$14HNO_3 + 3Cu_2O \rightarrow 6Cu(NO_3)_2 + 2NO + 7H_2O$$

Half-reactions

Redox reactions in aqueous solutions

Many interesting and useful redox reactions occur in aqueous solutions. The procedure for balancing the equations for aqueous reactions is based on the fundamental principles described earlier but with an important difference. The difference is the separation of the complete reaction into two **half-reactions**. One half-reaction involves the oxidized elements and the other involves the reduced elements. By separating the oxidation from the reduction and writing them separately, we make it easier to count electrons and establish charge balance.

Identifying half-reactions

To see where to split the reaction into half-reactions, we need to know the oxidation numbers of all the elements involved. Once these are known, we can see which are oxidized and which are reduced. Once we know the oxidation and the reduction parts, we can separate the complete reaction into half-reactions. When a zinc nail is placed in copper sulfate ($CuSO_4$) solution, the overall reaction can be explained with the half-reactions.

Why half-reactions are useful

It is very direct to see the transfer of electrons with half-reactions. The number of electrons given up by the oxidation half-reaction must be equal to the number of electrons received by the reduction half-reaction.

Solved problem

Find the half-reactions of the reaction $Zn(s) + CuSO_4(aq) \rightarrow ZnSO_4(aq) + Cu(s)$.

Given: *The rules for assigning oxidation numbers*

Relationships: *In solution, $CuSO_4$ and $ZnSO_4$ dissociate as follows:*

$CuSO_4$ into Cu^{2+} and SO_4^{2-} ions,

$ZnSO_4$ into Zn^{2+} and SO_4^{2-} ions.

The reaction may now be written as

$Zn(s) + Cu^{2+} + SO_4^{2-} \rightarrow Zn^{2+} + SO_4^{2-} + Cu(s)$

Zn is oxidized and Cu is reduced.

SO_4^{2-} is neither oxidized nor reduced. It is called a spectator ion.

Solve: *The half-reactions are*

$Zn(s) \rightarrow Zn^{2+} + 2e^-$ (oxidation)

$Cu^{2+} + 2e^- \rightarrow Cu(s)$ (reduction)

Chemistry terms

half-reactions: the oxidation and the reduction parts of a redox reaction.

The half-reactions method

Steps in the half-reactions method

Redox reaction equations can be balanced using the two half reactions. The method is called the *half-reactions* method for balancing redox reaction equations.

Step 1.   Write the complete unbalanced reaction showing explicitly all ions.

Step 2.   Identify which elements are oxidized and which are reduced. Find the spectator ions (those for which oxidation number does not change).

Step 3.   Write down the two unbalanced half-reactions.

Step 4.   Balance mass with elements other than oxygen and hydrogen. Balance oxygen by adding H_2O then balance hydrogen by adding H^+.

Step 5.   Balance the charge for both half-reactions.

Step 6.   Make the number of electrons in both reactions equal by adjusting the coefficients.

Step 7.   Add the two half-reactions

Step 8.   Simplify and check that both mass and charge balance.

An example redox reaction equation:

The plating of copper into zinc in a solution of copper sulfate provides a good example of the half-reaction method:

$$Zn(s) + CuSO_4(aq) \rightarrow ZnSO_4(aq) + Cu(s)$$

Step 1. Write the unbalanced equation showing all ions:

$$Zn(s) + Cu^{2+} + SO_4^{2-} \rightarrow Zn^{2+} + SO_4^{2-} + Cu(s)$$

Step 2. Identify oxidation, reduction, and spectator ions:

Step 3. Write down the two unbalanced half-reactions:

$$\text{Oxidation: } Zn(s) \rightarrow Zn^{2+}(aq)$$
$$\text{Reduction: } Cu^{2+}(aq) \rightarrow Cu(s)$$

Step 4. Balance the mass for both half-reactions,

$$Zn(s) \rightarrow Zn^{2+}(aq)$$
$$Cu^{2+}(aq) \rightarrow Cu(s)$$

We see that it is already balanced.

Balancing the charge in half-reactions

Why charge balancing is necessary

It is possible, even likely, that mass will balance for both half-reactions, but one half-reaction uses more electrons than the other one yields. In a fully balanced electrochemical reaction, the number of electrons given up in the oxidation half-reaction is the same as the number of electrons used in the reduction half-reaction.

Step 5. Balance the charge for both half-reactions. Add electrons to balance changes in oxidation numbers:

- $Zn(s) \rightarrow Zn^{2+}(aq) + \mathbf{2e^-}$: Add two electrons to the right side.

- $Cu^{2+}(aq) + \mathbf{2e^-} \rightarrow Cu(s)$: Add two electrons to the left side.

Step 6. Make the number of electrons in both reactions equal by adjusting the coefficients:

- $Zn(s) \rightarrow Zn^{2+}(aq) + 2e^-$
- $Cu^{2+}(aq) + 2e^- \rightarrow Cu(s)$

Step 7. Add the two half-reactions:

- $Zn(s) + Cu^{2+}(aq) \rightarrow Zn^{2+}(aq) + Cu(s)$
  Mass and charge are balanced.

- Return the spectator ions and adjust coefficients to maintain charge neutrality.

$$Zn(s) + Cu^{2+}(aq) + SO_4^{2-}(aq) \rightarrow Zn^{2+}(aq) + SO_4^{2-}(aq) + Cu(s)$$

Step 8. Simplify the equation and check for mass and charge balance:

- Reactants are Zn, Cu^{2+}, and SO_4^{2-}, for 0 net charge.
- Products are Zn^{2+}, Cu, and SO_4^{2-}, for 0 net charge.
- Mass and charge are balanced.

At the end of the analysis we could write the final balanced equation as

$$Zn(s) + CuSO_4(aq) \rightarrow ZnSO_4(aq) + Cu(s)$$

What the half-reactions tell us

However, this does not tell us that two electrons were transferred. If this reaction were part of a battery or biochemical process, the fact that two electrons were exchanged might create an electrical current!

A redox reaction with chlorine

Chlorine dioxide (ClO_2) is used for water treatment. The OH^- indicates that the reaction occurs in a basic solution for which an element that appears in the reactants is both oxidized and reduced.

Solved problem

Using the half-reactions method, balance the equation
$$ClO_2 + OH^- \rightarrow ClO_2^- + ClO_3^-$$

Solve: *Follow the steps for balancing redox equations.*

Step 1. *Write the complete unbalanced reaction explicitly showing all ions:*
$$ClO_2 + OH^- \rightarrow ClO_2^- + ClO_3^-$$

Step 2. *Identify which elements are oxidized and which are reduced:*
ClO_2 is oxidized to ClO_3^-. Cl goes from +4 to +5: Cl is oxidized.
ClO_2 is reduced to ClO_2^-. Cl goes from +4 to +3: Cl is reduced.
Note that Cl is both oxidized and reduced in this reaction.

Step 3. *Write down the two half-reactions:*
$ClO_2 \rightarrow ClO_3^-$ (oxidation half-reaction)
$ClO_2 \rightarrow ClO_2^-$ (reduction half-reaction)

Step 4. *Balance the mass for both half-reactions:*

Cl is balanced in both reactions.

Balance O and H of the oxidation half-reaction:
Balance O by adding H_2O and OH^-: $ClO_2 + 2OH^- \rightarrow ClO_3^- + H_2O$.
O and H of the reduction half-reaction are balanced: $ClO_2 \rightarrow ClO_2^-$.

Step 5. *Balance the charge for both half-reactions. Add electrons to balance changes in oxidation numbers:*
$ClO_2 + 2OH^- \rightarrow ClO_3^- + H_2O + e^-$: Add an electron to the right side
$ClO_2 + e^- \rightarrow ClO_2^-$: Add an electron to the left side

Step 6. *The number of electrons is equal in both reactions.*

Step 7. *Add the two half-reactions:*
$2ClO_2 + 2OH^- \rightarrow ClO_3^- + ClO_2^- + H_2O$ (no spectator ions)

Step 8. *Simplify the equation, if needed, and check for mass and charge balance:*
$2ClO_2 + 2OH^- \rightarrow ClO_3^- + ClO_2^- + H_2O$
Mass and charge are conserved.

15.4 Electrochemical Cells

Exchanged electrons and electrochemical cells

The movement of electrons from oxidized compounds to reduced compounds is the essence of electrochemistry. If we physically separate the oxidation and reduction reactions, we can force the electrons to be exchanged by moving through a wire. Electrons moving through a wire make an electrical *current*. A device that creates a separation of oxidation and reduction reactions is an *electrochemical cell*. An **electrochemical cell** is a device in which redox reactions may produce electrical energy or in which electrical energy is used to produce a chemical reaction.

Parts of electrochemical cells

There are three main components of an electrochemical cell:

1. two **electrodes**, where the oxidation and reduction reactions occur:
    a. the **anode** electrode, where oxidation occurs, and
    b. the **cathode** electrode, where reduction occurs;

2. the **electrolyte**, which is a conductive solution inside which the electrodes are immersed, and
    a. contains free ions and
    b. conducts electricity;

3. the conducting path that connects the electrodes externally.

When we analyze electrochemical cells we must keep in mind the following:

1. the connection between oxidation and reduction,
2. the flow of electrons from the anode to the cathode, and
3. the chemical reactions that occur at the anode and the cathode.

electrochemical cell: a device in which redox reactions take place.
electrode: the part of a cell where oxidation and reduction reactions occur.
anode: the electrode at which oxidation occurs.
cathode: the electrode at which reduction occurs.
electrolyte: the conductive solution in which the electrodes are immersed.

Types of electrochemical cells

Types of cells

The relation between the chemical reactions and the electrical current divide electrochemical cells into two categories.

Voltaic cells

1. **Voltaic cells**:
   A voltaic cell is an electrochemical cell in which spontaneous chemical reactions at the electrodes generate electrical current. Voltaic cells are named after Italian scientist Alessandro Volta, who invented the battery in 1800. Another name for a voltaic cell is a **galvanic cell** after Luigi Galvani, who is considered the father of electro-chemistry. A battery is a voltaic cell.

Electrolytic cells

2. **Electrolytic cells**:
   In an electrolytic cell an externally applied electrical current drives nonspontaneous chemical reactions at the interface between the electrolyte and the electrodes. Electroplating and electrolysis are done with electrolytic cells.

Half-cells

Both voltaic and electrolytic cells are constructed with two half-cells. One of these half-cells corresponds to the anode, which is related to the oxidation half-reaction. The other half-cell corresponds to the cathode, which is related to the reduction half-reaction.

Batteries are voltaic cells

Batteries are voltaic cells. The positive and the negative terminals of the battery correspond to the electrodes of the cell. The positive terminal is connected to the cathode half-cell where reduction occurs and the negative terminal is connected to the anode half-cell where oxidation occurs.

When an external circuit such as a light bulb is connected between the electrodes, electrons flow from the anode electrode to the cathode electrode.

The flow of electrical current is completed inside the battery. Here nega-tive ions move from the cathode to the anode and positive ions move in the opposite direction, from the anode to the cathode to maintain electroneutrality.

Anode (oxidation)

Cathode (reduction)

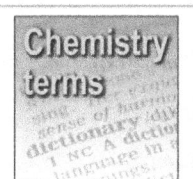

Chemistry terms

voltaic cell: an electrochemical cell in which chemical reactions generate electricity.

galvanic cell: another name for voltaic cell.

electrolytic cell: an electrochemical cell in which chemical reactions result from the application of electrical current.

Chemistry in a voltaic cell

Constructing a voltaic cell

To construct an electrochemical cell we start with the two half-cells. Electrons are released in the oxidation part (anode). Electrons are absorbed in the reduction part (cathode). We connect the two cells so that electrons flow from the anode to the cathode.

Mg–Cu voltaic cell

To illustrate the process, consider a voltaic cell using Mg and Cu as the electrodes. The magnesium electrode is immersed in a $MgSO_4$ solution that contains Mg^{2+} ions. The copper electrode is immersed in a $CuSO_4$ solution that contains Cu^{2+} ions. The half-reactions that describe the oxidation of Mg and the reduction of Cu are:

$$Mg(s) \rightarrow Mg^{2+}(aq) + 2e^- \quad \text{(oxidation at the anode)}$$

$$Cu^{2+}(aq) + 2e^- \rightarrow Cu(s) \quad \text{(reduction at the cathode)}$$

Magnesium loses electrons more easily than Cu. When the two electrodes are connected by a wire (or a bulb), the electrons released by Mg at the anode move through the wire to the cathode. This flow of electrons gives electrical current, *but only for a very short time*! The current stops because the Mg^{2+} ions that are generated at the anode have nowhere to go. The electrons and the Mg^{2+} ions are attracted to each other and the reaction stops as soon as it starts.

No path to complete the circuit means no current flow

No reactions means no electrons released

Mg^{2+} Cu^{2+}
SO_4^{2-} SO_4^{2-}

In order to solve this problem we must provide a path for positive ions to move from the anode half-cell to the cathode half-cell. The addition of positive ions to copper sulfate balances the addition of electrons and maintains charge neutrality. You might think that such an effective path can be created by mixing the two solutions. If we mix the solutions, Cu^{2+} ions will come in contact with Mg, generating localized redox half-cells, which are not going to produce any useful electrons *flowing in the wire*. The electrons in this case are exchanged locally and do not pass through the external circuit. We need a better solution.

Salt bridge

Salt bridge

An effective source of ions is provided by a *salt bridge*. A **salt bridge** is a connection between the oxidation and the reduction half-cells. An ideal salt bridge provides a path for ions to flow between the half-cells, but it does not permit mixing of the half-cell solutions. A common salt bridge is a tube that contains an electrolyte such as potassium chloride (KCl) whose ends are plugged with a porous material. The bulk of the material can't leak out, but ions such as K^+ and Cl^- can pass through. For short experiments, a strip of filter paper soaked in KCl makes an effective salt bridge.

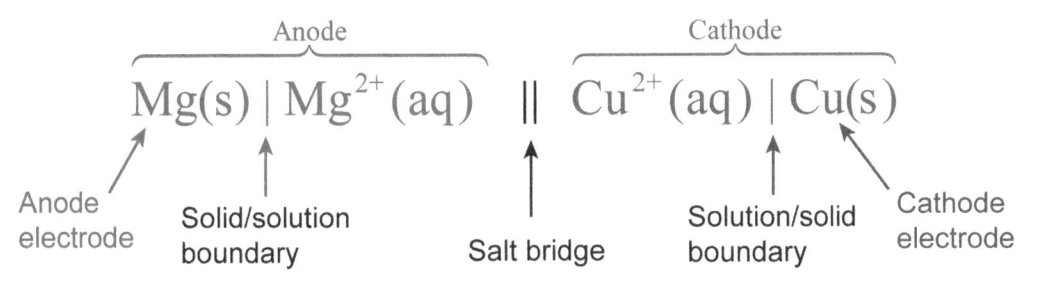

$$Mg(s) \rightarrow Mg^{2+} + 2e^-$$

$$Cu^{2+} + 2e^- \rightarrow Cu(s)$$

There is a compact way for representing the reaction and the electrochemical cell in general. For the magnesium–copper voltaic cell, this representation is shown here:

$$\underbrace{Mg(s) \mid Mg^{2+}(aq)}_{Anode} \; \| \; \underbrace{Cu^{2+}(aq) \mid Cu(s)}_{Cathode}$$

Anode electrode   Solid/solution boundary   Salt bridge   Solution/solid boundary   Cathode electrode

The double vertical lines in the middle indicate the salt bridge. The anode, or the oxidation half-cell, is always written on the left of the double lines, and the cathode, or reduction half-cell, is written to the right of the double lines.

The electrodes of the cell are written on the extreme left (anode) and the extreme right (cathode) of the expression. The two single vertical lines on the left and the right represent the boundaries between the solid and the solution.

Chemistry terms

salt bridge: an electrical connection between the oxidation and the reduction half-cells of an electrochemical cell.

Electromotive force

Electrical potential

The movement of electrical charge from one point to another requires there to be a difference in the potential energies between these points. Electric charge moves from a point of higher potential to a point of lower potential. The energy that is required in order to move a certain amount of charge depends on the amount of charge moved and the potential difference.

anode (-)   cathode (+)

Electron movement

In an electrochemical cell, the electrons that flow from the anode to the cathode are "pushed" by the force that is generated by the potential difference between the anode and the cathode.

Electromotive force

This difference in potential between the anode and the cathode is called the **electromotive force (emf)** of the cell and is denoted by E_{cell}, also called **cell emf**.

Cell energy

Once we know the emf of an electrochemical cell, we can calculate the amount of energy that the cell can provide when a certain amount of reactants are consumed. This energy is given by the equation:

$$Work_{cell} = nFE_{cell}$$

Power

F is the Faraday constant, which is equal to 96,500 C, and n is the number of moles of electrons that are produced in the reaction. The amount of power that the cell can provide is the amount of work that the cell can do. The amount of power is calculated by dividing $Work_{cell}$ by time:

$$Power_{cell} = Work_{cell} / time.$$

Voltaic cells generate energy

If we are given a certain cell reaction, we can calculate the electrical energy that the cell can provide when a certain amount of reactants is consumed. All we need to do is determine the number of moles of electrons released by the anode as the electrode is consumed. We then multiply the number of moles by Faraday's constant and the voltage of the cell E_{cell}.

$$Mg(s) \rightarrow Mg^{2+} + 2e^-$$

1 mole of Mg

2 moles of electrons

in $W_{cell} = n F E_{cell}$, $n = 2$

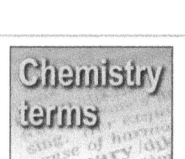
Chemistry terms

electromotive force (emf): the difference in the electrical potential between the anode and the cathode of an electrochemical cell.

cell emf: abbreviation for the electromotive force of a cell.

Cell voltage and energy

The cell emf (E_{cell}) gives us a measure of the driving force of the cell reaction. As we know, the cell reaction is the sum of two half-reactions: the oxidation reaction, which occurs at the anode, and the reduction reaction which occurs at the cathode.

Solved problem

The Mg–Cu cell has E_{cell} = 2.71 V. The cell reaction is
$$Mg(s) + Cu^{2+}(aq) \rightarrow Mg^{2+}(aq) + Cu(s).$$

Calculate the total energy that can be obtained from this cell if 2.43 g of Mg is consumed in the reaction.

Given: *The cell reaction, the emf voltage, and the amount of reactant consumed*

Relationships: *The equation that relates the number of moles of electrons and the cell voltage with the energy released is $W_{cell} = nFE_{cell}$*

The half-reactions are: $Mg(s) \rightarrow Mg^{2+}(aq) + 2e^-$
and $Cu^{2+}(aq) + 2e^- \rightarrow Cu(s)$

Solve: *From the half-reactions we see that 1 mole of Mg generates 2 moles of electrons.*

One mole of Mg weighs 24.3 g. Therefore, 2.43 g of Mg corresponds to 0.1 moles of Mg.

0.1 moles of Mg corresponds to 0.2 moles of electrons and so we have n = 0.2.

Substitute into the energy equation:
$$W_{cell} = 0.2 \times 96,500 \times 1.10 = 21,230 \, J$$

Answer: *2.43 g of Mg release 21,230 J.*

The total cell voltage (E_{cell}) is a combination of the potential at each half-cell. We define E_{cell} as

$$E_{cell} = \text{reduction potential} + \text{oxidation potential}$$

$$E_{cell} = E_{reduction} + E_{oxidation}$$

For example, if the voltage associated with the reduction half-reaction

$$Mg^{2+}(aq) + 2e^- \rightarrow Mg(s)$$

is –2.37 V, then the voltage associated with the reverse reaction

$$Mg(s) \rightarrow Mg^{2+}(aq) + 2e^-$$

is $-(-2.37) = +2.37$ V.

Standard reduction potentials

Since $E_{oxidation} = -E_{reduction}$, chemists have decided for convenience to only keep track of the $E_{reduction}$ voltages. Since the rate of chemical reactions depends on conditions such as temperature, pressure, and concentration the reduction potentials are tabulated for defined or standard conditions. These standard conditions are

- Temperature of   25°C

- Pressure of   1 atm (for gases), and

- Concentration of   1 M (for solutions).

Standard reduction potential

The cell voltage under these conditions is called the **standard reduction potential** and it is labeled as E^{o}_{cell}. Since it is not possible to measure the potential of single electrodes the standard reduction potentials are given with respect to a well-defined reference half-cell. The reference used is the hydrogen reference half-cell, which has the half-reaction

$$2H^+(aq) + 2e^- \rightarrow H_2(g)$$

The standard potential for this half-reaction is 0 V and the potential of all other cells is measured with respect to it. Standard reduction potentials are given in Table 15.4.

Solved problem

Using the standard reduction potentials calculate the cell voltage (E^{o}_{cell}) of the cell Zn(s) | Zn²⁺(aq) || Cu²⁺(aq) | Cu(s).

Asked: *E^{o}_{cell} of the reaction Zn(s) + Cu²⁺(aq) → Zn²⁺(aq) + Cu(s)*

Given: *The cell reaction and the standard reduction potentials*

Relationships: *The standard potential of the reduction half-reaction*
Zn²⁺(aq) + 2e⁻ → Zn(s) is –0.76 V.
Therefore that of the corresponding oxidation reaction
Zn(s) → Zn²⁺(aq) + 2e⁻ is –(–0.76 V) = 0.76 V. $E^{o}_{oxidation}$ = 0.76 V.
Cu²⁺(aq) + 2e⁻ → Cu(s); $E^{o}_{reduction}$ = 0.34 V
$E^{o}_{cell} = E^{o}_{reduction} + E^{o}_{oxidation}$

Solve: *Substitute the values for $E^{o}_{oxidation}$ = 0.76V and $E^{o}_{reduction}$ = 0.34 V to get E^{o}_{cell} = 0.34 V + 0.76 V = 1.10 V.*

Answer: *The cell voltage is 1.10 V.*

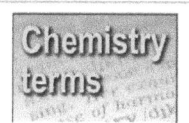

standard reduction potential: the potential of a cell measured under standard conditions of temperature, pressure, and concentration.

Standard reduction potentials

TABLE 15.4. Standard reduction potentials

Reduction half-reaction	$E°$ (V)	
$Li^+(aq) + e^- \rightarrow Li(s)$	−3.04	Strong reducing agent, strong tendency to be oxidized, strong tendency to give up electrons, weak oxidizing agent, tendency to occur in the reverse direction
$Na^+(aq) + e^- \rightarrow Na(s)$	−2.71	
$Mg^{2+}(aq) + 2e^- \rightarrow Mg(s)$	−2.38	
$Al^{3+}(aq) + 3e^- \rightarrow Al(s)$	−1.66	
$2H_2O(l) + 2e^- \rightarrow H_2(g) + 2OH^-(aq)$	−0.83	
$Zn^{2+}(aq) + 2e^- \rightarrow Zn(s)$	−0.76	
$Cr^{2+}(aq) + 2e^- \rightarrow Cr(s)$	−0.74	
$Fe^{2+}(aq) + 2e^- \rightarrow Fe(s)$	−0.41	
$Ni^{2+}(aq) + 2e^- \rightarrow Ni(s)$	−0.23	
$Sn^{2+}(aq) + 2e^- \rightarrow Sn(s)$	−0.14	
$Pb^{2+}(aq) + 2e^- \rightarrow Pb(s)$	−0.13	
$Fe^{3+}(aq) + 3e^- \rightarrow Fe(s)$	−0.04	
$2H^+(aq) + 2e^- \rightarrow H_2(g)$	0	Reference half-cell; assigned zero potential
$Cu^{2+}(aq) + 2e^- \rightarrow Cu(s)$	0.34	
$O_2(g) + 2H_2O(l) + 4e^- \rightarrow 4OH^-(aq)$	0.40	
$Cu^+(aq) + e^- \rightarrow Cu(s)$	0.52	
$Ag^+(aq) + e^- \rightarrow Ag(s)$	0.80	
$ClO_2(g) + e^- \rightarrow ClO_2^-(aq)$	0.95	
$O_2(g) + 4H^+(aq) + 4e^- \rightarrow 2H_2O(l)$	1.23	
$Cl_2(g) + e^- \rightarrow 2Cl^-(aq)$	1.36	
$PbO_2(s) + 4H^+(aq) + 2e^- \rightarrow Pb^{2+} + 2H_2O(l)$	1.46	
$Au^{3+}(aq) + 3e^- \rightarrow Au(s)$	1.50	
$H_2O_2(aq) + 2H^+(aq) + 2e^- \rightarrow 2H_2O(l)$	1.78	
$F_2(g) + 2e^- \rightarrow 2F^-(aq)$	2.87	Strong oxidizing agent, strong tendency to be reduced, strong tendency to attract electrons, weak reducing agent, tendency to occur in the forward direction

Reaction spontaneity

ADVANCED AP

Spontaneous and non-spontaneous reactions

Using the standard potentials given on Table 15.4, we can calculate the cell emf (E°_{cell}) of any redox reaction. The sign of E°_{cell} indicates whether the reaction is **spontaneous** or **nonspontaneous**. A spontaneous reaction is one that occurs in the indicated direction, reactants to products. A nonspontaneous reaction is one that does not proceed in the indicated forward direction.

A positive E°_{cell} indicates a spontaneous (product-favoring) reaction. A negative E°_{cell} indicates a nonspontaneous (reactant-favoring) reaction:

$E^\circ_{cell} > 0$ (spontaneous reaction.)

$E^\circ_{cell} < 0$ (nonspontaneous reaction.)

Solved problem

Determine whether the reaction Zn(s) + Ni^{2+}(aq) → Zn^{2+}(aq) + Ni(s) is spontaneous under standard conditions.

Given: *The reaction and the table of standard reduction potentials*

Relationships: *The half-cells and their half-cell potentials are*

$$Zn(s) \rightarrow Zn^{2+}(aq) + 2e^-, \quad E^0_{oxidation} = +0.76\,V$$

$$Ni^{2+}(aq) + 2e^- \rightarrow Ni(s), \quad E^0_{reduction} = -0.23\,V$$

Solve: *Now we need to calculate the total cell potential. Add*

$$Zn(s) \rightarrow Zn^{2+}(aq) + 2e^-, \quad E^0 = +0.76\,V$$

$$Ni^{2+}(aq) + 2e^- \rightarrow Ni(s), \quad E^0 = -0.23\,V$$

together to get:
$$E^0_{cell} = E^0_{oxidation} + E^0_{reduction} = -0.23\,V + 0.76\,V = +0.53\,V$$

Answer: *Since the total cell voltage is a positive number, the reaction is spontaneous and proceeds as indicated.*

The reactions at the bottom of Table 15.4 [F$_2$(g) + 2e$^-$ → 2F$^-$(aq)] have a tendency to occur in the forward direction. The reactions at the top of Table 15.4 [Li$^+$(aq) + e$^-$ → Li(s)] have a tendency to occur in the reverse direction.

The relative position of the half-reactions on the table tells us whether the redox reaction is spontaneous. Any reduction half-reaction will be spontaneous if it is paired with the reverse of the half-reaction above it in Table 15.4.

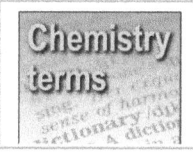
Chemistry terms

spontaneous: refers to a reaction that occurs in the indicated direction without any energy input.

nonspontaneous: refers to a reaction that does not occur in the indicated direction.

Nernst equation

Batteries run out of energy

The battery is a voltaic cell. The voltage of a battery is related to the emf of the battery cell. We are all familiar with the fact that batteries run out. This is because the chemical energy stored in the battery is used up. Since the chemical energy is released by redox reactions, something must happen to these redox reactions inside the battery as time goes on.

The relationship between reactants and products changes as the redox reactions proceed in an electrochemical cell. Reactants are consumed by the reaction and products are generated. This implies that the concentration of every substance in the cell changes as reactions proceed. As the reactants decrease their concentration decreases, and equivalently the concentration of the products increases. We expect that the voltage output of a battery depends on the concentration of reactants and products.

The relationship that describes this dependence is the **Nernst equation**, which is given by

$$E_{\text{cell}} = E^0_{\text{cell}} - \frac{0.0592}{n} \log(Q)$$

Standard cell potential

number of moles

$Q = \dfrac{\text{product concentration}}{\text{reactant concentration}}$

The parameter n is the number of moles of electrons generated by the reaction and Q is the ratio of product to reactant concentrations.

Under standard conditions, $Q = 1$, and since $\log(1) = 0$, $E_{\text{cell}} = E^0_{\text{cell}}$.

Using a battery

As a battery is used, the concentration of the products is increased and the concentration of reactants is decreased. This makes Q greater than 1, so $E_{\text{cell}} < E^0_{\text{cell}}$. The battery voltage is decreased, and the battery runs out.

Recharging a battery

When a battery is recharged, the concentration of reactants increases and the concentration of products decreases. This decreases Q and drives E_{cell} toward E^0_{cell}. The battery is then fully recharged when $Q = 1$ and $E_{\text{cell}} = E^0_{\text{cell}}$.

Battery discharging	Battery charging
[reactants]: decrease [products]: increase	[reactants]: increase [products]: decrease
Q increases	Q decreases
log(Q) increases	log(Q) decreases
E_{cell} decreases	E_{cell} increases

Chemistry terms

Nernst equation: the mathematical equation that relates the electrical potential of a cell to the standard reduction potential and the state of the reaction as given by the concentration of reactants and products.

Electrolytic cells

Voltaic vs. electrolytic cells

In the voltaic cell, spontaneous redox reactions are used to generate electrical current. In an **electrolytic cell**, externally applied electricity is used to drive a nonspontaneous redox reaction.

The result of the induced chemical reaction in an electrolytic cell is called **electrolysis**. Many useful substances, including aluminum and chlorine, are commercially produced using electrolysis.

When a battery is used it acts as a voltaic cell; chemistry generates electrical current. When we recharge a battery, we switch the type of cell from voltaic to electrolytic. A rechargeable battery is both a voltaic cell and an electrolytic cell.

Water decomposition

The decomposition of water into its constituent elements is a nonspontaneous reaction. This means that the reaction

$$2H_2O(l) \rightarrow 2H_2(g) + O_2(g)$$

does not proceed without the addition of energy.

The oxidation number of hydrogen in H_2O is +1 and the oxidation number of hydrogen in H_2 is 0. Therefore H_2O is reduced to H_2. Similarly, since the oxidation number of oxygen in H_2O is –2, H_2O is oxidized to O_2.

This is a redox reaction for which the reduction and oxidation half-reactions and the associated reduction potentials are:

$$2H_2O + 2e^- \rightarrow H_2 + 2OH^-, \quad E^o_{red} = -0.83 \text{ V} \quad \text{(reduction)}$$

$$2H_2O \rightarrow O_2 + 4H^+ + 4e^-, \quad E^o_{ox} = -1.23 \text{ V} \quad \text{(oxidation)}$$

For simplicity, we have used the abbreviation *red* for *reduction* and the *ox* for *oxidation*. The cell potential of this redox reaction is $E^o_{cell} = -2.06$ V. Since this is a negative number, the reaction is nonspontaneous. We must provide energy in order to break up water into hydrogen and oxygen.

Hydrogen generation

Hydrogen is being considered as an energy source for the future. However, hydrogen gas does not exist as a free gas on Earth, so has to be produced from water, fossil fuels, or biomass. The production of hydrogen from water is the cleanest but most expensive way of producing hydrogen. The production of hydrogen corresponds to energy storage in hydrogen. The energy is extracted when hydrogen gas is oxidized to form water.

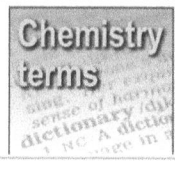

Chemistry terms

electrolytic cell: an electrochemical cell in which chemical reactions result from the application of electrical current.

electrolysis: the result of a chemical reaction in an electrolytic cell.

Catalytic converters: chemistry for a cleaner environment

The catalytic converter is a device in the exhaust system of automobiles. It is located between the engine and the muffler, and it changes harmful pollutants released by the engine into less harmful compounds.

Catalytic converters play a major role in the reduction of air pollution in populated areas. Automobiles produce three major types of air pollutants:

Catalytic converter

1. nitrogen oxides (NO and NO_2, also labeled NO_x),

2. uncombusted hydrocarbons (uncombustable fuel), and

3. considerable amounts of carbon monoxide (CO).

Automobile engineers have searched for ways to reduce these harmful pollutants with careful engine design, but they have found that, under normal driving conditions, it is impossible to decrease them to an acceptable level. The catalytic converter was designed to reduce the quantity of these pollutants in the exhaust before they are released into the air. Catalytic converters are very effective in removing the harmful gases. Approximately 96% of the uncombusted hydrocarbons and carbon monoxide are converted to CO_2 and H_2O, and approximately 76% of the nitrous oxides (NO_x) are reduced to harmless nitrogen gas (N_2). You might wonder why automobile exhaust is such a source of pollution in our major cities if our catalytic converters work so well. This is because there are so many people driving! Our population is soaring and this is increasing the overall amount of pollution.

The warm temperatures and the mountains surrounding the city of Los Angeles trap the harmful gases in the valley, causing them to reach dangerous levels. Los Angeles was the first city in the United States to use catalytic converters to reduce smog.

Catalytic converters selectively oxidize and reduce dangerous gases in our exhaust.

As part of the exhaust system of a car, catalytic converters perform two very distinct functions:

1. They reduce nitrogen oxides to nitrogen gas:

$$NO(g) \text{ and } NO_2(g) \rightarrow N_2(g) \quad \text{(reduction)}$$

2. They oxidize carbon monoxide and uncombusted hydrocarbon fragments to CO_2 and H_2O:

$$CO(g) \text{ and } C_xH_y(g) \rightarrow CO_2(g) + H_2O(g) \quad \text{(oxidation)}$$

In effect, catalytic converters work like antioxidants for our cars. In the catalytic converter, nitrogen in NO or NO_2 is reduced because its oxidation number goes from +2 or +4 to zero in N_2 gas.

Carbon in CO or methane (CH_4), which is a type of hydrocarbon, is oxidized because it goes from having an oxidation of +2 or –4 to a +4 oxidation state in CO_2.

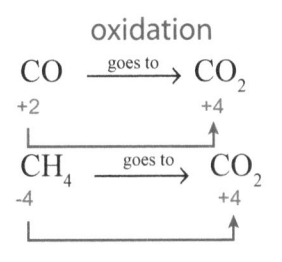

These redox reactions take place on the surfaces of metals such as platinum (Pt), palladium (Pd), and rhodium (Rh). These are called transition metals in the periodic table. The role of these metals is to increase the rate of the redox reactions, and thus they are called catalysts.

The processes of oxidation and reduction require two different catalysts in the same way that the electrodes of electrochemical cells were made of different materials. These catalysts are heterogeneous, because the catalyst is in the solid phase and the reacting molecules are in the gas phase.

Companies that make catalytic converters mix these metals with metal oxides such as CuO and Cr_2O_3 and other materials to make a "wash coat." The wash coat decreases the required amount of these very expensive transition metals. The wash coat is sprayed onto a bricklike ceramic substrate that looks like a sponge or honeycomb structure. This acts as a support structure for the catalyst. This ceramic structure is engineered to increase the surface area of the catalyst, so it is very porous.

By spraying the noble metals onto this surface, more of the exhaust comes into contact with the catalyst. This increased contact of gas molecules is very important in the catalytic process, because the gases are moving through the exhaust very quickly.

Typically these chemical reactions facilitated by the catalyst occur in four steps:

1. Adsorption and activation of the reactant molecules, such as CO or NO_2.

   Adsorption is the binding of molecules to a surface.

2. Migration of the adsorbed molecules along the surface.

3. Reaction among the adsorbed substances. The catalyst promotes dissociation (breaking apart) of the molecules such as NO or CO. For NO_x the N–O bonds weaken, and this allows the nitrogen atoms to bond and form N_2. For CO and C_xH_y, the C–O or C–H bonds are weakened so oxygen can bond to form CO_2 and H_2O molecules.

4. Escape or desorption of the products.

Preparation of these catalysts has a tremendous effect on their properties. The development of catalytic converters is always being improved, and it is a major area of research in the automotive and environmental areas of science. Without catalytic converters, our air, particularly in urban areas, would be much more polluted.

Chapter 15 Review

Vocabulary

Match each word to the sentence where it best fits.

Section 15.1

electrochemistry	antioxidants
free radicals	rust
electron charge	electroneutrality
coulomb	voltage
proton charge	volt
electrical current	resistance
Ampere	ohm
electrical potential difference	Ohm's law
	electron

1. Molecules that have an unpaired number of electrons are called _____.

2. The science that combines chemistry and the flow of electricity is called _____.

3. Iron _____ results from a process called oxidation.

4. _____ are molecules that protect us from the harmful effects of free radicals.

5. The unit of electrical charge is called the _____.

6. The charge of the proton is equal but opposite to the charge of the _____.

7. The _____ is -1.602×10^{-19} coulombs.

8. The movement of electrical charge gives _____.

9. The _____ is $+1.602 \times 10^{-19}$ coulombs.

10. Electrical current is measured in _____.

11. The property of _____ describes a balance between the positive and the negative charges.

12. The difference in electrical potential is called _____.

13. Voltage is measured in _____.

14. Electrical charges experience a/an _____ as they move in a conductor.

15. Electrical resistance is measured in _____.

16. _____ describes the relationship among current, voltage, and resistance.

Section 15.2

redox	oxidation number
oxidized	oxidizing agent
reduced	reducing agent
charge conservation	

17. An element is _____ when it loses electrons.

18. An element is _____ when it gains electrons.

19. Chemical reactions in which elements are oxidized and reduced are called _____ reactions.

20. Redox reactions obey the principle of _____.

21. The charge state of an atom is described by the _____.

22. An element that oxidizes another element is called a/an _____.

23. An element that reduces another element is called a/an _____.

Section 15.3

reduction half	balance charge
balance mass	half-reactions
	oxidation half

24. Balanced redox equations must _____.

25. Redox reactions can be separated into two _____.

26. One of the half-reactions is called the
_____ and the other is called the
_____.

Section 15.4

electrochemical cell	electromotive force
electrode	cell EMF
electrolyte	standard reduction potential
anode	
cathode	spontaneous
voltaic cell	non-spontaneous
galvanic	Nernst equation
electrolytic cell	electrolysis
salt bridge	hydrogen reference half-cell

27. A device in which redox reactions produce electrical current is called a/an _____.

28. A device in which electrical energy produces redox reactions is called a/an _____.

29. Voltaic and electrolytic cells are called _____.

30. The part of a voltaic cell on which oxidation occurs is called the _____.

31. The part of a voltaic cell on which reduction occurs is called the _____.

32. The cell electrodes are immersed in a solution called a/an _____.

33. Redox reactions occur at the interface between the electrolyte and the _____.

34. A battery is a/an _____.

35. A voltaic cell is also called a/an _____ cell.

36. A/An _____ is the connection between the oxidation and the reduction half-cells.

37. _____ means cell electromotive force.

38. The electrical potential difference between the anode and the cathode is called the _____.

39. The cell voltage under standard conditions of temperature, pressure, and concentration is called the _____.

40. The standard reduction potentials are measured with respect to the _____.

41. When the cell voltage is greater than zero, the reaction is _____.

42. When the cell voltage is less than zero, the reaction is _____.

43. The _____ gives the cell potential under nonstandard conditions.

44. The result of the induced chemical reaction in an electrolytic cell is called _____.

Conceptual Questions

Section 15.1

45. What are free radicals?

46. Why are free radicals harmful?

47. How do antioxidants protect us from free radicals?

48. What is the science of electrochemistry?

49. Give four examples of devices or natural process that are based on electrochemistry.

50. What is electrical current?

51. What is electroneutrality, and how does it affect electrical current flow?

52. What is voltage, and how is it related to electrical energy?

53. If the voltage increases, what happens to the current flow? Does it increase, decrease, or stay the same, and why?

54. If the electrical resistance increases what happens to the current if the voltage stays the same?

55. If the electrical resistance increases by a factor of 2 and the current decreases by a factor of 2, what happens to the voltage? Does it increase, decrease, or stay the same? Explain your answer.

Chapter 15 Review

Section 15.2

56. What does it mean when an element is oxidized?

57. What happens when an element is reduced?

58. What is the oxidation number of a free element?

59. How is the oxidation number of a monoatomic ion related to its charge?

60. What is a redox reaction?

61. Describe how charge conservation applies in redox reactions.

62. What is the sum of the oxidation numbers of all individual elements in a neutral molecule?

Section 15.3

63. Describe the basic steps that we have to follow when balancing redox reaction equations.

64. What are half-reactions, and how are they used when balancing redox reactions?

Section 15.4

65. What are the three major parts of a voltaic cell?

66. What do electrodes do in an electrochemical cell?

67. Describe the differences between a voltaic and an electrolytic cell.

68. Describe the role of the salt bridge in an electrochemical cell.

69. What is electrolysis, and how is it used to extract hydrogen and oxygen from water?

70. What is cell voltage, and how is it related to electromotive force?

71. Describe how a voltaic cell generates energy.

72. What are standard reduction potentials, and how are they measured?

73. How is reaction spontaneity related to cell voltage?

74. Describe how changes in the concentrations of reactants and products affect the voltage of a voltaic cell.

Quantitative Problems

Section 15.1

75. A voltage of 10 V is applied across a resistor that has a resistance of 5 Ω. What is the amount of current that flows through the resistor?

76. If we want to move a charge of 1 C from a potential of 1 V to a potential of 2 V, how much energy must we provide?

Section 15.2

77. Find the oxidation number for each element in the following compounds:
    a. CO_2
    b. HCl
    c. $NaCl$
    d. HNO_3

78. What is the oxidation number of each atom in the following ions?
    a. ClO_2^-
    b. Ca^{2+}
    c. ClO_4^-

79. What is the oxidation number of carbon in each of the following compounds?
    a. CO
    b. CH_4
    c. C_3H_4
    d. CO_3^{2-}

80. What is the oxidation number of nitrogen in the following compounds?
    a. N_2O
    b. N_2
    c. NO_2^-

81. For each of the following reactions, identify the elements that are oxidized and the elements that are reduced.
    a. $4Fe(s) + 3O_2(g) \rightarrow 2Fe_2O_3(s)$
    b. $Fe(s) + CuSO_4(aq) \rightarrow FeSO_4(aq) + Cu(s)$
    c. $2H_2O(l) \rightarrow 2H_2(g) + O_2(g)$
    d. $2Na(s) + 2H_2O(l) \rightarrow 2NaOH(aq) + H_2(g)$

82. For each reaction in #81, identify the oxidizing agent and the reducing agent.

83. Determine whether each of the following reactions are redox reactions. If not, tell what type of reaction it is (e.g precipitation).
    a. $NaOH(l) + HNO_3(l) \rightarrow NaNO_3(l) + 2H_2O(l)$
    b. $4Li(s) + O_2(g) \rightarrow 2Li_2O(s)$
    c. $Pb(NO_3)_2 (aq) + 2KI (aq)$
       $\rightarrow PbI_2 (s) + 2KNO_3 (aq)$
    d. $2Al(s) + 3H_2SO_4(l)$
       $\rightarrow Al_2(SO4)_3(l) + 3H_2O(g)$

Section 15.3

84. Balance the following reactions:
    a. $CH_4(g) + O_2(g) \rightarrow CO_2(g) + H_2O(l)$
    b. $O_2(g) + Cu_2S(s) \rightarrow Cu(l) + SO_2(g)$
    c. $NaOH(aq) + HCl(aq) \rightarrow NaCl(aq) + H_2O(l)$
    d. $NaOH(s) + Cl_2(g)$
       $\rightarrow NaCl(s) + NaClO(s) + H_2O(l)$

85. Balance the following redox reactions using the oxidation and reduction half reactions:
    a. $Al(s) + Fe^{2+}(aq) \rightarrow Al^{3+}(aq) + Fe(s)$
    b. $Zn(s) + Sn^{2+}(aq) \rightarrow Zn^{2+}(aq) + Sn(s)$

86. Balance the following redox reaction equations using the oxidation and reduction half reactions. All reactions occur in acidic solutions.
    a. $Cl_2(g) + S_2O_3^{2-}(aq) \rightarrow Cl^-(aq) + SO_4^{2-}(g)$
    b. $Cl_2(g) \rightarrow HClO(aq) + Cl^-(aq)$
    c. $Fe^{2+}(aq) + Cr_2O_7^{2-}(aq)$
       $\rightarrow Fe^{3+}(aq) + Cr^{3+}(aq)$

87. Balance the following redox reaction equations using the oxidation and reduction half reactions. All reactions occur in basic solutions.
    a. $O_3(aq) + Br^-(aq) \rightarrow O_2(g) + BrO_3^-(aq)$
    b. $MnO_4^-(aq) + S^{2-}(aq) \rightarrow S(s) + MnO_2(s)$

Section 15.4

88. Make a sketch of the electrochemical cell with the following reaction equation:
    $Mg(s) + Ni^{2+}(aq) \rightarrow Mg^{2+}(aq) + Ni(s)$
    Label the anode and the cathode. Use a KCl salt bridge and label the direction of movement for the K^+ and Cl^- ions. Label the direction of the electron flow through an external path.

89. Write the cathode and the anode half-reactions of the following cells:
    a. $Ni(s) \mid Ni^{2+}(aq) \parallel Ag^{1+}(aq) \mid Ag(s)$
    b. $Cr(s) \mid Cr^{2+}(aq) \parallel Au^{3+}(aq) \mid Au(s)$
    c. $Fe(s) \mid Fe^{2+}(aq) \parallel Ag^{1+}(aq) \mid Ag(s)$

90. Calculate the cell voltage for all the cells in the previous question under standard conditions.

91. An electrochemical cell has the following reaction occurring at the anode:
    $Mg(s) \rightarrow Mg^{2+}(aq) + 2e^-$
    Which of the following reduction reactions occurring at the cathode will produce the highest cell voltage under standard conditions?
    a. $Au^{3+}(aq) + 3e^- \rightarrow Au(s)$
    b. $Fe^{3+}(aq) + 3e^- \rightarrow Fe(s)$
    c. $Ni^{2+}(aq) + 2e^- \rightarrow Ni(s)$
    d. $Cu^{2+}(aq) + 2e^- \rightarrow Cu(s)$

92. The development of the field of electrochemistry has an extensive history with many scientists' contributions. Research the history of electrochemistry and organize the following years, names, and accomplishments into a timeline. (Note that two events occurred in 1800 and the items below are not in order.)

    Years: 1786, 1800, 1800, 1805, 1839
    Scientists: Brugnatelli, Faraday, Galvani, Nicholson/Ritter, Volta
    Contributions: invented the first battery, invented electroplating, discovered laws of electrochemistry, discovered "animal electricity," succeeded in the electrolysis of water

CHAPTER 16
Solids and Liquids

How are solids and liquids different from gases?

How are solids different from liquids? How are they similar?

What makes some solids different from each other?

What makes some liquids different from each other?

At 1,500°C, steel flows like thin syrup, and can be poured from the furnace into molds of any shape. Liquid steel has no *strength* at all, just like liquid water. However, at room temperature, steel is hard, tough, and extremely strong. A single strand of wire the thickness of a thread can easily support your whole weight.

You might be surprised to know that steel is not one substance, but many. All steel contains mostly iron and a little carbon, but there are many variations. Car frames are made of 1010 carbon steel, which is 99% iron with 0.1% carbon and a few other elements. Most tableware is made of 304 stainless steel, also known as 18/8 because it contains 18% chromium and 8% nickel. In the past year you probably came in contact with more than 100 different types of steel. Each one is a mixture (or alloy) with its own specific chemistry matched to the uses for which the steel is intended.

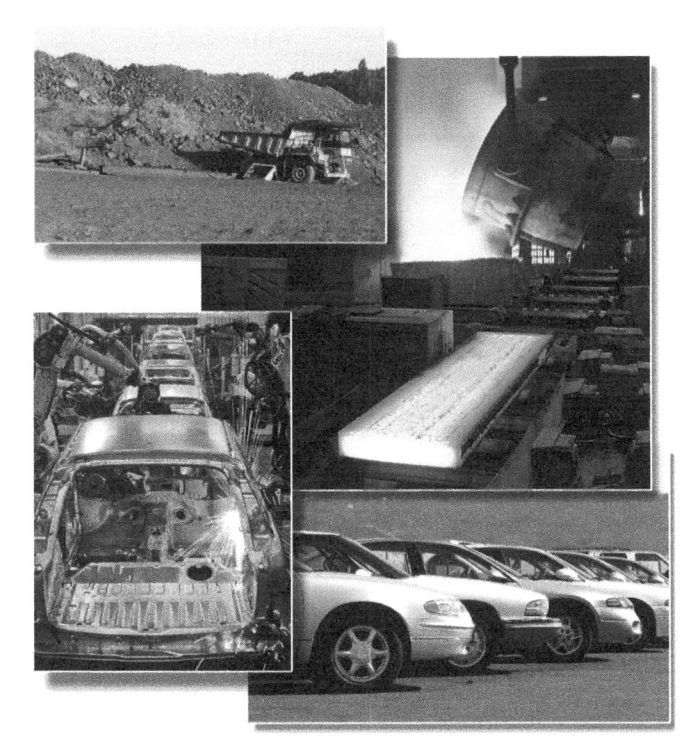

Melt metal in your hands

Melting steel in your hand would be foolish and painful. However, melting chocolate or butter in your hand is probably something you have already done, and you probably felt no ill effects from it at all! The difference, of course, is the melting point. Most metals melt at well over 1,000°C; however, there are some that melt at much lower temperatures. Pure gallium metal has a very low melting point, an incredible 29.8°C (85.6°F). *This is lower than the temperature of your body.*

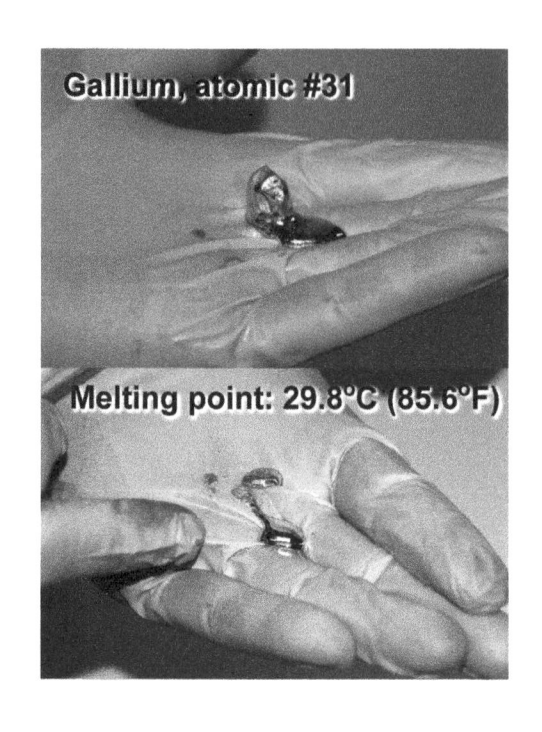

Gallium, atomic #31

Melting point: 29.8°C (85.6°F)

Gallium is a heavy metal and, like mercury, should not be handled with bare hands. Here is what we used:

- safety glasses and gloves,
- 1 g of pure gallium, and
- a petri dish for catching any excess gallium.

First, put the solid gallium in the petri dish. Next, pour some hot water over it. Watch what happens as the metal warms to the water temperature. Poke it with your gloved finger. How does the solid gallium deform? How does it deform when it melts?

Warm water — Solid gallium

Liquid gallium

How does liquid gallium change under the force of gravity? Now hold the gallium in your hand over the tray. How does the gallium deform if you poke it? How does it deform under the force of gravity? Finally, add a few ice cubes to the petri dish and watch the gallium freeze (solidify).

1. The solid gallium should hold its shape under the forces of gravity and your finger.

2. The liquid gallium should deform under external forces, including gravity and your finger.

5	6	7
B	**C**	**N**
10.811 boron	12.011 carbon	14.007 nitrogen

		13	14	15
		Al	**Si**	**P**
group 11	group 12	26.982 aluminum	28.086 silicon	30.974 phosphorous

29	30	31	32	33
Cu	**Zn**	**Ga**	**Ge**	**As**
63.546 copper	65.4 zinc	69.723 gallium	72.61 germanium	74.922 arsenic

| 47 | 48 | 49 | 50 | 51 |

16.1 The Properties of Solids

Properties of some typical solids

How would you describe the differences among rubber, glass and copper? How about the differences between aluminum and copper, or between soft and hard plastic? You might think of aspects such as color, hardness, flexibility, clarity, and density. These are some of the many physical properties that distinguish one solid from another.

Various solids. How are they different? How are they similar?

Hard plastic

Soft plastic

Glass

Copper   Aluminum

Examples of physical properties

Property	Description	Examples
Density	The amount of matter per unit volume	Steel has a density of 7.8 g/cm³, whereas polyethylene plastic has a density of 2 g/cm³
Hardness	The resistance of a material to small deformation, like scratches	Glass is harder than copper, but copper is harder than plastic
Elasticity	The ability to stretch and rebound without breaking	Rubber is often very elastic, and glass is hardly elastic at all
Transparency	The ability for light to pass through a material	Glass and plastic can be transparent, whereas rubber and metals are typically opaque
Strength	The amount of force a material can withstand before breaking	Steel is much stronger than aluminum, and aluminum is stronger than rubber or plastic
Electrical conductivity	The ability for electrical current to flow through a material	Copper and aluminum are excellent conductors but glass, rubber, and plastic are insulators
Thermal conductivity	The ability for heat to flow through a material	Metals are good heat conductors; rubber and plastics are moderate heat conductors

The microscopic causes of physical properties

Macroscopic physical properties ultimately come from the microscopic world of molecules and chemistry. That connection is the subject of this chapter. How do the properties of molecules explain the observable physical properties of liquids and solids? The converse statement is even more interesting. *How can we affect the molecular structure and chemistry of materials to achieve the physical properties we desire?*

Material properties vs. object properties

The properties of a *material* are different from the properties of an object. For example, rubber is not that strong, but a rubber rope as thick as your arm could easily support your weight. A steel wire the thickness of a heavy thread can achieve the same feat with far less matter. Steel as a material is intrinsically stronger than rubber. When we talk about *material properties*, we need to separate from our thinking any considerations of shape, size, or design of objects.

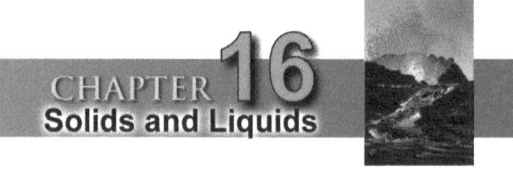

Density

Materials have a wide range of densities	Solid materials have a wide range of densities. One of the densest metals is platinum with a density of 21.4 g/cm³. Platinum is twice as dense as lead and almost three times as dense as steel. A ring made of platinum has three times as much mass as a ring of the exact same size made of steel. Rocks have lower density than metals, between 2.2 and 2.7 g/cm³. As you might expect, the density of wood is less than rock, ranging from 0.4 to 0.6 g/m³.

TABLE 16.1. Densities of some common materials

Material	Density (g/cm³)	Material	Density (g/cm³)
Platinum	21.4	Graphite	2.1
Lead	11.3	Polyethylene	2.0
Steel	7.8	Brick	1.6
Titanium	4.5	Rubber	1.2
Diamond	3.5	Liquid water	1.0
Aluminum	2.7	Ice	0.92
Glass	2.7	Oak (wood)	0.60
Calcite ($CaCO_3$)	2.7	Pine (wood)	0.44

Factors affecting density

The density of a substance is affected by two factors:

1. the mass of the molecules or atoms of which the substance is made and

2. how closely the atoms or molecules are packed together.

The atomic weight of platinum is 195 g/mole, and that of lead is 207 g/mole. Platinum has a lower atomic mass but nearly twice the density of lead. That tells us that platinum atoms must be packed together more closely than lead atoms. In a more extreme case, the molecular weight of polyethylene is more than 200,000 g/mole, yet its density is much lower than platinum. The conclusion is that density is strongly dependent on how tightly atoms or molecules can be packed together.

The packing fraction

The atoms in most metals are packed as tightly as they can get. The *packing fraction* is the volume taken up by atoms compared to the total volume of a substance. The atoms in most metals are arranged in a hexagonal pattern that nests each layer into the adjacent layer for the highest possible packing fraction. This is the primary reason for the high density of metals compared to other substances. Polyethylene is a long-chain molecule. It is not possible to pack large molecules efficiently, so molecular substances tend to have lower densities.

Cubic packing

packing fraction = 0.68%

Hexagonal packing

packing fraction = 0.74%

Hardness

Hardness

The **hardness** of a material describes how easy it is to move molecules out of their places by scratching the surface with a relatively small force. Diamond is the hardest known substance. Diamond is hard because it is a network covalent substance. A diamond is like a single huge molecule because every carbon atom is bonded to four other carbon atoms. It is very difficult to deform a diamond at all. In fact, the only thing that can cut a diamond is *another diamond*. Diamond polishers use special disks, like fine sandpaper, made of diamonds to polish bigger diamonds.

The Mohs scale of hardness

The **Mohs hardness scale** is a scale used for describing hardness. The Mohs scale goes from 1 to 10, with 10 being the hardest. The scale is based on the relative hardness of other materials. Your fingernail is about a 2.5. If something is harder than your fingernail, then it can scratch your nail and has a higher Mohs hardness. If a substance is softer than your fingernail, then your fingernail can scratch it! That substance would have a lower Mohs hardness. Since diamond is a 10, it can put a scratch in anything!

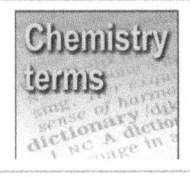

hardness: the ease of deforming a material by a small amount.

Mohs hardness scale: a scale that describes how easy it is to scratch one material with another.

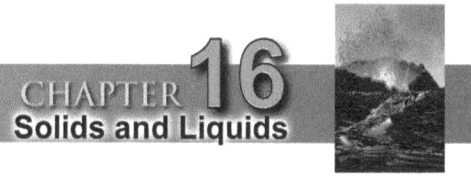

Strength

| The meaning of "strength" | The strength of a solid material really is about failure. The only way to know the strength of a material is to push it to its limit, where it isn't strong enough. Strength has three primary aspects, which are described by the following questions: |

1. How much will a material deform under a given force?

2. Does a material stretch before breaking or does it snap suddenly?

3. How much force can a material ultimately withstand before it breaks?

All of these may be strongly affected by chemistry.

Deformation under pressure
(stiffness, elasticity, hardness)

Stretch or crack?

(ductile or brittle)

Maximum pressure before failure

(tensile strength)

Deformation under pressure

Elastic materials such as rubber and soft plastics can deform a great deal under a relatively small pressure. These are materials you think of as "soft." Metals deform much less for the same amount of pressure. For example, 500 N of force (about 100 lb) on a 1 cm cube of rubber will compress the cube to 0.5 cm. The same pressure applied to a 1 cm cube of steel will deform the steel by only 0.02 millimeters, less than the thickness of your hair!

Ductility and brittleness

A **ductile** material will bend or deform substantially before breaking. Think about stretching a roll of soft clay. The clay deforms a lot before it finally breaks. Metals are typically ductile. For example, gold is so ductile it can be hammered out into very thin sheets without breaking. A **brittle** material will break before it deforms much. Ceramic and glass tend to be brittle. Ionic solids, including most mineral crystals and rocks, tend to be brittle materials.

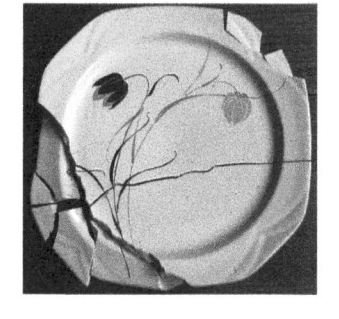

Tensile strength

The **tensile strength** of a material is the maximum pressure it can sustain in tension before breaking. Tension is a straight pulling force, like a weight hanging from a wire. Most materials will stretch a certain amount, then snap.

Chemistry terms

ductile: a property of materials that describes ease of stretching or moulding and lack of brittleness.

brittle: a property of materials that are hard and require little energy to fracture.

tensile strength: a measure of the energy needed to break a material in two.

16.2 The Microstructure of Solids

Molecules in a gas

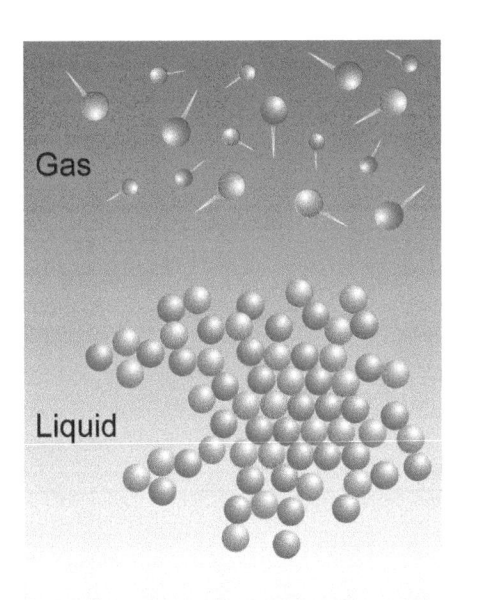

Gas

Condensed matter includes liquids and solids

Liquid

Solid

In a gas, the molecules are free to go where they please. They fly around at very high speeds, colliding with each other and everything in their way. However, except for the brief instants of their collisions, molecules do not interact with each other.

Solids and liquids are collectively called *condensed matter*. **Condensed matter** is made of molecules (or atoms) that are essentially touching each other. In a solid, the molecules are not only touching, but they are stuck tightly to each other in a rigid arrangement. Solids hold their shape because the molecules cannot move independently of each other. In a liquid, the molecules are still touching each other, but the connections are looser and more slippery than in solids. Liquid gallium flows because the atoms can slide around each other. It does not expand to fill space the way a gas would because the atoms are not energetic enough to completely break away from each other.

Competition between thermal agitation and attractive forces

Liquids and solids are "condensed" because the attractive intermolecular forces acting between molecules (or atoms) are stronger then the disruptive forces of thermal motion. In a solid, thermal agitation is much too low to overcome attractive forces. In a liquid, thermal agitation is almost enough, but not quite. However, as a liquid is heated to its boiling point, thermal agitation wins and the molecules escape to become a gas.

TABLE 16.2. Properties of solids, liquids and gases

	Solids	Liquids	Gases
Fixed volume	Yes	Yes	No
Fixed shape	Yes	No	No

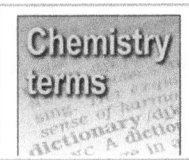

Chemistry terms

condensed matter: matter in which atoms or molecules are closely packed together and strongly interacting; includes both liquids and solids.

516

Crystalline and amorphous solids

Two types of solids

Solids are solid because the molecules are bound in one of two possible *microstructures*. **Microstructure** refers to the detailed arrangement of molecules (or atoms) in a material. In a crystalline solid, the molecules have an ordered pattern, like bricks in a wall. In an **amorphous** solid there is no repeating pattern, and molecules are randomly squeezed together without any long-range order. **Crystalline** solids include minerals and gemstones you think of as "crystals," but they also include metals and even some plastics. Amorphous solids include glasses and most plastics. Biological solids such as wood and bone have both crystalline and amorphous components, so they are mixtures of the two.

Crystals have ordered structures

A **crystal** is defined by its structure. *Crystal structures* describe how the molecules or atoms bond to each other. They tell us how far apart neighboring atoms are and at what angles the bonds are. You can see examples of natural crystals all around you. Look closely at an aluminum traffic pole, and you will notice "grains" of the aluminum metal. Each grain is a single crystal of aluminum. Under a magnifying glass, you can tell that the salt in your salt shaker is made of little cubic crystals!

Crystal structure and shapes

The microscopic arrangement of molecules in a crystalline solid will often show up in the shape of an object. Snowflakes are a lovely example. Snowflakes have six-way symmetry because water molecules align in six-sided rings.

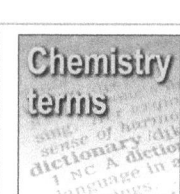

Chemistry terms

microstructure: the spatial arrangement of atoms and molecules in matter.

amorphous: a microstructure that does not have any ordered pattern.

crystalline: a microstructure with a repeating, ordered pattern.

crystal: a piece of solid, nonamorphous matter in which the microstructure is uniform and continuous over the entire piece.

Glasses

Glass has a
disordered
structure

Glass is an amorphous solid that does not have an ordered structure. There is no "bricklike" order to the molecules inside a glass; they just bond to each other wherever they can. The bond lengths are all different, and the angles are all different too.

Given enough time, glasses will sag under their own weight. This slow deformation is common to all amorphous substances. They are *deforming*, since the lack of order means they can't hold their shape forever. Also, the higher the temperature is, the faster the deformation occurs.

Amorphous

On the molecular level, an amorphous solid is like an "immobile" liquid. There is a fixed shape and volume like a solid, but the molecules are loosely packed and disordered like a liquid. The hotter an amorphous substance gets, the more it behaves like a liquid. Amorphous things do not "melt" in the same way crystals do. Crystals melt at only one temperature. Amorphous materials just get softer as it gets hotter.

• Oxygen   • Silicon

Metallic glasses

Most glasses we use everyday are made of sand, or silica. They are called *oxide glasses* because they are made mostly of silicon dioxide (silica). There are also some very special glasses called **metallic glasses**. By cooling a metal down very, very fast, you can freeze the atoms into a glass. These metallic glasses have amazing properties. They transmit energy very well. That's why the fanciest golf clubs have heads made out of metallic glass.

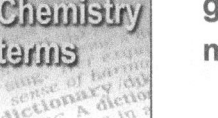

glass: a solid structure with no long-range order for bond lengths and angles.
metallic glass: a special form of glass made by cooling metal extremely quickly.

Crystal structures

Crystal structures

Crystals can look quite different from each other. Some are square (such as table salt), some are rectangular, some are hexagonal (quartz and snowflakes), and some have other geometric shapes. The similarity is a well-defined **crystal structure**. A crystal structure describes exactly the 3D repeating pattern of atoms and molecules.

Bravais lattices

Simple cubic   Face-centered cubic   Body-centered cubic

Simple tetragonal   Body-centered tetragonal   Hexagonal

Simple orthorhombic   Body-centered orthorhombic   Base-centered orthorhombic   Face-centered orthorhombic

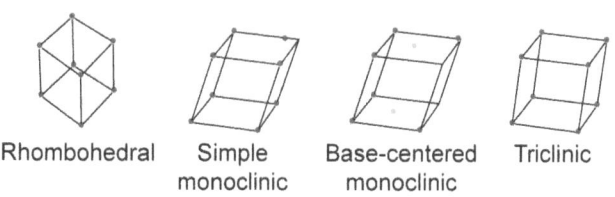

Rhombohedral   Simple monoclinic   Base-centered monoclinic   Triclinic

There are 14 geometrically unique crystal structures known as the 14 **Bravais lattices**. The Bravais lattices are used to classify crystal structures into groups with common properties.

If they are undisturbed while cooling, crystalline materials tend to form solids along the same geometry as their structure. A good example is calcite, a mineral crystal with a rhombohedral lattice.

calcite, a rhombohedral crystal

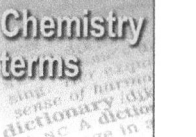
Chemistry terms

crystal structure: a system that describes the distances and angles between atoms in a crystal.

Bravais lattices: fourteen groups of crystal structures used to help group the many different types of crystal structures.

Crystal defects

Perfect crystals are never found in nature. There are defects even in the most flawless diamonds. Because crystals are three-dimensional structures, defects can have up to three dimensions to them. Some common defect types are point, also called zero-dimensional (0-D); line or one-dimensional (1-D); and surface or two-dimensional (2-D). Each type of defect has a different effect on the properties of the crystal.

Point defects (0-D)

Point defects occur when one atom is somehow different from the rest of the crystal. A *vacancy* occurs when an atom is missing from the crystal structure. An *interstitial* occurs when there is an extra atom wedged in between others. A third point defect is a *substitutional defect*, where there is a different type of atom or molecule present than in the rest of the crystal. Substitutional defects are the reason why rubies and sapphires have their colors. Both rubies and sapphires are made of nearly pure Al_2O_3. Their color comes from chromium substitutional defects. Very small changes in the chemistry of Al_2O_3 are what make beautiful gems.

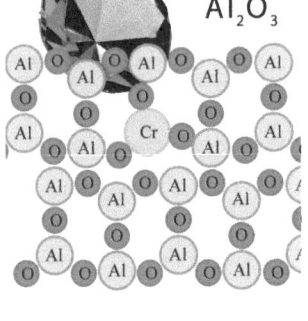

Ruby
Al_2O_3

Line defects (1-D)

Line defects occur when a line of atoms is somehow different from the rest of the crystal. These most often take the form of **dislocations**, or an extra "half-plane" of atoms in a crystal. Dislocations form the main mechanism of deformation in crystals.

Grains and grain boundaries

You don't normally think of metal as being a crystal. That is because most crystalline materials are polycrystalline. Polycrystalline materials contain millions of tiny crystals, called *grains*, connected to each other. Almost all metals are fine grained, meaning the grain size can be seen only with a microscope. The image on the right shows the grains in a sample of metal. The surfaces between grains are called **grain boundaries** and are the most common two-dimensional defect in a crystal. If a crystalline solid has only one large grain, it is a *single crystal*, or *monocrystalline*. The mineral "crystals" you see are actually large monocrystals.

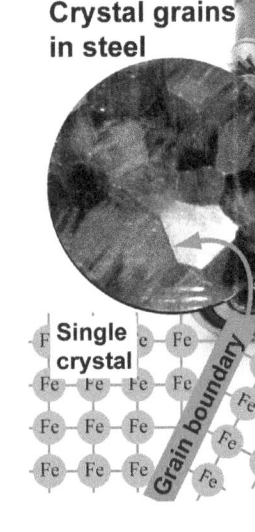

Crystal grains in steel

Single crystal

Grain boundary

Single crystal

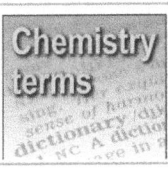
Chemistry terms

point defects: zero-dimensional single atom defects in a crystal.

dislocation: a 1-D defect involving a missing half-plane of atoms in a crystal.

grain boundary: the interface between two grains in a polycrystalline solid.

A NATURAL APPROACH TO CHEMISTRY

16.3 Metals and Alloys

Metallic bonding

Metals can be very strong, they are good conductors of heat and electricity, and they are easily formed by melting and bending. All of these characteristics come from the way metallic bonds behave. Because their ionization energies are low, the valence electrons in metals are not strongly bound to their parent atoms. In solid metal, the valence electrons become detached but do not reattach to another atom. A good analogy is that a metal is a fixed lattice of positive ions in a sea of free electrons.

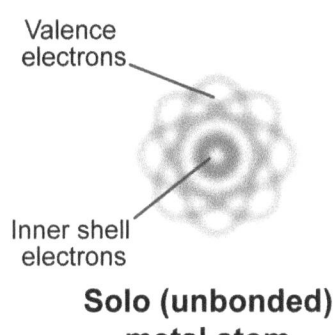

Valence electrons

Inner shell electrons

Solo (unbonded) metal atom

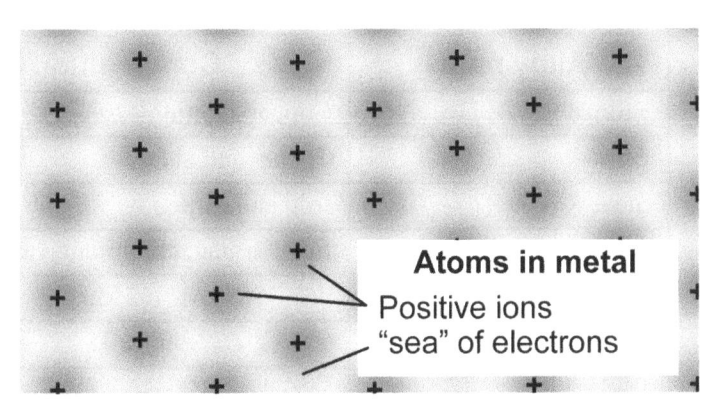

Atoms in metal
Positive ions
"sea" of electrons

Thermal and electrical conductivity of metals

Electrons are small, light, and therefore *fast*. The high electrical conductivity comes directly from the fact that metals have many charged electrons that are free to move around. The thermal conductivity of metals is high for the same reason. Moving electrons can carry energy quickly, and when they get heated, the heat spreads rapidly through the metal. The *thermal conductivity* describes how many watts of *heat* would flow through a 1 cm cube of a material if there were a 1°C temperature difference between its opposite sides. The *electrical conductivity* tells us how many *amperes* of electrical current would flow through a 1 cm cube if 1 V were maintained across the sides.

Thermal conductivity
1 W/(cm·°C) means 1 watt of heat flows through 1 cm for 1°C temperature difference

1°C   2°C

1 W of heat

Electrical conductivity
1 A/(cm·V) means 1 amp of current flows through 1 cm for 1 volt potential difference

0 V   1 V

1 A of current

Material	Thermal conductivity [W/(cm·°C)]	Electrical conductivity [A/(V·cm)]
copper	4	600,000
aluminum	2.2	380,000
polyethyene plastic	0.004	0.1
glass	0.01	10^{-10}

Comparing metals and nonmetals

Note how different the conductivity values are between metals and nonmetals, such as polyethylene and glass. The electrical conductivity of copper is 6 million times higher than it is for polyethylene plastic. The thermal conductivity of copper is 1,000 times higher than it is for polyethylene.

Alloys: solid solutions of elements

Alloys are solid solutions of elements

Alloys are a special class of solid mixtures of two or more elements where the element in the largest proportion is a metal. The atoms in an alloy are not bound up in molecules but are bound to each other with metallic bonds. The table below lists some common alloys and their uses. For example, bronze was perhaps the first important alloy discovered by humans. Bronze is an alloy of copper and tin. Other common examples of alloys include brass (copper and zinc) and steel (iron and carbon).

Alloy name	Composition	Uses
Bronze	Copper and tin	Coins, tools, bells, statues
Brass	Copper and zinc	Musical instruments, plumbing
Steel	Iron and carbon	Buildings, bridges
Stainless steel	Iron, carbon, chromium, vanadium	Where corrosion resistance is needed
6061 aluminum	96%–98% Al, 1% Mg, 0.5%–1% Si	Bicycle frames, aircraft, boats
6-4 titanium	6% Al, 4% V, 90% Ti	Bio-implants
14k gold	58% Au, 42% of Ni, Cu, Ag	Jewelry
Sterling silver	92% Ag, 8% Cu	Jewelry, silverware

6061 Aluminum   Steel   Brass   Bronze

Alloys improve physical properties

Early metalworkers discovered that by melting copper and tin together, they could create bronze, a metal that was stronger than both. This is perhaps the most important property of alloys. Alloys often have better physical properties than any of their constituent pure elements. Most pure metals, even iron, are naturally very soft. As a result, almost everything made of metal today is made of an alloy. Some of the most important discoveries in the rise of modern civilization were the alloys of bronze and iron. The Bronze Age and the Iron Age were periods of civilization named after them.

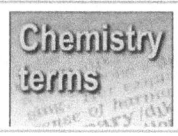
Chemistry terms

alloy: a solid material made up of two or more elements (usually metals) that is evenly mixed on the microscopic level.

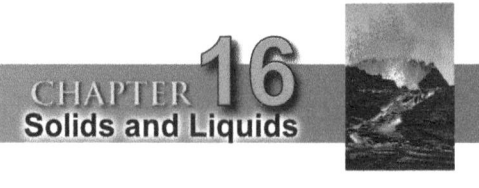

Alloys: chemistry and properties

Chemistry changes properties

Adding two or more elements together in the form of a metal alloy creates a material with different physical properties than any of the original elements. Simple alloys made of two elements are called **binary alloys**. Sometimes it only takes a small amount of the **alloying element** in a binary alloy to greatly affect the properties of the alloy. For example, adding less than 0.5% carbon by weight to iron can create incredibly strong steel.

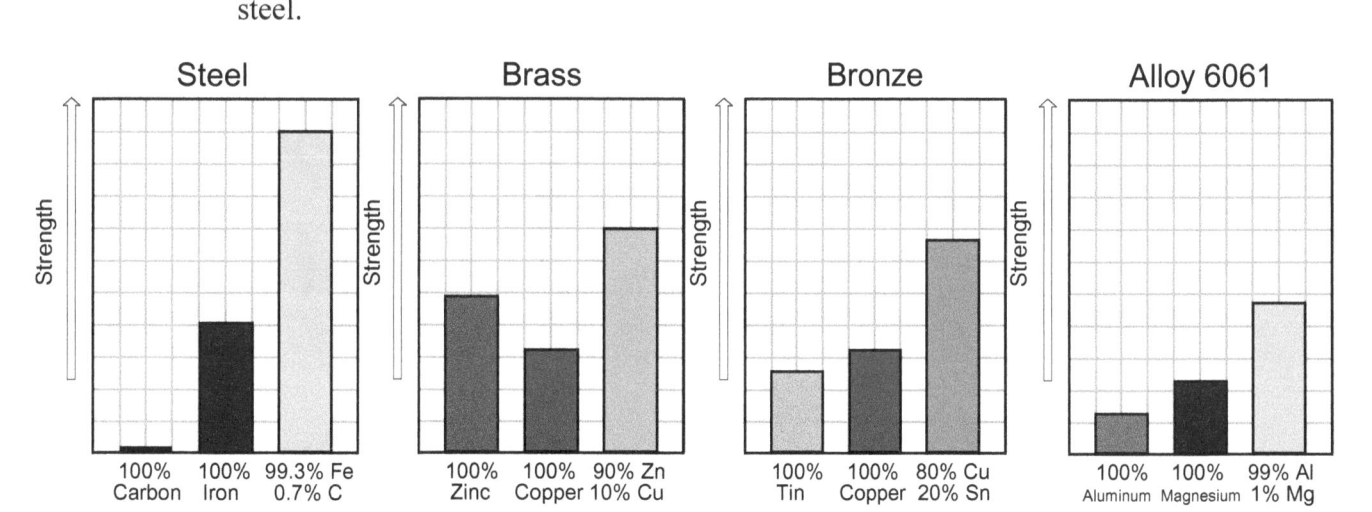

Complex alloys

Three or more alloying elements can be combined to produce complex alloys with even more interesting properties. For example, steel is made of iron and carbon. Adding more elements to the mix further changes the properties. This is explored further in the Chemistry Connection in this chapter.

The latest military aircraft are made of complex alloys of titanium, vanadium, and zirconium. Mixing them in the correct proportions creates an alloy that is incredibly strong and tough. If the chemistry of the alloy is off by even a tiny bit, the properties of the aircraft alloy will be greatly affected, leading to reduced strength, brittleness, or other problems.

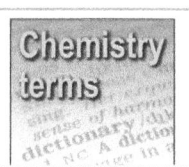

Chemistry terms

binary alloy: an alloy made up of only two different elements.

alloying element: one of the elements that make up a certain alloy.

Binary phase diagrams

Binary phase diagrams

The properties of alloys depend on their composition in unusual ways. For example, fitting two *different* atoms into a crystal lattice changes the crystal structure and that also changes how an alloy melts or freezes. A **binary phase diagram** shows how the composition of an alloy changes its melting point. You may have heard of "sterling silver." Sterling silver is an alloy in which 12% of the atoms are copper (Cu) and 88% are silver (Ag). This works out to 7.5% copper by mass.

Sterling silver contains 12 atoms of copper for every 88 atoms of silver
(Cu = 12% by atoms)
(Cu = 7.5% by mass)

Interpreting the diagram

A silver–copper alloy is a liquid solution of copper and silver in the blue-shaded region of the diagram. It is a solid solution below 779°C. Above 779°C, the mixture may be a mixed state or a liquid, depending on its composition. The mixed state is neither fully solid nor fully liquid.

Alloys may have a lower melting point

Pure silver melts at 991°C and pure copper melts at 1,085°C. Sterling silver melts at 779°C! The phase diagram shows that a silver–copper alloy becomes liquid at a much lower temperature than the typical freezing point of either pure metal.

The eutectic point

A silver–copper alloy has a single melting point at 779°C when the composition is 39% copper (by atoms). This is called the *eutectic point*. The **eutectic point** is the composition with the lowest melting point. *Solders* are metals that are designed to melt at low temperatures and are used for assembling electronic devices or sealing water pipes. The composition of solder is chosen so it corresponds to the eutectic point.

Chemistry terms

binary phase diagram: a graph showing the phase of an alloy at different temperatures and compositions.

eutectic point: the temperature and composition where an alloy's melting point is the lowest.

16.4 Physical Properties of Liquids

Liquids are more weakly bound than solids

Liquids, unlike solids, do not have a network of permanent intermolecular bonds. Instead, intermo-lecular bonds are continuously made and broken. The making of bonds allows liquids to hold together, and the breaking of bonds allows liquids to **flow**. It is a characteristic of liquids that they flow under a force (such as gravity) rather than just fall.

Energy of solid versus liquid

Because they can flow, liquids lack a rigid molecular structure like a crystal. On the molecular level, liquids are like amorphous solids, except that intermolecular bonds are not strong enough to overcome thermal agitation. The energy of a liquid is higher than that of a solid. The higher energy allows the bonds formed in a liquid to break quickly. The speed at which these bonds are made and broken, along with the strength of these bonds, leads to the unique physical properties of different liquids.

Freezing rate and solid microstructure

It is important to note that the same liquid can freeze (solidify) into a crystal or a glass. For example, sand and quartz are *crystalline* forms of SiO_2. Window glass is an *amorphous* form of SiO_2. You get liquid SiO_2 if you melt quartz or window glass. The molten liquid doesn't remember whether it came from a crystal or a glass! Depending on how it is cooled, the same liquid SiO_2 can become a glass (if it is cooled fast) or a beautiful quartz crystal (if it is cooled very slowly). Virtually all materials display differences in their solid microstructure depending on how fast they solidify. This is the basis for heat treating steel, glass, aluminum, and other materials.

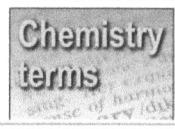
Chemistry terms

flow: the ability of a liquid to move and change shape under a force, such as gravity.

Cohesion

Cohesion in liquids

Liquids tend to stay together, even if forces such as gravity are acting on them. We call this property *cohesion*. **Cohesion** is an attractive force between molecules in a liquid. Cohesion is quite striking in the weightless environment of an orbiting space station. In microgravity, cohesion causes liquid drops to come together as tight as possible in perfect *spheres*. A sphere is the shape that results in the least surface area for the most volume. A liquid drop assumes this shape to maximize the number of liquid molecules that can bond together.

Courtesy of NASA

Cohesion in nature

Cohesion explains why rain falls in raindrops and how clouds form. Water vapor in the atmosphere tends to stick together because cohesion keeps liquids together. These droplets get bigger and bigger until they become visible as clouds. When it rains, tiny water droplets in clouds come together to make bigger and bigger droplets until they are so heavy that they fall as rain. Cohesion keeps these raindrops together as they fall to the ground.

Cohesion in mercury

Mercury is a liquid metal at room temperature

Some liquids are more cohesive than others. For example, water is a fairly cohesive liquid. Liquid mercury, a liquid metal, is very cohesive. The drops in liquid mercury are held together so tightly by cohesion that they form almost perfect spheres.

Chemistry terms

cohesion: the property of a liquid that causes it to hold together.

A NATURAL APPROACH TO CHEMISTRY

Adhesion

Adhesion

You may have also noticed that liquids tend to stick to things. We call this property **adhesion**, and it describes how liquids stick to surfaces. When something is "wet," we mean that liquid is *adhering* to it. Different surfaces can also *be wet* by the same liquid differently; we call this property *wettability*. Liquids that adhere to things very well are called *adhesives* and are commonly used as glues or put onto tape to make it sticky. Geckos use the property of adhesion to stick to surfaces such as the walls and ceilings of houses.

Meniscus

A good way to determine whether a liquid is more cohesive or adhesive is to put it into a test tube and observe the **meniscus**, or the top of the column of liquid. A cohesive liquid will try to stay together instead of sticking to the walls of the cylinder. A more adhesive liquid will stick to the walls of the cylinder and form a "U" shape. Water is a more adhesive liquid, whereas mercury is more cohesive. Adhesion

Water   Mercury

also explains why droplets of water stick to glass, such as windows. Liquids such as water are very adhesive, and adhesion is strong enough to hold large drops of water from falling.

Adhesion and capillary action

Water passes through these tubes

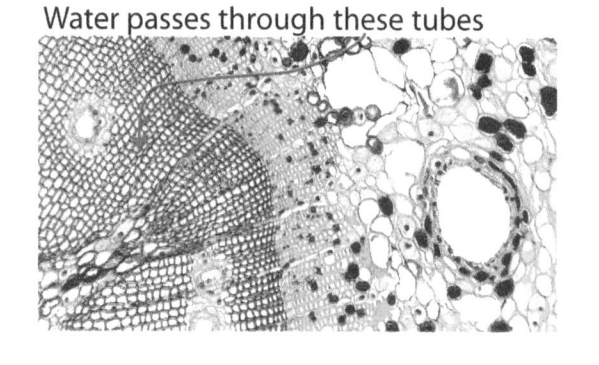

Plants use adhesion to draw water up from roots to leaves. The water adheres to the tubes inside the plant, and **capillary action** causes the water to be drawn up the empty tube to the top of the plant. Even very high trees move water this way. Adhesion is the force that causes capillary action. Without adhesion, plants could not use water.

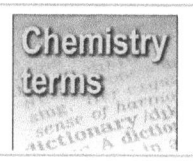

Chemistry terms

adhesion: the property of a liquid that causes it to stick to surfaces.

meniscus: the curved top of a column of liquid.

capillary action: an effect where liquid is pulled up a thin tube by adhesion.

A NATURAL APPROACH TO CHEMISTRY

Viscosity

Viscosity is resistance to flow

While the making and breaking of bonds allow a liquid to flow, the frequency and strength of the bonds controls how *easily* it flows. The "thick" or "runny" aspect of a liquid is called *viscosity*. **Viscosity** is a measure of *resistance to flow*. **Nonviscous** liquids have very low viscosity, are very runny and will flow very easily. Water and alcohol are good examples of liquids with low viscosities. A liquid with a high viscosity flows slowly. Oil and corn syrup are liquids with high viscosities.

Viscosity in nature

We can find liquids with very different viscosities in nature. Snails and slugs use mucus, a *very* high viscosity substance, to help them stick to surfaces and move. Magma, or molten rock, has different viscosity depending on the silica (SiO_2) content. High-silica magma is sticky and **viscous**. It is sticky enough to allow pressure to build up and potentially cause a violent volcanic eruption. Low-silica magma is runny and has a lower viscosity. This type of magma forms the lava in the spectacular fire fountains in Hawaii.

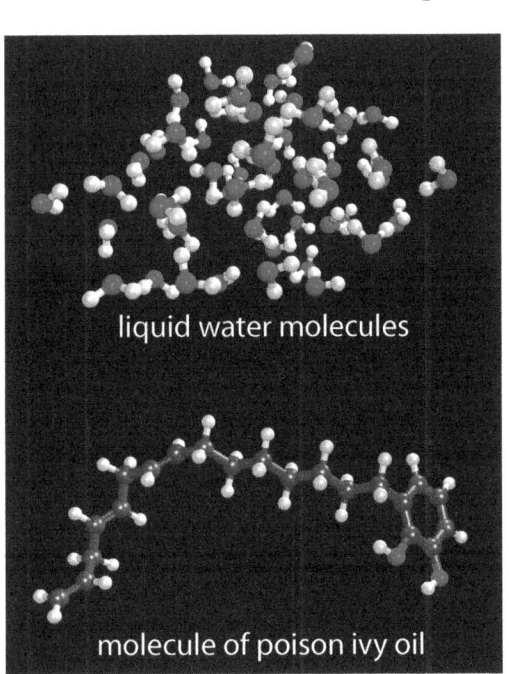

liquid water molecules

molecule of poison ivy oil

Viscosity is determined mostly by two variables: the strength of the intermolecular bonds and the shape of the molecules. If there are relatively strong intermolecular bonds, a liquid will be more viscous. Molten metals have a high viscosity because the bonds are strong. Liquids with polar or hydrogen bonding, such as water, will be more viscous than nonpolar liquids, such as liquid nitrogen.

Viscosity is also affected strongly by molecular size and shape. Water has a lower viscosity than oil because water molecules are small and can move around each other easily. The molecules in oils are very long, like worms. Long-chain molecules can be easily entangled and this slows down the flow. A good analogy is to think about pouring a cup of cooked spaghetti and another of sand. The sand flows quickly because the particles are small and slide over each other easily. The spaghetti gets tangled and pours very slowly. Liquids made of long-chain molecules tend to flow like entangled spaghetti and therefore have high viscosity.

Chemistry terms

viscosity: the resistance of a liquid to flow under an applied force.

nonviscous: a fluid property indicating a lack of cohesiveness or resistance to flow.

viscous: a fluid property indicating a high resistance to flow.

Surface tension

The strength of
a free surface

When you pour water onto a plate, you may have noticed that it forms a *surface*. It takes energy to actually *break* that surface. It obviously doesn't take too much energy, since you are able to poke your finger in without any trouble. However, there is a measurable energy required to break the surface of a liquid, and the physical property that measures this energy is called the **surface tension** of the liquid. You may be able to break the surface of water easily, but insects such as the *water strider* are so light and spread their weight out so far that they can actually rest *on top* of the surface of the water! They are not floating on the water but resting upon it because of surface tension!

What surface
tension does

Surface tension is what causes liquid to actually stay together. It makes the entire surface of a liquid act like a big elastic band, pulling back when the liquid is stretched out. Gravity is much stronger than surface tension on Earth, so water spilled on a flat table spreads out into a thin sheet. Without surface tension, gravity would squish the liquid into a perfectly thin sheet of water. In space, where there is *no* gravity, spilled water pulls itself into the tightest possible shape—a *sphere!* Surface tension is also what causes rain to fall in *drops*, rather than in sheets or any other shape.

Soaps

Soap reduces surface tension

Soaps work partly by lowering surface tension. The active molecules in soap are medium-length chains with one polar end and one that is nonpolar. The polar end tends to adsorb to the water surface and this breaks up the surface tension. Traditional soap consists of sodium or potassium salts of fatty acids. Soap is made by reacting common oils or fats with a strong alkaline solution, usually sodium hydroxide or lye.

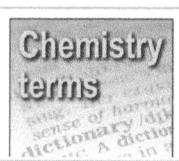
Chemistry terms

surface tension: a property of liquids to resist having their surface broken, usually measured in J/m².

Measuring surface tension

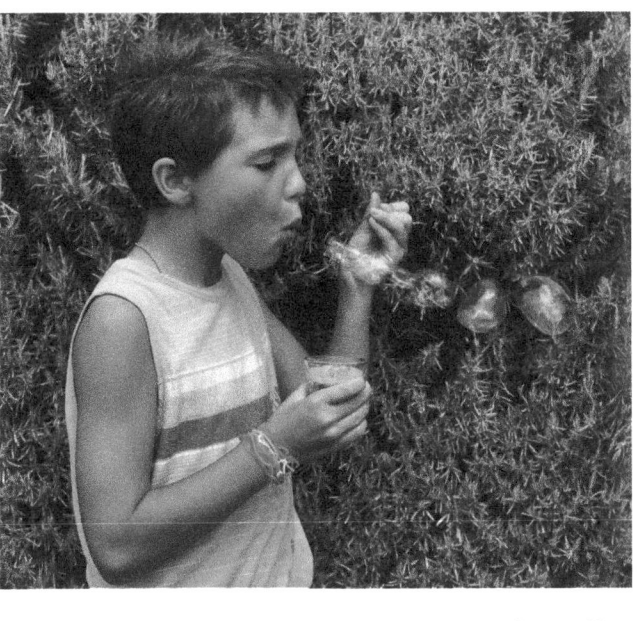

Surface tension is measured in energy per unit area (J/m^2). It represents the energy needed to break a certain amount of area of a liquid's surface. A very easy way to measure surface tension is to blow a bubble of a liquid. If you carefully measure the pressure needed to pop the bubble and the size of the bubble when it pops, then you can calculate the surface area of the bubble and therefore the surface tension.

You can observe surface tension's amazing effects with a few simple materials. Pour water into a beaker to just near the top. Now keep adding water with a dropper. Notice how the water level is *above* the top of the beaker! Now carefully place a paper clip on the surface of the water with a pair of tweezers. Metal is much denser than water, but surface tension can support the weight of the paper clip. How many paper clips can you add before they sink?

We can cause liquids to break up more easily by reducing their surface tension. Materials that do this are called **surfactants**, and they are most commonly found in soaps and detergents. They cause the sticky liquids to break up into smaller and smaller pieces, which are more easily washed away.

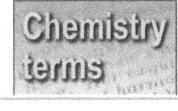

surfactant: a substance that reduces the surface tension of a liquid.

A NATURAL APPROACH TO CHEMISTRY

Steel: the most useful alloy

Steel is perhaps the most important alloy we use today. Steel is the building block for thousands of different things in our everyday lives, from cars to buildings to household objects. The discovery and development of steel marked one of mankind's greatest achievements.

All steels must contain both iron and carbon. In its simplest form, *carbon steel*, carbon and iron are the only ingredients in the alloy. The more carbon, the harder the steel can become. Over time and with much ingenuity, metallurgists have developed thousands of different steel alloys with very different physical and chemical properties. The two most common methods to change the properties of steel are 1. changing the size, type, or distribution of crystal defects and 2. changing the chemistry by adding or adjusting component elements in the alloy.

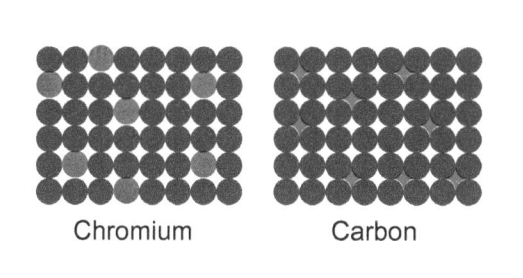

Chromium   Carbon

Carbon atoms are much smaller than iron atoms, so they exist as *interstitials* in an iron crystal. The chromium atoms in stainless steel exist as *substitutional* defects, because the Cr and Fe atoms are close to the same size. Adding chromium makes the steel very *corrosion resistant*, meaning that it is very hard to make it rust. This is why it is called *stainless*, because it is difficult to get anything to react and stain the metal.

The various defects present in steel can *significantly* change its properties. Metallurgists have added and controlled the types of defects in steel to change its properties. By controlling the grain size and the frequency of crystal defects, a skilled metallurgist can control hardness, strength, corrosion resistance, hardenability, and many other properties. For example, we can change the shapes and sizes of the grains by working the steel by forging, hot working, cold working, drawing, quenching, annealing, and tempering. Dislocations move well through grains, but not through grain boundaries. Working the steel and quenching it will make smaller grains and therefore more grain boundaries. The more grain boundaries, the harder it is for dislocations to move, and the harder the steel. In contrast, annealing (slow cooling) the steel will increase the grain size and make the steel softer.

Steels can also be joined together in fascinating ways. *Pattern-welded steel* is made of two or more types of steel, folded together in different ways. Objects made from pattern-welded steel often have properties of both the original steels, and they often have artistic patterns caused by the folding, like in this pattern-welded knife.

Changing the chemistry of steel greatly affects its properties. Just changing the amount of carbon in steel completely changes the nature of the steel. Very little carbon produces *mild steel*, or just iron with carbon. Adding more carbon produces *pearlite*, a microstructure of steel that is both strong and hard. Adding even more carbon can produce *carbides*, or particles of iron carbide (Fe_3C). These are very hard, but they can make the steel brittle.

Chapter 16 Review

Vocabulary

Match each word to the sentence where it best fits.

Section 16.1

solids	gases
liquids	

1. _____ have a fixed volume but no fixed shape.

2. _____ have no fixed volume and no fixed shape.

3. _____ have both a fixed volume and a fixed shape.

Section 16.2

crystal	slip systems
glass	close-packed directions
amorphous	
crystal structure	hardness
Bravais lattices	Mohs hardness scale
metallic glass	strength
point defects	brittle
dislocations	ductile
grain boundaries	alloy
inclusions	alloying elements
	binary alloy

4. The property of a solid that describes the energy needed to break it is called _____.

5. _____ are one-dimensional (1-D) defects in a crystal that consist of a missing half-plane of atoms.

6. A/an _____ is a solid solution of two or more elements.

7. A material that breaks easily is described as being _____.

8. _____ materials behave like both solids and liquids and have no long-range order to their molecular structures.

9. Interstitials, vacancies, and substitutionals are examples of _____ in a crystal.

10. A/an _____ is an ordered arrangement of atoms in a solid.

11. A/an _____ is an example of an everyday amorphous material.

12. _____ describes the ability of a material to resist deformation.

13. A material that stretches a lot before breaking is said to be _____.

14. A/an _____ is an alloy made up on only two elements.

15. Crystals often deform by activating _____, where planes of atoms will slide over each other.

16. A/an _____ is a three-dimensional (3-D) defect in a crystal, like a crystal within a crystal.

17. The _____ compares materials by their scratch resistance, with diamond at the top.

18. _____ are the elements that go into an alloy.

19. Slip systems are often activated on _____ in a crystal.

20. A/an _____ describes a specific arrangement of atoms.

21. The 14 _____ describe the 14 general possible ways to arrange one type of atom.

22. _____ are two-dimensional (2-D) defects in a crystal.

23. _____ is a special type of material, formed by cooling metal at a very high rate.

Section 16.3

phase diagram	binary phase diagram
triple point	eutectic point
critical point	

24. The _____ is the temperature and pressure where a material can be a solid, a liquid, and a gas at the same time.

25. A/an _____ shows the phase and crystal structure of an alloy depending on chemistry and temperature.

26. A/an _____ shows the phase of a material depending on the temperature and the pressure.

27. The _____ on a binary phase diagram shows the alloy composition with the minimum melting point.

28. The _____ on a phase diagram shows the point where the line between liquid and gas begins to blur.

Section 16.4

flow	viscosity
cohesion	viscous
adhesion	nonviscous
meniscus	surface tension
capillary action	surfactant

29. The resistance of a material to flow is called _____.

30. A/An _____ material has a high viscosity, and a/an _____ material has a low viscosity.

31. _____ describes when a group of molecules in a liquid hold together. It describes why water in space forms a sphere.

32. The movement of a liquid under an external force such as gravity is called _____.

33. You can observe the balance between cohesion and adhesion in a liquid by pouring it into a test tube and looking at the _____.

34. Plants draw water up their stems by _____.

35. Water can stick to a glass surface because of _____.

36. A water strider and some lizards can walk on water because of _____.

37. _____, such as soaps and detergents, are effective at encapsulating dirt and oil.

Conceptual Questions

Section 16.1

38. Why is bonding between molecules stronger in solids? Why don't the molecules escape?

39. Why does adding energy in the form of heat melt a solid? What does it do to the bonds?

40. What would happen to the molecules in a balloon filled with air if you popped it in outer space? How far would the molecules go?

41. What does it mean for a material to be hard? Does it have to be strong to be hard?

42. How would you use the Mohs hardness scale to determine the relative hardness of a new material?

43. What does it mean for a material to be strong? Does it have to be hard to be strong?

44. Name some materials that you know are brittle. Name some materials that you know are ductile. How would you figure out whether a new material is brittle or ductile?

Section 16.2

45. Why are NaCl (salt) crystals cubic? Why are snowflakes hexagonal? (Hint: The answers are the same.)

46. What would happen to a glass if you left it alone at room temperature for one year? How about at 1,000°F for one year? Why?

47. What would happen to a glass if you left it alone at room temperature for millions of years? Why?

Chapter 16 Review

48. Why do we say that glasses have no "long-range order?" Do glasses have a crystal structure? Why or why not?

49. How do you make a metallic glass? Why do we use it on energy-impact surfaces, such as golf club heads?

50. Try and find an example of each of the 14 Bravais lattices in nature. Look at different kinds of crystals, rocks, and gemstones.

51. Name the three types of point defects in a crystal. Describe each one.

52. Describe the four types of dimensional defects in a crystal.

53. What is a slip system? Why do crystals deform using slip systems? What does it mean if a crystal breaks without using a slip system at all?

54. Why do slip systems occur first on close-packed directions?

Section 16.3

55. Why do we use alloys? Why don't we just use pure metals?

56. Describe two alloys in which changing the chemistry changes the properties.

57. Research a complex alloy that is interesting to you. Describe what each alloying element does to change the properties of the alloy.

58. Describe how to use a phase diagram to tell what phase would exist in a material at a given temperature and pressure.

59. What does the triple point mean? What does the supercritical point mean?

60. How do you tell whether an alloy is a solid or a liquid, depending on its temperature and chemistry?

61. What is the eutectic point for an alloy? Why is it useful? Name three places where we use eutectic alloys in our lives.

Section 16.4

62. What would happen to the molecules in a water balloon if you popped it in outer space, where there is no gravity?

63. Why do liquids flow? Why don't solids flow?

64. Why does rain fall as drops instead of any other shape?

65. What property allows geckos to crawl on ceilings? How do we use this property in our everyday lives?

66. Design an experiment to measure the ratio of cohesion to adhesion for a number of liquids.

67. How do we measure viscosity? Design an experiment to measure viscosity.

68. Describe how the molecular shape of a molecule can lead to its viscosity. Why is water non-viscous? Why is oil so viscous?

69. How can a something heavier than water "float" on top?

70. How would you reduce the surface tension of a liquid? What would you add to it?

71. Why can a water strider walk on water?

72. Why can some lizards run on water? What would happen if they stood still?

73. What would happen if you ran on water? Why?

Chemistry Connection

74. What is steel in its most basic form?

75. Why is steel such an important alloy for us?

76. Name five alloying elements (besides carbon) that can be added to steel, and explain what they do.

77. Name five places where steel is used in our everyday lives. What alloying elements would you add to steel in each situation to improve its properties?

Quantitative Problems

Section 16.3

78. Research the names of 10 common alloys on the Internet or at the library. Make a graph of their strength versus their hardness. Do you see a pattern?

79. Research aluminum alloy 6061. Make a graph of the amount of magnesium versus strength. Do you see a pattern?

For questions 80–83, examine the phase diagram of water:

Phase diagram of water

80. What phase is water at STP (25°C, 0.1 MPa)? Before proceeding with the solution discuss the meaning of STP with your teacher or your classmates.

81. What is the triple point of water? Give the temperature and pressure.

82. What is the melting point of water on Earth (0.1 MPa)? What is the melting point of water on Mars (0.01 MPa)? What is the melting point of water in outer space (~0 MPa)? Does it melt?

83. What is the critical point of water? What happens at this temperature and pressure?

For questions 84–86, examine the phase diagram of CO_2:

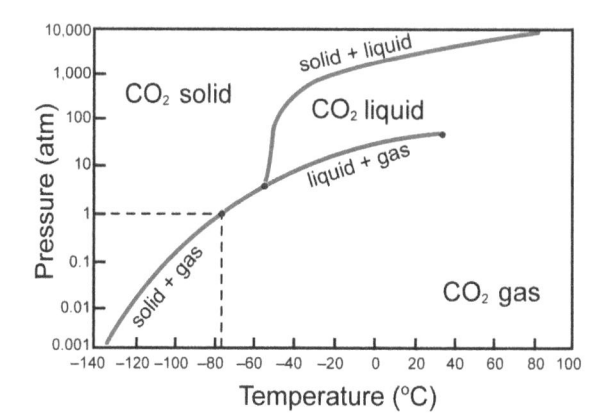

84. What is the freezing point of CO_2 on Earth (1 atm)? What is its melting point? Does it freeze? Does it melt?

85. When can CO_2 exist as a liquid?

86. Frozen CO_2 is called "dry ice." Why do we call it "dry" ice? Show why on the phase diagram.

For questions 87 and 88, examine the binary phase diagram for lead and tin:

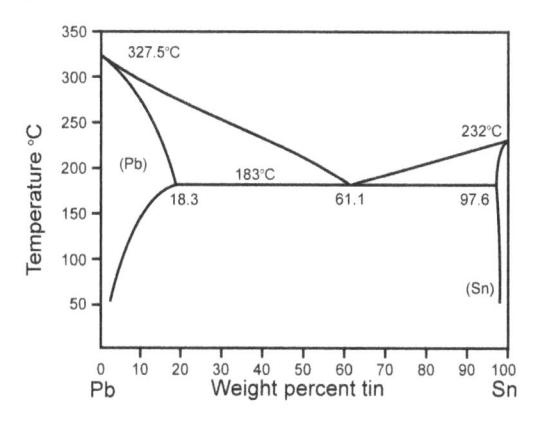

87. What is the melting point of lead? Of tin? Of the eutectic point?

88. Where do we use lead–tin eutectic? Why is it so useful to us?

CHAPTER 17
Organic Chemistry

What is so special about carbon?

Why is carbon so abundant in nature?

Are organic molecules "alive?"

Does "organic" chemistry involve the study of foods grown without harmful pesticides?

What exactly is plastic made of?

If you look around your classroom or home, you might be surprised by the fact that almost everything you see is made up of compounds containing carbon! Several million carbon-containing compounds are known to exist, and that number continues to grow. It is remarkable that carbon can make so many compounds. Organic chemistry is the study of carbon-containing compounds and their properties. These carbon-containing compounds vary widely in their size and complexity. The term "organic" in chemistry does *not* mean foods without harmful pesticides. You will find that you are already familiar with many organic chemicals. One important group of organic compounds is fossil fuels, such as gasoline, kerosene, natural gas, and coal. We use organic compounds to heat our homes and provide us with energy in our daily lives. Fossil fuels provide us with energy when we break the covalent bonds holding the molecules together.

Organic substances have changed people's lives in very significant ways. For instance, can you imagine our society without nylon, velcro, or plastic? We have become dependent on many synthetic organic substances.

We consume organic chemicals all the time! Artificial sweeteners, flavorings, and foodstuffs are produced by organic chemists.

Lastly, and perhaps most importantly, our understanding of the human body and living systems centers around the study of organic chemistry.

Vanillin molecule

Vanillin is used as a flavoring for vanilla ice cream

Mixing molecules

What chemicals are "organic"? To begin our study of organic chemistry, we will start by observing some of the important properties of these chemicals. Here we will examine the solubilities of three substances: candle wax, vegetable oil, and petroleum jelly. We will place each of them in contact with a different solvent. To each watch glass, we will add drops of alcohol, mineral oil, and water.

After making some observations we will mix the substances with a toothpick.

water   mineral oil   water   mineral oil   water   mineral oil
unmixed dissolved   unmixed unmixed   unmixed dissolved
  alcohol   alcohol   alcohol
  unmixed   unmixed   unmixed

In the first picture we can see that mineral oil dissolved in the petroleum jelly, but the alcohol and water did not. In the second one, candle wax does not appear to dissolve in anything. In the third case, vegetable oil dissolved in mineral oil, but not in alcohol or water.

What do our observations tell us about organic compounds such as wax, vegetable oil, and petroleum jelly?

Organic compounds must not be attracted to water or alcohol molecules. For substances to mix, the attractive forces must be similar between molecules. In this chapter we will learn more about the molecular structures of these molecules. Why these substances do not mix will be understood in more detail. The environmental impact of an oil spill is a good reason to understand these principles!

When oil spills in the ocean, as it did in 2010 in the Gulf of Mexico, it floats to the surface of the water. Chemicals called "dispersants" are used to break up the

oil into small pieces. The larger surface area of the smaller pieces makes it easier for the naturally occurring microorganisms to break up the oil. Even though oil dispersants move the oil from the surface of the water into the water column, and so help protect birds and shore life, the long-term effect that it may have on ocean organisms is not known, and so we must be very careful using them.

17.1 Carbon Molecules

Carbon has the ability to make four bonds

Carbon has a unique ability to form many strong bonds to itself and create carbon networks; no other element on the periodic table shares this ability. Carbon can also form strong bonds to other nonmetals, such as hydrogen and nitrogen. In this section, you will learn about some simple organic molecules. Understanding their molecular structures will help you to understand their properties and why they are important in our daily lives.

To begin, it will be helpful to review some of the concepts covered in the bonding chapter. Carbon, given its placement on the periodic table, has the ability to make four bonds. When carbon is bonded to four atoms, it will always take the geometric shape of a tetrahedron. This tetrahedral structure is very strong! The fact that diamonds are arranged in a tetrahedral lattice is one reason why they are the hardest substance we know of. The nonpolar or "perfect" covalent nature of the C–C bond is another factor in the strength of diamonds.

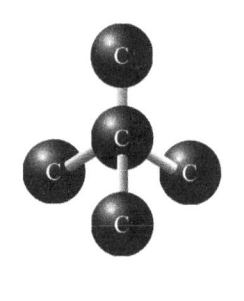

The fact that carbon contains four valence electrons requires it to make four bonds. As you know, it can bond to fewer than four atoms if it makes a multiple bond.

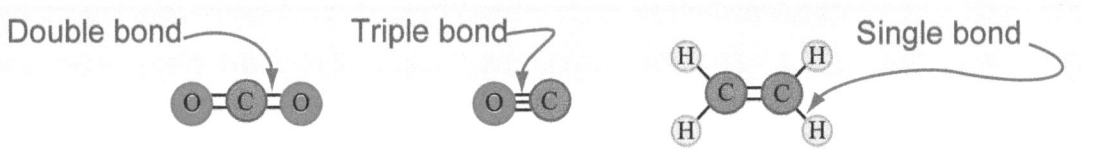

Hydrocarbons contain carbon and hydrogen

The simplest organic compounds are called **hydrocarbons**, and they contain only the elements carbon and hydrogen. There are two types of hydrocarbons: saturated and unsaturated. In a saturated hydrocarbon each carbon atom makes four bonds, the maximum number possible. **Saturated** hydrocarbons contain only single carbon-to-carbon bonds. In an **unsaturated** hydrocarbon, the carbon-to-carbon bonds contain double and triple bonds. Because of the double or triple bonds, it is possible for carbon to bond to one more atom, so these hydrocarbons are considered "unsaturated."

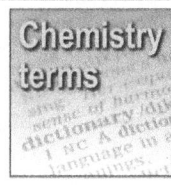
Chemistry terms

hydrocarbon: a molecule made entirely from hydrogen and carbon atoms.

saturated hydrocarbon: a hydrocarbon containing only single carbon-to-carbon bonds.

unsaturated hydrocarbon: a hydrocarbon containing multiple bonds between the carbon atoms.

Alkanes

Saturated hydrocarbons are called **alkanes**. Alkanes can form straight chains or branched chains. The simplest alkane is methane, because it contains only one carbon.

The pattern for alkanes

Ethane (C_2H_6) has two carbons attached by a single bond. Propane (C_3H_8) has three carbons attached by single bonds. Butane (C_4H_{10}) has four carbons attached by single bonds. As the length of the carbon chain grows, we can see a pattern in the formula for alkanes. They all follow $C_nH_{(2n+2)}$, where n represents the number of carbon atoms.

TABLE 17.1. Formulas of the first ten straight chain alkanes

Name	Condensed formula	Structural formula
Methane	CH_4	CH_4
Ethane	C_2H_6	CH_3CH_3
Propane	C_3H_8	$CH_3CH_2CH_3$
Butane	C_4H_{10}	$CH_3CH_2CH_2CH_3$
Pentane	C_5H_{12}	$CH_3CH_2CH_2CH_2CH_3$
Hexane	C_6H_{14}	$CH_3CH_2CH_2CH_2CH_2CH_3$
Heptane	C_7H_{16}	$CH_3CH_2CH_2CH_2CH_2CH_2CH_3$
Octane	C_8H_{18}	$CH_3CH_2CH_2CH_2CH_2CH_2CH_2CH_3$
Nonane	C_9H_{20}	$CH_3CH_2CH_2CH_2CH_2CH_2CH_2CH_2CH_3$
Decane	$C_{10}H_{22}$	$CH_3CH_2CH_2CH_2CH_2CH_2CH_2CH_2CH_2CH_3$

Observe the structure of butane

The best way to visualize an alkane is to build it with a molecular model. Try building a molecule of butane as an example.

When you observe the structure of butane, you will see that a "straight" chain is really not straight nor linear

Butane isn't perfectly "straight" because carbon makes a three dimensional tetrahedral structure. This is because it wants the single covalent bonds to be spaced out as far apart as possible to minimize the electron repulsions between the bonds. Look closely at your molecule of butane. Can you move the atoms around?

Butane

Can the hydrogens change positions? Did you notice that the atoms can rotate around the single bonds? It is important to see that the hydrogens can occupy different positions as the carbon atoms rotate. The carbon atoms can also occupy different positions that make the ends of the chain closer together or further apart. You will see that as the alkane gets longer and the carbon chain grows, the molecule will have different properties.

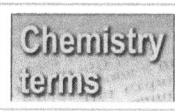

Chemistry terms

alkane: a hydrocarbon containing only single bonds; a saturated hydrocarbon.

Naming alkanes

Naming hydrocarbons with single bonds

The naming process for alkanes is very systematic, and it can easily be applied by following simple rules. The prefixes for the first ten alkanes are listed in Table 17.2.

To name an alkane we simply count the number of carbon atoms in the longest chain and add the suffix -ane. For example $CH_3CH_2CH_2CH_2CH_3$ has five carbons in the chain and is called pentane.

TABLE 17.2

Number	Greek root
1	meth
2	eth
3	prop
4	but
5	pent
6	hex
7	hept
8	oct
9	non
10	dec

Pentane

5 carbons ⟵⟶ alkane

Organic chemists call this *n*-pentane, where the *n* indicates the longest straight chain. Note how there are only single bonds between the carbons.

Count the longest continuous chain of carbons

For a branched chain alkane, we look for the longest continuous chain of carbons that gives us the name of the **parent compound**. The parent compound tells us the base alkane name. Do not lift your pencil off the paper as you count carbon atoms; this helps you identify the *longest continuous chain*. Consider the example:

Longest chain →

CH_3—CH_2—CH_2—CH—CH_2—CH_2—CH_3

Shortest chain ⟶ CH_2
                    |
                    CH_3

This may also be written with an R representing the CH_2CH_3 branch

CH_3—CH_2—CH_2—CH—CH_2—CH_2—CH_3
                    |
                    R

Here the longest carbon chain contains seven carbons. We call the parent compound heptane. The two-carbon chain that is not included is called an ethyl group. Eth- stands for "2 carbons" and -yl indicates it is a "substituent," or an add-on. For the exact name of the compound, we count the number of carbons over to the ethyl group. Here it is on the fourth carbon, so we name it 4-ethyl-heptane. The ethyl group can also be referred to as an **R group**. The R group notation is used as a shorthand way of writing a hydrocarbon side chain attached to the parent compound.

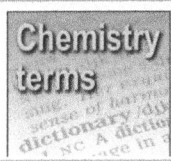
Chemistry terms

parent compound: the longest continuous chain of carbons in an organic compound, which tells us the base alkane name.

R group: any group of atoms in an organic formula, typically H or a hydrocarbon side chain of any length.

540

Structural isomers

Branching of the carbon chain forms new structures

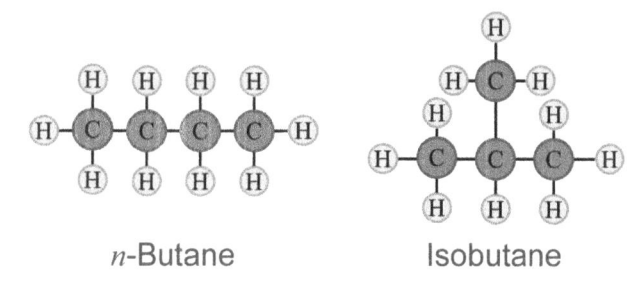

n-Butane   Isobutane

When a carbon chain contains four or more carbon atoms, it may form a "branched" chain alkane. For example, let's take the butane molecule and remove one atom of carbon by pulling apart the covalent bond. If we place it in the middle of the remaining carbon chain with three atoms, we will have changed the bonding arrangement. If we try to place it anywhere but in the middle, we end up with straight-chained butane again.

When a molecule has the same number and type of atoms, but a different bonding pattern, it is known as a **structural isomer**. If you compare the two butane molecules above, you will see that they have the same structural formula of C_4H_{10}.

Pentane has five carbon atoms

Let's draw the structural isomers of pentane (C_5H_{12}). First begin by making a chain of five carbon atoms:

$$-C-C-C-C-C-$$

Now we add the hydrogen atoms so that each carbon atom makes four bonds in total:

This is called *n*-pentane or normal pentane, which indicates the straight-chain form. Now we can remove one carbon and form a branch in one position. We can also remove two carbons and form a symmetrical branched structure.

Structural isomers for pentane

branching carbons

2-Pentane   Isopentane

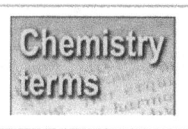
Chemistry terms

structural isomer: molecule with the same number and type of atoms as another molecule but a different bonding pattern.

Petroleum chemistry

Octane, or gasoline, forms structural isomers!

Petroleum undergoes reactions at high temperatures with specific catalysts, which create structural isomers. These reactions cause some of the linear octane molecules to become branched. Branched-chain hydrocarbons burn better in your car's engine, because they burn more slowly and smoothly. Much research has been focused on how to get gasoline to burn effectively, and one of the discoveries was that increased branching allowed for better combustion by the engine. The more branched the fuel is, the more complete the combustion of the fuel is, because it burns slower.

Octane

Isooctane

Branched-chain hydrocarbons have higher octane ratings. At the fuel pump, the octane ratings are based on a ratio of branched isooctane to linear heptane. Linear heptane has an octane rating of zero, and isooctane has an octane rating of 100. Gasoline is a mixture of hydrocarbons. When we look at the gas pump and see the number 87, this tells us that this ratio is 87% isooctane to 13% heptane. Isooctane is a branched alkane formed during the refining of petroleum. *Isomerization reactions are used to produce large amounts of branched-chain alkanes.*

This is an important application of structural isomers.

Performance cars require high-octane fuels

Branched-chain hydrocarbons such as isooctane have higher octane ratings. This means that these molecules can withstand the high compression of the cylinders in a high-performance car. High-performance cars have engines that are designed to operate under a higher compression. The high compression produces more energy when the fuel is burned; this gives the car more power. If normal gasoline is used in high-compression cylinders, the pressure can cause it to ignite and make small explosions, which damages the engine cylinders. High-performance cars run on high-octane fuels because they burn slower and produce more power, allowing these engines to perform at their best.

Properties of hydrocarbons

Hydrocarbons are nonpolar

Thinking back to Chapter 8 when you studied intermolecular forces, you might remember that methane (CH_4) is a nonpolar molecule. Do you remember why? This is because carbon has four of the same C–H bonds, all at equal angles, which share the electrons relatively equally between their nuclei. Symmetrical molecules such as methane have no net dipole or charge separation; therefore they are considered nonpolar. Nonpolar molecules are held together with London dispersion forces. London dispersion forces can be a relatively "weak" attractive force between hydrocarbon molecules that have low molecular weights such as methane. Because of this many of these molecules exist as gases at room temperature.

The longer the hydrocarbon chain, the stronger the attractive forces between molecules

London dispersion forces

Name	Molecule	Boiling point (°C)
Methane	CH_4	−161
Ethane	C_2H_6	−88.5
Pentane	C_5H_{12}	36
Hexane	C_6H_{14}	68.7
Octane	C_8H_{18}	125.6

However, as the hydrocarbon chain grows in length, London dispersion forces *increase significantly*. As the length of the chain increases, it allows for a larger surface area, which in turn allows the molecules to be in greater contact with each other. The increased attraction causes many longer chain hydrocarbons to be liquids at room temperature.

Surfactants and bacteria are used to clean up an oil spill

These nonpolar properties have been given important consideration so that we can better help our environment. A thorough understanding of these properties has allowed scientists to design effective ways to clean up oil spills. Initially, some of the oil is skimmed off the surface of the ocean water. Chemicals called surfactants are then added to the oil to help it mix with the ocean water. Surfactants are detergent-like chemicals that break apart the nonpolar attractions, causing the oil to be dispersed into smaller regions. Bacteria are then added to help engulf or "eat" the smaller, more manageable amounts of oil.

Image courtesy of NOAA.
The pink color comes from oil consuming bacteria

Unsaturated hydrocarbons

Multiple bonds require more energy to break

Unsaturated hydrocarbons contain multiple bonds between carbon atoms. You may remember that double bonds take more energy to break than single bonds, and triple bonds require more energy to break than double bonds. This is because the distance between the nuclei of the atoms is shorter. Just remember that the more bonds there are between the atoms, the more energy is required to pull them apart. Ethene is used to make the plastic polyethylene. Polyethylene is simply a long chain formed by joining ethene molecules. Ethene is an example of an **alkene**. Alkenes are hydrocarbons that contain one or more double bonds in their structure.

Ethene

Ethyne contains triple bonds

Acetylene gas, used in welding torches, contains ethyne (C_2H_2). Acetylene is the "common name" or slang term used for the ethyne molecule. Ethyne has a triple bond between the two carbon atoms. Ethyne is an example of an **alkyne**, which is a hydrocarbon containing one or more triple bonds. Here the prefix eth- still means two carbons and the -yne ending tells us there is a triple bond. When ethyne is burned in air the triple bond is broken, releasing a large amount of energy. Acetylene torches reach temperatures up to 3,300°C (6,000°F)! This is enough to melt steel!

Acetylene Torch

Naming alkenes and alkynes

All alkenes end by using -ene; the parent names are the same ones we used for the alkanes (see Table 17.1). For example, the name propane means a three-carbon chain alkane. When there is a double bond, we replace -ane with -ene. We use -yne if there is a triple bond. We will always use the name of the longest parent chain, so it is important to identify it correctly if the molecule is long.

Propene
3 carbons — alkene

Propyne
3 carbons — alkyne

> **Chemistry terms**
>
> **alkene:** a hydrocarbon containing one or more double bonds.
> **alkyne:** a hydrocarbon containing one or more triple bonds.

Stereoisomers

Spatial relationships of atoms can also result in isomers

When atoms are bonded in the same order, but the three-dimensional positions of the atoms in space are different, the resulting isomers are called **stereoisomers**. There are two types of stereoisomers.

The first type is called a **geometric isomer**. Geometric isomers form when a double bond is present between two carbon atoms. The double bond prevents rotation and the carbons are in "fixed" positions relative to each other.

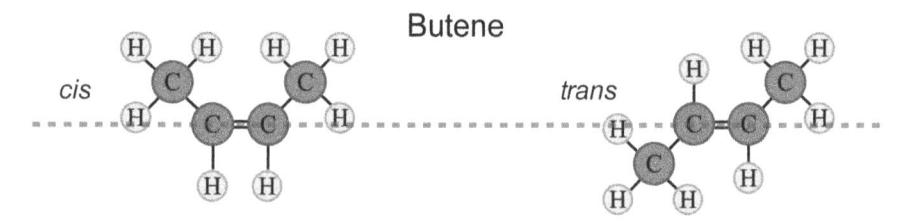

Butene

The *cis* configuration results when –CH_3 groups of the molecule are both on the same side. The *trans* configuration results when the –CH_3 groups of the molecule are across from each other. It is helpful to make these molecules with molecular models. This allows you to observe the differences firsthand.

Making two mirror image tetrahedrons

The second type of stereoisomer is called an **optical isomer**. Optical isomers result when the central carbon atom has four different atoms or groups attached to it. Optical isomers rotate light differently with respect to each other. When plane-polarized light (light polarized in one direction) shines on an optical isomer, the molecule rotates the light either clockwise

or counterclockwise. Here we will consider four different atoms (H, F, Cl, and Br) attached to a central carbon atom. These isomers look the same at first glance. But place one model on top of the other and you will see that no matter how you turn them, they cannot be superimposed! This is just like your left and right hands. They are mirror images if you hold them facing each other. If you place one on top of the other, your thumbs do not line up. Compare your tetrahedrons and see.

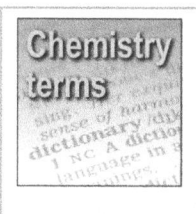

Chemistry terms

geometric isomer: a molecule with the same sequence of atoms, but different placement of groups around a double bond, as another molecule.

optical isomers: "mirror image" compounds that form when the carbon atom has four different groups attached to it.

stereoisomers: compounds whose atoms are bonded in the same order but have different spatial orientation.

Aromatic hydrocarbons

Vanilla and cinnamon have pleasant aromas

Organic compounds with distinct aromas that were originally discovered in spices and flavorings are called **aromatic hydrocarbons**. Some of these compounds include vanillin, cinnamon, cloves, and wintergreen.

Cinnamaldehyde   Eugenol   Wintergreen oil   Vanillin

Cinnamon   Cloves   Wintergreen   Vanilla bean

Benzene is common to many aromatic hydrocarbons

When scientists examined these aromatic hydrocarbons to see what gave them their pleasant odors, they discovered that they all had one feature that was the same! Each contained a six-membered ring structure known as **benzene**. Benzene (C_6H_6) is a six-membered carbon ring with alternating double bonds between the carbon atoms.

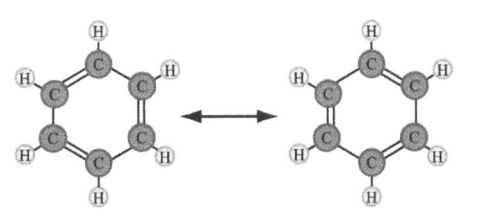

Because electrons are always moving, benzene's double and single bonds are never actually static, or fixed in place. The alternating double bond structures represent two "resonance" structures that help us to visualize the bonding pattern. Benzene never actually exists as either of the resonance structures but is a "blend" of the two structures, because the electrons are evenly distributed throughout the structure. A simpler representation of benzene is a six-membered ring with a circle inside it.

The circle represents the electrons being shared equally between the six carbons. This equal distribution and sharing of the electrons gives benzene a special stability. The electrons in benzene's double bonds are referred to as "delocalized," because they have the ability to move around the entire molecular structure.

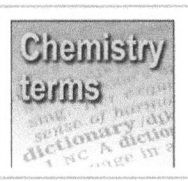
Chemistry terms

aromatic hydrocarbon: a hydrocarbon containing one or more cyclic ring structures.

benzene: an aromatic hydrocarbon (C_6H_6) modeled with alternating single and double bonds between the carbon atoms in the ring.

546

17.2 Functional Groups

Functional groups give a molecule its special properties

The term "functional group" refers to a group of elements that give an organic compound very specific properties. In fact, most organic chemistry is dictated by the type of functional groups attached to the molecule.

Many common products that we use contain functional groups that give each product specific characteristics. These characteristics make each product useful in a different way.

Let's use an analogy to help us understand how the functional groups might influence the behavior of the hydrocarbon chain. Humans can perform different activities depending upon what we have attached to our feet! If we are wearing skis, then we can slide down a snow-covered mountain. If we are wearing rollerblades, then we can roll along a paved street. Without skis or rollerblades, humans still have the capability to walk or run. Hydrocarbon chains are, for the most part, similar to each other in their chemical behavior. However, when functional groups are added, the organic compounds gain special abilities. Functional groups give organic molecules the ability to do different things, just as skis and rollerblades give us different capabilities. The different types of functional groups that we will cover in this chapter are listed in Table 17.3.

TABLE 17.3 Common functional groups

Recall that R refers to any hydrocarbon chain. In the table it represents CH_3 each time.

Name	Functional group	Example
Alcohol	$R-OH$	CH_3CH_2OH
Ether	$R-O-R$	CH_3-O-CH_3
Aldehyde	$R-\overset{\overset{O}{\|\|}}{C}-H$	$CH_3\overset{\overset{O}{\|\|}}{C}-H$
Ketone	$R-\overset{\overset{O}{\|\|}}{C}-R$	$CH_3\overset{\overset{O}{\|\|}}{C}-CH_3$
Carboxylic acid	$R-\overset{\overset{O}{\|\|}}{C}-OH$	$CH_3\overset{\overset{O}{\|\|}}{C}-OH$
Ester	$R-\overset{\overset{O}{\|\|}}{C}-O-R$	$CH_3\overset{\overset{O}{\|\|}}{C}-O-CH_3$

Alcohols and ethers

Alcohols contain a hydroxyl group

Hydrocarbons that contain a hydroxyl (–OH) group are classified as **alcohols**. Methanol and ethanol are likely the most familiar alcohols to you. Rubbing alcohol has methanol in it, whereas wine and beer contain ethanol. Alcohol has

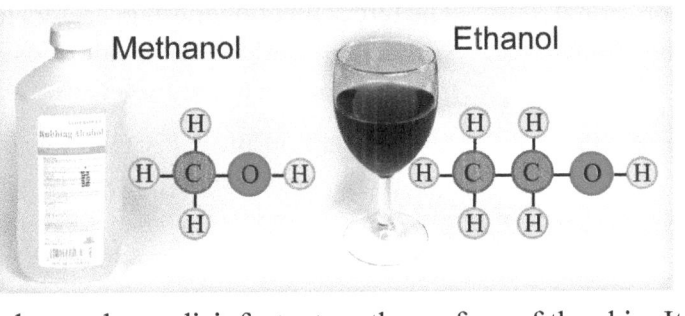

chemical properties that allow it to be used as a disinfectant on the surface of the skin. It breaks apart lipids and precipitates proteins; because of this it kills organisms (bacteria, fungi, and most viruses) on our skin. It evaporates easily, leaving a cool feeling. The – OH group is often referred to as a "hydroxyl group." Ethanol is used in medical wipes and antibacterial hand sanitizers. It is also used extensively as a fuel source or fuel additive to gasoline. Most American gasolines have 10% ethanol content.

Alcohols can form hydrogen bonds

The –OH or hydroxyl group is capable of hydrogen bonding and this makes short-chain alcohols able to easily dissolve in water. The strong hydrogen bonds cause these alcohols to be liquids at room temperature; without the –OH functional group, the one- and two-chain hydrocarbons would be gases. However, alcohols such as methanol and ethanol vaporize easily because they readily absorb heat from their surroundings.

Ethers readily vaporize

Ether molecules have hydrocarbon chains on either side of an oxygen molecule. Ethers are volatile, meaning they easily form vapors. Recall that a substance can go from being a liquid to a vapor easily if the attractive forces between the molecules are weak. One type of ether, diethyl ether, has been used as an anesthetic in medical surgery for over 150 years. It was first used in surgery by an American doctor in the mid 1800s. When inhaled, diethyl ether causes patients to become unconscious for a period of time, allowing surgery to be

Early use of diethyl ether as an anesthetic

performed. Dimethyl ether is used as a propellant in aerosol cans. The gas suspends the particles inside the can and allows a mistlike spray to be formed when the can is used.

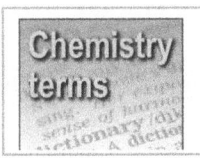

Chemistry terms

alcohol: a hydrocarbon with a hydroxyl group (–OH) attached.

ether: a molecule where oxygen is bonded to two carbon groups, often hydrocarbon chains.

Aldehydes and ketones

Nature provides us with fragrant smells

A wide variety of familiar smells and flavors come from aldehydes and ketones. These organic compounds are similar in their structures. In both an **aldehyde** and a **ketone**, functional groups contain a central carbon atom double bonded to an oxygen. In an aldehyde, the carbon always has one hydrogen bonded to it,

and on the other side the carbon is bonded to a hydrocarbon. In a ketone, the carbon is bonded on both sides to a hydrocarbon. The carbon double bonded to the oxygen (C=O) is referred to as a **carbonyl group**. This carbonyl group shared by both the aldehydes and the ketones is quite polar, which increases the reactivities of these molecules.

Flavoring molecules found in nature are also produced artificially

Many different aldehydes and ketones have been isolated from plants and animals in nature. They are so popular that larger quantities of the molecules are often produced on an industrial scale. For example, vanillin is found in vanilla beans and is used as a flavoring in ice cream and cookies. You may have heard of "artificial" vanilla flavoring and "pure" vanilla flavoring from extracts. The pure extract costs more to purchase, but most agree that it tastes better than the artificial vanilla flavoring.

Cinnamon's aroma is also an aldehyde. It comes from the bark of cinnamon trees. The smell and flavor of cinnamon comes from the molecule cinna-maldehyde, which, as its name indicates, is an aldehyde.

Formaldehyde is used to preserve tissues and as a fixative for viewing tissues under the microscope for medical diagnosis. It also has a distinct smell.

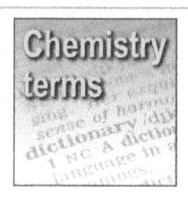

Chemistry terms

aldehyde: a functional group in which the central carbon makes a double bond with oxygen and is then bonded to hydrogen on one side and to another hydrocarbon.

ketone: a functional group in which the central carbon makes a double bond with oxygen, and is then bonded to two hydrocarbons one on each side.

carbonyl group: group formed when a carbon atom is double bonded to an oxygen atom (C=O).

Aldehydes and ketones

Acetone and testosterone are ketones

There are also many ketones that you may be familiar with. A biological example of a ketone would be testosterone, the male sex hormone. Another common ketone is acetone, which is also the simplest molecular example of a ketone molecule. Acetone is found in fingernail-polish remover and paint thinner. The smell you notice when you open the fingernail-polish remover is actually acetone. Interestingly, our bodies make small amounts of acetone that is used as a building block for other molecules. Acetone is widely used as a solvent because it mixes well with water and dissolves organic substances. Acetone is used in the lab and in industry as a cleaning agent. Acetone is synthesized in large amounts for use in the production of polymers.

Carbohydrate molecules are aldehydes and ketones

Perhaps one of the most important examples of aldehydes and ketones in nature are carbohydrate molecules. The sugar glucose ($C_6H_{12}O_6$) is a six-carbon aldehyde sugar that contains several hydroxyl groups. In contrast, fructose, which is commonly found in fruit, is a ketone.

Glucose   Fructose

Although it is much easier to identify the aldehyde and ketone functional groups when looking at the linear structures, these sugars are generally found in the ring form shown here on the right.

Disaccharide

Carbohydrates and energy

Carbohydrates are the primary source of energy for most animals. These aldehyde and ketone sugars make disaccharides. A disaccharide is a two-unit sugar molecule (from di-, meaning two, and saccharide, meaning sugar.) Sucrose, or table sugar, is a disaccharide formed by connecting a glucose molecule to a fructose molecule. Starch molecules from pasta and potatoes are also formed by connecting many glucose molecules in a chain.

Carboxylic acids

Carboxylic acids are widespread in nature. A **carboxylic acid** contains a functional group composed of four elements (COOH), called a carboxyl group.

Acetic acid is an example of a carboxylic acid. You can see its structure on the right. Acetic acid is present in sour foods such as vinegar and citrus fruits. Red ants contain another type of carboxylic acid, called formic acid. They use formic acid as a chemical weapon! Spoiled foods also contain carboxylic acids.

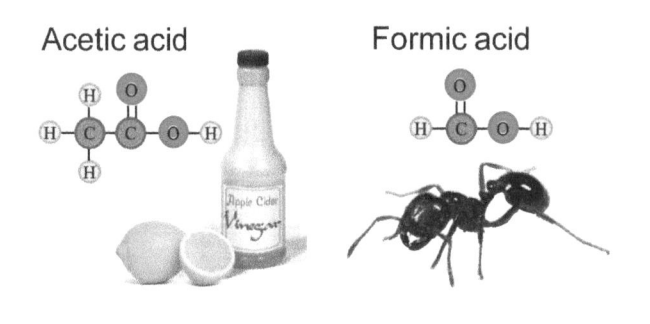

Acetic acid   Formic acid

Carboxylic acids are weak acids

As the name indicates, carboxylic acids have acidic behavior. You may remember that acids are proton (H^+) donors. The structure of the carboxyl group gives it the ability to lose the hydrogen attached to the oxygen molecule, and this is responsible for the acidic properties of these molecules. The electronegative oxygens draw the electrons in the bonds more toward themselves; this leaves the hydrogen bonded to the oxygen with a slight positive charge. The positive charge is attracted to a nearby water molecule, which causes it to be pulled off, or ionized. Although this only happens approximately five percent of the time, this partial ionization still produces significant amounts of H^+ ions in solution.

Electrons pulled to oxygen

||| indicates bonds

Water attracts H

Carboxyl groups form hydrogen bonds

Another important property of molecules containing carboxyl groups is that they can form strong hydrogen bonds, and this increases their melting and boiling points.

Carboxylic acids are one of the key functional groups of all amino acids. In the next chapter, you will see that this group is involved in the bonding of amino acids to make proteins. Carboxylic acid functional groups are also present on long-chain fatty acid molecules.

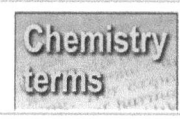
Chemistry terms

carboxylic acid: an organic molecule containing a carboxyl group (COOH).

Amines

Amines are found in amino acids

Alanine

Amine group

Amines are organic compounds that contain an amino group (NH_2). The amino group is an important functional group on amino acids. You may recall that amino acids make up all of the proteins in our bodies! The amino group forms a bond with the neighboring carboxyl group, which links the amino acids together in a chain. As you will see in the next chapter, these proteins regulate most of the chemical reactions in our bodies.

As a class of molecules, the amines have several important applications. The first and foremost is protein synthesis. Amines are also used to make dyes and to treat allergies. Chlorpheniramine, shown here, is the active ingredient in many allergy medications. This medication is also effective in reducing the side effects of other drugs that may cause allergic reactions.

Clorpheniramine
allergy medication

Amine group

Amines are weak bases and also form hydrogen bonds

Amines have basic properties, because the lone pair on the top of the nitrogen atom allows them to accept a proton or hydrogen ion (H^+). The high electronegativity of the nitrogen atom also contributes to the molecule's high polarity, making it capable of forming strong hydrogen bonds. The amine functional group causes amino acids to have basic behavior in aqueous solutions; because of this, pH plays an important role in the functional group's behavior.

Lone pair accepts H^+

indicates bonds

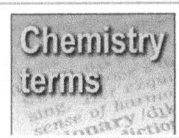

Chemistry terms

amines: organic molecules containing an amino group (NH_2).

Esters

Esters smell good!

Esters are very common in nature. They are often responsible for the lovely fragrances of flowers and ripened fruit. On the right you can see the molecule responsible for the smell of lavender. The **ester** functional group resembles a carboxyl group, except that it has a carbon group attached to the oxygen instead of a hydrogen atom (H).

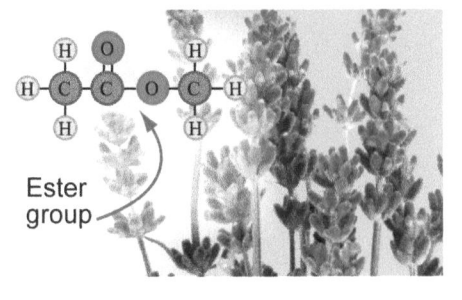

Ester group

Esters are added to foods and drinks

Flavor comes from a unique combination of taste and odor. Fragrances and tastes are often due to a complex blend of several esters, instead of just one. Manufacturers often add specific esters to make their foods and drinks taste better. Esters are also added to shampoos to give the desired fragrance. Using the appropriate mixture, you can make things smell like strawberries without using actual strawberries!

Isobutylacetate

Fats and oils are esters too! Long-chain fatty acids are attached by ester bonds to the glycerol molecule. Ester bonds can be formed by joining carboxylic acids and alcohols.

Esters cannot form hydrogen bonds among themselves because they have no hydrogen atoms that are directly attached to an electronegative atom of nitrogen or oxygen. Esters can, however, accept a hydrogen bond on the oxygen's lone pairs. Esters cannot make a hydrogen bond to donate. Because of this lack of hydrogen bonding, esters vaporize more readily than carboxylic acids.

Polyesters are polymers with the ester group attached

Polyesters are commonly used in clothing and in foods. Polyesters are polymers that contain the ester functional group on the hydrocarbon chain. One of the most common synthetic fibers is polyethylene terephthalate (PET). Polyester clothing made from these fibers is very popular because it does not wrinkle easily.

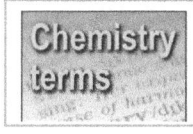
Chemistry terms

ester: an organic molecule containing a –COOR group, responsible for many smells and tastes in fruits and flowers.

17.3 Organic Reactions

Organic compounds undergo some important chemical reactions that we will discuss in this section. Organic reactions have been used to create heat and light early in human history. Humans have long taken advantage of the fact that hydrocarbons burn rapidly in the presence of oxygen at sufficiently high temperatures. Industrial production of solid shortenings such as Crisco® and of textiles and fabrics are dependent upon organic reactions. Plastics are widely used in our society, and the formation of plastics takes place through polymerization reactions, which are an important type of organic reaction.

Let's begin with combustion reactions, since you are already familiar with them. Earlier we studied combustion reactions in several areas, including stoichiometry, chemical reactions, and thermochemistry. Combustion reactions have been used to generate electricity and to power vehicles and machinery. Because of this, the alkanes are widely used as a fuel source all over the world.

Hydrocarbons burn rapidly at high temperatures

Here are two typical combustion reactions:

$$C_3H_8(g) + 5O_2(g) \rightarrow 3CO_2(g) + 4H_2O(l) + heat \quad 2C_4H_{10}(g)$$
$$+ 13O_2(g) \rightarrow 8CO_2(g) + 10H_2O(l) + heat$$

In all "complete" combustion reactions, the products are always carbon dioxide and water. Here we are assuming complete combustion. In real life, when hydrocarbons are burned there are uncombusted hydrocarbon fragments remaining after the combustion process. These fragments contribute to air pollution.

Let's look at what happens structurally to the alkane molecule as we burn (or combust) it. Some of us use natural gas to heat our homes. Natural gas contains several alkanes, but is primarily methane (CH_4). High temperatures are necessary to break the highly stable carbon hydrogen (C–H) bonds and initiate the reaction. However, when the more stable bonds in CO_2 and H_2O form as products, energy is given off and released to the surroundings. The amount of heat released is *more* than the amount necessary to initiate the reaction, so overall the reaction provides us with energy.

Reactions of alkanes

Alkanes have low reactivity

Overall, the alkanes as a group are considered to be relatively unreactive. This low reactivity comes in part from the high strength of the C–C and the C–H bonds. These bonds are very stable. At room temperature, alkanes do not react easily with substances like acids and bases that often cause chemical reactions. However, when light energy is added or when the temperature is raised, their reactions can be very useful to us.

A new atom is substituted for hydrogen

Alkanes undergo substitution reactions. In **substitution reactions**, one or more hydrogen atoms on the alkane are removed and replaced by different atoms. The name substitution reaction comes from the fact that a different atom is *substituted* for one or more of the hydrogen atoms. For example, by using a halogen such as Cl_2 or Br_2, methane will undergo a substitution reaction referred to as *chlorination* or *bromination*.

First Cl added   Second Cl added

The light used in the equations above indicates that energy in the form of light ($E = h\nu$) is required to break the covalent Cl–Cl bond and form free chlorine radicals (Cl•) with an unpaired electron via the following equation: $Cl_2(g) + h\nu \rightarrow Cl\bullet + Cl\bullet$. The chlorine radical is very reactive, and is able to break the C–H bond on the hydrocarbon molecule. The overall result is that a chlorine atom is substituted for a hydrogen atom. This process can be repeated until several or all of the hydrogen atoms are replaced on the hydrocarbon. Interestingly, alkanes become more reactive when modified by substitution reactions. This is because the bond between carbon and the new element is not as strong as the original C–H bond. The difference in electronegativity causes the new bond to be more polar and therefore more reactive.

Removal of H_2 forms double bonds

Alkanes also undergo **dehydrogenation reactions**. Dehydrogenation reactions remove hydrogen (H_2) from the alkane, causing the formation of double bonds. Dehydrogenation causes areas of desaturation along a hydrocarbon chain.

Ethane   Ethene   Hydrogen

Chemistry terms

substitution reaction: a reaction in which one or more hydrogen atoms on an alkane are removed and replaced by different atoms.

dehydrogenation reaction: reaction in which hydrogen (H_2) is removed from the alkane, causing formation of double bonds and resulting in the formation of unsaturated alkenes.

Reactions of alkenes and alkynes

Double and triple bonds are more reactive!

The presence of double and triple bonds in their molecular structures make alkenes and alkynes much more reactive than alkanes. Compounds that are more "reactive" are more likely to react with other chemicals. The presence of these multiple bonds allows them to undergo addition reactions and polymerizations. Both of these reaction types are widely used for industrial purposes to make plastics and synthetic fibers. In an **addition reaction**, atoms are added to the two carbon atoms forming the multiple bond. **Hydrogenation** is one of the most common types of addition reactions. In hydrogenation reactions, hydrogen atoms are added to the carbon atoms forming double bonds. The process of hydrogenation is used to make solid shortenings, such as Crisco. Removing double bonds allows the hydrocarbon molecules to pack tighter, allowing the intermolecular forces to have stronger associations. This causes the liquid oil to become a solid.

Hydrogenation reaction

Predict the product of the hydrogenation of 2-pentene (C_5H_{10}):

$$H-\underset{\overset{|}{H}}{\overset{\overset{H}{|}}{C}}-\overset{H}{C}=\overset{H}{C}-\underset{\overset{|}{H}}{\overset{\overset{H}{|}}{C}}-\underset{\overset{|}{H}}{\overset{\overset{H}{|}}{C}}-H$$

Given: *Structure of 2-pentene*

Relationships: *In hydrogenation, H atoms are added across the double bond:*

$$H-\underset{\overset{|}{H}}{\overset{\overset{H}{|}}{C}}-\underset{\overset{|}{H}}{\overset{\overset{H}{|}}{C}}-\underset{\overset{|}{H}}{\overset{\overset{H}{|}}{C}}-\underset{\overset{|}{H}}{\overset{\overset{H}{|}}{C}}-\underset{\overset{|}{H}}{\overset{\overset{H}{|}}{C}}-H$$

Discussion: *The hydrocarbon 2-pentene is now saturated and contains only single bonds.*

addition reaction: a chemical reaction that adds atoms to the carbon atoms forming multiple bond(s) in a molecule.

hydrogenation reaction: a type of addition reaction where hydrogen gas, H_2, is added to a double or triple bond in a hydrocarbon, causing the structure to become saturated.

Trans fats and "partial" hydrogenation

Now that you understand hydrogenation, we will review how trans fats are formed. Trans fats were created by accident through the **partial hydrogenation** of unsaturated fats. The term "partial" means that some double bonds still remain in the structure of the fat and that the fat is not completely hydrogenated. Partial hydrogenation causes the remaining double bonds to have a *trans* orientation on either side of the double bond.

The *cis* and *trans* configuration

In their natural forms, fats have *cis* double bonds. Elaidic acid and oleic acid are examples: These fats are geometric isomers, which means they have identical structures except for the double bond configuration. Elaidic acid is the main ingredient of partially hydrogenated vegetable oils, and it has the *trans* configuration. Oleic acid is found in olive oil, and has the *cis* configuration shown.

Remember that the partial hydrogenation process does not fully hydrogenate all of the double bonds. This gives the fat a semisolid texture. Unsaturated fats such as corn oil, olive oil, and peanut oil are organic hydrocarbons. Because of the presence of double bonds in their structures, these fats are liquids at room temperature.

Unsaturated fats are liquids at room temperature

The process of partial hydrogenation causes food that contains oil, such as potato chips, to last longer on the shelf in a grocery store. Manufacturers use this process to cut down on spoilage in foods that contain unsaturated fats. Now that research has shown trans fats to be harmful to our health, scientists have had to come up with ways to process oils that do not produce the harmful trans fats. In fact, most manufacturers advertise "no trans fats" on the labels of their products so that consumers will purchase them.

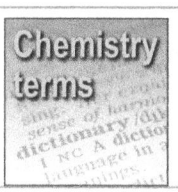

partial hydrogenation: a chemical reaction where only some of the unsaturated fat is hydrogenated; in this case, some double bonds remain in the structure, causing the formation of trans fats in place of the naturally occurring *cis* configuration.

Petroleum refining

Organic matter formed petroleum

Today's petroleum was formed from the remains of prehistoric plankton and algae! This organic material settled to the bottom of ancient lakes and seas in large amounts, and over time it formed crude oil under conditions of extreme pressure and temperature.

Crude oil, or **petroleum**, is a blend of hydrocarbons. Most of the mixture is composed of straight-chain and branched-chain alkanes. There are also small amounts of aromatic hydrocarbons, such as benzene, and some organic compounds that contain sulfur, oxygen, and nitrogen. Petroleum in its crude form is not very useful! It needs to be refined and separated into parts called fractions. Fractions have different sizes, weights, and boiling temperatures depending on the length of the carbon chains.

Petroleum must be separated into fractions

The refining of petroleum begins by distillation. The distillation process heats the crude oil to temperatures above 1,000°F (600°C). The mixture boils and forms vapor, which then enters the fractionating column. The fraction condenses at the point in the column equal to its boiling point. Fractions are removed and separated from the crude oil mixture as they reach their boiling point. Each fraction is a mixture of hydrocarbons.

A process called **cracking** is used to break larger hydrocarbons down into smaller ones. For example, when the demand for gasoline is high, fractions with longer hydrocarbon chains and higher molar masses are broken down, or *cracked,* to form gasoline and kerosene. The cracking process requires very high temperatures and a catalyst. Ethylene and other alkenes are produced during the cracking process; these are used in the production of plastics. Low-molar-mass alkanes and hydrogen gas are also produced as by-products of the cracking process. These are useful as raw materials in the chemical industry. Crude petroleum provides us with many different molecules that serve as fuels or as building blocks for new materials.

Crude oil — fractionating column

Temp.	Carbons	
20°C	4	gas
40°C	8	gasoline
70°C	12	kerosene
120°C	16	diesel
200°C	36	lubricating oil
300°C	44 +	
600°C		heavy oil for cracking

boiler

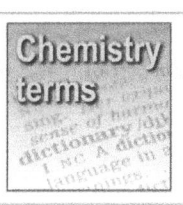
Chemistry terms

petroleum: a blend of hydrocarbons, formed from prehistoric organic matter, containing mainly straight- and branched-chain alkanes.

cracking: a process used to break long-chain hydrocarbons down into smaller hydrocarbon fragments, requiring high temperatures and a catalyst.

Polymerization

Long-chain molecules

Many important biological molecules are polymers. **Polymers** are long-chain molecules. The word comes from two Greek words, "poly," which means many, and "meros," meaning parts. Here we will review some information covered earlier in the bonding chapter. We make a chain by connecting the units called **monomers** together. Monomers are small molecules that make up the polymer chain. The small molecules are joined together by covalent bonds. The chemical reaction that joins the monomers is called **polymerization**.

Where are polymers?

For example, starch is a polymer made of sugar molecules, called a polysaccharide, which is found in foods such as potatoes and wheat. Many polysaccharides are also complex carbohydrates. Polymers formed in nature make up the majority of polymers we are exposed to in our daily lives. Cotton, silk, and rubber are all examples of natural polymers. Synthetic polymers began to be produced during World War II after our supply of raw materials became limited. Our country needed to produce materials that could be used in place of the scarce but naturally available polymers. Polyethylene and polyester fabrics were among the first synthetic polymers.

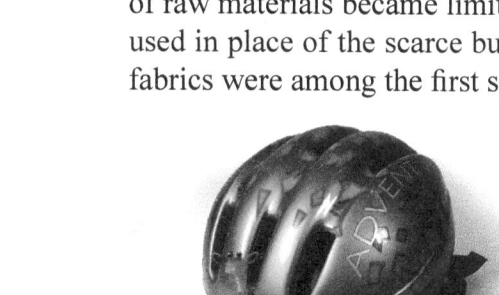

Plastics are also polymers. Can you imagine what we would do without all the different forms of plastic? Plastics have completely revolutionized our modern society! Each of the products shown uses some form of polymer. Think about the plastics you use each day, and imagine how things would change if we did not have plastic. Making a large molecule by connecting lots of small monomers together is very practical. The process of connecting molecules to make a long chain occurs in two different types of chemical reactions. We will learn about these reactions in the next few pages.

Chemistry terms

polymer: a long-chain molecule formed by connecting small repeating units with covalent bonds.

monomer: a small molecule that is a building block of larger molecules called polymers.

polymerization: a chemical reaction that assembles a polymer through repeated additions of smaller molecular fragments.

Addition polymers

Polyethylene is the most widely used plastic

One of the simplest and most widely used polymers in the world is polyethylene. Polyethylene is used to make plastic shopping bags, shampoo bottles, children's toys, and many other consumer products. It is a strong but flexible plastic with thousands of uses.

Polyethylene forms through a simple polymerization reaction called **addition polymerization**. Addition polymerization attaches monomers using their double bonds. Initially, the double bond is broken by a **free radical**. A free radical is a very reactive molecule with an unpaired electron. The double bond then opens up, and the two electrons are used to make new C–C single bonds. In this way, the unsaturated monomers are added to the right side of the chain with the unpaired electron. The repeated addition of these monomers creates a long, saturated polymer. The polymerization reaction shown below uses ethylene monomers to create polyethylene.

Polymerization of ethylene

The softness of polyethylene can be controlled by the length of the chain. If the chain is short (~100 units), the plastic will be soft. If the chain is longer (~1,000 units), the plastic becomes more rigid. The branching of the polymer chain also affects its properties. High-density polyethylene (HDPE) is formed from polymer chains without many branches. The density increases because the polymers can pack closer to other nearby chains. In low-density polyethylene (LDPE), the polymer chains are more branched and the plastic is thinner, more like a film. Sandwich bags are made from LDPE.

Chemistry terms

addition polymerization: the process of forming a polymer by adding monomers together using their double bonds.

free radical: a molecule or atom having one or more unpaired valence electrons.

Condensation polymers

Monomers connected by the loss of a small molecule

Another general type of reaction used by nature and industry to synthesize polymers is called **condensation polymerization**. Here the polymer is formed by eliminating a smaller molecule, such as water. This type of polymerization process does not involve double bonds and can occur between any two monomers. The monomers are joined in a repetitive fashion from head to tail. Nylon is an important industrial polymer, and it is a good example of condensation polymerization. Nylon is used for clothing, carpets, and ropes. Over one million tons of nylon are produced in the United States each year!

In this reaction a water molecule is removed; this is what joins the polymer together. The bond that is formed is called an **amide linkage**. You may recall that the amine functional group was $-NH_2$, and an amide is formed when an amine is linked to a carbon double bonded to an oxygen, or a carbonyl group (C=O). The chain continues to grow as more of these bonds are formed, adding on to the carboxylic acid and amino ends of the chain. A water molecule is lost each time a monomer is joined.

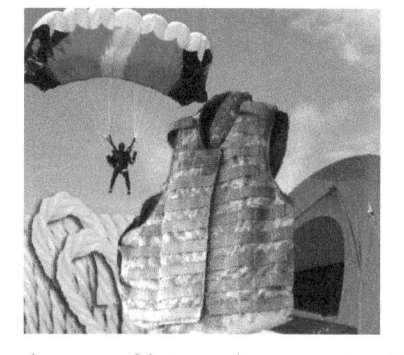

Kevlar® is another polymer formed through condensation polymerization. It is a very strong material, having about five times the strength of steel. It is best known for its use in bulletproof vests. Kevlar is unique because it is both lightweight and very strong. Prior to the discovery of Kevlar, materials that were strong were also very heavy, which limited movement and made them uncomfortable. Kevlar's strength is partially due to crystallinity in its structure. Its molecules are very organized, with a high degree of internal symmetry. The individual polymer strands of Kevlar are held together with hydrogen bonds. Stephanie Kwolek, a researcher for Dupont, developed Kevlar in the late 1960s. It is likely the most important polymer discovery to date.

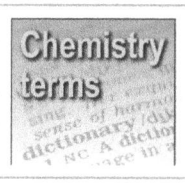

Chemistry terms

condensation polymerization: type of polymerization reaction that links monomers through the loss of a small molecule such as water.

amide linkage: a type of bond formed between an amine group ($-NH_2$) and a carbonyl group (C=O).

Diapers, milkshakes, and polymers

Polymers called *hydrogels* have many different real-life applications. These polymers are very good at absorbing water, and are thus termed "hydrogels." Did you know that the same type of polymers used in baby diapers are also used to make fast food milkshakes? In diapers, these polymers are used for their absorbent properties. They can hold up to 300 times their own weight in water. In milkshakes, a small amount of these polymers can act as a gelling agent. When the polymer is added to the milkshake it forms a gel, sort of like Jello®, but not as thick. Have you ever noticed that your milkshake doesn't melt even at warm temperatures?

There are several different types of hydrogel polymers. Chemically, hydrogels are cross-linked polymers that contain strong hydrophilic groups. *Hydrophilic* means "water-loving." The most common synthetic hydrogel is sodium polyacrylate. A common natural hydrogel is sodium alginate, which is extracted from certain types of seaweed.

Hydrogels work by forming hydrogen bonds with water molecules in aqueous solutions. The water molecules are drawn into the hydrogel by osmosis. Osmosis is the flow of water from a low to a high concentration. Water always moves into the polymer because there is no water inside of it initially. There are negatively charged portions along the polymer chain that attract the positive ends of water molecules. As water is added to the hydrogel, it is slowly pulled in, forming hydrogen bonds. This process continues until the polymer is saturated, or "full," holding as many water molecules as it is capable of holding.

Water is attracted to inside of polymer via osmosis

H bond holds water

Once the water molecules are hydrogen bonded to the oxygen, they are "held" or absorbed by the polymer. These hydrogel polymers can hold between 300 to 500 times their own weight in water. The absorbency range depends upon the amount of salt in the solution. When salt is present, the positive ion can selectively bind to the oxide anion, leaving less room for hydrogen bonds to form. Basically this means that the absorbent properties of hydrogels are greater in pure water or in solutions with dilute salt concentrations. Large amounts of salt can cause the absorbency to decrease by roughly 80%.

Today, sodium polyacrylate is most commonly used in diapers. If you open up an unused diaper and look underneath the first layer of material, you will see small crystalline beads of this superabsorbent polymer.

As water is absorbed, the little beads swell and become heavier. Urine does contain some salt, but the amount is so dilute that the liquid is still absorbed effectively.

Inside a dry diaper

After adding 3 cups of water to the same diaper

Many uses have been developed for these superabsorbent polymers. One very important application is their use in farming. In very dry regions of the world this polymer is worked into the soil, so that when it rains it absorbs water. The polymer absorbs much more water than the soil would normally hold on its own. The polymer retains the water until the soil once again becomes extremely dry. It then slowly releases the water back into the soil, allowing crops to continue to grow. A major benefit of this super absorbent polymer technology is that it also allows these communities to conserve precious drinking water, because they need to use less of it to water their crops and gardens.

"Growing sponge" toys that children love to watch grow in water are also made from sodium polyacrylate! As they grow each day, they absorb water until they reach a point of saturation, and at this point they are full size. Remember that the chemical properties of the polymer, hydrogen bonding, and osmosis are what allow these structures to grow. Without dye, sodium polyacrylate is white, and this polymer is frequently used to make a wintry scene in movies and plays, where real snow would be impractical.

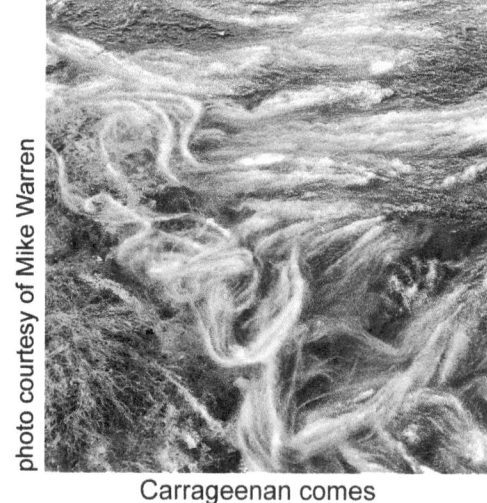

photo courtesy of Mike Warren

Carrageenan comes from seaweed

Fast food restaurants commonly use polysaccharide polymers such as *carrageenan* to gel their milkshakes. Carrageenan is a linear polymer made of about 25,000 galactose monomers. Galactose is a natural sugar made by our bodies, and it is also found in dairy products and vegetables. Carrageenan comes from a red seaweed native to the coast of Ireland. When this seaweed is boiled for 20 to 30 minutes and removed, it leaves behind a gelatinous layer of carrageenan. Carrageenan has the ability to form complexes with calcium and milk proteins. These complexes help to thicken and "stabilize" products such as ice cream and milkshakes, protecting them so that they do not thaw easily. Vegetarians use carrageenan in many products that commonly use gelatin so they can avoid eating animal by-products, since some gelatin is derived from boiling animal bones!

Chapter 17 Review

Vocabulary

Match each word to the sentence where it best fits.

Section 17.1

hydrocarbon	parent compound
R group	saturated hydrocarbon
alkene	
alkane	unsaturated hydrocarbon
structural Isomer	alkyne
optical isomers	benzene
aromatic hydrocarbon	geometric isomers

1. The longest continuous chain of carbons is called the _____.

2. An organic compound containing only hydrogen and carbon is called a/an _____.

3. Sometimes an organic formula is written with a/an _____, which is a shorthand notation that represents a hydrocarbon side chain.

4. A hydrocarbon compound that contains multiple bonds is said to be a/an _____.

5. Some molecules have the same chemical formula but a different bonding pattern. These molecules are referred to as _____.

6. A hydrocarbon that contains only single bonds is called a/an _____.

7. An aromatic ring structure with the formula of C_6H_6 is called _____.

8. Ethene is an example of a/an _____.

9. The *cis* and *trans* isomers are also called _____ because their atoms are arranged differently with respect to their double bonds.

10. _____ contain one or more cyclic rings in their structures.

11. Isomers that rotate light differently with respect to one another are called _____.

12. An organic molecule such as butyne belongs to the class of molecules called a/an _____.

Section 17.2

aldehyde	ether
alcohol	carboxylic acid
ketone	amines
carbonyl group	esters

13. A/An _____ is an organic molecule where oxygen is bonded in the middle with single bonds, with hydrocarbon chains on either side.

14. Methanol is an example of a/an _____.

15. Cinnamon and vanilla are types of _____, giving us familiar smells and flavors.

16. Fructose is an example of a/an _____, which is a functional group containing a carbon to oxygen double bond with hydrocarbon groups on both sides.

17. An organic acid containing a COOH group is called a/an _____.

18. The _____ functional group is an important part of amino acids; it also has the ability to act as a weak base in aqueous solutions.

19. _____ are responsible for the fragrances of many flowers and ripened fruits.

Section 17.3

dehydrogenation	substitution
hydrogenation	addition
partial hydrogenation	petroleum
cracking	polymer
monomer amide	polymerization
linkage	condensation polymers

20. Hydrogenation is a type of _____ reaction that adds hydrogen atoms to the double bonded areas of an unsaturated hydrocarbon molecule.

21. During a/an _____ reaction, hydrogen atoms are removed from an alkane and replaced with different atoms, often a halogen.

22. The process of _____ was used to make food stuffs containing oils last longer on the shelf at the grocery store. It was later discovered that this process also created trans fats.

23. Removal of hydrogen through the process of _____ creates double bonds in the structure of a saturated alkane.

24. A long chain molecule formed by connecting many small repeating units with covalent bonds is called a/an _____.

25. The process used to break long-chain hydrocarbons into smaller fragments is called _____.

26. The small repeating unit of a polymer is called a/an _____.

27. _____ is a blend of hydrocarbons formed from prehistoric organic material.

28. A chemical reaction that joins monomers together is called _____.

29. Some polymers form linkages by the loss of a water molecule between the monomer units. These are called _____.

30. A bond formed between an amine group and a carbonyl group is called a/an _____.

31. Polyethylene is formed through the common process of _____ polymerization, where double bonds are opened up and a growing chain is created.

Conceptual Questions

Section 17.1

32. Consider a straight-chain alkane with seven carbons.
    a. Write its formula.
    b. Name the compound.
    c. Show one branched form of this compound.

33. Using the formula $C_nH_{(2n+2)}$, write the compound containing 12 carbon atoms.

34. Consider a straight-chain alkane with four carbons.
    a. Write its formula.
    a. Name the compound.

35. Draw the formula for two structural isomers of pentane.

36. What is the name of the parent compound in the structure below?

$$CH_3—CH_2—CH_2—CH_2—CH—CH_3$$
$$\underset{\underset{CH_3}{|}}{\overset{|}{CH_2}}$$

37. The alkane butane is referred to as a straight-chain alkane. Is this an accurate description of what the molecule looks like? Explain.

38. How many hydrogen atoms are bonded to a carbon atom in a saturated alkane?

39. Write the structures for two unsaturated alkanes.

40. Which alkane is referred to as gasoline? Write its chemical formula.

41. When we read the numbers on a typical gas pump, we see the numbers 87, 89, and 93 referring to gasoline quality.

    a. What do these numbers tell us about the gasoline? Explain.

    b. Which number would be the best choice in a race car? Why?

42. Which is the smallest alkane that has a structural isomer? Explain and show structures to support your answer.

43. Compare the boiling points of ethane and hexane. Clearly explain why one is so much higher than the other.

44. What types of intermolecular forces are present between hydrocarbon molecules?

45. Water and oil do not mix. Explain why this is so using your knowledge of intermolecular forces.

46. What is the structural feature that indicates whether a hydrocarbon is an alkene?

47. Write the chemical structure that represents each of the following compounds:

    a. 2-butene

    b. 1-heptyne

    c. 3-propene

    d. 2-methyl-butane

48. Identify which of the following geometric isomers has the *trans* configuration.

49. Write the *cis* and *trans* isomers for 3-hexene.

50. What is an optical isomer? Sketch an example using a tetrahedral geometry.

51. Explain how an optical isomer is different from a structural isomer.

52. How did aromatic organic compounds get their name?

53. List the names of two aromatic compounds that are commonly used in the kitchen.

54. Why is the benzene ring (C_6H_6) written using a six-sided ring structure with a circle in the middle of it?

Section 17.2

55. Without looking in the book, try to write the structural formula and the name for each of the following functional groups:

    a. alcohol

    b. aldehyde

    c. ketone

    d. amine

    e. ester

    f. ether

    g. carboxylic acid

56. Which functional group does ethanol belong to?

57. Which functional group does acetic acid belong to?

58. Look at the compounds shown below and try to identify the functional group to which each molecule belongs.

    a. $CH_3CH_2CH_2CH_2OH$

    b. $CH_3CH_2-O-CH_2CH_3$

    c.
$$CH_3CH_2\overset{\overset{\displaystyle O}{\|}}{C}-OH$$

    d. CH_3NH_2

59. Consider aldehydes and ketones.

    a. What feature distinguishes the difference between them?

    b. What do their structures have in common?

60. List one example of a commercial use for an aldehyde and a ketone.

61. Sketch the structure for acetylsalicylic acid, the active ingredient in aspirin, and circle the portion of the structure that is an ester. You may look up the structure online.

62. Acetone is the active ingredient in fingernail-polish remover. Draw its structural formula and label which functional group it belongs to.

63. Using a sketch, show why carboxylic acids, such as acetic acid in vinegar, behave like weak acids in water.

64. List two functional groups that would *not* be very soluble in water. Explain your choice.

65. Amines have basic properties. Using a sketch, show how methylamine can act as a base in aqueous solution.

Section 17.3

66. Identify the type of alkane reaction shown here: $C_3H_8(g) + O_2(g) \rightarrow CO_2(g) + H_2O(g) + heat$ What are some uses for this type of reaction?

67. Name the type of reactions represented by the following equations:

    a. $CH_3-CH_2-CH_3g) + F_2(g)$
       $\rightarrow CH_3-CH_2-CH_2F + HF$

    b. $CH_3-CH_2-CH_3 \rightarrow CH_3-CH=CH_2 + H_2$

    c. $CH_3-CH=CH-CH=CH_2 + H_2(g)$
       $\rightarrow CH_3-CH_2-CH_2-CH_2-CH_3$

68. Predict the products and write the balanced chemical equation for each of the following reactions:

    a. $C_3H_8(g) + O_2(g) \rightarrow$

    b. $C_6H_{14}(g) + O_2(g) \rightarrow$

69. Explain how corn oil can be converted into a solid form that could be used for shortening.

70. Write the chemical equation that represents each of the following reactions: a. ethene burned in air.

    b. propene being hydrogenated with the aid of a platinum (Pt) catalyst.

71. In a couple of sentences, describe what happens in a substitution reaction.

72. Write the chemical reaction that represents the dehydrogenation of ethane.

73. Name the process in which trans fats are formed. Why was this process originally used?

74. Look on three food labels at home and record the type of food (and brand) and the amount of total fat, saturated fat, and trans fat.

75. Are fats healthy to eat as long as they are not trans fats? Explain briefly.

76. The process called "cracking" is widely used in petroleum refining. What is its overall purpose?

77. What types of substances originally formed petroleum?

78. Using plastic snap beads as an example, explain how polymers are formed.

79. List at least five of the plastic polymers you use on a daily basis.

80. Write out the steps for addition polymerization.

81. How are addition and condensation polymerization different? Explain the specifics.

82. List two different materials formed from condensation polymers.

83. Select two different types of polymers, and go online and look up two large chemical manufacturers that make them. What are the building blocks that they use?

CHAPTER 18
The Chemistry of Living Systems

What are the molecules of life?

How are these molecules formed?

Where does the energy that living things need come from?

Do all living things have the same molecules?

Are you familiar with the molecules that make up living things? You may have learned about them in biology class. Often one's first encounter with biological molecules can be overwhelming. Don't let that discourage you! When we study the molecules of life from a chemical perspective, we will see that what looks like a very large molecule is really made of small repeating units.

Most important biological molecules are polymers. The molecules that make up living things are very large. One of the truly amazing things about living systems is that they are able to make these extraordinary molecules. For instance, how do organisms get the energy they need to make large molecules? They do so by eating proteins, fats, carbohydrates, and sugars. Our daily diet determines how well our bodies can build these important molecules. The expression "you are what you eat" is actually true to a large extent! Molecules also carry important information that allows organisms to reproduce. The molecules that are passed on to our offspring are read by other molecules. Our growth and development depend on molecular information. Enzymes, which are actually proteins, help to regulate how many molecules are made and of what types. The molecular systems in living organisms work together in a very specialized way. We are alive because of these molecules! In this chapter you will see how many of the concepts you have learned throughout the year fit together to create the molecules that keep us alive and healthy.

Chlorophyll: protein in leaves

Do you know how plants absorb sunlight? They do so by using a special molecule called *chlorophyll*. We will learn about this very important molecule in this experiment. Chlorophyll allows plants to use the energy from sunlight to carry out chemical reactions that make sugars and oxygen. The molecular structure of chlorophyll is similar to another molecule that is also very important to us: hemoglobin. Chlorophyll is made up of a four-

Chlorophyll

membered ring structure, called a porphyrin ring, which contains alternating double bonds. These alternating bonds allow this molecule to strongly absorb energy in the visible region of the spectrum. Magnesium metal (Mg) is held on the inside of the molecule. In turn, animals get this energy by eating the plants.

Using paper chromatography we are going to separate chlorophyll pigments from leaves. First we will need three large leaves (spinach leaves will work). The leaves are cut or chopped into very small pieces using scissors or a knife. Pour a small amount of rubbing (isopropyl) alcohol over the pieces of leaves, just enough to cover the surface. Smaller pieces of leaves will allow the chlorophyll pigment to be absorbed in the alcohol. Cover the jar loosely with plastic wrap and let it sit for 30 minutes.

After 30 minutes, swirl the glass beaker and check to see whether the alcohol has absorbed any color. The darker the color, the better your results will be. Place a long strip of filter paper in the jar so that it just touches the surface of the alcohol. Tape the other end to a pencil or glass stirring rod and place it horizontally over the glass beaker. The alcohol will be absorbed by the filter paper, and it will bring the pigment molecules with it. Watch the filter paper and you will see color start to rise. The filter paper will allow all of the pigments dissolved in the alcohol to migrate up the paper, where they will be separated according to their molecular weights by gravity and capillary action. The smaller molecules will travel the furthest. What do we see? The olive-green-colored band represents chlorophyll-b. The brighter colored green band is chlorophyll-a. The two other pigments we see are carotene, which is light orange, and xanthophyll, which is yellow.

There are two types of chlorophyll in plants, chlorophyll-a and chlorophyll-b. Each of these pigments absorbs light in different regions of the visible spectrum. Both chlorophyll molecules absorb blue (400–500 nm) and red (610–700 nm) light the best. Each type of chlorophyll captures light in slightly different regions of the red and blue spectrum; this accounts for the different colored bands. Leaves appear green because that color is reflected from the leaves to our eyes. Life exists because of the chlorophyll molecule! Without chlorophyll, plants could not carry out photosynthesis.

18.1 Fats and Carbohydrates

Fats and carbohydrates store energy

All animals need to eat to survive. If this seems obvious, then the reason why must be obvious too! Living things get their energy from food. Without energy for our bodies processes, we would not survive. We get a large portion of our daily energy from **fat** and **carbohydrate** molecules that we consume. Our bodies are capable of breaking apart fat and carbohydrate molecules and obtaining energy from them. A fat molecule is made of fatty acids and a glycerol molecule. Fats are used and formed by animals as an efficient means of storing energy. Carbohydrates are made of both short- and long-chain polymers of sugar molecules. All organisms, including plants, release energy from carbohydrate molecules.

Nature uses fat and carbohydrate molecules
for energy and for structural purposes

Let's look at a few examples. If we consume a big meal of spaghetti, we are filling up on starch. Starch is a type of carbohydrate. Athletes often eat large meals of pasta, especially before a big race, so that they have full stores of energy to allow them to perform longer. Polar bears, on the other hand, prefer to eat fatty meats, such as seals. Seals fill up the fat stores on the polar bears' bodies; this gives them energy during long periods with no food. Plants use cellulose, which is a also a type of carbohydrate, for structural purposes. The cellulose found in plant cell walls allows trees and some plants to grow tall without falling over!

Energy	Warmth	Structure

Carbohydrates and fats have very different molecular structures. In the next few pages, we will explore how their molecular structures allow for their different functions in nature.

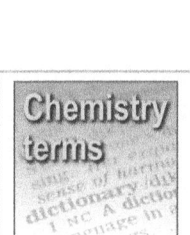

Chemistry terms

fat: nonpolar molecules made from fatty acids and a glycerol molecule, efficient for storing energy for many types of animals and are not soluble in water.

carbohydrates: short- and long-chain polymers of sugar molecules, used by all organisms as a main source of energy.

Carbohydrates

Carbohydrates are the most abundant bio-molecules

Carbohydrates are the most abundant type of biomolecules. The word *carbohydrate* literally means carbon atoms with water molecules. You may remember from the last chapter that carbohydrates are aldehydes or ketones with many hydroxyl groups attached. Simple carbohydrates refer to sugar molecules and "complex" carbohydrates refer to starches or grain products. Plants make starch as a storage form of energy, and animals make glycogen to store some of the energy from carbohydrates.

The smallest repeating unit of a carbohydrate is called a **monosaccharide**. Monosaccharides are individual sugar molecules. The chemical properties of these sugar units are similar. Most monosaccharides have a sweet taste and are crystalline, colorless, and water soluble. Glucose and galactose are examples of monosaccharides.

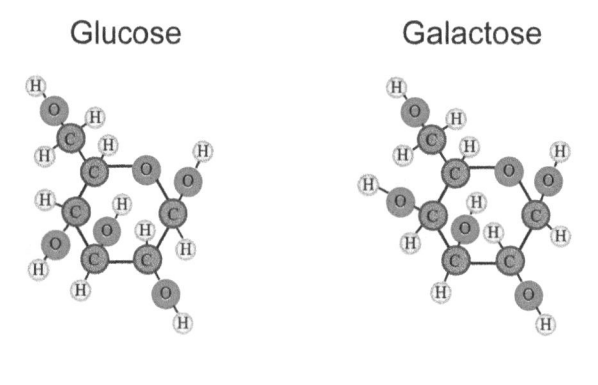

Glucose   Galactose

Galactose is found in certain vegetables, such as sugar beets, and in dairy products. When glucose and galactose are linked together through condensation polymerization, they form the sugar *lactose*, which is found in milk. Small chains are formed by linking 2–10 monosaccharides units together; these small chains are called **oligosaccharides**. Lactose is an example of an oligosaccharide. Both monosaccharides and oligosaccharides are referred to as sugars.

Long chains of more than 10 monosaccharides form **polysaccharides**. Polysaccharides form starches, glycogen, and cellulose. These naturally occurring, long chains of sugars serve many purposes in nature. Starch is the primary ingredient in rice, cereal, potatoes, and corn. Glycogen is the backup supply of carbohydrates in animals. It is stored in the liver and in muscle tissue, where it can be broken down and used as a fuel source. Cellulose is the primary structural material in plants. It is the main component of straw, wood, and cotton. Cellulose cannot be digested by humans, because we do not have the necessary enzymes to break the molecules apart. Some ruminant animals such as cows and termites can break apart cellulose and use it as a food source.

Chemistry terms

monosaccharide: a single sugar unit.

oligosaccharides: a molecule made of 2–10 monosaccharides linked together in a chain.

polysaccharide: a long chain of more than 10 monosaccharides connected together, such as starch, cellulose, and glycogen molecules.

Monosaccharide ring structures

Sugars such as glucose form a ring structure

When carbohydrates are made, the monomer units or monosaccharides are not linear molecules. The sugar molecules form a ring, or a cyclic structure, and it is the ring structures that are joined in a long-chain polymer. *These ring structures contain carbons with optical centers, or chiral carbons.* Recall from the previous chapter that carbon forms stereoisomers when four different groups are attached to it. In most living things, the isomers that rotate light *clockwise* are the ones that are utilized.

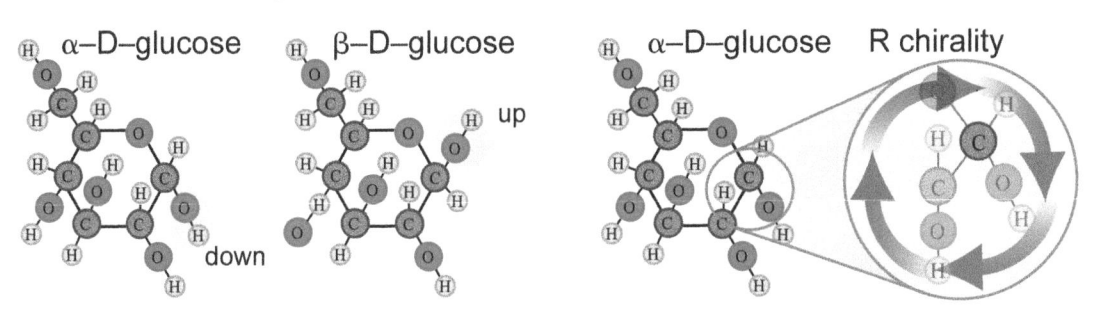

If you look carefully at the structures above, you will see that the hydroxyl group on the first carbon is oriented downward in alpha-D-glucose, and it is positioned upward in β-D-glucose. *This single difference is an important aspect of carbohydrate chemistry!* D-glucose is an optical isomer that rotates light clockwise, or to the right. Our bodies cannot metabolize L-glucose, the mirror image of D-glucose, which rotates light to the left (counterclockwise).

α-D-Glucose is connected in carbohydrates using a condensation reaction

When these cyclic sugar molecules are used to make polysaccharides, they are joined in a very specific way. For example, in starch, which is formed from repeating glucose units, α-D-glucose is connected exactly the same way each and every time.

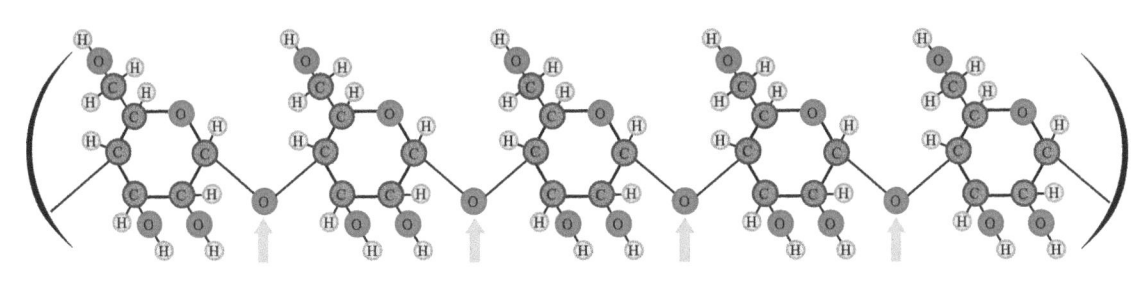

In sucrose, which is a disaccharide, the glucose and fructose rings are connected. Sucrose, or sugar, occurs naturally in every fruit and vegetable. Forming sucrose is the primary way that plants transform the Sun's energy into food. Notice here that glucose is a six-membered ring and fructose is a five-membered ring. This should help you to recognize the structure for sucrose.

Sucrose
(disaccharide)

Carbohydrates in our diet

Excess carbohydrates are stored as fat

When we consume carbohydrates in our food, our body utilizes what it needs and stores the excess. Some of the excess is stored as glycogen in our muscles and liver tissue. These tissues, however, are not capable of storing large amounts of excess carbohydrates. Once the stores of glycogen are restocked, the excess carbohydrate is *converted to fat* and stored on our bodies. So it is important to understand that overeating carbohydrates will increase your body fat. You do not need to eat lots of fatty foods to become overweight!

Some carbohydrates are digested quickly, but others are not

We take in two types of carbohydrates when eating food: simple carbohydrates and complex carbohydrates. Simple carbohydrates are digested more quickly. They do not contain much fiber, and their molecular structure allows our digestive process to get glucose molecules into the bloodstream quickly. Sometimes we get a "sugar rush" from consuming these on an empty stomach. Complex carbohydrates such as brown rice, pasta, whole wheat bread, and vegetables take much longer to digest. They have a high fiber content, and they are rich in vitamins and minerals. The slow digestion of these carbohydrates leaves us feeling full longer. Complex carbohydrates take longer to break down owing to their longer chains and branched molecular structures. Selecting the right types of carbohydrates is an important part of our daily nutrition. You have likely heard the phrase "empty calories." These are calories from which we get little or no nutrition. Foods high in sugar such as candy bars and donuts do not fill us up, and they leave us feeling hungry again in a short time.

TABLE 18.1. Carbohydrates

Simple carbohydrates	Complex carbohydrates
fruit, fruit juice, yogurt, molasses	brown rice, whole-wheat pastas, vegetables, whole-grain breads and cereals
processed sugars, white cane sugar, candy, high-fructose corn syrup	white enriched flour, white breads, instant rice, sugared and processed cereals

There is much information based on current research that suggests that 55% of our daily diet should come from carbohydrates. It is highly recommended that we eat a variety of carbohydrates to ensure that we get adequate amounts of nutrients. Complex carbohydrates are especially good for our bodies' overall health. Whole grains are put through fewer chemical and mechanical processes, so more of the vitamins and minerals remain for our bodies to absorb and use.

Fats and oils

Fats come mainly from animals

Fats and oils come from plant and animal tissue. For example, soybean oil comes from soybeans and butter is made from milk fat. Plants generally make oils rather than fats. The fact that fats are solids at room temperature while oils are liquids at room temperature is one helpful distinguishing feature. The formation of fats and oils is an efficient way for plants and animals to store energy. By efficient, we mean that they provide more energy per gram than carbohydrates. You may already be aware of the fact that some fats are better for you than others.

Why does it make any difference what type of fat you consume?

Unsaturated fats are best for us

The answer to this lies in the *molecular structure of the fat molecule* and how our bodies can break it up. For example, fried foods are considered bad for us but fish oil is considered quite healthy. The primary difference in the molecular structure of good and bad fats lies in the number and position of the double bonds between the carbon atoms. Saturated fats contain no double bonds and are solids at room temperature. These types of fats are less healthy because they remain solid in our bodies, potentially causing blockages in our arteries, as well as being more difficult to break apart and extract energy. Trans fats are unhealthy for the same reason. Nutritionally, we want to consume fats that our bodies can readily use for energy. Unsaturated fats, which have double bonds in their molecular structures, are much easier for our bodies to metabolize.

Fats have useful body functions

In this scan of normal fat distribution in a human body the adipose tissue is yellow

Certain fat molecules help to protect us from diseases and keep our bodies functioning properly. For example, our nerve cells and spinal cord have a fatty coating, called *myelin*, that helps to protect and insulate them. Our cell membranes contain fats, or a lipid bilayer, that helps to maintain a barrier between the inside and outside of our cells. Fats that make up adipose tissue in our bodies also provide cushions to protect our vital organs.

Fats have been important in our existence throughout history. Oil was used in lanterns long before electricity was discovered, and fats were also used to waterproof clothing and other fabrics. This helped humans to survive during periods of bad weather while living and working outdoors.

Fat molecules

Fats dissolve in nonpolar solvents

We have already established that fats are important molecules in life systems. But what are they, and what do they look like? Let's look closely at the molecular structure of a fat molecule. You can see ester bonds where fatty acid chains attach to glycerol.

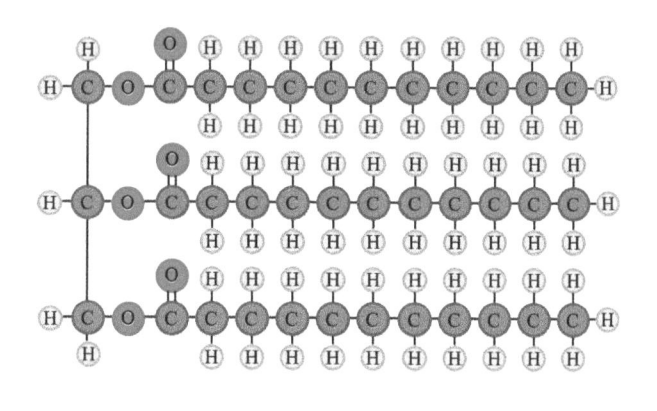

The nonpolar glycerol molecule is attached to three fatty acids to form a fat molecule. Fatty acids have long, nonpolar hydrocarbon chains. Along the length of the hydrocarbon chain there are London dispersion forces, which attract other fatty acid chains. Fats tend to aggregate together for this reason.

Fats, or lipids as they are often called, are actually classified by scientists based on their solubility in nonpolar solvents. This means they dissolve in organic liquids such as benzene, hexane, or other liquid oils (vegetable oil). Recall that "like dissolves like."

Also remember that our blood and body fluids are mostly water. For a molecule to dissolve in water, it must have the ability to form hydrogen bonds or it must carry some form of a charge, either a partial dipole–dipole or an ionic charge. We use *lipoproteins* to carry fat molecules in our bloodstream. Lipoproteins are small spherical assemblies of fats and proteins with hydrophilic groups on their exterior; these allow them to be soluble in our blood. Fat is found inside the lipoprotein.

Lipoprotein in blood

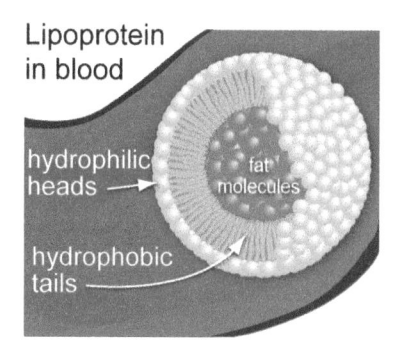

hydrophilic heads

fat molecules

hydrophobic tails

Fats with unsaturated double bonds tend to be liquids at room temperature

Fats can vary depending upon the fatty acid molecules that are attached. The fatty acids can all be the same molecule, or they can be different in length. Fatty acid molecules range from 4 to 24 carbons in length. In humans, fatty acid chains of 16 to 18 carbons are the most common. The fatty acid chains can also contain saturated single bonds or unsaturated double bonds. The reason fats are solid at room temperature is because they contain more saturated single bonds. Oils are liquids at room temperature because they contain more unsaturated double bonds. This explains why oils are healthier for us to consume: because the unsaturated double bonds are easier to break and get energy.

Omega-3 fatty acid

Triglycerides

Triglycerides store energy for humans

Fats and oils are made of **triglyceride** molecules. Fats are transported by our blood-stream in the form of triglyceride molecules. A triglyceride molecule is made of three fatty acid molecules attached by ester bonds to a glycerol molecule.

The image on the right shows tristearin, which is the main type of fat in beef. Fatty acids are long-chain (C_{12} to C_{24}) hydrocarbon molecules with a carboxyl group at the end.

The special texture of chocolate

Most naturally occurring triglycerides have 16, 18, or 20 carbon chain fatty acids. Natural fats contain a mixture of these fatty acids, not just one type. Because of this they have a melting *range*, not a melting point. A good example of a popular fat, cocoa butter, comes from the cacao tree. Chocolate contains only three triglycerides, and this allows it to melt without feeling greasy. The smooth chocolate texture is due to a blend of fats melting slowly in your mouth.

We obtain a good deal of energy from fat molecules. Long-chain fatty acids yield large amounts of ATP when they are oxidized. For every two carbons on the fatty acid chain of the triglyceride, we can make more than 15 ATP molecules. Longer fatty acid chains yield more energy when they are metabolized. This is because there are more C–C bonds to break, which in turn release more energy.

If we consume more fat than our body needs for energy, some of the excess is stored on our bodies in adipose (fat) tissue. We obtain most of our fat in our diet, but the body can also make triglycerides in the liver and fatty tissues when necessary. When we eat foods that contain triglyceride molecules, our body digests them in our intestines and breaks them apart into smaller molecules, some of which are glycerol and fatty acid molecules. If we consume too much fat in our diet, our blood will have a larger amount of triglycerides floating around in it. The number of fat molecules circulating in the bloodstream has been shown to contribute significantly to blocked blood vessels and arteries. For this reason, our blood should be tested during routine physical exams to determine its triglyceride levels.

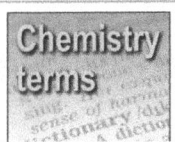

triglyceride: a fat or lipid molecule used for energy storage, made of a glycerol molecule and three long-chain fatty acids.

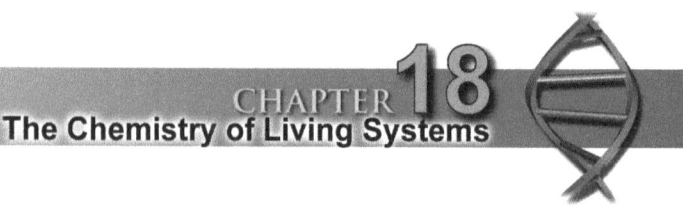

Phospholipids

Phospholipids are important in our cells

One very important type of lipid molecule in our bodies is called a **phospholipid**. These fat molecules are important because they make up our cell walls, which protect the internal environment of our tissues. A phospholipid has a long hydrocarbon chain with a phosphate group for a head. These molecules have a unique ability to

Polar head

Non polar tails

orient themselves in water because of the difference in polarity on different ends of the molecule. The phosphate portion of the molecule is polar and is attracted to water. This portion is called hydrophilic, which means "water loving." The hydrocarbon tail is nonpolar and repels, or pushes away, the water molecules. The hydrocarbon tail is hydrophobic, which means "water hating." As a result, these molecules are able to

Micelles

organize themselves in a spherical fashion in water, forming **micelles**. The micelle spheres form because the nonpolar hydrocarbon tails want to be together, near each other and away from water!

Phospholipid molecules have polar and nonpolar regions

Hydrophilic head

Phospholipid bilayer

Hydrophobic tails

In an aqueous environment such as the one in our bodies, the hydrophobic tails come together and form a layer that excludes water, whereas the phosphate heads are pushed out-ward to be near the water. This causes a layer to form. In our cells, these molecules make up our lipid bilayers in cell membranes.

The fact that phospholipids have long nonpolar regions and small polar heads causes them to aggregate together, or stick near one another. The layer that is formed acts as a barrier in our cells to keep needed nutrients inside and to keep unwanted substances from mixing with the cell's interior. There is some fluidity to our cell membranes because these phospholipid molecules can move or migrate within their own layer; however, they cannot change from one layer to another layer very easily.

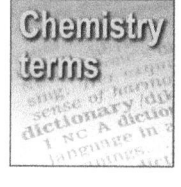

Chemistry terms

phospholipid: a lipid that has a phosphate group attached, giving it a polar head and a nonpolar tail; the phosphate group is the polar region of the molecule and the hydrocarbon chain is the nonpolar region.

micelle: a collection of phospholipid molecules that form a small sphere, which allows the nonpolar tails to be away from the aqueous solvent in the center of the sphere.

18.2 Photosynthesis and Respiration

Plants use sunlight to make sugars and starches

In the previous section, we established that the energy that living things need comes from food. The sugar molecule (glucose) is the most important energy-yielding molecule in living systems. Here we will look at how the glucose molecule is formed in a process called **photosynthesis**. Plants harness sunlight, using its energy to convert water and carbon dioxide molecules into sugars and starches during the process of photosynthesis. Photosynthesis is the first step in this natural pathway, which uses carbon atoms from carbon dioxide as building blocks to make complex organic molecules. Plants use the energy they harness to grow and transport nutrients. Photosynthesis also makes food energy available to animals that eat plants. Animals that consume plants take the energy harnessed in the molecules and use it to carry out life processes. The overall equation for photosynthesis is

Plant absorbing sunlight

$$6CO_2(g) + 6H_2O(l) \xrightarrow{\text{light}} C_6H_{12}O_6(s) + 6O_2(g)$$

This equation may look familiar from biology or from the chemical reactions you studied in Chapter 10, when you were learning about endothermic reactions.

Carbon dioxide and water are the building blocks

Plants, algae, and some bacteria are capable of using sunlight to make glucose. Plants use water and carbon dioxide gas as the building blocks for sugar molecules. These sugar molecules are turned into starch for more efficient storage. Luckily for us, oxygen is also produced! Plants get the carbon dioxide that they need either from the air or from water, depending on where they grow. Plants need a certain amount of sunlight and water to flourish. Many of us who have raised plants have seen this firsthand.

Chlorophyll

Energy is required to make sugars from stable molecules such as CO_2 and H_2O. So how do plants use the energy in sunlight to make larger six-carbon molecules? The answer to this lies in a pigment molecule called chlorophyll. **Chlorophyll** is a large molecule capable of absorbing sunlight in the blue, violet, and red wavelengths of the visible spectrum. Chlorophyll transfers this absorbed light energy to electrons within its molecular structure, and these electrons increase in energy. These high-energy electrons make the process of photosynthesis work by indirectly providing the energy to break chemical bonds and form new ones.

Chemistry terms

photosynthesis: the chemical reaction that occurs almost exclusively in plants and algae and combines CO_2 and H_2O to form glucose $C_6H_{12}O_6$ and oxygen. The reaction is endothermic and is driven by sunlight.

chlorophyll: a pigment molecule that absorbs sunlight and uses it to excite electrons in its molecular structure, thereby storing energy to use in photosynthesis.

Overview of photosynthesis (part 1)

How does a plant put carbon dioxide and water molecules together to form glucose and oxygen? The first part of this process involves water molecules being split apart using the energy absorbed by sunlight. These are often referred to as the "light-dependent" reactions of photosynthesis, because they depend upon sunlight. Chlorophyll molecules absorb light, which allows the water molecules to be split apart. Each water molecule is split into two electrons, two H^+ ions, and one oxygen atom. As electrons continue to be removed from water, oxygen is released into the air. The reaction looks like this:

$$2H_2O(l) \rightarrow 4H^+(aq) + O_2(g) + 4\ e^-$$

NADPH

These four electrons are passed onto special "carrier molecules" that are capable of *transferring the energy* obtained very efficiently. It takes very special molecules to do this. Nicotinamide adenine dinucleotide phosphate ($NADP^+$) is such a molecule. It is able to pass these high-energy electrons through a series of oxidation and reduction reactions. One $NADP^+$ molecule is capable of holding two high-energy electrons and a hydrogen ion to form **NADPH**. The formation of NADPH is one way that sunlight can be stored in a chemical form. The energy from sunlight is stored in the chemical bonds of a "carrier molecule" such as NADPH. NADPH can then be oxidized to once again form $NADP^+$.

ATP

Another very important molecule that stores energy is formed during these light-dependent reactions. This molecule is adenosine triphosphate, or **ATP**. ATP also "holds" and carries energy in its bonds, specifically in the bonds between each phosphate group. Look carefully at the picture on the right. The phosphate groups are broken off by the addition of water molecules, and the energy that is released is used to power chemical reactions that require energy.

ATP

ATP and NADPH carry energy to chemical reactions

The important thing to understand about ATP and NADPH is that they carry energy from spontaneous reactions to nonspontaneous reactions. These molecules that are formed provide the energy for the next step of photosynthesis.

Chemistry terms

NADPH: a molecule that carries two high-energy electrons and stores sunlight as chemical energy.

ATP: adenosine triphosphate; a molecule that carries chemical energy from spontaneous chemical reactions to nonspontaneous reactions.

Overview of photosynthesis (part 2)

CO₂ is added to carbon molecules to make glucose

Sunlight is not required in the second phase of photosynthesis, called the **Calvin cycle**. These reactions are sometimes referred to as the "dark reactions" in contrast to the light reactions.

During the Calvin cycle, carbon dioxide is added to other carbon molecules, and a six-carbon molecule of glucose is formed

The steps in this process require energy and are nonspontaneous. They could not occur without the NADPH and the ATP molecules formed in the first part! The energy harnessed in these molecules helps to put together the six-carbon sugar of glucose.

NADPH and ATP provide the energy for these reactions

The way nature works in simple yet interconnected ways is amazing.

Here you can see that the light-dependent reactions take in water and light, releasing ATP and NADPH molecules that feed into the Calvin cycle. The Calvin cycle takes in carbon dioxide and the high-energy molecules to make glucose. The Calvin cycle recycles the high-energy molecules back to the light dependent reactions. Together, the light and dark reactions use six carbon dioxide molecules to make a single six-carbon molecule of glucose.

Plants work continuously removing CO₂ from our atmosphere and making energy-rich sugar molecules

Plants use glucose for their own energy needs and to make more complex molecules, such as cellulose and starch. These complex molecules are used for structure and growth.

Chemistry terms

Calvin cycle: a series of chemical steps that makes energy-rich sugars from CO₂ by using the high-energy molecules ATP and NADPH formed in light-dependent reactions.

Cellular respiration

Cellular respiration provides energy for life processes

We now need to understand how we use food molecules to give us energy. How is the six-carbon sugar (glucose) metabolized and utilized by our bodies? We know that chemicals store energy in their bonds, but how do living systems obtain this energy and use it for life processes? The glucose molecule gives us energy through the process of **cellular respiration**. During cellular respiration, glucose and other food molecules are broken apart in the presence of oxygen, releasing energy.

Athletes get their energy from cellular respiration

The overall chemical equation for cellular respiration is as follows:

$$6O_2(g) + C_6H_{12}O_6(s) \rightarrow 6CO_2(g) + 6H_2O(l) + energy$$

Oxygen is a powerful electron acceptor in this process. Without oxygen, cellular respiration cannot take place. This equation is greatly oversimplified, because it makes the process appear to happen all at once. Just like other chemical reactions, it actually occurs in a series of steps.

The slow release of energy from glucose allows for its capture

The three-step cellular respiration process helps to control the slow release of energy from glucose

If the release of energy from the bonds of the glucose molecule is not slow, too much of the energy will be lost as heat and therefore be made unavailable to use for other life processes. There must be a way to capture some of the energy released when the chemical bonds in glucose are broken. Each of the three steps in cellular respiration captures energy. The energy captured by forming ATP molecules provides the energy for transporting nutrients across cell membranes, powering muscle contractions during movement, and maintaining body temperature. Many of the body's chemical reactions require energy, and the ATP molecule provides it.

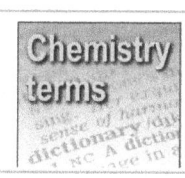
Chemistry terms

cellular respiration: a chemical reaction that breaks down glucose and other food molecules in the presence of oxygen, releasing energy that is used to carry out life processes.

Glycolysis: the first step in cellular respiration

The first step in cellular respiration is **glycolysis**. Glycolysis is carried out in the cytoplasm (cellular fluid) of plant and animal cells. During glycolysis one molecule of glucose is broken in half, yielding two three-carbon molecules.

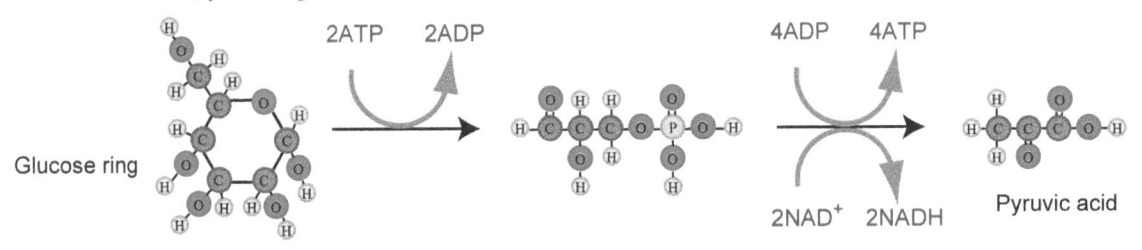

Some energy is required to split the glucose molecule

You'll notice that in the first step two ATPs are required to split the glucose molecule apart, but four ATPs are produced in the second step. *A little energy needs to be added at the start of the reaction, but more energy is obtained in the overall process.* This is similar to pushing a boulder over a hill to get it down a mountain. At first you have to put some energy into the boulder to get it to the top; however, once it gets going it really takes off! By putting a small amount of energy into the boulder, you get a larger return of energy. Glycolysis also gives a larger return!

In the second step you will see that two **NADH** (nicotinamide adenine dinucleotide) molecules are formed. Like NADPH in photosynthesis, NADH is a high-energy electron carrier molecule. NADH is made of two nucleotides, adenine and nicotinamide, which are connected through their phosphate groups. In its oxidized form, after it loses the two electrons it carries, NADH becomes NAD^+. Each NAD^+ molecule is able to accept two high-energy electrons, becoming reduced to NADH once again. NADH acts as a strong reducing agent. In cellular respiration, NADH sends the electrons to a pathway, where they are used to make ATP molecules.

The overall energy yield of glycolysis is small

The overall energy yield of glycolysis is small; however, it can produce energy quickly and without oxygen. When oxygen is present, a second step called the Krebs cycle is able to proceed. The three-carbon molecules of pyruvic acid are passed on to the Krebs cycle, where they release even more energy.

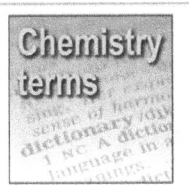

Chemistry terms

glycolysis: the first step in cellular respiration, in which one molecule of glucose is broken in half, yielding two three-carbon molecules of pyruvic acid.

NADH: nicotinamide adenine dinucleotide; a molecule capable of carrying high-energy electrons and transferring them to another pathway.

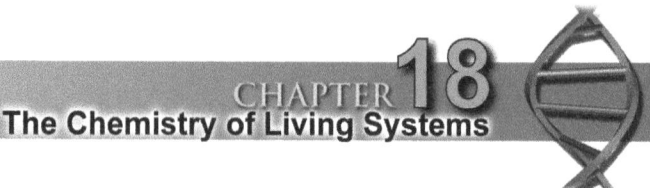

The second and third steps: the Krebs cycle and electron transport

The Krebs cycle

Glycolysis only uses a small portion (about 10%) of the energy available in the glucose molecule. The majority of the energy still remains locked inside the pyruvic acid molecules. These three-carbon molecules then enter the **Krebs cycle**. The Krebs cycle is a sequence of chemical reactions that remove energy while breaking pyruvic acid down to carbon dioxide.

During the steps of the Krebs cycle, the three carbons in pyruvic acid are lost as single carbons in the form of carbon dioxide. The breakdown of pyruvic acid yields several more ATP molecules for the cell to use. The rest of the energy is released in the form of high-energy electrons. NADH and other carrier molecules bring these high-energy electrons to the **electron transport chain**. The electron transport chain uses these high-energy electrons from the Krebs cycle to make more ATP molecules. To accomplish this, the electron transport chain uses special proteins called *cytochromes* to transfer the electrons, which we will discuss in the next section about proteins. In general, each pair of electrons that moves along the chain has enough energy to form three ATP molecules.

Oxygen is the final electron acceptor

At the end of the electron transport chain, hydrogen ions (H^+) and electrons combine with oxygen to form water:

$$4H^+ + 4e^- + O_2 \rightarrow 2H_2O(l)$$

Oxygen serves as the final electron acceptor. Oxygen is necessary to remove the low-energy electrons and hydrogen ions, which are considered waste molecules. Overall, the process of cellular respiration uses roughly 38% of the energy in the glucose molecule. The other 62% is lost as heat.

Chemistry terms

Krebs cycle: a series of energy-extracting chemical reactions that break pyruvic acid down into $CO_2(g)$ during cellular respiration.

electron transport chain: a sequence of biologically important chemical reactions that uses high-energy electrons from the Krebs cycle to make ATP molecules.

18.3 Proteins

Proteins are the workhorses in our bodies

Proteins are another very important type of molecule that performs numerous functions inside our bodies and all living organisms. Perhaps you have heard about how important it is to have enough protein in your diet. Proteins are involved in *every* cell process within our bodies! For example, our bodies break apart the protein we digest and use it to build and repair our muscle tissue.

plant seed protein

What are proteins? They are polymers made of compounds called **amino acids**. Amino acids are molecules that have an amino (NH_2) group on one end and a carboxyl group on the other end. Proteins are large polymers containing more than 100 amino acids linked together. There are over 20 different amino acids found in nature, and this gives rise to tremendous diversity. The large size of the protein chain and the variety of amino acids used allows for many different combinations, over 20^{100} to be exact!

Proteins are required for almost all chemical reactions that take place in our bodies!

Proteins help make chemical reactions faster

One of the primary functions of proteins is to facilitate chemical reactions. You may recall from Chapter 12 or from biology class that many proteins are catalysts and that **catalysts** speed up the rate of chemical reactions. *Chemical reactions would be so slow at body temperature that we could not survive without these protein catalysts!*

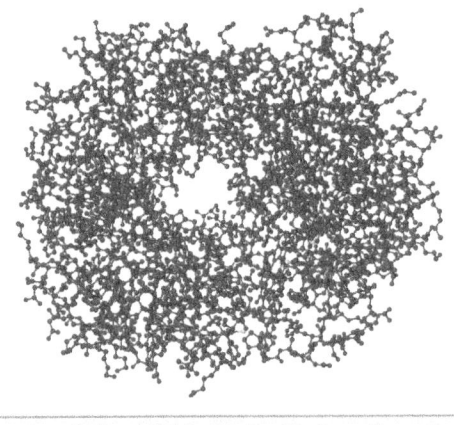

Proteins also make up our hair, muscles, and cartilage. They also transport and store oxygen and nutrients to our tissues. For example, hemoglobin is a bundle of four proteins, responsible for transporting oxygen from our lungs to our tissues. This protein can bind to an oxygen molecule, holding onto it until it gets to a place in the body where it is needed. In muscle tissue, hemoglobin changes its shape and releases the oxygen molecule so that the muscles have the oxygen that they need.

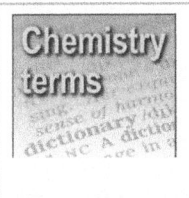
Chemistry terms

protein: a biologically functional polymer of amino acids, typically a very large molecules with 100 or more amino acids.

amino acid: a chiral molecule that has an amino group on one end and a carboxyl group on the other.

catalyst: a substance that speeds up the rate of a chemical reaction, by providing a pathway with a lower activation energy

Amino acids

To understand how proteins are formed, it is important to have a basic understanding of what amino acid molecules are. There are 20 different naturally occurring amino acids commonly found in most proteins (see the table on the next page). Each amino acid has an amino group (NH_2) and a carboxyl group (COOH) covalently bonded to the central carbon atom.

The R group determines the chemical properties of the amino acid

Because the *central carbon atom has four different groups attached to it, it is chiral and forms an optical isomer*. Each amino acid also contains a hydrogen atom and a side chain (R hydrocarbon chain). The side chain significantly affects the chemical properties of the amino acid. These R groups are unique for each amino acid.

Chemically some R groups are nonpolar, whereas others are polar. Amino acids such as alanine or valine contain R groups that are nonpolar, and in an aqueous environment they would be found on the interior of a protein molecule. Inside the protein these hydrophobic R groups are "shielded" or protected from an aqueous environment. Other amino acids such as serine or aspartic acid contain polar R groups, and these are found on the exterior of a protein molecule. These amino acids would form hydrogen bonds with water molecules. The R group determines the functionality of a protein in solution.

Alanine

COOH
|
$H_2N–C–H$
|
CH_3

nonpolar

Serine

COOH
|
$H_2N–C–H$
|
CH_2OH

polar

Side chains can be either polar or nonpolar

Some amino acids have both acidic *and* basic properties

COOH
|
$H_2N–C–H$
|
CH_2
|
CH_2
|
COOH

acidic

COOH
|
$H_2N–C–H$
|
CH_2
|
CH_2
|
CH_2
|
NH
|
$C=NH_2$
|
NH_3

basic

Some amino acids contain acidic and basic R groups, such as glutamic acid and arginine. In the body these side chains are exposed to a roughly neutral pH of approximately 7.35. The pH changes can be used to separate proteins in the laboratory, because these amino acids can be made to come apart and "denature" under conditions of high or low pH. Biochemists take advantage of this when they want to isolate proteins.

Table of amino acids

Twenty amino acids

Nonpolar

Glycine

COOH
|
H_2N-C-H
|
H

Alanine

COOH
|
H_2N-C-H
|
CH_3

Valine

COOH
|
H_2N-C-H
|
CH
/ \
CH_3 CH_3

Leucine

COOH
|
H_2N-C-H
|
CH_2
|
CH
/ \
CH_3 CH_3

Phenylalanine

COOH
|
H_2N-C-H
|
CH_2

Tryptophan

COOH
|
H_2N-C-H
|
CH_2
|
C=CH
NH

Methionine

COOH
|
H_2N-C-H
|
CH_2
|
CH_2
|
S
|
CH_3

Isoleucine

COOH
|
H_2N-C-H
|
$H-C-CH_3$
|
CH_2
|
CH_3

Polar

Tyrosine

COOH
|
H_2N-C-H
|
CH_2

OH

Serine

COOH
|
H_2N-C-H
|
CH_2OH

Threonine

COOH
|
H_2N-C-H
|
H-C-OH
|
CH_3

Cysteine

COOH
|
H_2N-C-H
|
CH^2
|
SH

Proline

COOH
|
C-H
/ \
H_2N CH_2
| |
H_2C—CH_2

Asparagine

COOH
|
H_2N-C-H
|
CH_2
|
C
/ \\
H_2N O

Glutamine

COOH
|
H_2N-C-H
|
CH_2
|
CH_2
|
C
/ \\
H_2N O

Acidic

Aspartate

COOH
|
H_2N-C-H
|
CH_2
|
COOH

Glutamate

COOH
|
H_2N-C-H
|
CH_2
|
CH_2
|
COOH

Basic

Lysine

COOH
|
H_2N-C-H
|
CH_2
|
CH_2
|
CH_2
|
CH_2
|
NH_3

Arginine

COOH
|
H_2N-C-H
|
CH_2
|
CH_2
|
CH_2
|
NH
|
$C=NH_2$
|
NH_2

Histidine

COOH
|
H_2N-C-H
|
CH_2
|
C-NH
‖   \\
C-N   CH
H   //

Chirality in nature

Most amino acids have the L or left-handed (S) configuration

Interestingly, it seems as though nature almost exclusively uses one particular form of amino acid stereoisomer. Nature is said to exhibit homochirality, which means it utilizes only one type of isomer. There are many theories as to why one particular form is favored. One theory is based upon the fact that the L configuration amino acids are favored when dissolved in water. This would make them readily available in aqueous environments, which is where life forms are thought to have evolved. Another intriguing theory is that the L amino acids were brought to Earth by meteorites. Meteorites, such as the Murchinson meteorite that landed in Australia in 1969, contain primarily L amino acids. Scientists think this is because they were formed by circularly polarized light from the stars! If one chiral form was available back when life was first developing, then perhaps nature adapted itself to utilize that one form!

The chirality of the amino acids commonly found in nature is almost always left handed

Other things in nature exhibit what we call "handedness." Most seashells for example are formed in the right-handed direction. Snails and plants also show tendencies toward one specific chirality. This has been of great interest to biologists. Snail shells either twist to the right or to the left. Which type of chirality is expressed is determined by genetic factors.

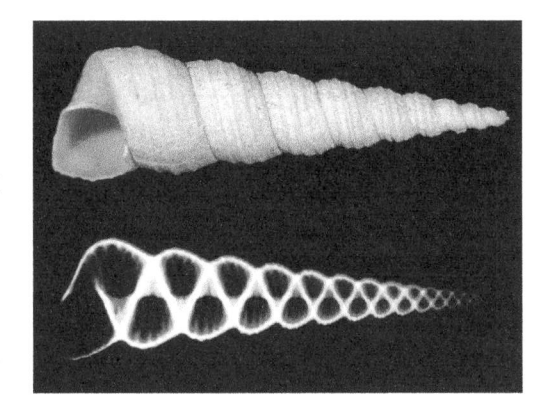

Our body chemistry functions are designed with a preference toward one stereoisomer. As mentioned earlier, sugar molecules utilized by the body for energy are all in the D or right-handed conformation. *Chemical reactions are carried out in the body by recognizing very specific molecular structures.* This is what allows our bodies to function properly.

One very important application of chirality can be seen in medicine. Many widely used medications are derived from nature. For example Taxol, which is a drug used for chemotherapy, was discovered from the bark of the Pacific yew tree. When a useful drug is discovered in nature, scientists try to isolate the different active molecules to identify which one works. When we try to synthesize these molecules artificially, we find that a mixture of both the isomers is made. But nature specifically makes only one isomer! Stereoisomers have been shown to have very different effects in the body. *Molecules of different chirality have completely different biological activities.* Because of this, over 50% of medications must be specifically one chiral form.

Functions of proteins

One example is muscle tissue

Proteins are used in numerous ways by our bodies. Perhaps you have been told to eat meat so that your muscles will grow. It is true that muscles are mainly made up of protein. Athletes and body builders who have to increase their muscle mass often consume protein shakes. The protein helps them to build up their muscle fibers. For a while, creatine was a popular body-building supplement taken by athletes. It helped to build muscle mass faster and without the damaging side effects of steroids. Creatine is a protein naturally found in meats, and taking a supplement provided muscles with more energy. However, it was later found that taking creatine causes liver and kidney damage, because our bodies cannot break it down it effectively.

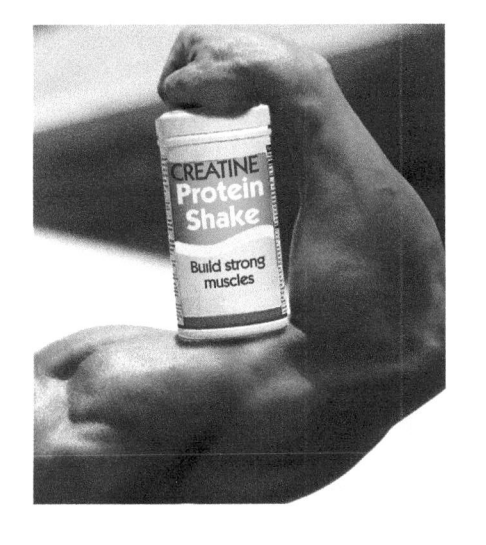

TABLE 18.2. Functions of proteins

Function	Example
Movement	Muscle is primarily made up of protein. Certain protein molecules allow muscle cells to contract.
Structure	Tendons, skin, bones, fingernails, and claws are made up of structural proteins. So are fibers such as wool or hair.
Catalysis	Enzymes, which are proteins, catalyze almost all chemical reactions in living systems.
Transport	Oxygen is carried by proteins to our tissues by hemoglobin.
Storage	Proteins store or hold onto minerals needed by the body.
Protection	Blood-clotting proteins such as fibrinogen protect us from bleeding too much. Antibodies such as interferon are proteins that protect cells from viral infection.
Energy transfer	Living cells contain cytochromes, which are proteins. Cytochromes transfer electrons in a series of oxidation–reduction reactions during cellular respiration (metaboliz-ing food molecules).

Protein composition: primary structure

The information for building proteins comes from our hereditary information. Our genes contain the instructions for which amino acids to link together when forming specific proteins.

Amino acids are linked together chemically by a **peptide bond**. A peptide bond joins the carboxyl group and the amino group of adjacent proteins.

Carboxyl group   Amino group   Peptide bond

Amino acids are linked together with peptide bonds

The formation of a peptide bond involves the loss of a water molecule. As you saw in Chapter 17, this is called condensation polymerization. A bond is formed between two monomers, in this case amino acids, and a polymer is formed. Each amino acid in the sequence is added on the right end of the polymer as it continues to grow. All of the amino acids have a carboxyl group and an amino group, which allows them to be put together in any combination.

Amino acid sequence determines protein function

The amino acid sequence is what makes one protein have different chemical properties than another. Remember that a protein sequence must be at least 100 amino acids long! Although these proteins are long, a sequence for a protein is very specific. A change in just one amino acid in the protein chain can result in very different chemical properties. The sequence of amino acids in a protein chain is called its **primary structure**.

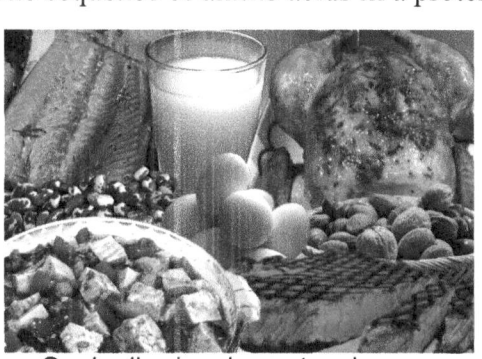

Our bodies break apart and reuse the amino acid building blocks

You might wonder where we get all the amino acids necessary to build a protein. Our bodies can make 10 of the necessary amino acids, but the other 10 we need to get from our diet. When we eat protein-containing foods, these proteins must be broken apart and put back together to make new proteins for our bodies to use.

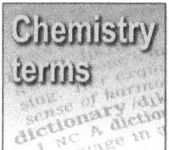

Chemistry terms

peptide bond: a bond between the amino group and the carboxyl group of two amino acids, formed through condensation polymerization or the loss of water molecules.

primary structure: the sequence of amino acids in a protein chain.

Secondary structure of proteins

The way a protein is put together is very important. The sequence of amino acids influences the way a protein functions. The next piece to this puzzle is to understand how

Proteins are three-dimensional

the chain of amino acids orients itself three dimensionally. There are two spatial arrangements that are commonly seen in nature, the **alpha helix** and the **pleated sheet**. The alpha helix resembles a spiral staircase or a slinky. It slowly winds around in a coil that is primarily held in place by hydrogen bonds. The alpha helix is one of the most important and common secondary structures. The pleated sheets resemble a folded paper fan or an accordion.

Hydrogen bonds are important in forming and holding the protein's shape

The regular coils of the alpha helix give it some elasticity and stretchiness. These properties influence the protein's function. For example, many fibers such as wool, hair, and tendons have the alpha helix shape. The alpha helix shape is held together by hydrogen bonds formed between a carbonyl group (C=O) and a nearby amino group (N–H). The formation of a helix is designed so that the hydrogen bond associations are perfectly aligned. The twist of the helix causes the side chains or R groups to be on the outside of the helix, where they have more room and can interact with their environment. Some amino acids, such as tyrosine and tryptophan, have large and bulky side chains that do not fit well into an alpha helix. These amino acids prefer to form pleated sheets.

The pleated sheet is made up of two or more protein chains located side by side. This spatial arrangement causes the protein to be *flexible and strong but resistant to stretching*. Pleated sheet proteins are found in muscle tissue and in natural fibers like silk. Both muscle fibers and silk have a very high tensile strength—in fact, stronger than steel! Similar to the alpha helix, hydrogen bonds hold the pleated sheet together, but these hydrogen bonds are formed *between adjacent proteins*, not between groups along the same chain.

alpha helix: a common form of the secondary structure of a protein that forms a spiral or twist similar to a Slinky® or a spiral staircase, in which a single protein chain is held together by hydrogen bonding attractions.

pleated sheet: a secondary structure of a protein that forms a folded or pleated pattern similar to an old-fashioned fan, formed by two or more side-by-side protein chains held together by hydrogen bonding.

A Natural Approach to Chemistry

Tertiary structure of proteins

Tertiary structure

A protein's shape involves a great deal of chemistry. You have learned about hydrogen bonds, electrostatic attractions between charged or polar molecules, and you have learned about hydrophobic and hydrophilic interactions. Here we will apply all of this knowledge to our study of tertiary protein structures. Proteins fold or bend their secondary alpha helix structures into what is called a **tertiary structure** or a "globular" protein. It is this tertiary structure that defines the functionality of the protein. The term globular is a good one because the protein looks like a glob of amino acids stuck together. A globular protein has a unique tertiary structure that makes it capable of performing a very specific function. To imagine this structure, think of a phone cord wrapped around itself with several twists and turns until it is all knotted together. This is what a globular protein looks like.

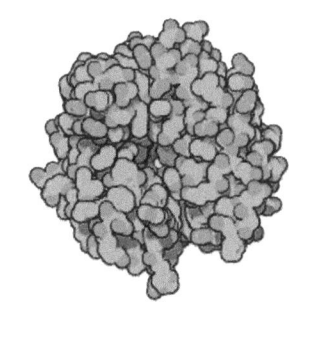

Intermolecular forces stabilize the tertiary structure

The interactions of the side chain R groups greatly affect the shape of the tertiary structure. Most proteins in living systems are in aqueous water environments. The nonpolar side chains tend to be tucked inside the tertiary structure and away from the polar water molecules, whereas the polar side chains are on the outside so that they can interact with the aqueous environment. These intermolecular forces are what stabilize the tertiary structure and keep it in the proper shape so that it can perform its role in living organisms.

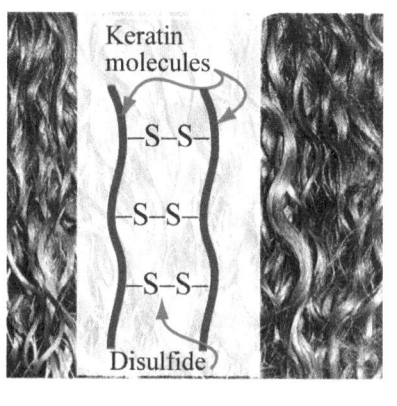

Keratin molecules

—S–S—

—S–S—

—S–S—

Disulfide

The amino acid cysteine plays an important role in stabilizing tertiary structure as well. Two nearby cysteine groups can form a covalent disulfide (S–S) bond, which is very strong and can hold two parts of a protein chain together, forming a bend. The keratin in our hair contains these disulfide bonds. When we get our hair "permed" at the hairdresser, some of these disulfide bonds in our hair shafts are broken and new ones are formed that hold a curl. As our hair grows, new protein is formed that does not have the same bonds holding its shape.

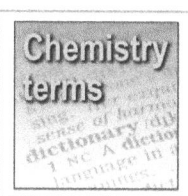
Chemistry terms

tertiary structure: a protein structure held together by intermolecular attractions, hydrophobicity of nonpolar regions, and ion–dipole interactions, that forms from the bending or folding of the secondary alpha helix.

Enzymes

Enzymes are proteins that orchestrate chemical reactions in living systems

Now that you understand a little more about proteins, we can study an important class of proteins called enzymes. Almost all enzymes are proteins! Enzymes serve a wide variety of roles inside living systems. As mentioned earlier in Chapter 12, enzymes dramatically speed up chemical reactions. Living systems have an incredibly complex system of integrated chemical reactions. Enzymes orchestrate these complex systems so that living organisms can survive. Enzymes are able to turn molecules "on" and "off" at appropriate times as they are needed by living organisms. Enzymes were mentioned earlier when we were studying the rates of chemical reactions.

Luciferase lights up a firefly

Enzymes lower the energy needed for a chemical reaction to take place; because of this they speed up chemical reactions.

Bio-luminescence

Some enzymes, such as luciferase, are responsible for "bioluminescence." If you have ever seen a firefly light up in the dark, then you have seen this enzyme in action.

The shape of the enzyme determines what molecules bind to it

Enzyme   Substrate

active site

Enzymes are large proteins with molecular weights ranging from approximately 10,000 amu to 1 million amu. Enzymes help bind other molecules called **substrate** molecules. The substrate is the "reactant" in the chemical reaction taking place. The substrate binds in a small region of the enzyme called the **active site**. The active site makes up only a small section (three or four amino acids) of the enzyme molecule. When these substrate molecules are bound by the enzyme, the enzyme and the substrate can change shape, molding to each other. These large enzyme molecules have very high specificity for the substrates that attach. Generally an enzyme will only allow one type of substrate molecule to fit in its active site. *The shape of the active site is determined by the tertiary structure of the protein.*

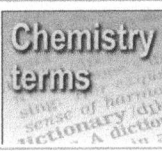

Chemistry terms

substrate: a reactant molecule that is able to be bound by a particular enzyme.

active site: a small region of an enzyme molecule that is responsible for "binding" or holding on to the substrate molecules.

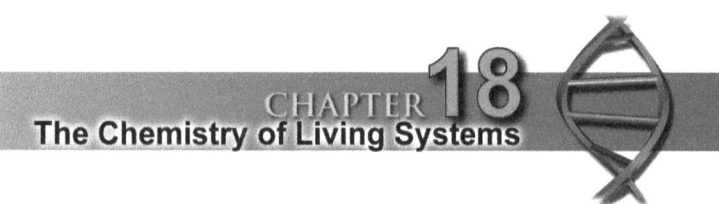

Cytochrome proteins

Cytochrome proteins transfer electrons in the electron transport chain

The **cytochrome proteins** involved in cellular respiration are one of the most important proteins in nature. A cytochrome molecule is any type of iron-containing protein with heme groups. The electron transport chain contains several types of cytochromes. The cytochrome protein molecules are responsible for the transfer of electrons in the electron transport chain. You may recall from earlier in the chapter that the electron transport chain makes ATP using high-energy electrons originally from food molecules. The electron transport chain

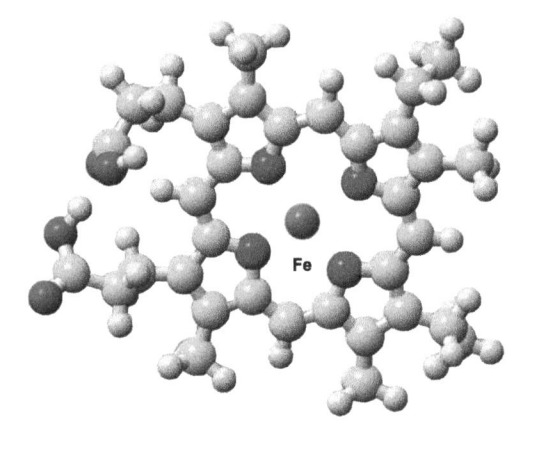

slowly releases the energy with the help of cytochrome molecules. The electrons are passed slowly along, and the energy is released in manageable amounts. Cellular respiration relies on the slow release of energy achieved by these cytochrome proteins, which are located in the inner mitochondrial membranes inside our cells.

All organisms that carry out respiration use cytochrome proteins

Oxidation–reduction cycle of iron catalyzed by cytochrome

The cytochrome system functions to catalyze oxidation of iron(II) to iron (III) and the reduction of iron(III) to iron(II). The molecular structure of a cytochrome is made up of a large organic ring structure, called a porphyrin, with an iron atom held at its center. The cytochrome molecule picks one electron up and gets reduced from Fe^{3+} to Fe^{2+}. When the electron is transferred to the next carrier protein, Fe^{2+} is

oxidized back to Fe^{3+}. These electron transfers are used to pump H^+ ions into the cell against the concentration gradient. When the H^+ ions diffuse back out of the cell, they go through a protein channel, which couples the energy released when the H^+ flows out to the formation of ATP. Each pair of electrons produces roughly three ATP molecules.

Chemistry terms

cytochrome protein: any iron-containing protein with heme groups, important as catalysts in oxidation–reduction reactions in the electron transport chain.

18.4 DNA and Molecular Reproduction

DNA nucleotides contain three parts

What is a DNA molecule? How can it possibly carry enough information to encode an entire living organism? These questions will help us focus on this unique molecule. **DNA** is a polymer that stores and transmits genetic information. The DNA polymer is made up of units called nucleotides. A **nucleotide** has three molecular parts. The first part is a five-carbon sugar called deoxyribose. The second part is a phosphate group, derived from phosphoric acid (H_3PO_4). Finally, a nitrogen-containing organic base is the third part. DNA molecules are *huge*, with molar masses ranging from 5 to 20 million amu, and possibly more!

Nucleotide Structure

Phosphate group

Sugar

Nitrogenous base (guanine)

Even with only four different building blocks, there are an incredibly large number of possible sequences of DNA nucleotides. DNA molecules carry all of the hereditary information necessary for an organism to grow and survive. Almost every cell in the human body has the same DNA!

Life is only possible because cells can pass on their genetic material to new cells during replication

Nitrogen-containing bases are different for each of the nucleotides

The **nitrogenous bases** are the only difference among nucleotides.

Did you know that humans share about 99% of the same DNA? That means only 1% causes the differences we observe along with environmental and developmental effects.

Cytosine

Thymine

Adenine

Guanine

Chemistry terms

DNA: a long polymer chain of nucleotides that stores and transmits genetic information.

nucleotide: a molecular unit composed of a five-carbon sugar, a phosphate group, and a nitrogenous base.

nitrogenous base: a nitrogen-containing base; one component of nucleotides.

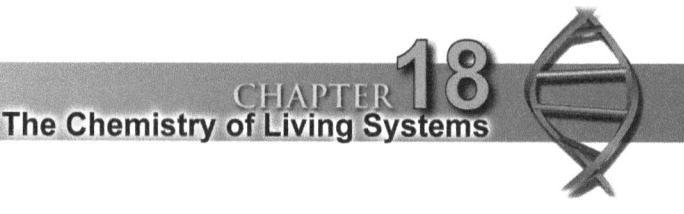

DNA double helix

Nucleotides are linked by a condensation reaction

Individual strands of DNA polymers are formed by joining nucleotides together in a condensation reaction. The nucleotides are linked together when a phosphate group on one nucleotide bonds with the hydroxyl (–OH) group on a deoxyribose sugar molecule of the other nucleotide. A water molecule is lost in this condensation reaction when two monomers are joined. As you can see, *each DNA polymer has a central backbone formed from the sugar and the phosphate group on each nucleotide.* This backbone holds the polymer together. Notice that the nitrogenous bases stick out from the backbone.

In the double helix, which consists of two individual strands of DNA, the nitrogenous bases play a key role in DNA's structure and function. Each nitrogenous base has a partner, or a "complementary base," which is determined by the number of hydrogen bonds formed. Adenine (A) always bonds to thymine (T) forming two hydrogen bonds, and guanine (G) bonds to cytosine (C) forming three hydrogen bonds between them.

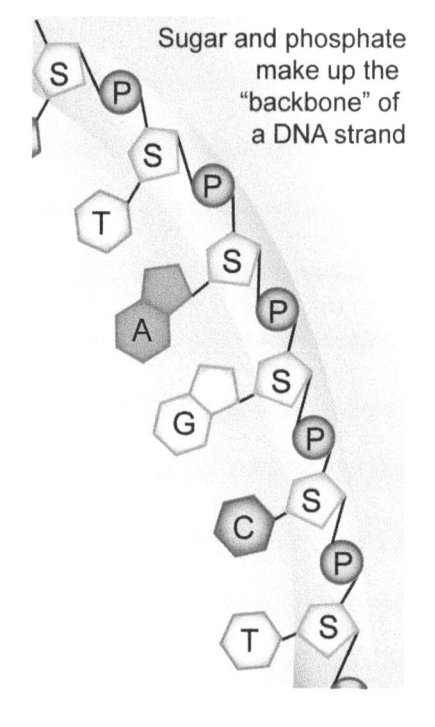

Sugar and phosphate make up the "backbone" of a DNA strand

Nitrogenous bases (G,C,A,T) play a key role in the double-helix structure

Hydrogen bonds

It is interesting to see how the nitrogenous base structures on one strand match up with the opposite strand, allowing them to form uniform hydrogen bonds of two or three depending upon the base pairs. The formation of the double helix and the spacing in the turns of the helix are just right, allowing for only these specific pairings of the bases. Pairings like A to G do not fit properly!

Hydrogen bonds and London dispersion forces hold together the DNA double helix.

DNA replication

A human cell contains approximately one meter of DNA. How can a strand that long fit into such a tiny cell?

DNA needs to be folded many times and coiled tightly to be packed effectively inside a cell

DNA exists in a condensed form that is coiled around proteins

We might expect DNA molecules to be very long because they carry so much information. Human DNA coils around proteins called *histones*. DNA forms intricate weaving patterns around these histone proteins. This allows the DNA to fit inside the cell. Only some of our DNA codes for our genes; there are long sections that have only structural purposes.

DNA coils around histones

Condensed DNA "opens up" to replicate

The fact that this long polymer can replicate itself with relatively few mistakes is truly amazing. During cell division, the double helix unwinds so that new complementary strands can be formed from each of the original strands. *Enzymes cause the hydrogen bonds between the base pairs to come apart; this allows for the "unzipping" of the DNA double helix.* As the strand unzips, new base pairs are added to the individual strands. Because certain bases only pair with certain others, we can predict what the sequence of nucleotides will be.

Each new cell is made from an existing cell. The ability of these strands to replicate allows for each of the two cells to have an exact copy of the original DNA molecule. The genetic information is stored like a "code" in the sequence of the base pairs (A, T, G, C). For each amino acid the code is three letters long, but there can be more than one three-letter code for each amino acid. For example CGA, CGG, CGC, and CGT all code for the amino acid alanine. Scientists speculate that this allows for some flexibility and error when the sequences are formed.

DNA and protein synthesis

DNA stores information necessary to make proteins

DNA also carries the code to make proteins that an organism needs to live. As discussed in the previous section, proteins are necessary for all life processes. All chemical reactions that occur in the body require proteins. A segment of DNA, called a **gene**, is the code for a specific protein. All organisms, including humans, consume proteins in the foods that they eat, but these proteins are not the same ones required by the organism to survive. Individual organisms require specific instructions for the proteins they need.

The DNA code stores the information for a sequence of amino acids that is passed on to the cell machinery (ribosomes). Recall that the sequence of amino acids represents the primary structure of the protein.

RNA carries the information from DNA to where proteins are made

How is the information stored in DNA used by the cell to make protein molecules? Depending upon the type of organism, the DNA is stored either in the cytoplasm or in the nucleus of the cell. Another nucleic acid called **RNA** (**ribonucleic acid**) is responsible for transmitting the information to the cell machinery where proteins are made. RNA is similar to DNA except for a few distinguishing features. It contains a different sugar called ribose that contains a hydroxyl (–OH) group on the second carbon in the five-carbon ring structure. It also uses one different nitrogenous base called uracil (U). Uracil is used in place of thymine (T) when RNA is formed. RNA molecules are also much smaller than DNA polymers. RNA molar masses are typically between 20,000 and 40,000 g whereas DNA's molar mass is in the billions of grams.

RNA is made following the pattern of the gene for a specific protein. RNA carries this information to a ribosome. Ribosomes are like little factories where the proteins are made. Once the instructions for the pattern reaches the ribosome, it makes the protein. Specific amino acids are then brought to the ribosomes following the instructions from the RNA. Scientists have discovered that RNA has a wide variety of functions, which has led to the possibility that perhaps it evolved before DNA. For example, RNA also plays an important role as a catalyst of chemical reactions, similar to enzymes.

Chemistry terms

gene: a segment of DNA that contains the code for a specific protein.

RNA: a polymer composed of nucleotides that contain a five-carbon sugar called ribose, a phosphate group, and a nitrogenous base; transmits the information stored in DNA to cell "machinery."

Biotechnology, farming, and green chemistry

CHEMISTRY
CONNECTIONS

For thousands of years, people have been using "biotechnology" to improve their lives. The selective breeding of plants for maximizing crop yield was the earliest application of biotechnology. Now, as the world population continues to increase, biotechnology is expected to help improve the quality of life by helping to provide food and medicine, and also to help us deal with environmental issues. Biotechnology has already made a significant contribution toward improving people's lives. The vaccinations that we receive and the antibiotics that we take are derived from applications of biotechnology. Thanks to biotechnology, deaths from diseases such as malaria, meningitis, hepatitis, and many others have been almost totally eliminated.

Biotechnology is based on the sciences of biology and chemistry. Recent developments in genetic science and engineering have provided new tools and techniques. From medicine to the control of environmental pollution, biotechnology techniques provide useful solutions but have also led to many concerns.

While the development of medicines is generally desirable, there are other applications that are very controversial. Since the birth of the first cloned animal, a sheep called Dolly in 1996, many people worry that biotechnological genetic modification has no ethical or moral boundaries.

Gene therapy is both very promising and highly controversial. The prospect of human cloning is creating ethical issues that must be addressed as gene therapy advances. Also, the use of genetically modified organisms for developing genetically modified foods is generating many opportunities and concerns. On one hand, crop yields can be greatly increased, feeding many more people. On the other hand, there are concerns that biotechnology might be counterproductive to agriculture over the long term. There are also indications that certain genetically modified foods could be poorer in nutrition and could introduce new allergens.

Biotechnology will play a major role in our everyday lives for many years to come. It is up to us to use this powerful tool with great caution and a sense of responsibility.

Over the years, commercial farming has relied on chemical pesticides to grow healthier crops and increase crop yields. Now with the rise of *green chemistry*, there has been a dramatic shift in how pesticides are being made and used. By definition, "green chemistry" is the design of chemical products and processes that reduce or eliminate the use of hazardous substances. Since the late 1990s, people have been buying

more and more organic produce. Many of us know that organic fruits and vegetables are good for us. In fact, buying organic has become very important in our society.

What is so important about buying organic vegetables anyway? Of course, it has to do with chemicals! Over the past 50 to 60 years, chemicals used by farmers as pesticides have become a topic of great concern. We have learned that these chemicals, used to kill insects and pests, sometimes cause cancer and other illnesses in our bodies. They also can have adverse effects on our environment.

598

A NATURAL APPROACH TO CHEMISTRY

Science has shown that some widely used pesticides can persist in the soil and in the environment for long periods of time. For example, dichloro-diphenyl-trichloroethane (DDT) is a synthetic pesticide that was widely used by U.S. farmers during the 1950s and 1960s. This product has been banned since 1972 in the United States. It was found that DDT remained active in the soil for up to 30 years after it was used.

We are replacing chemicals like DDT with pesticides that have lower energy barriers for decomposition, which means that they persist in the environment for shorter periods of time.

An example of one of these chemicals is glyphosate. Glyphosate is an analog of glycine, which means it is similar to the amino acid glycine. Glyphosate interferes with plants' abilities to make amino acids.

Glyphosate is replacing an herbicide known as Simazine, which has been associated with several human health risks. It also stays in the environment for relatively long periods of time. The U.S. Environmental Protection Agency (EPA) has placed a limit of 4 ppb in drinking water for Simazine. This kind of progress, replacing harmful chemicals like Simazine with less harmful alternatives like glyphosate, is the focus of green chemistry.

Glyphosate

$C_3H_8NO_5P$

Glycine

$C_2H_5NO_2$

You will be happy to know that pesticide use is currently declining in the United States. Farmers are using pesticides more wisely. Also, better pesticides are being designed and made by chemists. Finally, organic farming deliberately avoids the use of all pesticides!

What does it mean to be organic? Organic foods must be certified by the U.S. Department of Agriculture (USDA) and must be grown without synthetic pesticides or chemical fertilizers. Regulations also specify that such produce must not be grown from bioengineered crops. However, organic farmers can use natural pesticides and fertilizers. Some chemicals such as sulfur, copper sulfate, pyrethrins, and compounds from a soil bacterium have been approved for organic use. Pyrethrins come from the seed cases of the chrysanthemum flower (chrysanthemum cinerariaefolium). Pyrethrins break down easily when exposed to sunlight and oxygen, becoming inactivated.

Organic produce

Overall, green chemistry is successfully helping farmers improve their methods for treating insects and weeds. These achievements directly affect our food supply, our bodies, and our surrounding environment in a very positive way!

Chapter 18 Review

Vocabulary

Match each word to the sentence where it best fits.

Section 18.1

fat	carbohydrates
oligosaccharides	monosaccharides
polysaccharides	triglyceride
phospholipid	micelle

1. All organisms use _____ as a primary source of energy.

2. A/An _____ is a single sugar unit.

3. Lipids, or _____ molecules, are nonpolar and therefore do not dissolve in water.

4. Starch and cellulose are examples of _____.

5. A fat molecule made of glycerol and three long-chain fatty acids is called a/an _____.

6. A chain of 2–10 monosaccharide units linked together is called a/an _____.

7. A lipid that has a phosphate group attached to it is called a/an _____.

8. A small sphere made up of phospholipids is called a/an _____.

Section 18.2

chlorophyll	Calvin cycle
ATP	cellular respiration
photosynthesis	glycolysis
NADPH	NADH
Krebs cycle	electron transport chain

9. The process of _____ uses sunlight to convert carbon dioxide and water into glucose and oxygen.

10. _____ is an electron carrier molecule used by plants to store the energy from sunlight.

11. Adenosine triphosphate, or _____, is a molecule that carries chemical energy to nonspontaneous chemical reactions.

12. Plants contain a pigment molecule called _____ that absorbs energy from the sun to be used in photosynthesis.

13. _____ breaks down glucose and other food molecules in the presence of oxygen, releasing energy for life processes.

14. The _____ is also sometimes referred to as the "dark" reactions, because sunlight is not required for this part of photosynthesis.

15. During _____, which is the first step in cellular respiration, glucose is broken into two three-carbon molecules.

16. In cellular respiration, a high-energy electron carrier molecule called _____ is used to transfer electrons.

17. The _____ is a series of chemical reactions that break pyruvic acid down into carbon dioxide during cellular respiration.

18. High-energy electrons from the Krebs cycle are transferred to the _____, where they are used to make ATP molecules.

Section 18.3

protein	primary structure
amino acids	pleated sheet
peptide bond	tertiary structure
alpha helix	cytochrome protein
substrate	active site

19. _____ are polymers of amino acid molecules, which are used in every cell process in our bodies.

20. There are 20 different naturally occurring
_____.

21. The _____ of a protein is its sequence of
amino acids.

22. A bond formed between the amino group of one
amino acid and the carboxyl group of another is
called a/an _____.

23. The secondary structure of a protein can have
two different structural forms, called a/an
_____ and a/an _____.

24. An enzyme has a/an _____ that can
change shape once the specific substrate molecule
is bound to it.

25. A reactant molecule that can bind to an enzyme is
called a/an _____.

26. A/An _____ is an iron-containing heme
protein that is important in the electron transport
chain.

27. Proteins fold or bend their secondary structures
into a/an _____ that is the result of
molecular interactions.

Section 18.4

nucleotide	DNA
gene	RNA
nitrogenous bases	

28. Different pairs of _____ match up by the
number of hydrogen bonds they can make.

29. The _____ molecule forms an alpha
helix, a long polymer chain of nucleotides used to
transmit genetic information.

30. A/An _____ is made up of a five-carbon
sugar, a phosphate group, and a nitrogenous base.

31. A segment of DNA that contains the code for a
specific protein is called a/an _____.

32. The _____ molecule
uses uracil (U) instead of thymine (T).

Conceptual Questions

Section 18.1

33. Give three examples of how living systems use
fats and carbohydrate molecules.

34. Distinguish between a monosaccharide and an
oligosaccharide. Give one example of each.

35. Sketch the structures of glucose and galactose.
Explain how these molecules are different from
one another.

36. Do our bodies use alpha-D-glucose or beta-D-
glucose? Explain why.

37. When forming a polysaccharide, which carbon
atoms in the glucose molecule are used to bond
the molecules together as the chain forms?
Explain.

38. Explain how glucose and fructose are different
from each other.

39. When glucose and fructose are linked together,
what do they form?

40. List four examples of carbohydrates that are
considered good for you.

41. Why is it better to consume complex
carbohydrates rather than simple carbohydrates?

42. What is cellulose?

43. Where is cellulose most commonly found?

44. When you eat more carbohydrates than your body
needs, what happens to these extra carbohydrates?
Explain.

45. In our daily diet:
a. how much should come from carbohydrates?
b. how much should come from fats?

46. Explain the basic differences between fats and
oils.

Chapter 18 Review

47. Explain the difference in the molecular structures of a saturated fat and an unsaturated fat.

48. Why are unsaturated fats better for us to consume? Explain, and be sure think back to the organic chemistry chapter for some help with the specifics.

49. Fats serve several different useful purposes in our bodies. List three examples and briefly explain the purpose of each.

50. Do animals store most of their energy in the form of fats or carbohydrates? Briefly explain why.

51. Consider a typical fat molecule.
    a. Name the types of molecules that make it up.
    b. How are these molecules joined together and what is the bond called?

52. What physical property is used to classify fat molecules from other biological molecules such as proteins or carbohydrates?

53. Answer the following.
    a. What are lipoproteins?
    b. Explain why lipoproteins are needed to carry fat molecules in our blood.

54. Based on the molecular structure, why are some fats solid at room temperature whereas others are liquid?

55. Give two examples of foods you could eat that contain unsaturated fatty acids.

56. What type of fat comes from beef?

57. Longer fatty acid chains yield more energy than shorter ones. What is it about the molecular structure of longer fatty acids that makes this true?

58. Consider micelles.
    a. What type of fat molecule are micelles made up of?
    b. Draw a simple sketch that describes what you think a micelle would look like.

59. Consider phospholipids.
    a. Which end of the phospholipid molecule is attracted to water? Explain why.
    b. Describe the purpose of the phospholipid bilayer in our cells.

Section 18.2

60. Consider photosynthesis.
    a. Write its chemical reaction.
    b. What living systems carry out photosynthesis?
    c. Show the Lewis structure for the gas that is produced.

61. Consider photosynthesis.
    a. What molecule is responsible for the process of photosynthesis?
    b. In what regions of the visible spectrum does this molecule absorb light?

62. Consider photosynthesis.
    a. In the first part of photosynthesis, how is the energy from sunlight captured?
    b. What carrier molecule holds onto the high-energy electrons?
    c. Where does this carrier molecule store the energy?

63. Why are carrier molecules so important in the overall process of photosynthesis?

64. In a general way, describe what happens in the Calvin cycle.

65. For what purposes do plants use glucose?

66. Where is the energy stored in the ATP molecule?

67. Once the carrier molecules transfer their energy in the Calvin cycle, what happens to them?

68. Write the overall equation for cellular respiration.

69. What is oxygen's role in the chemical reaction responsible for cellular respiration? Explain.

70. List the three steps involved in cellular respiration.

71. Why is it important that the energy from the glucose molecule be released in three steps?

72. What happens to the glucose molecule during glycolysis?

73. How many ATP molecules are produced as a result of glycolysis?

74. Is the first step in glycolysis spontaneous? Explain.

75. In the second step of glycolysis, two NADH molecules are formed. Is NADH a strong reducing agent or an oxidizing agent? Explain.

76. Do the processes of glycolysis and the Krebs cycle require oxygen in order to occur?

77. What is the net result of the Krebs cycle? Explain.

78. Write the reduction half reaction where oxygen acts as the final electron acceptor. What are the waste species that oxygen gets rid of?

79. Does cellular respiration use most of the energy in the glucose molecule? Explain.

Section 18.3

80. Draw an amino acid molecule, and label the three parts that all amino acids have in common.

81. What is the primary function of proteins in our bodies?

82. How do animals get the protein they require?

83. How many different amino acids are there?

84. Give an example of an acidic amino acid. Label the portion of the molecule that makes it acidic.

85. Give an example of a basic amino acid. Label the portion of the molecule that makes it basic.

86. List four examples of where proteins are found in our bodies.

87. What type of amino acid stereoisomer is commonly found in nature? Why do scientists think nature prefers to use that form?

88. What is chirality? Give two examples in nature where chirality is observed.

89. List the six different functions of proteins in our bodies.

90. Select two amino acid molecules and show how they come together to form a peptide bond. Label the peptide bond.

91. What is a primary structure of a protein?

92. Create a protein sequence with 10 amino acids.

93. Name and contrast the differences between the two secondary structures found in proteins.

94. How are enzymes important to living systems?

95. Explain briefly what an active site is.

96. What happens to an enzyme when the substrate attaches?

97. What is the enzyme in saliva responsible for breaking down carbohydrates?

98. In what part of cellular respiration are the cytochrome proteins important?

99. What metal is bound to the inside of the heme groups in a cytochrome protein? How is this metal important in the transfer of electrons from one cytochrome to another?

Section 18.4

100. What are the three molecular components of a nucleotide?

101. What part of the nucleotide structure forms the structural backbone of a DNA strand?

102. What types of attractive forces hold together a DNA molecule?

103. Which nitrogenous base pairs with guanine (G)? Why do these two bases match up?

104. Explain how large amounts of DNA are able to fit inside a small cell.

105. During cell replication how does the DNA double helix come apart? Explain.

106. Make a small table that lists the differences between DNA and RNA.

CHAPTER 19

The Chemistry of the Earth

How do chemical reactions in the atmosphere affect life?

What is the role of water on Earth?

How are elements and molecules recycled on Earth?

How is chemistry applied to environmental issues?

All living things are made up of matter, and matter is made from elements. How do the elements used by us become available in our environment? If we take a walk in nature and pay close attention to all that is around us, we become aware of the great diversity of living things. All of these life forms exist because of the intricate balance among chemicals that are present here on Earth. In this chapter we will study how these chemical balances are maintained.

Chemicals cycle among the atmosphere, ocean, land and living things. Factors that affect one of these things will eventually affect all of them, because they are all connected. For this reason, green chemistry and the study of "sustainability" have come to the forefront of scientific research today. Earth's resources need to be consumed at a rate at which they can be replaced. We observe the effects of chemical imbalance when conditions such as severe climate change occur. The difficult part is that the effects of chemical imbalances are not readily apparent, so our awareness of them only comes when significant changes have taken place. The lag time between noticeable changes and the initial imbalance makes it hard to correct problems. As a global society, we are now learning that we need to plan ahead and study the chemical balances of our planet. To do this, we need to understand Earth's composition and its cycles.

Investigating the water cycle

In this chapter you will learn about the atmosphere, the land, and the ocean. The water molecule plays an important role in each of these systems! Water is recycled and redistributed through each of these Earth systems. Without this recycling process, our living systems could not be supported.

Have you ever wondered why rain does not have mud in it? Think about it: If rain falls to Earth and flows through the ground, could it possibly have mud or soil in it? Here you will get to see first hand how the water molecule can be easily transferred from one phase to another, and what happens to the mud.

1. Fill one large test tube about 2/3 of the way up with some muddy water. Place the test tube in the Lab-Master probe system heater, and attach the heater. Set the temperature initially for 140°C. As the water heats up, observe what happens to it. Record your observations for the first minute.

   - What naturally heats the water molecules here on Earth?
   - From where do you think most of the water molecules vaporize?

2. As the water warms, place the condenser over the top of the test tube. Place a small beaker under the condenser to collect your condensate.

   - How will the condenser unit affect your system?
   - Record your observations.
   - What happens to the mud as water changes from one physical state to another?

3. Turn off your heater once you have evaporated most of the water. How does the water look? Describe the appearance of the condensate.
   If we consider water here on Earth, what causes condensation to occur naturally? Here on Earth, water condenses in the clouds.

4. Look carefully at your system. Can you tell what happens to the water molecules after they condense? Support your answer with observations.

5. Where did the water in the test tube go? Using common observations explain this concept and draw analogies between it and the water cycle phenomenon of the Earth.

Now let's consider how these changes occur in nature. Think about the recycling of water. We know energy is required to loosen and separate the hydrogen bonds holding the water molecules together. The addition of energy in the form of heat is used to cause these changes; in nature the Sun provides this energy and the oceans provide most of the water. When we remove heat, the molecules come closer together and the hydrogen bonds re-form. In nature, this happens as water vapor rises higher in the atmosphere. The water cycle is a physical process. The molecule itself remains intact throughout the cycle. The fact that it can undergo physical changes and remain together as a molecule is what allows the water cycle to work.

19.1 Chemistry of the Atmosphere

Our atmosphere determines the environment in which we live. Have you ever wondered what is in the air or what our atmosphere is made of? Most of us tend to take our atmosphere for granted. We live and breathe it everyday, and for the most part, as far as we know its composition stays the same.

We live in the troposphere

The atmosphere around Earth has four layers of gases that have been given specific names depending on their distance from the surface. The **troposphere** is the layer closest to Earth's surface, and it extends for about 10 km. The weather that we experience all happens in the troposphere. The troposphere is more turbulent than the other layers, which causes gases in this layer to mix more rapidly. When you fly on large jet airplanes, you are flying at the top of the troposphere.

The next layer of gases is called the **stratosphere**. This region of gases begins approximately 10 km above the surface and goes up to about 50 km. Very important chemical reactions take place in the stratosphere, the most significant being the formation of the ozone (O_3) molecule. Approximately 90% of the ozone that protects Earth from high-energy photons is formed in the stratosphere.

Meteors burn up in the mesosphere

The mesosphere is the "middle" layer of gases around Earth. In this layer the temperatures are very cold. The higher the altitude, the colder the temperature becomes due to decreased heating from the Sun. Waves created by gravitational pull in the mesosphere cause gases to circulate around the globe. Meteors burn up in the mesosphere when they collide with the gas particles contained in this layer. The energy created by these collisions produces a lot of heat, causing most meteor fragments to vaporize before reaching Earth. The mesosphere contains high concentrations of metal atoms such as iron (Fe) because of these meteor collisions.

The thermosphere is the outermost layer, beginning at 85 km above Earth's surface. In this layer, ultraviolet light from the Sun causes ionization of the gases contained there. For example, oxygen loses an electron when absorbing UV radiation:

$$O_2(g) + photon(h\nu) \rightarrow O_2(g)^+ + e^-$$

These ionized gases are attracted to the Earth's poles and are responsible for the auroras seen at the polar regions.

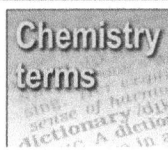

Chemistry terms

troposphere: the layer of gases closest to the Earth, extending up to approximately 10 km above the Earth's surface.

stratosphere: the second layer of gases after the troposphere, extending from 10 to 50 km above the Earth.

Composition of the atmosphere

Heavier gas molecules stay closer to Earth

The atmosphere contains primarily nitrogen (78%) and oxygen (21%) molecules. The remainder of the atmosphere is made up of carbon dioxide and noble gases. Most of the mass of the atmosphere is contained in the troposphere, because the majority of the heavier molecules are found close to Earth's surface. Earth's gravitational field causes the lighter molecules and atoms to rise higher in the atmosphere. The Sun plays an important role in the chemistry of our atmosphere. The molecules contained in the atmosphere are constantly being hit by radiation from the Sun. These energetic collisions have significant chemical effects. We will learn about these effects in this section.

TABLE 19.1.
Composition of dry air

Element	% by volume
N_2	78.08
O_2	20.95
Ar	0.93
CO_2	0.037
Ne	0.0018
He	0.00052
CH_4	0.00020

Why are these gases so abundant in our atmosphere? Let's look at the four most abundant gases. We think most of the nitrogen gas in our atmosphere was brought from inside the Earth by volcanoes. Nitrogen gas is heavy; its molar mass of 28.02 g/mole causes it to tend to stay near Earth's surface and not float up to the higher regions of the atmosphere. Photosynthesis is responsible for the oxygen gas present in our air today. The production of oxygen by plants has greatly influenced Earth's chemistry. Oxygen is a more reactive molecule than nitrogen. Because of this it is responsible for many important chemical reactions in the atmosphere. Argon is also a heavy gas, with a molar mass of about 40 g/ mole. Most of the argon in the air was produced by the radioactive decay of other elements in Earth's crust, such as potassium (K). Lastly, the carbon dioxide gas present was created by respiration of animals.

Water vapor in the air keeps Earth warm

Water is also present in the atmosphere as moisture. It enters the air through evaporation from the oceans and from the transpiration of plants. Water is an important contributor to Earth's relatively moderate temperature, because it absorbs infrared radiation and helps holds heat.

The weather patterns we experience in the troposphere are the result of how the Sun heats our planet. Different places on Earth are heated at different angles, and this unequal heating is what causes the wind and ocean currents to circulate. Winds are formed when warm air rises and cool air sinks. This process sets up movement of air currents around the globe. Weather patterns help to cycle chemicals among the atmosphere, living organisms, and the ocean. This continuous movement of air distributes nutrients to living systems.

These cycles can be disrupted by pollution or environmental changes, which are causes for much concern. The majority of the pollutants found on Earth come from the widespread use of combustion reactions.

Chemical reactions in the air

Nitrogen and oxygen gas molecules make up about 99% of the atmosphere. These molecules are involved in many of the chemical reactions that take place in our atmosphere because they are present in such high concentrations. To help you better understand some of the chemical reactions that take place in our atmosphere, we will review some of the properties of nitrogen and oxygen molecules.

Nitrogen is nonreactive because of its triple bond

Recall that nitrogen (N_2) contains a triple bond and that oxygen (O_2) has a double bond holding its atoms together. The triple bond in nitrogen has a high bond energy, requiring 946 kJ/mole of energy to break it. The strength of the triple bond makes nitrogen a relatively inert, nonreactive gas found close to Earth's surface. Under high temperatures, such as in a combustion engine, nitrogen can be broken apart. The double bond in oxygen requires significantly less energy to come apart because it has a bond energy of 495 kJ/mole. *In the atmosphere, oxygen is a more reactive molecule than nitrogen because it requires less energy to split its atoms apart.* Remember: For atoms to react, they have to come apart so they can interact with new atoms.

Cars produce nitrous oxide

There are several important chemical reactions that take place in the troposphere that we need to understand, primarily because they are close to us and we experience their effects directly. For instance, most of us have seen smog. Smog is formed when pollutant gases are trapped in a highly populated city or urban area. The smog effect is created in these areas because the exhaust emissions contain nitrous oxides. Cars or vehicle engines provide the energy necessary for some of the nitrogen in the air to react with the oxygen in the air, producing nitrous oxide (NO):

$$N_2(g) + O_2(g) \rightleftharpoons 2NO(g), \quad \Delta H = 181 \text{ kJ}$$

In the air, nitrous oxide (NO) is quickly converted to $NO_2(g)$ through oxidation:

$$2NO(g) + O_2(g) \rightleftharpoons 2NO_2(g) \quad \Delta H = -113 \text{ kJ}$$

Los Angeles was the first city to experience the full effects of smog. The temperature in the city is hot and the mountains trap the gases down in the valley, causing them to become concentrated. When photons from the Sun with wavelengths of 393 nm or less strike the NO_2 molecules, they dissociate into NO(g) and atomic oxygen (O). This atomic oxygen can react with oxygen gas to make ozone, which is another primary pollutant in smog. The reaction is $O(g) + O_2(g) \rightarrow O_3(g)$. Ground-level ozone is very toxic and is dangerous for us to breathe. Ozone in the upper atmosphere protects us, but ozone in the troposphere is a serious health hazard.

Chemical reactions in the troposphere

Formation of sulfur dioxide comes primarily from fossil fuels

Like smog, other gases in our atmosphere have significant effects even though they are only present in small amounts. The combustion of coal and oil releases significant amounts of sulfur in the form of sulfur dioxide (SO_2), one of the most harmful pollutant gases in our air. SO_2. The combustion process causes the sulfur present in these fuels to react with oxygen in the air to produce SO_2:

$$S(s) + O_2(g) \rightarrow SO_2(g)$$

Small amounts of sulfur are released naturally into the environment, primarily through the decomposition of organic materials. However, most of the sulfur is released from the use of fossil fuels. Approximately 80% of the sulfur dioxide in the air comes from coal that provides us with electricity. The SO_2 in the air readily reacts with oxygen in the air to form SO_3, which in turn reacts with water vapor to form sulfuric acid:

$$SO_3(g) + H_2O(l) \rightarrow H_2SO_4(aq)$$

Acid rain is formed from sulfur and nitrogen oxides

Sulfuric acid is a strong acid! This has significant environmental and health impacts. Sulfuric acid is one of the acids responsible for acid rain, which has damaged many ecosystems in the Northeast and Great Lakes regions of the United States. For example, in New York there are no fish in hundreds of lakes and ponds because of the low pH caused by acid rain. Certain lakes and streams contain bicarbonate (HCO_3^-) buffer, which helps to counteract the effects of acid rain. In areas where the amounts of acid rain are extremely high, the pH can get as low as 4.0. But even naturally occurring rain is acidic, having a pH of approximately 5.5 to 5.8. This is because natural rainwater absorbs carbon dioxide in the air, reacting to form the weak acid called carbonic acid (H_2CO_3):

$$CO_2(g) + H_2O(l) \rightarrow H_2CO_3(aq)$$

Natural rainwater is acidic because of the absorption of CO_2

Carbonic acid is responsible for lowering the pH of our rainwater. Nitrous oxides also react with water vapor to form nitric acid (HNO_3):

$$3NO_2(g) + H_2O(l) \rightarrow 2HNO_3(aq) + NO(g)$$

On an environmental level, acid rain can damage forests and crops, and it also lowers the pH of lakes and streams. You may remember that strong acids react with carbonates such as limestone ($CaCO_3$), and this is why it causes damage to stone and buildings. These strong acids also react with many different metals, causing corrosion. Overall these effects have serious economic and environmental impacts.

Chemical reactions in the upper atmosphere

The outer layers of the atmosphere absorb dangerous UV radiation

The outer layers of the atmosphere act like a shield protecting us from damaging forms of radiant energy. These outer layers of the atmosphere, beyond the thermosphere, are constantly being struck by high-energy particles from the Sun. The gas molecules here are exposed to continuous high levels of radiation. The Sun produces photons with a wide range of wavelengths. The short-wavelength photons in the ultraviolet region of the spectrum (below 400 nm) are very damaging to living organisms. These high-energy photons can damage cellular DNA, causing mutations and possibly cancer. However, the outer layers of our atmosphere are able to absorb most of these high-energy photons, and they do not travel down close to the surface and cause harm.

Chemical changes are caused by high-energy photons

How are these photons absorbed? The gas molecules in the upper atmosphere absorb these high-energy photons. Chemical changes are caused by high-energy photons colliding with the molecules in these layers. One of these important chemical changes is called **photodissociation.** Photodissociation is the breaking of a chemical bond in a molecule caused by the absorption of a photon. Because of nitrogen's high bond energy the oxygen molecule (O_2) is the principal absorber of high-energy photons in the upper atmosphere. No ions are formed when a bond is broken by the process of photodissociation. The bonding electrons are divided equally between the two atoms, and two neutral particles are created. The amount of energy required to split the double bond between the oxygen atoms is equal to the bond energy of 495 kJ/mole.

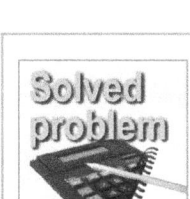
Solved problem

Calculate the wavelength of a photon emitted by the Sun that contains enough energy to dissociate the oxygen molecule.

Asked: *Wavelength of a photon that can split an O_2 molecule*

Given: *The bond dissociation energy for O_2 is 495 kJ/mole.*
Avogadro's number = 6.022×10^{23}, Planck's constant = $6.63 \times 10^{-34} J\,s$

Relationships: $E = hc/\lambda$

Solve:

$$\frac{495\ kJ}{mole} \times \frac{mole}{6.022 \times 10^{23}\ molecules} = 8.22 \times 10^{-22}\ \frac{kJ}{molecule} = 8.22 \times 10^{-19}\ \frac{J}{molecule}$$

$$\lambda = \frac{hc}{E} = \frac{6.63 \times 10^{-34}\ J \cdot s\left[3.0 \times 10^8 \left(\frac{m}{s}\right)\right]}{8.22 \times 10^{-19}\ J} = 242 \times 10^{-9} m\left(\frac{10^9 nm}{1\ m}\right) = 242\ nm$$

Discussion: *A photon with a wavelength of 242 nm is energetic enough to break the double bond in the oxygen molecule.*

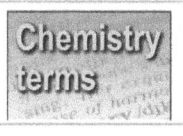
Chemistry terms

photodissociation: the breaking of a chemical bond in a molecule caused by the absorption of a photon.

A NATURAL APPROACH TO CHEMISTRY

Chemical reactions in the upper atmosphere

Molecules absorb short-λ of UV light, causing them to lose an e⁻

Another type of reaction that is very important in absorbing high-energy radiation is **photoionization**. When a molecule absorbs a photon of sufficient energy, it can eject an electron and ionize. Photoionization in the upper atmosphere absorbs photons in the high-energy region of the ultraviolet spectrum. These short wavelengths would be very harmful if they reached Earth's surface. It is important to understand that when a molecule absorbs a photon of high energy, a chemical change occurs. Here the change is a loss of an electron. This chemical change in the molecule "uses up" the energy in the photon, so that it no longer has this damaging energy to pass on. Here are some examples:

$$O_2(g) + \text{photon}(h\nu) \longrightarrow O_2^+(g) + e\text{-}$$

$$N_2(g) + \text{photon}(h\nu) \longrightarrow N_2^+(g) + e\text{-}$$

In both of these cases, a photon with a wavelength between 80 and 100 nm is absorbed and a positively charged ion is formed.

Stratospheric ozone (O_3) acts as a protective shield against longer λ UV light

The other important chemical reaction that occurs just above the stratosphere is the formation of ozone (O_3). Ozone forms when atomic oxygen, formed from photodissociation, collides with molecular oxygen: $O(g) + O_2(g) \rightarrow O_3(g)$. Ozone acts as a shield protecting us from the longer ultraviolet wavelengths. The ozone molecule absorbs high energy radiation between 240 and 310 nm. Ozone has a natural cycle of formation and decomposition. Once it collides with an ultraviolet photon, it splits apart into atomic oxygen (O) and molecular oxygen (O_2). These two molecules are then available to react again and form ozone. Basically, the ozone molecule splits when it absorbs sufficiently energetic light and then comes back together by undergoing molecular collisions.

Ozone

Discussions about the "ozone hole" have been in the news since the late 1980s. The production and use of chlorofluorocarbons (CFCs) in aerosols and air conditioners were causing destruction of the ozone layer. The highest concentrations of ozone are in the stratosphere, where it protects us. But remember, near the surface it is toxic and is considered a pollutant! Up in the stratosphere, we do not breathe it, and it has a useful purpose.

Chemistry terms

photoionization: process that occurs when a molecule absorbs a photon and ejects an electron causing it to become an ion.

The climate and global warming

The greenhouse effect can be a good thing

For a planet to be inhabited by living organisms, it must have a climate that is reasonably moderate so that life forms can adapt. A planet that has extreme fluctuations of temperature would not support life. In our atmosphere, carbon dioxide and water are the two most important molecules in maintaining a balanced temperature near Earth's surface. Earth takes in energy from the Sun,

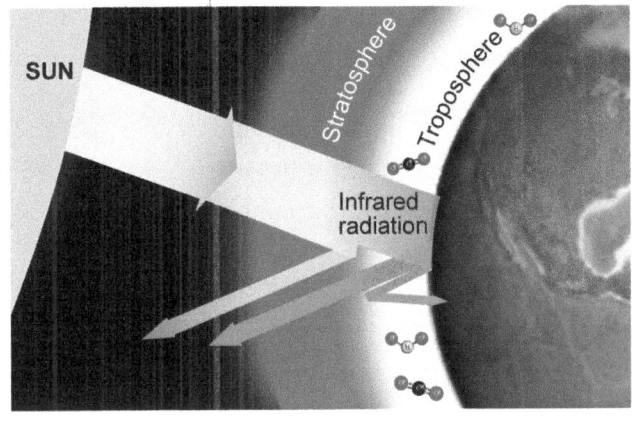

and it radiates that energy back out through the atmosphere. The greenhouse effect actually is necessary to maintain life on Earth. The gases close to Earth allow visible light to enter, but they absorb the longer wavelengths (infrared radiation) of light that are reflected by Earth's surface. When we discuss the greenhouse effect, we are focusing on the fact that Earth's gases are trapping too much heat and not allowing it to escape back into the atmosphere. We need the gases to trap some heat, but with the increased use of fossil fuels these gases are trapping too much heat.

Molecules trap infrared radiation in their bonds

How do water and carbon dioxide molecules trap heat? They absorb longer wavelength photons in the infrared region of the spectrum in their bonds. When these molecules absorb the energy in their bonds they are able to stretch, vibrate, and rotate. These motions allow the molecules to hold onto the energy for a short time before reradiating it back to Earth's surface. When the energy is released, or reradiated, it can go in any direction; about half of it returns to the surface.

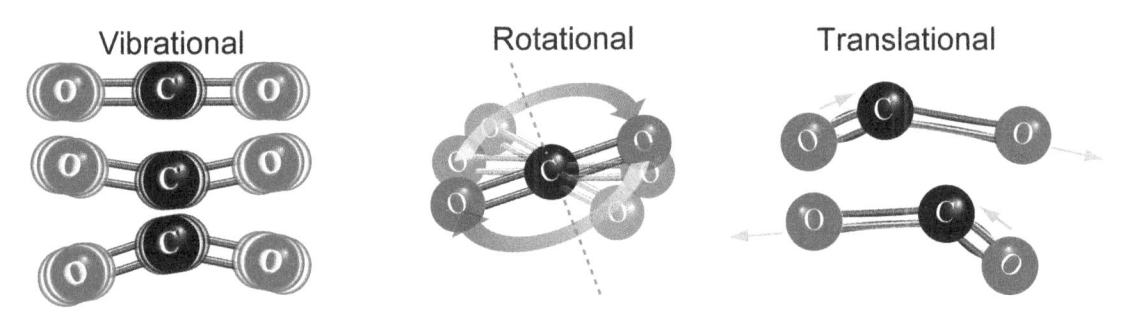

Vibrational   Rotational   Translational

Water molecules in our troposphere keep Earth warm at night, when there is no solar energy. In dry climates, such as the desert, it can get very cold at night because there are few water molecules absorbing warmth from Earth.

Chemistry terms

global warming: the warming of the surface of the Earth by gas molecules in the atmosphere that trap heat and reflect it back to the surface.

Trace amounts of chemicals in our atmosphere

Gases are measured in ppm

When measuring trace amounts of chemical substances in the air, we typically measure them using parts per million (ppm). You many recall that we used this same unit to measure amounts of chemicals in aqueous solutions in Chapter 2. The difference here is that we are dealing with gases and not water-based solutions.

Table 19.2. Concentrations of natural and human-made gases

Molecule	Sources	Typical Concentrations
Carbon dioxide (CO_2)	fossil fuel combustion, decom-position of organic materials, the ocean	375 ppm in troposphere
Methane (CH_4)	decomposition of organic mat-ter	1–2 ppm in troposphere
Carbon monoxide (CO)	industrial pollution, fossil fuels, and decomposing organics	0.05 ppm 1–56 ppm in urban areas
Nitric oxide (NO)	combustion, lightning, electricity	0.02 ppm in nonpolluted air 0.25 ppm in urban areas
Ozone (O_3)	photodissociation, electricity	0.01 ppm in nonpolluted air 0.55 ppm in urban areas
Sulfur dioxide (SO_2)	fossil fuel combustion, indus-try, volcanoes, fires	0.01 ppm in nonpolluted air 0.15–2 ppm in urban areas

Atmospheric chemists measure the partial pressures of pollutant gases

When we wish to measure relative amounts of gases, we measure the pressure of each individual gas. This is directly related to the moles of the gas given in the ideal gas equation ($PV = nRT$). Atmospheric chemists measure the partial pressure of pollutant gases in our atmosphere and decide whether the amount is dangerous. By using the partial pressure of a gas relative to the total pressure of the atmosphere, scientists can determine the mole fraction of a particular compound in our air. One part per million for a pollutant would be one mole of the compound per one million moles of total gas.

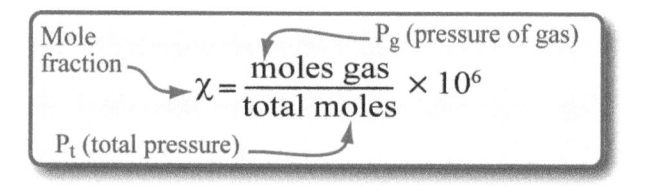

$$\chi = \frac{\text{moles gas}}{\text{total moles}} \times 10^6$$

Mole fraction — χ

P_g (pressure of gas)

P_t (total pressure)

Amounts of chemicals in our atmosphere

It is helpful to be able to quantitatively measure these small amounts of gases so that we can determine whether or not they are harmful to our health. Let's calculate the concentration in parts per million for carbon monoxide in a small city that has a total air pressure (P_t) of 702 torr. The partial pressure of CO for that day was measured to be 3.1×10^{-3} torr. To begin we first need to calculate the mole fraction (χ), the "fraction" or amount of moles present in the total sample.

How to
calculate ppm
of CO

$$\chi_{CO} \; \frac{P_{CO}}{P_t} = \frac{3.1 \times 10^{-3}}{702} = 4.42 \times 10^{-6} \, ,$$

The mole fraction is simply the number of moles of the gas as compared to the total moles in the air sampled. This tells us how much of the gas is present relative to the total gases in the air.

Next we multiply the mole fraction by 10^6 to calculate the parts per million. So $4.42 \times 10^{-6} \times 10^6 = 4.42$ ppm of CO is the concentration of carbon monoxide in this city.

Carbon monoxide is present in the troposphere in small concentrations, as our calculations just showed us. These concentrations vary in different areas owing to population differences and industrial activity (refer to Table 19.2 on the previous page). In some places the levels are quite low, but the gases can still travel in the air currents and affect more rural regions.

Let's try calculating the concentration of water vapor in the air in ppm.

Calculate the concentration of water vapor in ppm for a sample of air that contains a pressure of 0.83 torr of water vapor and a total air pressure of 729 torr.

Asked: *Concentration of water vapor*

Given: *Total pressure of air = 729 torr*
Partial pressure of H_2O vapor = 0.83 torr

Relationships: $\chi_{H_2O} = \dfrac{P_{H_2O}}{P_{total}}$

Solve: *Find mole fraction of water.* $\chi_{H_2O} = \dfrac{0.83 \, torr}{729 \, torr} = 0.0011$

Mole fraction multiplied by 10^6 is the ppm.

$0.0011 \times 10^6 = 1100 \, ppm$

Answer: *The concentration of water vapor in this sample of air is 1100 ppm.*

614

19.2 Chemistry of the Oceans

97% of Earth's water is in the oceans

The majority of Earth's water is contained in its oceans. Out of all the water on Earth, only about 0.5% is accessible to us! Roughly about 97% of the water on Earth is in the oceans, and another 2.3% is contained in ice caps and glaciers. The remaining 0.7% of our water is in groundwater, lakes, rivers, and salt marsh areas. Water is the most abundant liquid on Earth, and as mentioned earlier it is crucial to living systems.

You may recall that water's unique ability to dissolve other substances makes it known as the "universal solvent." Water's polarity allows it to form strong hydrogen bonds, which accounts for water's solvent properties and the majority of its chemistry. Water is present in almost all chemical reactions that happen in nature. Let's review how water plays a key role in chemical reactions.

Water plays a key role in chemical reactions

First, as a solvent it can separate ionic compounds or salts by surrounding them with water and hydrating them. This hydration process allows ions to be mobile and therefore transported to different areas in our bodies and in the oceans. Many minerals are key players in biological reactions, and hydration makes them available for organisms to use.

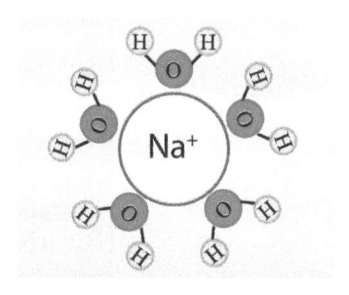

Second, water is important in the acid–base chemistry of the ocean because it is amphoteric. Water can accept a hydrogen ion from an acidic compound or it can donate a hydrogen ion to a basic compound. In the ocean, water reacts with carbon dioxide, forming carbonic acid in the reaction

$$H_2O(l) + CO_2(g) \rightarrow H_2CO_3(aq).$$

Once formed, the carbonic acid ionizes and is present the majority of the time as bicarbonate ions (HCO_3^-) and hydrogen ions (H^+). In the ocean, about 88% of inorganic carbon is in the form of bicarbonate ions.

Lastly, water can accept and donate electrons in oxidation–reduction reactions. The ocean is an electrolyte solution containing dissolved minerals and salts. These dissolved ions give the ocean water conductivity and allow for electron transfer reactions to occur.

Chemical reactions in the ocean are affected by temperature

Chemical reactions in the oceans are significantly affected by the temperature of the water. The ocean water absorbs energy from the Sun and carries this solar energy to different places in the ocean. Where this energy goes is dictated by the ocean currents. Gases are more easily dissolved in the cold waters of the ocean, just like your soda when it is cold! In warm conditions, the increased motion of the molecules allows more of the gases to escape into the air. Density is a key factor here as well. The warm waters of the ocean have more kinetic energy, and the molecules are more spread out. In cold water, the decreased kinetic energy allows the molecules to be closer together. In the ocean when ice freezes the salt ions are left behind; this increases the concentration of salt in the water, which also increases the density of the water. The saltier, denser water then sinks.

Chemicals in the ocean

Have you ever gone swimming in the ocean and experienced its saltiness? Ocean water is known for its **salinity**, or saltiness. The salinity of the ocean is approximately 3.5%. This means that about 3.5% of the water is composed of salt ions. Of the salt ions, chloride (Cl^-) is the most abundant followed by the sodium ion (Na^+).

Table 19.3. Chemicals found in the ocean

Ion	Amount (g/kg)	Concentration (M)
Chloride (Cl^-)	19.40	0.56
Sodium (Na^+)	10.75	0.48
Sulfate (SO_4^{2-})	2.70	0.030
Magnesium (Mg^{2+})	1.29	0.054
Calcium (Ca^{2+})	0.41	0.011
Potassium (K^+)	0.40	0.010
Bicarbonate (HCO_3^-)	0.145	2.75×10^{-3}
Bromide (Br^-)	0.068	8.5×10^{-4}
Boric acid (H_3BO_3)	0.026	4.1×10^{-4}
Strontium (Sr^{2+})	0.0080	9.2×10^{-5}
Fluoride (F^-)	0.0014	6.9×10^{-5}

Ocean water has a relatively constant composition

The salt concentration of ocean water remains relatively constant around the world. The concentration is maintained partly because all of the oceans are connected and because there is constant mixing of the water. These effects circulate the salts and chemicals in the water, giving it an even distribution.

How do these minerals and compounds find their way into the ocean water? Many come from erosion and runoff from the soil, some come from ocean sediments, and others are absorbed from the nearby air. When Earth first formed, volcanoes brought many minerals such as iron to the oceans. Volcanoes brought minerals up from deep within the planet and introduced them to ocean waters. Dissolved minerals are critical to living organisms who depend upon the dissolved minerals in ocean water to provide them with necessary nutrients. It is widely believed that early life developed in the ocean waters. Geothermal vents deep in the ocean floor provide sulfur for bacteria and other life forms that use it for energy.

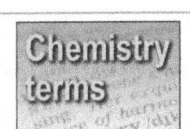
Chemistry terms

salinity: the concentration of salt in water.

The water cycle

Water is
constantly
being recycled

Where does all the water that living things require come from? Most of it comes from the ocean, but it also cycles around Earth, moving from the ocean to the air and from the air to the land. The fact that water readily changes from a liquid to a vapor allows it to be carried by the atmosphere from the oceans to the land, where it condenses and returns to the land as precipitation in the form of snow or rain. The patterns of the movement of water are described by the **water cycle** diagram shown below.

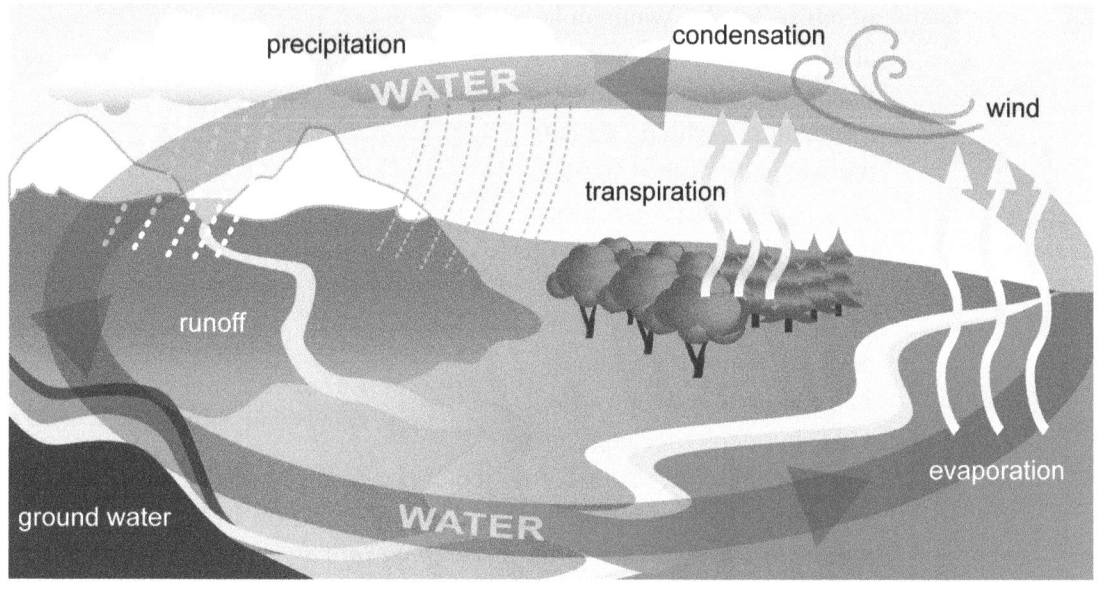

Evaporation
over the ocean
forms clouds

By looking at this diagram, you can see that water evaporates from the ocean and from the leaves of plants in a process known as **transpiration**. Over the course of a day the Sun's radiation is absorbed by the atmosphere. This warms the water vapor in the air. The warm air rises to a point in the atmosphere where it begins to cool. As it cools, it condenses into small droplets, which form clouds. The clouds bring the weather, which, depending on the location and time of year, brings either snow, sleet, or rain. Evaporation exceeds precipitation over the ocean, and this is what allows water vapor to be carried by the wind to the inland areas. On land precipitation exceeds evaporation, which sets up groundwater systems that eventually flow back to the oceans.

With the exception of photosynthesis, the water molecules that cycle through this process are not chemically changed. The water cycle is mainly a physical process rather than a chemical one.

Chemistry terms

water cycle: the process showing how water molecules move among the atmosphere, the land, and the ocean.

transpiration: the release of water from the leaves of plants as they carry out photosynthesis.

Ocean currents and climate

Here on Earth the ocean currents have a tremendous effect on our climate. The global currents are driven by differences in density. The density of ocean water is largely affected by two factors: temperature and salt concentration.

Cold ocean water is more dense and it sinks

To start to think about currents, let's begin at the poles where the temperature is cold. Water sinks at the poles because cold water has slower moving molecules, which causes them to pack slightly tighter, making the cold water more dense. This causes it to sink. The cold ocean water at the poles is also more dense because it contains a higher salt concentration. This happens because, as some of the cold water forms ice crystals, some of the salt does not freeze with it. The salt that is left behind increases the concentration in the remaining water. *The fact that cold salty ocean water sinks has a huge impact on our global climate!* As the cold water sinks, more water flows in to replace it. When this new water is pulled in it is cooled, which in turn causes it to slowly sink. It is this overall motion that sets up a current. This current moves very slowly, but it circulates large amounts of ocean water every year. The circulation brings minerals and nutrient-rich water near the surface of the ocean where algae and plankton depend on them to survive.

As cold water sinks more warm water is pulled in above it to take its place

Warm water rises to the surface and some evaporates, creating precipitation

Ocean currents carry cold water down and away from the North Atlantic. As these waters reach the Arctic they are cooled once again. Once the water flows back up to the equator it begins to be heated by the warm climate. The warmer water becomes less dense, and the water rises to the surface, where it can absorb more heat directly from the Sun. The ocean's surface water plays a key role in our weather because it evaporates and provides water molecules for precipitation here on land.

If the glacial ice melts because of the warming of Earth by greenhouse gases, it will introduce fresh water to the salty ocean water. As large quantities of fresh water are added to the ocean, the overall density of the surface water decreases. This means that the water will not sink as much. Overall changes such as this would lead to differences in the motion of the deep ocean currents. If we no longer had the deep ocean currents returning the warmer water north, the North Atlantic regions would become much colder.

The carbon cycle

Carbon is the fourth most abundant element in the universe

Carbon is used as the building block for all living organisms. It is present in the ground, the ocean, and the atmosphere. In fact, carbon is so widely used that it makes sense that it is recycled. The **carbon cycle** below shows us how carbon moves among the ocean, the land, and the atmosphere. Carbon *does* change its chemical form throughout the different phases of the cycle. For example, when it goes from CO_2 to glucose ($C_6H_{12}O_6$) and bicarbonate (HCO_3^-), each of these forms contains carbon as it cycles through its natural processes.

The largest amounts of carbon are present in the form of carbon dioxide contained in the atmos-phere and in the ocean. The four major areas that hold carbon are sediments and fossil fuels, plants, the ocean, and on land fresh water and soil. *The surface waters of the ocean contain the largest amount of carbon that is actively cycling around Earth.* The cycling of carbon can take millions of years when we include all of the geological aspects, or it can take days to thousands of years if we consider the biological and physical cycles.

Movement of carbon between the storage areas occurs because of biological activity and geological changes, both of these processes bring about chemical changes along with some physical changes. The amount of carbon dioxide released by Earth has roughly balanced the amount Earth absorbs. Lately, this has not been the case because of the increase of carbon dioxide from the burning of fossil fuels.

Bicarbonate (HCO_3^-) is essentially dissolved CO_2 in the ocean

Ocean chemistry revolves around formation of bicarbonate from carbon dioxide in the familiar reaction of carbon dioxide dissolving in water; $CO_2(g) + H_2O(l) \rightleftharpoons H_2CO_3(aq)$ The bicarbonate ionizes in water via the reaction $H_2CO_3(aq) \rightleftharpoons H^+(aq) + HCO_3^-(aq)$. The formation of the bicarbonate ion is favored, and this allows the ocean to hold large amounts of carbon dioxide.

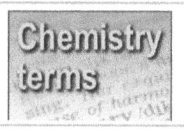
Chemistry terms

carbon cycle: the process showing how carbon moves among the atmosphere, the land, and the ocean in its different forms, such as CO_2, $C_6H_{12}O_6$, and H_2CO_3.

19.3 Chemistry of the Land

Scientists believe the Earth formed from a solar nebula

What types of matter and atoms is Earth made of? The actual composition of Earth was formed from relatively few elements. Scientists think that Earth was formed 4 to 5 billion years ago by a **solar nebula**. A solar nebula is a region of dust and gases that accompanied the formation of the Sun. This flat, circular area of dust orbiting the Sun eventually formed the planets. When we refer to the "land" we tend to think of the crust, which is the surface of Earth on which we live. The crust is approximately 40 km thick, and it is primarily made of the elements oxygen and silicon. The crust is actually the smallest portion of Earth.

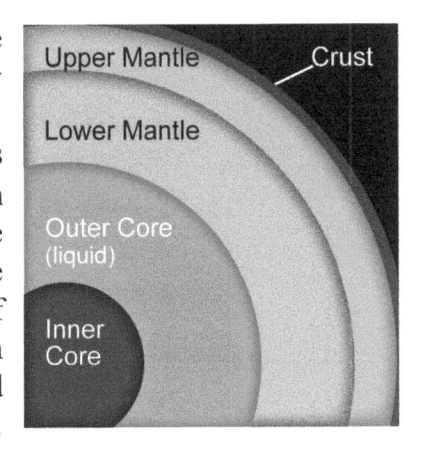

Si and O form the silicates that make up most of our rocks

Table 19.4. Elements of Earth's crust

Element	% by mass
O	46.6
Si	27.7
Al	8.1
Fe	5.0
Ca	3.6
Na	2.8
K	2.6
Mg	2.1

Understanding the composition of Earth requires an understanding of chemistry. There are eight elements that make up most (98.5%) of Earth's matter, with small amounts of other elements making up about 1.5% of the remaining mass. Of these eight elements oxygen (O) and silicon (Si) are the most abundant. They combine to form a class of compounds called the **silicates**. *Silicates make up most of the different types of rocks and minerals on Earth.* These silicates contain different amounts of the other eight elements, and these variations give different properties to the types of rocks they form.

If Earth is made up of mainly the same elements, then why are the layers different? As the Earth cooled and condensed it separated into layers as shown above. *The elements that were more dense sunk to Earth's center, forming the core.*

Conditions of high temperature and pressure affect the arrangement of atoms

Iron (Fe) is much more dense than the silicates formed from oxygen and silicon. This caused it to be concentrated in the center of Earth or the **core**. The conditions of high temperature and pressure below the surface have significant effects on the arrangement of the atoms. For example, under conditions of high temperature and pressure carbon forms diamond, which has a tetrahedral lattice and is very strong. On Earth's surface, carbon forms parallel planes of soft flaky graphite. Graphite has a trigonal planar arrangement of atoms within a layer, and it is held loosely between layers.

Chemistry terms

solar nebula: a disk-shaped region of dust and gases around a forming star, which can lead to planetary formation.

silicates: the most abundant class of minerals in the Earth's crust consisting primarily of $(SiO_4)^{2-}$ combined with various metal ions.

core: the center of the Earth, where temperature and pressure are very high.

The composition of Earth

Magma is the source of most of our rocks

You may wonder where all of the different types of rocks and soils that make up Earth come from. There is a great variety here on Earth's surface. Around the world we observe such variation in the land and rock formations that it may seem almost impossible that just a few elements give rise to such diversity, but they do! Different types of rock are formed from a substance called **magma**. Magma is molten rock, made up of silicates (Si and O). Magmas contain suspended crystals and dissolved gases as well. Most magma is formed just below the upper mantle region. As magma cools by crystallization it forms **igneous rock**. Most of Earth's upper crust is made of igneous rock. Igneous rock is widely studied for clues about Earth's inner composition.

Temperature plays an important role in rock formation

Temperature differences experienced as the rock crystallizes are important in the final composition of the rock. Basically all igneous rock is formed primarily from silicates. The variation seen in these rocks comes from the other six elements present in significant amounts. The term "rock" applies to **minerals** of several differ-

Feldspar   Quartz

ent types. Minerals are naturally occurring solids, not made up of organic mater, that have an organized internal structure and a definite chemical makeup. In other words, their atoms are arranged in a definite pattern. Most minerals are made of silicate materials. Quartz, feldspar, and mica are examples of silicates. Carbonates are an example of a common nonsilicate mineral, as are oxides. Some minerals are prized as gems because of their beautiful appearance, hardness, and color. For example, rubies are made of aluminum oxide (Al_2O_3) with impurities of chromium oxide (Cr_2O_3), a mineral known as corundum. Some elements are found in their pure forms on Earth such as gold, silver, copper, lead, and carbon in the form of diamond.

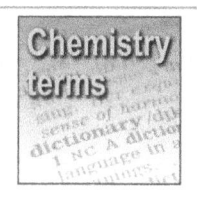
Chemistry terms

magma: molten rock found below the surface of the upper mantle.

igneous rock: rock that is formed from crystallized magma, and covers more than 90% of Earth's crust.

mineral: a natural nonorganic solid with an organized internal structure where the atoms have a definite pattern.

Volcanoes

Openings in the Earth are created where rigid crust layers meet

Most of Earth's crust is made up of igneous rock, and igneous rock is made from magma. How does magma get to the surface? The answer is through a volcano! A **volcano** is an opening in Earth's crust that allows magma, gases, and other materials to escape from the interior. Earth has about a dozen rigid plates that move independently of one another. These plates are in contact with each other, and as they move and shift some rock is pulled underneath. This rock sinks and, as it does, it heats up, which causes it to become less dense. Because it is less dense, it slowly rises towards Earth's surface again. If magma rises all the way up to the surface and is released, it becomes **lava** which cools down, solidifies, and becomes igneous rock.

Melting of rock is affected by pressure, temperature, and composition

Deep inside Earth the temperatures are very hot, reaching 1,000°C at a depth of 100 km. However, because of the high pressure experienced at that depth, most of the rock is not melted! The melting of rock depends not only on the temperature and pressure but also on the composition of the rock. As mentioned earlier rock is mainly silicon and oxygen, but these elements vary in their relative percentages. For example, basalt is one of three common types of lava. Basalt is made up of 45%–50% SiO_2. Basalt is considered to be a low-silica type of lava. Low-silica lavas flow the farthest, sometimes going for miles before they solidify. The chemical composition of the lava plays a key role here. In molten lavas and magmas silicates tend to form SiO_4^- anions, and these link together to form polymers. The higher the silicate content, the greater amount of polymerization. This polymer formation makes the lavas "thicker" or more viscous, which does not allow them to flow as far.

Water significantly decreases the melting temperature of rock

Most volcanoes appear at the edge of continents or on islands in the ocean. This is because water decreases the melting temperature of rock! Water has the opposite effect of pressure. Water finds its way deep into the Earth, particularly near or in the ocean where the rigid plates meet. Even in small amounts, water causes the rock to melt more quickly, forming magma. As this magma rises it is released from volcanoes as lava.

Chemistry terms

volcano: an opening in the Earth where magma, gases, and other materials can escape from inside the Earth.

lava: molten rock or magma released from the vent(s) of a volcano.

A NATURAL APPROACH TO CHEMISTRY

The rock cycle

Rocks are recycled within the Earth

The study of rock has greatly influenced our knowledge of Earth. Rock tells a story about Earth that reaches far beyond our human history record. Rocks cycle through a process that is ongoing, and in this way rocks can be considered to be "recycled" in the true sense of the word! The rock cycle shown on the right highlights the three main types of rock: igneous, sedimentary, and metamorphic. Each of these types comes originally from magma. **Geologists** study the matter that makes up the Earth. The study of the Earth has many

applications, including identifying areas where our natural resources can be found, such as oil, coal or precious minerals. Learning about Earth also gives us valuable information for understanding earthquakes and other natural dangers. In general, the information geologists gather can be used to protect and improve our environment.

Motion of rock layers occurs underneath Earth's crust

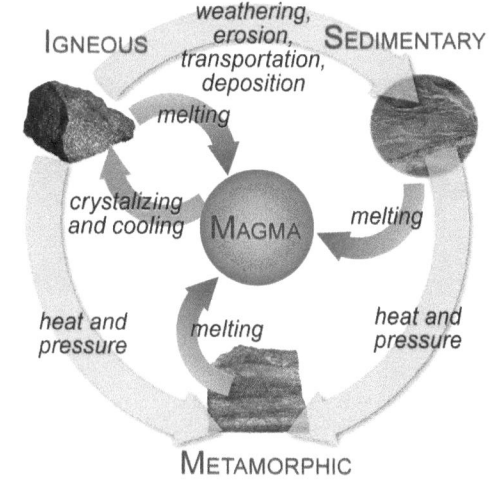

By studying different types of rock, geologists have discovered how they are all interconnected. Over time Earth changes a rock from one type to another. How does Earth do this? Motion under Earth's crust is responsible for the recycling of rock materials. The mantle layer slowly moves in response to density changes within the layers, and the rigid areas above called "plates" shift and cause some rock matter to move underneath them, where it experiences more pressure. Solidified magma forms igneous rock and this begins the cycle. The cycle continues as rocks are eroded over time by the environment. The resulting smaller pieces of rock are deposited in layers which are eventually compressed and cemented together to form **sedimentary rock**. Fossils are primarily found in the layers of sedimentary rocks. The third type of rock, **metamorphic rock**, is created when existing rocks of any type are subjected to different conditions of heat and pressure. The change in conditions causes the rocks, and the minerals that make them up, to "change form" into a new, metamorphic rock. All three types of rock can be melted and form a new type of magma, starting the cycle over once again.

Chemistry terms

geologists: scientists who study the Earth.

sedimentary rock: rock formed from the compression and cementation of eroded pieces of other rocks.

metamorphic rock: rock created when existing rock layers are subjected to different conditions of heat and pressure.

The nitrogen cycle

Nitrogen in the air (N_2) cannot be used by most living organisms

Nitrogen is a very important element. Essentially all living organisms use amino acids to make proteins, and amino acids contain nitrogen. In addition to amino acids, nitrogen is used to make nitrogenous bases for DNA and RNA molecules, and it is also used in the molecular structure of the porphyrin ring. You may recall that the porphyrin ring is important in cytochrome systems and in the hemoglobin molecule. Even though nitrogen is abundant here on Earth in the form of nitrogen gas, living organisms cannot use this form of nitrogen. Why can't we use the $N_2(g)$ in the air? The strong triple bond holding nitrogen atoms together requires too much energy. Because of this we cannot use them to make other molecules. We need nitrogen in a chemical form that our bodies can break apart and use to make our biological molecules. Animals simply inhale and exhale nitrogen gas.

Nitrogen cycle

How do we obtain the types of nitrogen our bodies can use? We eat plants and meat that contain nitrogen, and reuse it to make our own proteins. Living organisms can use nitrogen in the form of ammonia (NH_3) nitrate (NO_3^-) and nitrite (NO_2^-).

As you can see from the diagram above, there are three ways for nitrogen to become available to living organisms: atmospheric **nitrogen fixation**, bacterial nitrogen fixation, and through the production of synthetic fertilizers to grow plants. We will study the chemistry behind nitrogen fixation next.

Chemistry terms

nitrogen cycle: the process that shows how nitrogen moves from the atmosphere to the ocean, land, and living systems.

nitrogen fixation: the ability to use nitrogen gas from the atmosphere and convert it into a nitrogen compound such as ammonia or nitrate.

Nitrogen fixation

Nitrogenase allows bacteria to use atmospheric N_2

The ability to take nitrogen gas and make compounds requires special enzymes, lots of energy, or high pressure and a catalyst. Each of these processes is unique. In nature only certain types of soil bacteria can convert gaseous N_2 into a usable form of nitrogen compounds. These bacteria live in the soil and on the roots of plants. The reason they can break this strong double bond in the nitrogen molecule is because they have a special enzyme called nitrogenase. The nitrogenase enzyme catalyzes the reaction.

Nitrogen-fixing bacteria in root nodules in clover

$$N_2 + 8H^+ + 8e^- + 16ATP \rightarrow 2NH_3 + H_2 + 16ADP + 16P_i$$

As you can see this reaction is carried out in an acidic environment and it requires energy from ATP molecules. The nitrogenase enzymes can be damaged by the presence of oxygen, and for this reason the bacteria that carry out this process live in the soil and create environments where the amount of oxygen gas is minimal. Prior to the creation of synthetic fertilizers, farmers would fertilize with manure because it added the nitrogen that the animals consumed by eating grass back into the soil.

Nitrogen fixation also occurs when lightning reacts with the air. The energy necessary to split the triple bond is provided by the energy in the lightning, and this yields nitrogen-containing compounds such as NO_3^- and NO_2^-. The combustion of fossil fuels can also provide the energy necessary to convert atmospheric nitrogen into compounds such as NO and NO_2, which you learned about earlier with respect to acid rain.

The Haber–Bosch process is the largest nonbiological means of nitrogen fixation

The Haber–Bosch process is one of the most important commercial chemical processes used today, because we need more fertilizer than can be produced by nature alone. As Earth's population has grown, it has become necessary for us to produce larger amounts of food. The Haber–Bosch process produces approximately 100 million tons of nitrogen fertilizer each year, and this helps provide food for more than one third of our population. This process was discovered and refined by two German chemists, Fritz Haber and Carl Bosch, during the early 1900s. The production of ammonia from nitrogen and hydrogen gas requires high-pressure conditions, and the use of a catalyst and was *very challenging* to overcome. The equation for the Haber–Bosch process is

Haber and Bosch earned the Nobel Prize for their work

$$N_2(g) + 3H_2(g) \rightleftharpoons 2NH_3(g), \quad \Delta H = -92 \text{ kJ/mole}$$

Look carefully at this equation. Can you see why conditions of high pressure would favor the formation of NH_3? With increased pressure on the system, the reaction shifts to the products side where there are fewer moles of a gas, which decreases the overall pressure of the system. This is in agreement with Le Châtelier's principle. Chemical reactions that require high pressure can be very dangerous to carry out on a large industrial scale, but by using an iron oxide catalyst it was finally accomplished.

The phosphorus cycle

Similar to nitrogen, phosphorus (P) is another very important element in living systems. In living organisms, phosphorus is found in the form of the familiar polyatomic ion compound called phosphate (PO_4^{3-}), where it is bound to oxygen. You may recall that phosphorus is part of many biological molecules; DNA and RNA use phosphate molecules to form the backbone of their molecular structures. Important energy molecules such as ATP and ADP also incorporate phosphorus in the form of phosphate. The phospholipid bilayer of a cell membranes also incorporates the phosphate ion.

Phosphates (PO_4^{3-}) are important in living systems

Where do living organisms obtain this essential element?

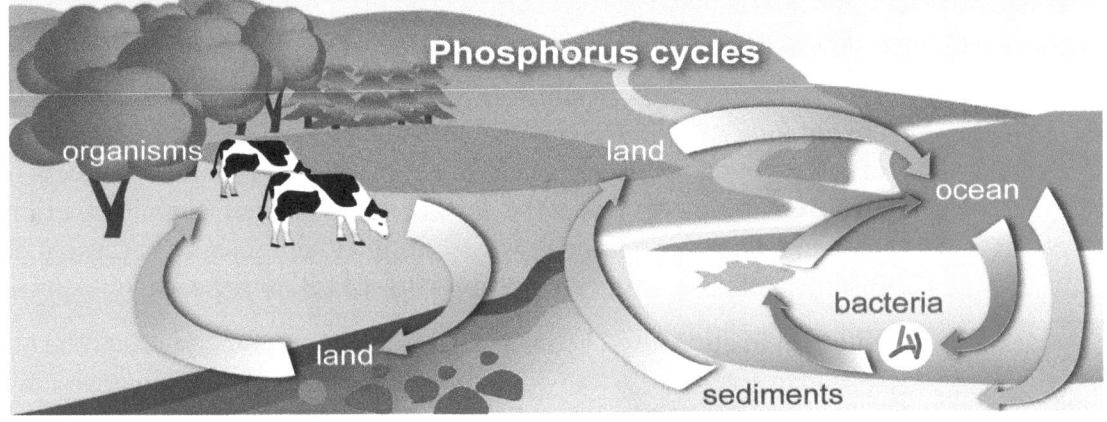

Phosphorus cycles between the land and the ocean

As you look carefully at the **phosphorus cycle** diagram above, you will notice a few interesting features. First, phosphorus does not actually enter the atmosphere like the other cycles we studied. The phosphorus cycle involves the land, living organisms, and the ocean. Phosphorus is found on land mainly in the form of rocks and minerals in the soil. A large amount of phosphorus, in the form of inorganic phosphate salts, is also found on the ocean floor as sediment. Plants are able to absorb phosphate that is dissolved in soil and water. When phosphate is taken up by plants, it is bound in organic compounds. Phosphate bound by plant or animal tissue is considered organic. Organic phosphate makes its way through the food chain. Soil and rocks release phosphate, plants absorb phosphate from the soil and water, and animals eat the plants and obtain phosphate. In the ocean, sediments can slowly bring phosphates to the land and to organisms who live in the sea. Living organisms eventually return the phosphorus back to land and sea at the end of their life cycle. Runoff can eventually return some phosphate back to the ocean. We can cause a disruption of the phosphorus cycle with the overuse of phosphates in our fertilizers and detergents. These phosphates make their way into the environment, creating levels that are too high.

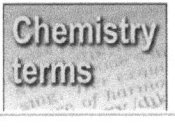

Chemistry terms

phosphorus cycle: the process that shows how phosphorus moves among the land, the ocean, and living systems.

Soil chemistry

Soil is a mixture of minerals, organic matter, water, and air

The chemical reactions that take place in soil play an important role in our environment. Originally, soil chemistry was primarily important to gardeners and farmers, but now it has become a very important developing field of science. Our environment is suffering from the increased global population and the significant increase in industrial production. Today, knowledge of soil science is essential for the cleanup of contaminated areas near industrial sites. What exactly is soil? Soil is a mixture of minerals (inorganic solids), organic matter (living microorganisms and decaying plant and animal matter), water, and air. Plants need soil to grow, and plants are required to support most living organisms here on Earth. Soils are formed initially from bare rock, which can come from volcanic lava or be exposed from melting glaciers. Soil develops over time from lichen and algae growing on these rocks. As lichen and algae grow, they cause some of the rock to break down and erode. Over time these organisms also add to the formation of soil. Gradually the soil becomes deep enough for small plants to grow, and as vegetation dies it continues to build layers of soil. The soil that develops over time is influenced by several factors, including climate, the types of minerals in the soil, organisms living in the soil, and the geography of the land itself.

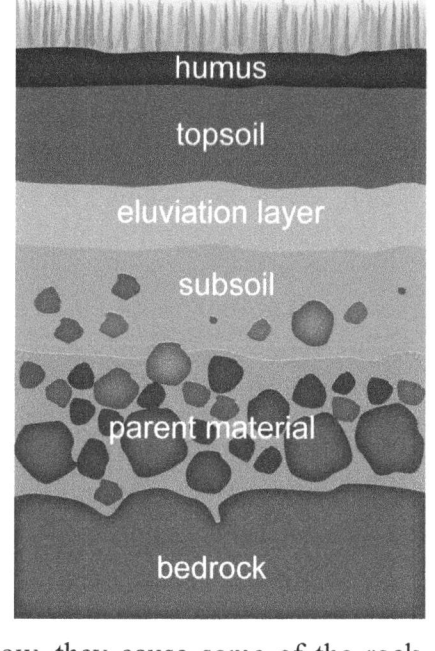

pH plays a key role in soil chemistry

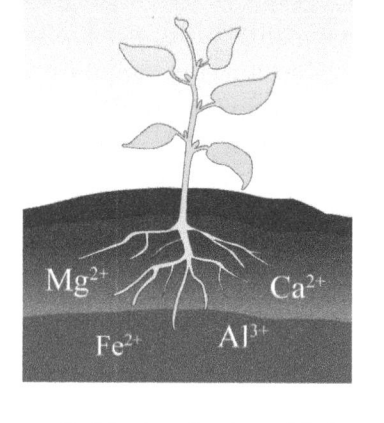

The chemical properties of soil are largely influenced by the pH of the soil. This is because the nutrient availability in soil is regulated by pH. Nutrients that are required by plants include cations such as Mg^{2+}, Ca^{2+}, Zn^{2+}, Fe^{2+}, Co^{2+}, Mn^{2+}, Cu^{2+}, and Al^{3+}. Elements such as nitrogen (N) and phosphorus (P) are also important for plant growth. The pH range of 6 to 7.5 makes these elements and divalent cations available to plants in the soil. When the pH gets too high, nitrogen, and phosphorus can form solid precipitates in the soil that make it impossible for plants to absorb them. Overly acidic conditions can make too many cations available to plants, which can lead to the leaching of nutrients from the soil too rapidly and to toxicity. Both of these conditions negatively impact plant growth. There are several ways soil can become acidic. These include the decay of organic matter, large amounts of rainfall, added fertilizers, and the type of minerals originally present in the soil.

Carbon sequestering

Earth's systems all play a role in the recycling of carbon, as you learned by studying the carbon cycle. One area of cutting-edge research today is how to decrease the amount of carbon dioxide being released into our atmosphere. Global efforts to slow down global warming trends are focusing on many different technologies to capture carbon dioxide. Carbon sequestering means holding carbon underground for long periods of time. The capturing of carbon in the form of carbon dioxide is one form of carbon sequestration.

If you think back to the carbon cycle, there are many natural ways that nature removes carbon dioxide gas from the air. The largest amount of carbon dioxide is absorbed by our oceans in the form of the bicarbonate ion (HCO_3^-). Research is now being done to determine how much more carbon dioxide the ocean can hold. It is believed that in some warm climates, the ocean has reached its full capacity to absorb carbon dioxide. Atmospheric chemists are measuring the partial pressure of carbon dioxide just above and below the surface of the ocean to see which is higher. The process of photosynthesis also absorbs carbon dioxide. Because of this we have become more aware of how important natural resources such as large forests actually are. Lastly, decaying organic matter remains in the soil for a period of time; this also keeps carbon out of the atmosphere.

CO_2 Reservoirs

Monoethanolamine

Diethanolamine

Beyond these natural means of absorbing carbon, scientists have been studying ways to decrease the release of carbon dioxide into our atmosphere. One of the biggest challenges of sustainability is how to decrease industrial emissions of carbon dioxide. One method currently being used is called carbon capture and sequestering. This method requires chemicals and significant energy to pump carbon dioxide deep into Earth's interior. In this process, the chemicals added are amine-based solvents, such as MEA (mono ethanol amine) or DEA (diethanolamine). These chemicals are added to the emission gases (flue gases) of natural gas, or coal-fired power plants or other industrial emissions containing carbon dioxide or hydrogen sulfide. The gases that would normally be emitted into the air through the stack are bubbled through an aqueous amine solution. The chemical equation that describes this process is:

$$CO_2 \;+\; H_2O \;+\; \underbrace{H_2NCH_2CH_2OH}_{\text{MEA}} \;\rightarrow\; \underbrace{HCO_3^-}_{\text{carbonate ion}} \;+\; \underbrace{H_3NCH_2CH_2OH^+}_{\text{MEA ion}}$$

In this process, cold aqueous solutions of amines are used to treat gases with carbon dioxide (CO_2) and hydrogen sulfide (H_2S). You may recall that these gases are both acidic gases. Chemically, the amine solvent acts as a weak base, because it contains an amino (NH_2) group. Recall that it is the lone pair on the nitrogen that attracts the H^+ ion. The weak base effectively neutralizes the weak acid contained in the dissolved gas. This forms ionic compounds that are much more soluble in the cold solution. The use of amine solvents helps to concentrate the CO_2 so that it can be collected. The first large-scale CO_2 sequestration project, called Sleipner, was located in the North Sea in 1996. Norway's StatoilHydro strips carbon dioxide from natural gas with amine solvents and disposes of this carbon dioxide in a deep saline aquifer.

CO₂ can be captured and sequestered by power stations.

unmineable coal beds

depleted oil and gas reservoir

The overall effect of this process is to keep the carbon dioxide dissolved in solution in the form of bicarbonate ions. This allows the carbon dioxide to be "captured," and therefore it is not released into our atmosphere. However, after it is captured, the amine solution is warmed and the carbon dioxide gas is released from it. The carbon dioxide is then injected deep into the ground. The capture of the carbon dioxide gas can be expensive, and it was initially challenging because CO_2 only makes up about 15% of the overall combustion gases produced. Geologists are studying ways to safely inject carbon dioxide back into the Earth. Currently, we use old oil wells or coal seams that cannot be mined. Geologically these areas appear to be ideal sites because carbon dioxide is soluble in oil. The United States has used the injection of CO_2 in depleted oil wells since the early 1970s. Injecting CO_2 into the oil well improved the ability of the oil to flow by increasing the adhesive forces between the surface molecules of the oil and the CO_2 gas molecules. Old oil fields also have a geologic barrier that help to contain the injected CO_2. Since a 1,000 kW coal-powered electrical plant is estimated to produce about 50 million barrels of carbon dioxide in one year, there is a lot of CO_2 that needs sequestering.

Another option is making natural processes occur at a faster speed. Some believe this to be the best and safest way to handle the removal of CO_2 from the atmosphere. One such process is fertilization of the ocean with iron (Fe). Adding iron to the ocean would increase the rate of photosynthesis by plankton and algae. This is a good idea, but it is not fully tested yet. There are environmental concerns about how the added iron would affect the nutrient balance and the overall ecosystem. As you can see, many chemical reactions are important in our pursuit to decrease the CO_2 in our air.

Chapter 19 Review

Vocabulary

Match each word to the sentence where it best fits.

Section 19.1

troposphere	stratosphere
photoionization	photodissociation
global warming	

1. Most of the ozone that protects Earth from high energy photons is formed in the _____.

2. When a molecule breaks a bond by absorbing a photon, the process is called _____.

3. Most of the atmosphere's mass is contained in the _____.

4. Gas molecules in the atmosphere absorb heat and reradiate it back to Earth, causing _____.

5. Sometimes a molecule undergoes _____, which causes it to become an ion by ejecting an electron.

Section 19.2

carbon cycle	water cycle
salinity	transpiration

6. Plants can release water in a process known as _____ when they carry out photosynthesis.

7. Measuring the _____ of water tells us its salt content.

8. The process that shows water moving through the atmosphere, ocean, and land is known as the _____.

9. Carbon moves among the different areas of our planet in a process known as the _____.

Section 19.3

solar nebula	core
igneous rock	magma
mineral	volcano
lava	sedimentary rock
geologists	metamorphic rock
nitrogen fixation	nitrogen cycle
phosphorus cycle	

10. Molten rock found below the surface of the upper mantle is called _____.

11. The Earth formed in the Sun's _____, which is a region of dust and gases.

12. Earth's _____ is its center.

13. A/An _____ is a nonorganic solid that has an organized internal structure; it is often called "rock."

14. Magma can rise to the surface of the Earth through an opening called a/an _____.

15. Scientists who study the matter making up the Earth are called _____.

16. Crystallized magma forms _____, which covers most of Earth's crust.

17. As igneous rock erodes, small pieces collect and form _____ when compressed.

18. Magma is called _____ after it is released from the vent of a volcano.

19. Under conditions of high heat and pressure _____ can form from igneous rock or sedimentary rock.

20. Plants can use atmospheric nitrogen (N_2) in a process called _____.

21. Nitrogen moves among the atmosphere, land, and ocean in a process known as the _____.

22. The _____ is unique in that it cycles between the land and the ocean without entering the atmosphere.

Conceptual Questions

Section 19.1

23. List the different layers of our atmosphere.

24. Explain why the troposphere has a larger total mass than the stratosphere, even though the stratosphere is so much bigger.

25. Explain why photodissociation of O_2 is more important in our atmosphere than photodissociation of nitrogen gas.

26. Draw the Lewis structures of ozone (O_3) and nitrogen dioxide (NO_2).

27. Where do the following pollutant gases come from? List both naturally occurring and human-made sources.
    a. NO
    b. CO
    c. CH_4
    d. SO_2
    e. O_3

28. What is the pH of naturally occurring rainwater? Explain why it is lower than a neutral pH of 7.

29. What happens in the thermosphere that causes the auroras seen in the polar regions?

30. Explain what role the mesosphere plays in protecting Earth.

31. List the four most abundant gases in the atmosphere.

32. What gases are important in keeping Earth warm?

33. Explain how each of the following gases came to be present in our atmosphere:
    a. CO_2
    b. Ar
    c. O_2

34. What are the primary gases responsible for smog? What causes smog to form?

35. Explain why natural rainwater is acidic. Show a chemical reaction to help explain why.

36. Acid rain is a major problem affecting the environment.
    a. List the two main gases responsible for the formation of acid rain.
    b. Show the chemical reactions for the formation of the two acids that form acid rain.
    c. What are some of the detrimental effects of acid rain on our environment?

37. What are two important chemical reactions initiated by the Sun that occur in the upper atmosphere?

38. What molecules are responsible for absorbing short-wavelength UV light? What about longer wavelength UV light?

39. What kind of electromagnetic radiation does carbon dioxide trap in the atmosphere? Explain how carbon dioxide molecules are able to trap heat.

40. Make a sketch of the Earth, and show with arrows how infrared radiation passes through our atmosphere, is reflected and then reradiated back to the surface.

41. What unit do we use to measure trace amounts of gases in our atmosphere?

Section 19.2

42. Explain how temperature can affect the density of ocean water.

43. Write the chemical reaction that shows how the ocean is able to absorb large amounts of CO_2.

44. List the four most abundant ions in ocean water.

45. Even though the ocean is vast it maintains a relatively constant composition. What factors help it to do this?

46. Consider the water cycle.

    a. Make a sketch and label the key features of the cycle.

    b. Where does most of the evaporation take place?

    c. Do water molecules change form chemically as they move through the cycle? Explain.

47. What are the two factors that affect the density of ocean water?

48. Explain how ocean currents are influenced by cold water near Earth's poles.

49. How does the melting of glaciers affect the density of the water at the poles? How might this affect deep ocean currents?

50. Make a sketch of the carbon cycle. Label the processes that bring carbon into the atmosphere with a red arrow. Label the processes that return carbon to the surface with a blue arrow. Do these processes appear to balance one another? Explain.

51. Where is the largest amount of carbon available to cycle around the Earth contained?

52. Photosynthesis and respiration are processes that use each other's waste products to function.

    a. Explain under what conditions photosynthesis and respiration would be able to balance each other.

    b. What human factors may influence this relationship?

53. Explain what will happen to the ocean's pH as it continues to absorb CO_2.

Section 19.3

54. Consider Earth's internal structure.

    a. Make a sketch showing the different layers of the Earth.

    b. What conditions caused these layers to form?

55. What two elements make up most of Earth's crust?

56. Explain why there is a high concentration of iron in the Earth's core.

57. What two factors affect the arrangement of atoms deep within Earth?

58. What type of rock is the most abundant on Earth's crust? What is the common source for all types of rock?

59. What is another common term for minerals? List three common types of minerals.

60. Some minerals form gemstones.

    a. List the chemical formulas for two different gemstones.

    b. What types of conditions are required to form diamonds?

61. Explain how silicate content affects the flow of lava.

62. Why are most volcanoes found near the ocean on the edges of continents?

63. What are some of the ways that geologists are helpful to us?

64. What are the two ways that metamorphic rock can be formed?

65. In what type of rock are fossils commonly found?

66. What is the primary source of nitrogen on Earth?

67. Make a sketch of the nitrogen cycle. Label the methods by which nitrogen can enter the land.

68. What are the forms of nitrogen that animals and humans can metabolize?

69. What are the three ways that nitrogen can become available to living organisms?

70. Why is N_2 not a usable form of nitrogen for animals?

71. Bacteria are vital in creating usable forms of nitrogen in a process called "nitrogen fixation."

    a. What do bacteria require to form ammonia (NH_3) from nitrogen?

    b. Write the equation for the bacterial fixation of nitrogen.

    c. What molecule is damaging to the bacteria that carry out this process?

72. Write the equation that represents the Haber–Bosch process.

73. What important biological molecules use the element phosphorus?

74. Where does most of our inorganic phosphorus come from?

75. Phosphates are commonly used in fertilizers and detergents. How can this upset the balance of phosphorus in our environment?

76. What is the primary source of phosphate in the ocean?

77. Compare the nitrogen and phosphorus cycles.

   a. List one major difference.

   b. List two similarities.

   c. What role do plants play in each of the cycles?

78. What is soil made up of?

79. What pH range is the best for most plants to grow in?

80. Compare the chemical effects on nutrient availability when the soil is too acidic or too basic.

Quantitative Problems

Section 19.1

81. Does a photon with a wavelength of 170 nm emitted by the Sun have enough energy to dissociate an oxygen molecule? The bond dissociation energy of an O_2 molecule is 495 kJ/mole. Show a calculation to support your answer.

82. Formaldehyde (CH_2O) is formed in car exhaust when fuels containing alcohol are combusted. Formaldehyde photodissociates and contributes to smog formation. A photon with a wavelength of 336 nm is energetic enough to cause the C–H bond to rupture and dissociate.

   a. In what part of the electromagnetic spectrum is this light found (visible, UV, IR, etc.)? Explain.

   b. Calculate the bond energy in kJ/mole of the bond that can be broken by a photon of 336 nm.

83. In polluted areas where there is a larger amount of NO_2 in smog, the formation of NO through photodissociation is an important factor:
$$NO_2(g) + h\nu \rightarrow NO(g) + O(g)$$
Light with a wavelength of 420 nm can cause this dissociation process.

   a. Where in the electromagnetic spectrum is light with a wavelength of 420 nm found?

   b. Calculate the bond energy in kJ/mole of the bond that can be broken by a photon of 420 nm.

84. In one sample of air from an urban area, the concentration of carbon monoxide (CO) was 4.5 ppm. What was the partial pressure of CO? The atmospheric pressure (total air pressure) was 702 torr.

85. Magnesium (Mg) is reclaimed from seawater by precipitation with calcium oxide, CaO, given by the equation
$$Mg^{2+}(aq) + CaO(s) + H_2O(l)$$
$$\rightarrow Mg(OH)_2(s) + Ca^{2+}(aq)$$
Calculate the amount of CaO in grams needed to precipitate 1.0 kg of $Mg(OH)_2$.

86. In one sample of air from New York City, the concentration of carbon monoxide (CO) was 3.7 ppm. What was the partial pressure of CO? The atmospheric pressure (total air pressure) was 718 torr.

87. The average concentration of carbon monoxide in air in Chicago, Illinois, was 4.1 ppm. Calculate the number of CO molecules in 2.0 L of this air. The atmospheric pressure was 738 torr and the temperature was 25°C.

88. The average concentration of nitrous oxide in the air in Los Angeles, California, was 0.30 ppm. Calculate the number of NO molecules in 1.0 L of this air. The atmospheric pressure was 756 torr and the temperature was 26°C.

89. Calculate the concentration of water vapor in parts per million for a sample that has a water vapor pressure of 0.76 torr, and a total air pressure of 709 torr.

CHAPTER 20
Nuclear Chemistry and Radioactivity

How do we write nuclear reactions?

How are nuclear reactions different from chemical reactions?

What is radioactivity, and how is it used?

What are the biological effects of radioactivity?

Where does nuclear energy come from?

Nuclear chemistry and nuclear processes are central to many products and devices that are used in our daily lives. Nuclear chemistry is at the core of many technologies, from the smoke detector in your home to medical procedures like x rays. The generation of energy from nuclear reactors is also based on the science of nuclear chemistry. Archeologists are able to date ancient objects by using nuclear chemistry techniques. The development of new drugs depends on nuclear procedures that are used to investigate and evaluate chemical reaction mechanisms.

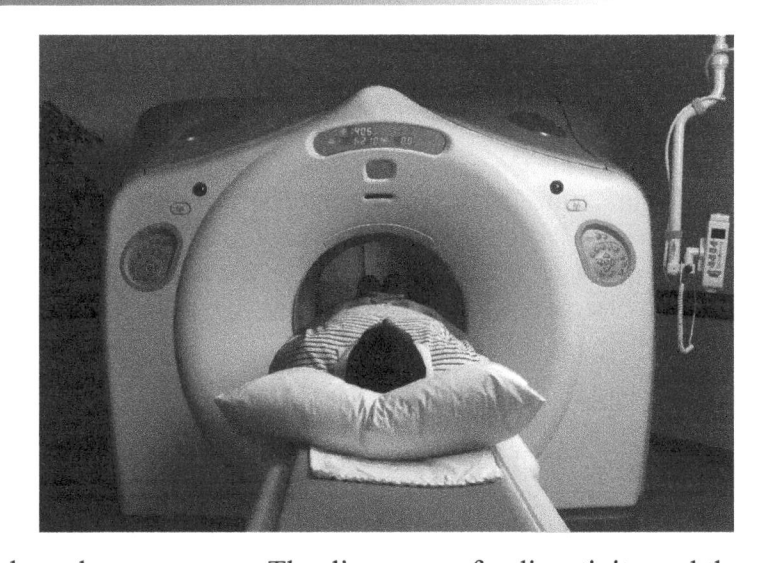

Radioactivity is the energy that is associated with nuclear processes. The discovery of radioactivity and the eventual development of the science of nuclear chemistry is one of the great accomplishments of humanity. It gave us tools to diagnose and treat conditions such as cancer and heart disease. However, it also led to the development of nuclear weapons.

Nuclear chemistry is a technology that presents us with the ultimate trade-off between benefit and risk. In this chapter we will learn the fundamentals of nuclear chemistry science, and so we will be able to accurately evaluate its impact on our lives.

Radioactivity: the invisible energy

Radioactivity is a natural phenomenon that occurs all around us and has been occurring since the Solar System condensed out of interstellar gases 4.3 billion years ago. Uranium, with 92 protons and 146 neutrons, is a remnant of the ancient exploded stars that contributed matter to our own Earth. Uranium is a radioactive element, and today it is mined and used in nuclear reactors.

Rocks that contain uranium have some very special properties. These properties led to the discovery of the nucleus and the dawn of the atomic age. The crucial experiment in which radioactivity was discovered was first done in 1896 by French scientists Antoine-Henri Becquerel and Marie Curie. You can do it too!

For the experiment we use three rocks and a piece of black and white photographic paper. One of the rocks is a mineral called pitchblende. The other two can be any type of rock you can pick up from outside. We will perform our experiment in a dark room so that the photographic paper is not affected by light. We place the three rocks on the paper and let them sit in a dark room or in a lightproof box for 24 hours.

In a completely dark room or using a darkroom safelight, place an unexposed piece of photographic paper and three rocks inside a light tight box

Close the box for 24 hours
Do not move or disturb the box

24 Hours

1 PM: Day 1   1 PM: Day 2

In a completely dark room or using a darkroom safelight, remove the paper, develop and fix it using photographer's chemicals

After 24 hours we remove the rocks and develop the photographic paper. We notice there is an *image* under the pitchblende rock, as if the rock gave off its own light. Some type of energy must have made this image. What type of energy was it? Where did it come from?

The invisible energy that exposed the photographic paper comes from uranium in the pitchblende rock. The source of the energy is a sequence of nuclear reactions that occur in uranium. In this chapter we will study these reactions and learn how energy is released by nuclear reactions.

20.1 Nuclear Equations

Nuclear versus chemical reactions

Unlike chemical reactions, which only involve the outer electrons of atoms, nuclear reactions involve and affect the nuclei of atoms. Nuclear reactions can change an element into a different element. This change means that the number of protons and neutrons is altered during a nuclear reaction. Therefore, to represent a nuclear reaction we must explicitly indicate the number of protons and neutrons for each nucleus involved in the reaction.

Chemical reactions create new compounds from elements

Nuclear reactions create new elements from other elements

Representing nuclei

The symbols that we use to represent the atomic nucleus contain information about the number of protons and neutrons in the nucleus. The number of protons is represented by the **atomic number (Z)**. The number of neutrons is given by the **neutron number (N)**. The **mass number (A)** is the total number of protons and neutrons in a nucleus.

$$\text{mass number} \rightarrow A$$
$$\text{atomic number} \rightarrow Z \quad X \quad element$$

Atomic number (Z): number of protons in a nucleus

Neutron number (N): number of neutrons in a nucleus

Mass number (A): number of protons and neutrons, A = Z + N

The helium-4 nucleus contains two protons and two neutrons and it is represented by $_{2}^{4}\text{He}$.

The hydrogen nucleus contains one proton and no neutrons and it is represented by: $_{1}^{1}\text{H}$.

Nuclear symbols

The nuclear equation that represents the disintegration of uranium-238 $\left(_{92}^{238}\text{U}\right)$ into thorium-234 $\left(_{90}^{234}\text{Th}\right)$ and helium-4 $\left(_{2}^{4}\text{He}\right)$ is written as

$$_{92}^{238}\text{U} \rightarrow {}_{90}^{234}\text{Th} + {}_{2}^{4}\text{He}$$

Balanced nuclear equation

Like a chemical equation, a nuclear equation must also be balanced:

1. There must be mass number balance. The sum of the mass numbers on both sides of the equation must be equal.

2. There must also be charge conservation. The sum of the atomic numbers on both sides of the equation must be equal.

Mass number balance

| 238 | = | 234 | + 4 Protons + neutrons |

$$_{92}^{238}\text{U} \longrightarrow {}_{90}^{234}\text{Th} + {}_{2}^{4}\text{He}$$

Charge balance

| 92 | = | 90 | + 2 Protons |

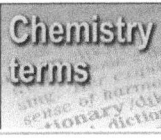

atomic number (Z): the number of protons in a nucleus.

neutron number (N): the number of neutrons in a nucleus.

mass number (A): the total number of protons and neutrons in a nucleus.

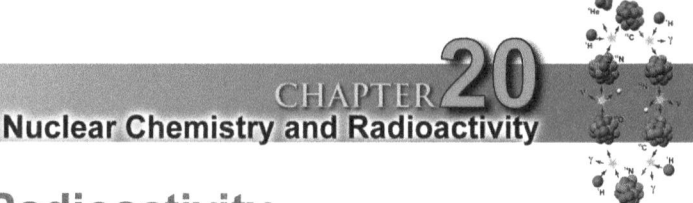

20.2 Nuclear Reactions: Radioactivity

Nuclear reactions can change one element into a different one. They can also change an isotope into a new isotope of the same element. Chemical reactions do not change the types of atoms involved. They only rearrange atoms to form different compounds.

Energy of nuclear reactions

Nuclear reactions involve much more energy than chemical reactions. The energy released by a chemical reaction is related to the rearrangement of the electronic structure of atoms, which involves electrical forces. For nuclear reactions, the energy released is related to the rearrangement of the atomic nucleus, which involves the strong nuclear force, the strongest force in the universe.

Reaction types

There are two main types of nuclear reactions:

1. Decay reactions, during which a nucleus spontaneously breaks up (disintegrates), and

2. Bombardment reactions, during which a nucleus is struck by another nucleus or some nuclear particle, such as a proton or a neutron.

Decay

Bombardment

Radioactivity

The four most common types of nuclear decay are alpha (α) decay, beta (β) decay, gamma (γ) decay, and positron emission (β⁺). The elements that decay by α, β, γ, or β⁺ decay are said to be radioactive. α, β, and positron emission release energy that is carried by particles. Gamma decay releases electromagnetic energy. Light, radio waves, microwaves and x rays are all forms of electromagnetic energy. **Radioactivity** is a general term used to describe the property of some elements to break up and release energy associated with matter or waves.

Alpha decay

helium

Beta decay

electron

Gamma decay

photon

Radiation

The transmission of energy, matter, or waves through space is called **radiation**. Radiation can be dangerous if it has high enough energy to break chemical bonds in molecules. Exposure to radiation over a long period of time can be harmful. Ultraviolet radiation from the Sun is an example of radiation that can be harmful to living organisms.

Chemistry terms

nuclear reactions: reactions that involve nuclei and that may change one element into another.

radioactivity: a process by which the nucleus of an atom spontaneously changes itself by emitting particles or energy.

radiation: the transmission of energy through space.

Intensity of radiation

ADVANCED AP

Intensity

The **intensity of radiation** measures how much energy flows per unit of area per second.

$$\text{intensity (W/m}^2) = \frac{\text{power (W)}}{\text{area (m}^2)} , \quad I = \frac{P}{A}$$

Intensity

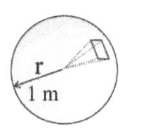

$$\underset{(W/m^2)}{\overset{intensity}{}} I = \frac{P \; power \; (W)}{A \; area \; (m^2)}$$

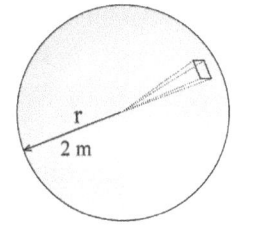

Area, $A = 4\pi r^2 = 12.6 \text{ m}^2$

Intensity, $I = \dfrac{100 \text{ W}}{12.6 \text{ m}^2}$
$\qquad\qquad = 7.96 \text{ W/m}^2$

On a clear day, the intensity of sunlight on the surface of the Earth is about 1,000 watts per square meter (W/m²). A good flashlight produces an intensity of about 100 W/m² in the brightest part of the beam at a distance of half a meter away.

Inverse square law

When radiation comes from a single point, the intensity decreases inversely over the square of the distance. This is called the **inverse square law**. If you get twice as far away from a radiation source, the intensity goes down by a factor of 1/4, which is one divided by the square of two ($1/4 = 1/2^2$). If you get 10 times farther away, the intensity goes down by a factor of 1/100 ($1/100 = 1/10^2$).

Area, $A = 4\pi r^2 = 50.4 \text{ m}^2$

Intensity, $I = \dfrac{100 \text{ W}}{50.4 \text{ m}^2}$
$\qquad\qquad = 1.99 \text{ W/m}^2$

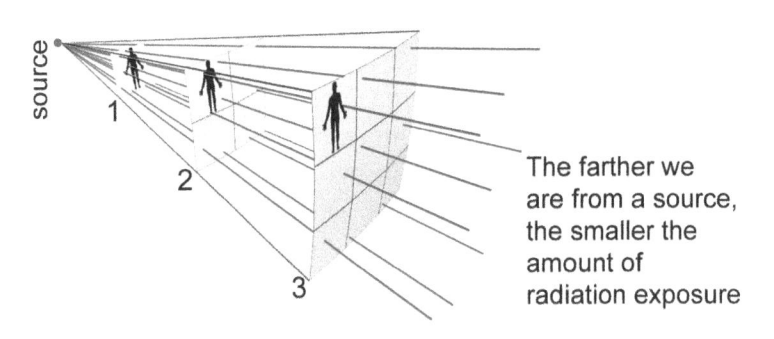

The farther we are from a source, the smaller the amount of radiation exposure

The inverse square law is a property of geometry. Think of a 100 W light bulb at the center of a sphere of radius *r*. The intensity at the surface of the sphere is 100 W divided by the area of the sphere ($4\pi r^2$). At twice the distance, the area of the sphere is four times greater. Since the same amount of power is spread over a larger area, the intensity goes down. Mathematically, the area goes up as the square of the radius, so the intensity goes down with the inverse square of the radius. This is the inverse square law.

Chemistry terms

intensity of radiation: the amount of energy that flows per unit area per time.

inverse square law: a law that states that the intensity of radiation emitted from a point source decreases inversely over the square of the distance.

A NATURAL APPROACH TO CHEMISTRY

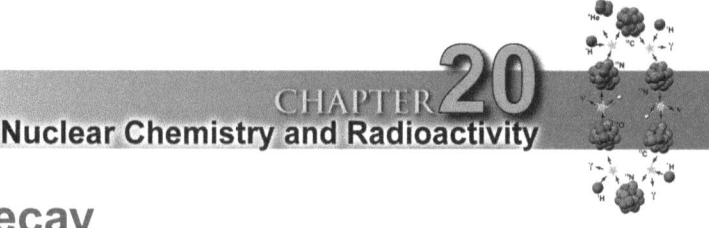

Decay reactions: alpha decay

Alpha decay

In **alpha decay** the original nucleus ejects two protons and two neutrons, which is the nucleus of helium-4 ($^4_2$He), also called an alpha (α) particle. During alpha decay the emitted radiation is also called **alpha radiation**, which is a fast moving $^4_2$He nucleus.

Uranium-238 decays by releasing an α particle ($^4_2$He) and thorium-234 ($^{234}_{90}$Th).

The original uranium atom is called the **parent nuclide**, and the thorium atom is called the **daughter nuclide**.

Alpha decay

⬤	Protons	Decrease by 2
⬤	Neutrons	Decrease by 2
	Atomic number	Decrease by 2
	Mass number	Decrease by 4

Parent → Daughter + He-4 nucleus

Alpha particles deposit their energy over small distances

When the α particle hits a molecule, it transfers energy to it and damages it. Damaged molecules in the cells of biological systems may result in cell death or the abnormal reproduction of cells. Since the α particles are very large, their ability to penetrate into matter is very limited. In fact α radiation can be stopped by a sheet of paper. However, an element that undergoes α decay is ingested, it is very dangerous. As the α source is carried throughout the body, the emitted α particles are in direct contact with the molecules in the cells of organs and can deposit their energy, causing great damage.

Solved problem

Write the complete nuclear equation for the α decay of the radium isotope $^{226}_{88}$Ra.

Relationships: *We need to find the type of the daughter nucleus X, the atomic number Z and the mass number A according to* $^{226}_{88}$Ra $\rightarrow ^{A}_{Z}$X $+ ^4_2$He

Solve: *First: Balance the atomic number and the mass number.*
By balancing the mass number, we obtain A = 222.
By balancing the atomic number, we obtain Z = 86.

Second: Look at the periodic table to determine the identity of the unknown daughter element.
Since the atomic number is 86, the daughter nuclide is radon (Rn).

Answer: *The complete α decay equation is* $^{226}_{88}$Ra $\rightarrow ^{222}_{86}$Rn $+ ^4_2$He

---

Chemistry terms

alpha decay: the decay that occurs when a nucleus emits a helium nucleus.
alpha radiation: the radiation associated with alpha decay.
parent nuclide: the original nucleus involved in a nuclear reaction.
daughter nuclide: the nucleus resulting from a nuclear reaction.

Beta decay

Beta decay

Beta decay is the process in which an unstable nucleus emits an electron. We know that the nucleus does not have any electrons in it. So where does the emitted electron during beta decay come from? It turns out that the electron is formed when a neutron in the nucleus changes into a proton and an electron. The radiation released during beta decay is called **beta radiation**.

Beta particles are electrons

Since the charge of the nucleus increases by +1 as the neutron changes to a proton, the formation of the electron, which has a charge of –1, maintains the overall charge of the nucleus. The electron released during beta decay is called a beta particle.

Beta decay
Nucleus converts a neutron to a proton

Parent → Daughter + $\ominus$ electron

The beta symbol is $_{-1}^{0}\text{e}$

The beta (β) particle is an electron. For consistency with the general nuclide symbol, and to help us with the balance of mass and atomic numbers, the β particle is written with the symbol $_{-1}^{0}\text{e}$.

$_{6}^{14}\text{C} \longrightarrow {}_{7}^{14}\text{N} + {}_{-1}^{0}\text{e}$

Parent → Daughter + $\ominus$ electron

Radium ($_{88}^{228}\text{Ra}$) could also decay by β decay according to $_{88}^{228}\text{Ra} \rightarrow {}_{89}^{228}\text{Ac} + {}_{-1}^{0}\text{e}$

Solved problem

Write the complete nuclear equation for the β decay of the radium isotope $_{88}^{228}\text{Ra}$.

Given: *The parent nuclide and the type of reaction*

Relationships: *We need to find the type of the daughter nucleus X, the atomic number Z and the mass number A according to* $_{88}^{228}\text{Ra} \rightarrow {}_{Z}^{A}\text{X} + {}_{-1}^{0}\text{e}$

Solve: *First: Balance the atomic number and the mass number.*
By balancing the mass number, we obtain A = 228.
By balancing the atomic number, we obtain 88 = Z – 1 or Z = 89.
Second: Look at the periodic table to determine the identity of the unknown daughter element.
The atomic number is 89; the daughter nuclide is actinium (Ac).

Answer: *The complete β decay equation is* $_{88}^{228}\text{Ra} \rightarrow {}_{89}^{228}\text{Ac} + {}_{-1}^{0}\text{e}$

Chemistry terms

beta decay: decay that occurs when an unstable nucleus releases an electron.
beta radiation: the radiation resulting from beta decay.

640

Gamma decay and positron emission

Gamma decay

Radioactive decay can also occur by the emission of electromagnetic radiation. **Gamma decay** (γ decay) occurs when an excited nucleus goes to a lower energy state by emitting high-energy electromagnetic radiation. The wavelength of this radiation is about 10^{-12} m. In some cases the emission of γ radiation, also called γ rays and denoted by $^{0}_{0}\gamma$, follows some other radioactive decay such as β decay or α decay.

Nucleus emits gamma radiation
and lowers its energy.

Gamma decay   Gamma
ray

●	Protons	Stay the same
●	Neutrons	Stay the same
	Atomic number	Stays the same
	Mass number	Stays the same

γ ray energy

The number of protons and neutrons does not change during γ decay. Gamma radiation has a high enough energy (greater than 10^{-13} J per disintegration) to break apart other atoms, making them dangerous to living organisms. The best way to stop γ rays is by using a thick shielding material made of lead or concrete.

The positron

The **positron**, denoted with the symbol $^{0}_{+1}e$ in nuclear equations, is a nuclear particle that has the same mass as the electron, but has a positive charge. Nuclear decay by **positron emission** occurs when an unstable nucleus emits a positron. In doing so it converts a proton into a neutron.

Nucleus converts a proton to a neutron

+ ⊕ positron

Positron emission

●	Protons	Decrease by 1
●	Neutrons	Increase by 1
	Atomic number	Decreases by 1
	Mass number	Stays the same

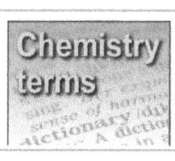
Solved problem

Determine the type of decay for the reactions

1. $^{234}_{90}\text{Th} \rightarrow {}^{234}_{90}\text{Th} + {}^{A1}_{Z1}X_1$ and 2. $^{95}_{43}\text{Tc} \rightarrow {}^{95}_{42}\text{Mo} + {}^{A2}_{Z2}X_2$

Asked: *Unknowns X_1 and X_2*

Given: *Mass and atomic numbers of the parent and daughter nuclides.*

Solve: *Balance the atomic numbers to find Z and mass numbers to find A:*

For reaction 1: 234 = 234 + A1, so A1 = 0; 90 = 90 + Z1, so Z1 = 0.

For reaction 2: 95 = 95 + A2, so A2 = 0; 43 = 42 + Z2, so Z2 = +1.

Answer: *For reaction 1, $^{A1}_{Z1}X_1 = {}^{0}_{0}X_1$, which denotes γ decay, so $^{A1}_{Z1}X_1 = {}^{0}_{0}\gamma$.*

For reaction 2, $^{A2}_{Z2}X_2 = {}^{0}_{+1}X_2$, which denotes positron decay,

so $^{A2}_{Z2}X_2 = {}^{0}_{+1}e$.

Chemistry terms

gamma decay: decay that occurs when a nucleus releases electromagnetic energy.

positron: a particle that has the same mass as the electron and positive charge.

positron emission: decay that occurs when a nucleus releases a positron.

20.3 Rate of Radioactive Decay

Carbon-14 ($^{14}_{6}C$) is an isotope of carbon that is produced when the neutrons generated by the cosmic rays (high energy radiation from the Sun and elsewhere in the universe) bombard nitrogen in the upper atmosphere:

$$^{1}_{0n}C + ^{14}_{7}N \rightarrow ^{14}_{6}C + ^{1}_{1}H$$

Carbon-14 ($^{14}_{6}C$)

Once a carbon-14 isotope is formed, it is oxidized into a $^{14}CO_2$ molecule, just like carbon-12, and it is taken up by plants during photosynthesis. In turn, carbon-14 enters the food chain when plants are consumed by animals. Even though $^{14}_{6}C$ is continuously generated, the fraction of carbon-14 to carbon-12 present in living organisms is constant at about 1 to 10^{12} $^{14}_{6}C$ to $^{12}_{6}C$ atoms.

Half-life

The reason for this constant ratio is that $^{14}_{6}C$ decays back to $^{14}_{7}N$ by β decay at a fixed rate. The rate at which an atom decays may be estimated by collecting a large number of them and then observing how many have remained after a certain period of time. The time that it takes for half of the initial atoms to disintegrate is called the **half-life** ($t_{1/2}$).

Radioactive decay of C-14

Half-life of carbon-14

The half life of $^{14}_{6}C$ is 5,730 years. For example, if we start with 1,000 carbon-14 atoms, after 5,730 years we will have 500 $^{14}_{6}C$ and 500 $^{14}_{7}N$ atoms. After another 5,730 years we will have 250 atoms of $^{14}_{6}C$, 750 $^{14}_{7}N$ atoms, and so on.

The half-lives of different isotopes vary greatly

Nuclide	Half-life	Decay type
$^{238}_{92}U$	4.5×10^9 years	alpha
$^{131}_{53}I$	8.05 days	beta
$^{18}_{9}F$	110 min	positron
$^{220}_{86}Rn$	55.6 s	alpha

Every radioactive element has a different half-life. Some of them, such as uranium-238 ($^{238}_{92}U$), have half-lives of billions of years. $^{238}_{92}U$ was created in the nuclear reactions of exploding stars, and it has been around since the formation of our Solar System. Others, such as iodine-131 ($^{131}_{53}I$), have half-lives measured in days. Some others, such as fluorine-18 ($^{18}_{9}F$) have half-lives of a couple of hours. The isotopes with short half-lives such as fluorine-18 do not occur naturally, and have to be generated in the laboratory.

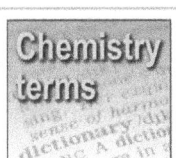

carbon-14: a radioactive isotope of carbon.

half-life: the time it takes for half of the atoms in a sample to decay.

A NATURAL APPROACH TO CHEMISTRY

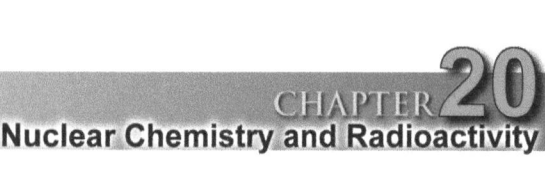

The mathematics of radioactive decay

ADVANCED AP

Rate of decay

The number of radioactive nuclei that decay per unit time, called the rate of decay, is directly proportional to the number of nuclei that are present in the first place. The number of decays per unit time is called the **rate of decay**, and it is given by:

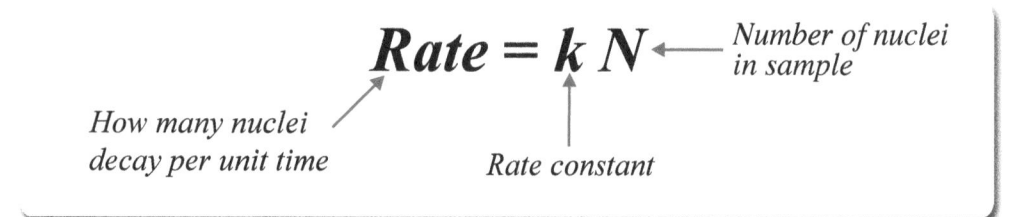

$$Rate = k\,N$$

Number of nuclei in sample

How many nuclei decay per unit time

Rate constant

Rate constant

The **rate constant** (k) is a parameter that describes how fast the radioactive nuclides decay. The rate constant k has the units [1/time] and is related to the half-life ($t_{1/2}$). The longer the half-life, the fewer radioactive decays will occur over a period of time and the smaller the rate constant.

- A short half-life implies a large rate constant.
- A long half-life implies a small rate constant.

The equation that relates k to $t_{1/2}$ is $t_{1/2} = 0.693/k$.

Solved problem

Carbon-14 and radium-220 have half-lives of 5,730 years and 1 minute (min), respectively. Calculate the rate constants for their decay, in units of 1/s.

Asked: *The rate constant k*

Given: *The half life $t_{1/2}$ for each radioactive decay process.*

Relationships: *The equation that relates $t_{1/2}$ to k: $k = 0.693/t_{1/2}$*

Solve: *For C-14, $t_{1/2} = 5730$ years and*

$$k = \frac{0.693}{5730\ year} \times \frac{1\ year}{365\ days} \times \frac{1\ day}{24\ h} \times \frac{1\ h}{60\ min} \times \frac{1\ min}{60\ s} = \frac{3.84 \times 10^{-12}}{s}$$

For Ra-220, $t_{1/2} = 1$ min and

$$k = \frac{0.693}{1\ min} \times \frac{1\ min}{60\ s} = \frac{1.155 \times 10^{-2}}{s}$$

Discussion: *Note that a small $t_{1/2}$ gives a large k. The rate constant k gives us an indication of the number of decays over a certain period of time.*

Chemistry terms

rate of decay: the number of radioactive decays per unit time.

rate constant: a number that describes how fast a radioactive nuclide decays.

Decay rate law

ADVANCED AP

Activity

The rate of decay of a radioactive sample is also called the **activity** of the sample. The activity of a sample is proportional to the number of nuclei present in the sample at any time. As time passes, the activity of radiation decreases since the number of parent nuclei decreases.

When making radioactive decay calculations, it is important to be able to answer the following question:

If we start with a radioactive sample that has a half-life $(t_{1/2})$ that initially contained N_0 nuclei, what is the number (N) of radioactive nuclei present in the sample after time t has passed?

The answer to this question is given by the equation $N = N_0 e^{-kt}$

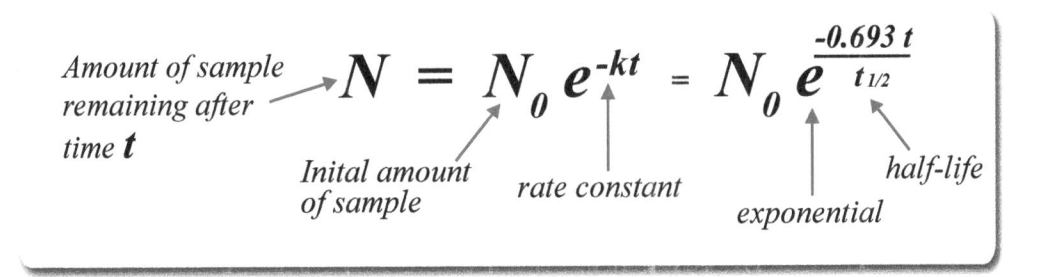

$$N = N_0 e^{-kt} = N_0 e^{\frac{-0.693\, t}{t_{1/2}}}$$

Amount of sample remaining after time t — Initial amount of sample — rate constant — exponential — half-life

The parameter e is the number 2.718, the base of the natural logarithm. This is one of the most important mathematical constants used in many areas of science and engineering.

Solved problem

Plutonium-236 decays by emitting an alpha particle and has a half-life of 2.86 years. If we start with 10 mg of Pu-236, how much remains after 4 years?

Asked: *Calculate N, the amount left after 4 years*

Given: *The half life $t_{1/2}$, the initial amount N_0, and the elapsed time t*

Relationships: *The equation that relates $t_{1/2}$ and N_0 to N is $= N_0 exp\left(-\frac{0.693t}{t_{1/2}}\right)$*

Solve: $N = 10 \text{ mg } 2.718^{\left(\frac{(-0.693)\,4 \text{ year}}{2.86 \text{ year}}\right)} = 3.79 \text{ mg}$

Discussion: *After 4 years, the initial 10 mg is reduced to 3.79 mg, which is 37.9% of the initial amount of Pu-236.*

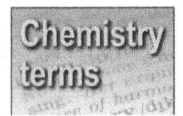

Chemistry terms

activity: the rate of decay of a radioactive sample.

A NATURAL APPROACH TO CHEMISTRY

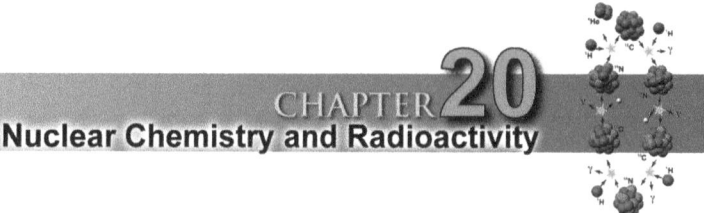

Carbon dating

$_{6}^{14}C$: Dating organic matter

Living things contain a large amount of carbon. The isotope carbon-14 ($_{6}^{14}C$) is used by archeologists to determine the age of things that were once alive. The ratio of carbon-14 to carbon-12 in the environment is a constant, determined by the balance between production and decay of carbon-14. As long as an organism is alive, it constantly exchanges carbon with the environment. Therefore, the ratio of carbon-14 to carbon-12 in the organism that is alive stays the same as in the environment.

When an organism dies, it stops exchanging carbon with the environment. All the carbon-12 in the organism remains because it is a stable isotope. Almost no new carbon-14 is created because most cosmic rays do not reach the ground. As the carbon-14 decays, the ratio of carbon-14 to carbon-12 slowly gets smaller with age. By measuring this ratio, an archeologist can tell how long it has been since the organism was alive. Carbon dating works reliably up to about 10 times the half-life, or 57,300 years. After 10 half-lives there is not enough carbon-14 left to measure accurately. Carbon dating only works on material that has once been living, including organic materials such as tissue, bone, or wood.

Dating non-organic matter

It is also possible to date nonliving matter by using other nuclear decay reactions. For example, the decay of uranium-238, which has a half-life of 4.5 billion years, has been used to determine the age of Earth.

How carbon dating works

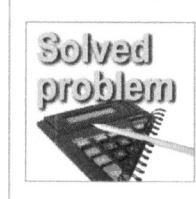
Solved problem

About 18% of the mass of a live animal is carbon. If 1 g of live bone contains about 90 billion carbon-14 atoms (half-life = 5,730 years), how many C-14 atoms remain in 1 g of bone 17,190 years after the animal dies?

Given: *The half-life and the number of carbon-14 atoms*

Solve: *Since 17,190 years is three half-lives, the initial amount must be reduced by a factor of $2 \times 2 \times 2 = 8$.*
90 billion / 8 = 11.25 billion.

Answer: *After three half-lives the amount of carbon-14 atoms is reduced by a factor of 8, from 90 billion to 11.25 billion.*

Applications of radioactive dating

 ADVANCED AP

Radiometric dating

The technique of dating archeological finds using carbon-14 was developed in 1949. Since then, this technique of radiometric dating has been a very important tool for archeology and other sciences.

A radiometric technique is also used by climate scientists who are working to understand the Earth's atmosphere over time. Scientists can measure the composition of the atmosphere over time by detecting differences in the concentration of oxygen isotopes ($_8^{18}O$ and $_8^{16}O$) that are present in ice cores and ocean sediments. This gives an indication of climate change over time. This is a very important area of research, as we are trying to understand how the release of various gases in the atmosphere could affect Earth's climate.

Geological dating

Scientists are also able to determine the age of rocks by measuring the ratio of Uranium–238 to Plutonium–239 that is present in the rock. Since uranium–238 decays with a half-life of 4.5 billion years, this technique allows geologists to determine the age of rocks that are billions of years old. The equation

$$N = N_o e^{-kt}$$

with $k = 0.693/t_{1/2}$ forms the basis for all calculations used in radiometric dating. If we know the half-life ($t_{1/2}$), the initial amount N_0, and the current amount N, then we can calculate the time t from the equation

$$t = -\ln \frac{N}{N_o}/k$$

Solved problem

An ancient Greek scroll written on an animal skin was discovered by archeologists in 2008. They isolated 10 g of it and measured the carbon-14 decay rate to be 111 disintegrations/minute. Calculate the age of the scroll. (Assume that living organisms have a carbon-14 decay rate of 15 disintegrations per minute per gram of C.)

Given: *The initial decay rate of C-14: N_0=15 disintegrations/(min·g).*
The present decay rate of C-14 is 11 dis/(min·g).
The half-life of C-14 is 5,730 years.

Solve: *The rate constant $k = 0.693/t_{1/2} = 0.693/5,730$ years*
$= 1.209 \times 10^{-4}$/years

and the time is $t = \dfrac{-\ln\dfrac{N}{N_0}}{k} = \dfrac{-\ln\dfrac{111}{150}}{1.209 \times 10^{-4}}$ *years* $= 2\ 491$ *years*

Discussion: *The animal skin on which the scroll was written was 2,491 years old It was written in about 483 BC.*

646

20.4 Nuclear Energy

Energy of nuclear reactions

For nuclear reactions, the energy released is related to the rearrangement of the atomic nucleus. The energy released by a chemical reaction is related to the rearrangement of the electronic structure of atoms. A chemical explosive such as dynamite results from a chemical reaction, and it is millions of times weaker than a nuclear explosion, which results from the rearrangement of nuclei.

Chemical reactions involve the electrons

Nuclear reactions involve the nucleus

Nuclear energy versus chemical energy

For example, the combustion of 1.0 g of carbon produces about 33 kJ of energy. By comparison, a nuclear reaction of 1.0 g of uranium produces about 8.2×10^7 kJ, more than 2 million times as much.

So where does this large amount of energy come from? We know that energy cannot be created out of nothing. It must be somehow stored in the nucleus. When a nuclear reaction occurs the nucleus is rearranged. As we have seen, the number of protons and neutrons in the nucleus changes. A result of this change is the release of energy.

Nuclear size and energy

The energy of the nucleus depends on the number of neutrons and protons that it has. In other words, it depends on the atomic number and the mass number. The nucleus with the lowest energy is iron-56 ($^{56}_{26}$Fe). Any nucleus that is larger or smaller than iron contains more energy per nucleon. **Nuclear energy** is released when the nuclear reaction produces a nucleus that is lower on the graph of energy.

Nuclear force and electro-magnetic force

The shape of the energy curve is caused by the competition between two forces that act on the protons and neutrons: the electromagnetic force, which causes protons to repel, and the strong nuclear force, which causes protons and neutrons to attract each other. Nuclei that are lighter or heavier than iron have more energy than iron because their nucleons are less tightly bound. You may think of the nuclei as trying to hold themselves together by balancing the electromagnetic force with the nuclear force. When they break up, either by bombardment or decay, they release some of the energy that they were using to hold themselves together.

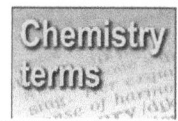

Chemistry terms

nuclear energy: the energy released during nuclear reactions.

Energy–mass equivalence

Mass and energy are related

The formula $E = mc^2$ is one of the most important formulas in science. It was developed by Albert Einstein in 1908, and it says that energy and mass are related.

$$\text{energy (J)} \longrightarrow E = mc^2 \quad \begin{array}{l} \text{mass (kg)} \\ \text{speed of light } (3 \times 10^8 \text{ m/s}) \end{array}$$

The equation tells us that for any mass (m) there is an associated energy (E), or for any energy (E) there is an associated mass (m).

If we consider the general chemical equation that represents an exothermic reaction:

$$\text{reactants} \rightarrow \text{products} + \text{energy}$$

we see that the amount of energy released must be related to the difference between the mass of the reactants and the mass of the products according to Einstein's formula:

$$\text{energy} = (\text{mass}_\text{reactants} - \text{mass}_\text{products})c^2$$

In other words, the change in mass ($\Delta m = \text{mass}_\text{reactants} - \text{mass}_\text{products}$) is related to the change in energy (ΔE) by

$$\Delta E = \Delta mc^2$$

As we have seen in Chapter 10, when carbon burns with oxygen it releases energy in the form of heat and light. Each mole of C, or 12 g of C, releases 393.5 kJ of energy:

$$C + O_2 \rightarrow CO_2 + 393.5 \text{ kJ/mole}$$

Even chemical reactions obey $E = mc^2$

The energy that is released by this chemical reaction is energy that is given off by the carbon and the oxygen. This energy is thus removed from the carbon–oxygen system. The loss of energy (change in energy) means that there should also be a loss of mass (change in mass). The total mass of C and O_2 is less than the mass of CO_2.

According to $\Delta E = \Delta mc^2$ the change in mass is:

$$\Delta m = \frac{\Delta E}{c^2} = \frac{3.935 \times 10^5 \text{ (kg} \cdot \text{m}^2/\text{s}^2)}{(3.0 \times 10^8 \text{ m/s})^2} = 4.37 \times 10^{-12} \text{ kg}$$

This mass of 4.37×10^{-12} kg or 4.37×10^{-9} g is a very small amount of matter, and it can't be detected even by the most accurate balance. However, the energy released by the reaction is very pronounced, and it is easily detected.

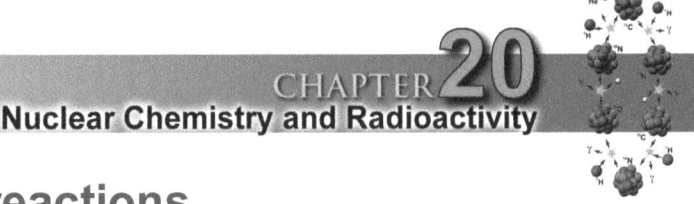
Mass change in nuclear reactions

The energy that is released during a nuclear reaction is related to a change in mass according to Einstein's formula.

We could for example create an oxygen nucleus in two different ways:

1. Combine 8 protons and 8 neutrons.
2. Combine $_2^4\text{He}$ with $_6^{12}\text{C}$ to obtain $_8^{16}\text{O}$.

Nuclear reactions change mass

Each one of these ways is a nuclear reaction. Let's calculate the energy that is released in both of these cases. In the first case, when we combine eight neutrons and eight protons, the difference in mass between them and the mass of the $_8^{16}\text{O}$ nucleus is:

$$8\ _1^1\text{H} + 8\ _0^1\text{n} \longrightarrow\ _8^{16}\text{O} + \text{energy}_1$$

$$\Delta m_1 = (\text{mass}_{8\ \text{neutrons}} + \text{mass}_{8\ \text{protons}} - \text{mass}\ _8^{16}\text{O})$$
$$= [(8 \times 1.0087) + (8 \times 1.0073) - 15.999]\ \text{amu} = 0.129\ \text{amu}$$

Although the molar mass for oxygen (15.999) includes the mass of the electrons, since the mass of the electrons is about 1/1,000th that of the protons, it is ignored in elementary calculations.

Mass is not conserved in nuclear reactions

When we combine $_2^4\text{He}$ with $_6^{12}\text{C}$, the difference in mass is

$$_2^4\text{He} + \ _6^{12}\text{C} \longrightarrow\ _8^{16}\text{O} + \text{energy}_2$$

$$\Delta m_2 = (\text{mass}\ _2^4\text{He} + \text{mass}\ _6^{12}\text{C} - \text{mass}\ _8^{16}\text{O})$$
$$= (4.0028 + 12.011 - 15.999)\text{amu}$$
$$= 0.015\ \text{amu}$$

So, since $\Delta m_1 / \Delta m_2 = \text{energy}_1 / \text{energy}_2$ and $\Delta m_1 / \Delta m_2 = 0.129 / 0.015 = 8.6$ it follows that $\text{energy}_1 = 8.6 \times \text{energy}_2$.

mass (amu)

16.128 — 8 $_1^1\text{H}$ + 8 $_0^1\text{n}$

This is the change in mass when He and C are formed from 8 protons and 8 neutrons

0.114 amu

Δm_1
0.129 amu

This is the change in mass when O is formed from neutrons and protons

16.014 — $_2^4\text{He}$ + $_6^{12}\text{C}$

Δm_2
0.015 amu

15.999 — $_8^{16}\text{O}$

This is the change in mass when O is formed from He and C

Nuclear energy

Let's look at the nuclear equation that represents the disintegration of radium-226 by α particle decay:

$$^{226}_{88}\text{Ra} \rightarrow {}^{222}_{86}\text{Rn} + {}^{4}_{2}\text{He}$$

From the periodic table we see that the masses of the nuclei involved in this reaction are 225.9771 amu (Ra), 221.9703 amu (Rn), and 4.0015 amu (He).

Therefore the change in mass that results from this reaction is

$$\Delta m = (225.9771 - 221.9703 - 4.0015)\ \text{g} = 0.0053\ \text{amu}$$

In grams the change in mass is:

$$0.0053\ \text{amu} \times 1.66 \times 10^{-27}\ \frac{kg}{amu} = 8.978 \times 10^{-30}\ \text{kg}$$

The energy associated with this change in mass is:

$$E = \Delta mc^2 = 8.798 \times 10^{-30}\ \text{kg}\ (3.0 \times 10^8\ \text{m/s})^2 = 7.92 \times 10^{-13}\ \text{J}$$

This is the change in energy for each Ra nucleus. To find the energy released for each mole of Ra, we just multiply by Avogadro's number (6.02×10^{23}).

We find that for each mole of Ra the energy released is 4.77×10^{11} J.

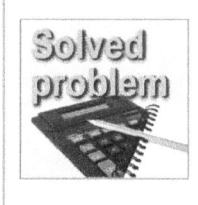
Solved problem

Calculate the energy released per mole of He-4 from the nuclear reaction

$$^{2}_{1}\text{H} + {}^{3}_{1}\text{He} \longrightarrow {}^{4}_{2}\text{He} + {}^{1}_{0}\text{n}$$
2.0134   3.0149   4.0015   1.0073 amu

Given: *The nuclear reaction and the molar mass of the nuclei involved*

Relationships: $E = \Delta mc^2$

Solve: *Calculate the change in mass (Δm):*
$\Delta m = (2.0134 + 3.0149 - 4.0015 - 1.0073)$ amu $= 0.0195$ amu
Convert amu to grams:
Molar mass in grams is equal to the nucleus mass in amu.
Therefore the change in mass for each mole of He-4 is
$\Delta m = 0.0195$ g and 0.0195 g $= 1.95 \times 10^{-5}$ kg
$E = \Delta mc^2 = 1.95 \times 10^{-5}$ kg $(3.00 \times 10^8$ m/s$)^2 = 1.76 \times 10^{12}$ J

Answer: *The energy released by this reaction is 1.76×10^{12} J per mole of helium (4 g of helium release 1.76×10^{12} J).*

Discussion: *This is one of the reactions that takes place in the Sun. The energy released is in the form of kinetic energy of the nuclei. Since hydrogen is lighter than He-4, it has most of the energy and moves faster.*

Nuclear binding energy

Binding energy   When protons and neutrons are combined to form oxygen, the mass changes. The mass of the oxygen nucleus is less than the total mass of the separated protons and neutrons. The energy that is released as a result of this change in mass is called the **binding energy**. The larger the binding energy, the tighter the nucleons are bound together.

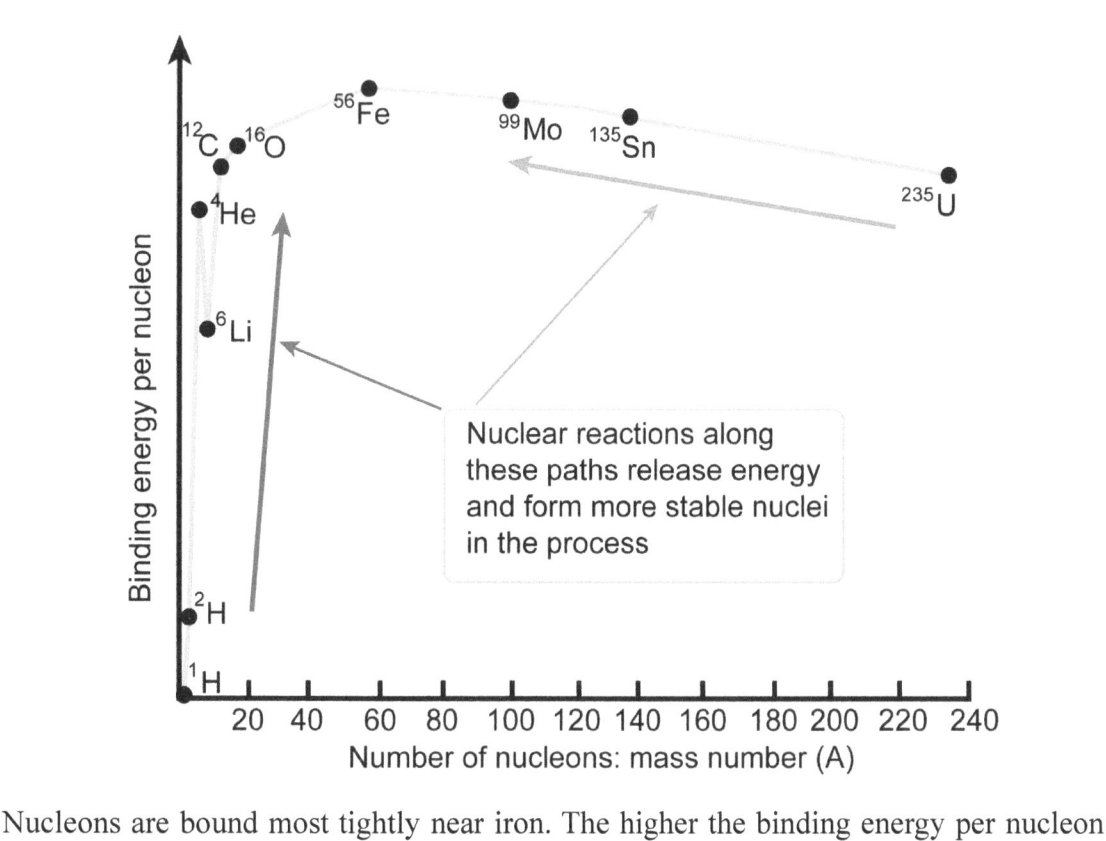

Iron is the most   Nucleons are bound most tightly near iron. The higher the binding energy per nucleon
stable element   (BE/n), the greater the stability of the nucleus. Iron, which has the highest binding energy per nucleon, is the most stable element. This is why iron is such an abundant element.

We can't get any nuclear energy out of iron. This is because the nucleons (protons and neutrons) in iron have the highest binding energy. Any other nucleus is less tightly bound. We can only get energy from nuclei to the left or to the right of iron.

High binding energy per nucleon

More stable nucleus

Less energy in the nucleus

Chemistry terms   **binding energy:** the energy that keeps nucleons inside a nucleus together.

Fission reactions

Fission reaction

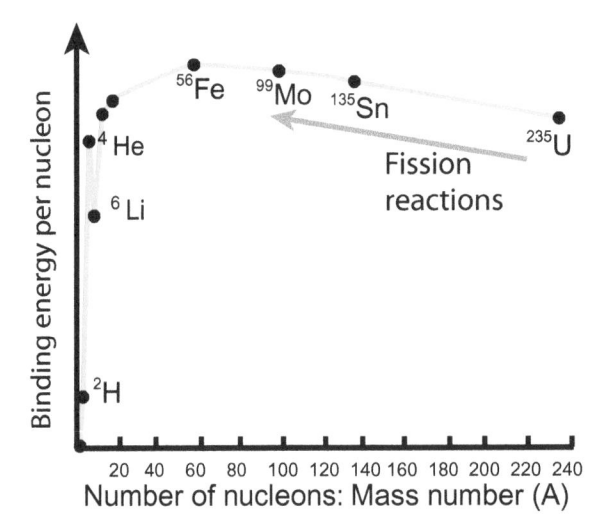

A **fission reaction** splits up a large nucleus into smaller pieces. For elements heavier than iron, breaking the nucleus into smaller pieces releases nuclear energy. For example, if a uranium nucleus is split, we end up with smaller nuclei.

These smaller nuclei have lower mass numbers, and their nucleons are bound tighter than the nucleons in the uranium nucleus. The energy that is released is equal to the difference in the binding energies of the uranium and the products of the reaction.

When $^{235}_{92}U$ is bombarded with a neutron ($^{1}_{0}n$) it fissions according to

$$^{1}_{0}n + ^{235}_{92}U \rightarrow ^{99}_{42}Mo + ^{135}_{50}Sn + 2^{1}_{0}Sn + energy$$

This is a bombardment reaction, and it happens when a neutron hits the nucleus with enough energy to make the nucleus unstable. The unstable nucleus then breaks up, or "fissions," into two smaller pieces and releases two neutrons.

Fission energy

Some of the fission energy released by the reaction appears as gamma rays, and some appears as kinetic energy of the smaller nuclei and the two neutrons.

Fission products

When a kilogram of $^{235}_{92}U$ fissions it releases 98 trillion J of energy. This amount of energy from a piece of uranium the size of a golf ball is enough to drive an average car 19 million miles! The by-products of this reaction are the $^{99}_{42}Mo$ and $^{135}_{50}U$ nuclei, which are called the **fission products**.

$$n + U^{235} \longrightarrow Mo^{99} + Sn^{135} + 2n$$
$$+ energy$$

+123 TJ	Energy of U nucleus
−25 TJ	Average energy of nuclei of Mo and Sn
+98 TJ	Energy released by fission of U into Mo and Sn

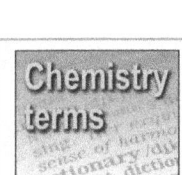

Chemistry terms

fission reaction: a reaction in which a large nucleus is split into smaller nuclei.
fission products: the smaller nuclei released when a large nucleus undergoes nuclear fission.

Energy from fission reactions

Chain reaction

A **chain reaction** occurs when the fission of one nucleus triggers fission of many other nuclei. In a chain reaction, the first fission reaction releases two (or more) neutrons. The two neutrons hit two other nuclei and cause two more fission reactions that release four neutrons in total. The four neutrons hit four new nuclei and cause fission reactions that release eight neutrons, and so on.

The number of neutrons increases rapidly. The increasing number of neutrons causes more nuclei to have fission reactions and enormous energy is released. This is the basic energy release mechanism that takes place in the cores of nuclear reactors.

The fission chain reaction

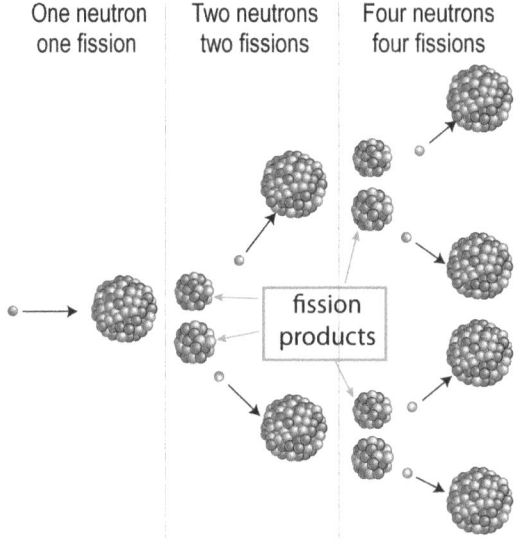

Nuclear power plants

In a **nuclear power plant**, the $^{235}_{92}U$ fission reaction is used to generate electricity. The process of getting electricity from nuclear reactions takes many steps. First, nuclear reactions in uranium produce heat in the reactor core. The heat is carried by high-pressure hot water into a steam generator. Heat in the steam generator boils water and makes steam. The steam turns a turbine. In the last step, the turbine is connected to an electric generator that makes electricity. Finally the steam is condensed and pumped back to the steam generator.

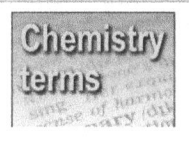
chain reaction: term used to describe when the neutrons produced in one fission reaction cause more fission reactions to take place, releasing yet more neutrons.
nuclear power plant: a reactor that creates electricity using a nuclear chain reaction.

Fusion reactions

Fusion
reactions

Fusion energy
from the Sun

A **fusion reaction** is a nuclear reaction that combines, or "fuses," two smaller nuclei into a larger nucleus. Fusion reactions can release a very large amount of energy. The Sun and other stars make their energy from fusion reactions. The temperature at the core of the sun is about 15 million degrees Celsius. Its density is so high that a tablespoon of the Sun weighs more than a ton. The primary fusion reaction that happens in the Sun combines hydrogen nuclei to make helium, converting two protons and two electrons into two neutrons along the way. All of the energy reaching Earth from the Sun comes from fusion reactions in the Sun's core.

Fusion
reactions
release a lot
of energy

For example, two carbon-12 (C-12) nuclei can fuse together to create a magnesium-24 (Mg-24) nucleus according to $C^{12} + C^{12} \rightarrow Mg^{24}$ + energy. The nucleons in the Mg nucleus are bound more tightly than the nucleons in carbon-12. The magnesium-24 nucleus has a lower energy. If the nuclei in a kilogram of carbon are combined to form magnesium, about 56 trillion joules of energy is released.

Fusion
reactions need
very high
temperatures

It is difficult to make fusion reactions occur because positively charged nuclei repel each other. The attraction from the strong nuclear force has a very short reach. Two nuclei must get very close for the attractive strong force to overcome the repulsive electric force. If the temperature is high enough, nuclei slam together with enough energy to almost touch, allowing the strong force to take over and lead to a fusion reaction. Temperatures greater than 10 million degrees Celsius are required for nuclei to get close enough for fusion reactions.

+104 TJ	Energy of C nucleus
-48 TJ	Energy of Mg nucleus
+56 TJ	Energy released by the fusion of 1 kg of C into Mg

Chemistry terms

fusion reaction: a nuclear reaction where two small nuclei are fused under conditions of high temperature and pressure, creating a large nucleus and vast amounts of energy.

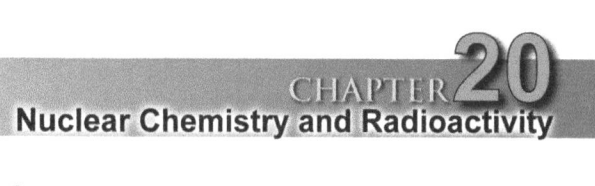
Energy from fusion reactions

Using nuclear energy

Today about 20% of electric power in the United States comes from nuclear fission plants. In some other countries such as France, 75% of their electricity comes from nuclear fission power. Nuclear fission is an energy source that does not use any fossil fuels, and thus it does not generate carbon dioxide or other air pollutants. However, it does generate highly radioactive waste.

Issues with nuclear energy

Even though the volume of waste generated by nuclear reactors is small, its radiation intensity is very high, making it extremely dangerous. In addition, the half-life of this radioactive waste is very long, meaning it must be safely stored for a long time.

Fusion: the future of nuclear energy

In the future it might be possible to use the energy from fusion reactions to generate electricity. Fusion reactions have all the benefits of fission, and in addition they generate a much smaller amount of waste. It is a very challenging thing to do since we have to create conditions found in the Sun to make fusion reactions possible.

Fusion fuel comes from seawater

The basic fuels for fusion energy are hydrogen isotopes. The nuclear reaction between deuterium ($_{1}^{2}H$), which is an isotope of hydrogen with one neutron, and tritium ($_{1}^{3}H$), which is an isotope of hydrogen with two neutrons, form the most basic fusion reaction:

$$_{1}^{2}H + _{1}^{3}H \rightarrow _{2}^{4}He + _{0}^{1}n + \text{energy}$$

Notice that the only by-products of this reaction are helium and a neutron. The reaction uses tritium, which is a highly radioactive but short-lived isotope ($t_{1/2}$ = 12.3 years). Tritium does not occur naturally, but it can be produced from lithium, which is a very common element on Earth. Deuterium is found naturally in sea water.

Nuclear fusion is in many ways an ideal energy source, since it uses inexpensive, abundant fuel and it generates little harmful waste. However, it is very difficult to build a fusion reactor capable of generating electricity. One difficulty is heating the deuterium and tritium fuel to more than 50 million degrees Celsius, about five times hotter than the core of the sun. Fusion fuel, in the form of a hot plasma, must be contained in a magnetic force field and kept isolated from solid materials. The tokamak reactor is the most successful experimental fusion reactor yet constructed.

20.5 Biological Effects of Radiation

Radioactivity is a dangerous natural phenomenon

Radioactivity is a natural phenomenon that can be both dangerous and useful. Exposure to a large amount of radiation can damage biological tissues. The damage could range from genetic defects, to increased cancer risk, to death. However, the use of controlled radiation sources can be a very useful tool for the diagnosis and treatment of many diseases.

Ionization

Ionizing radiation

Nonionizing radiation

The process by which radiation affects biological tissues is based on the principle of **ionization** of atoms. An atom is ionized when electrons are knocked out of their orbits. The energy that is required to remove electrons from their orbits comes from radiation. When the radiation energy is high enough to knock electrons out of their orbits, it is called **ionizing radiation**. When the energy is not high enough, it is called **non-ionizing radiation**.

Chemical bonds and radiation

Chemical bonds, which form by sharing or exchanging electrons, are affected when electrons are knocked out of their orbits. When the chemical bonds of biological molecules such as DNA break, the biological function of the molecule is affected. The human body and other biological systems have evolved to deal with low-level damage caused by naturally occurring low-level radiation.

Non-ionizing radiation
Energy is absorbed by electrons

Ionizing radiation
Energy is enough to knock electrons out of the atom

Radiation protection
-Shield
-Distance
-Time

There are several ways to protect ourselves when working with radioactive materials:

1. Use a shield such as lead to block the radiation. The radiation energy is absorbed by the shield and not by our body.

2. Limit the amount of time that we are close to a radiation source by working efficiently and quickly.

3. Keep as large a distance as we can from the radiation source. Because of the inverse square law, increasing the distance by a factor of 3 decreases the exposure by 89%.

$$\left(1 - \frac{1}{3^2}\right) \cdot 100 = 89$$

Chemistry terms

ionization: the process of removing one or more electrons from an atom.

ionizing radiation: radiation with high enough energy to remove electrons from their orbits.

non-ionizing radiation: radiation that cannot cause ionization of atoms.

Radiation units: dose

Radiation dose

A **dose** of radiation refers to the amount of radiation absorbed by the body. The units for measuring radiation dose are the **rad** and the **rem**.

rad

The *rad* corresponds to 0.01 J of energy absorbed by 1 kg of body tissue:

$$1 \ rad = 0.01 \ \text{J/kg body tissue}$$

rem

The *rem* measures the effectiveness of radiation in causing biological damage. For example, α radiation has a much higher biological effectiveness compared to γ radiation. The reason for this is that alpha radiation is absorbed over a very short distance. This results in a very concentrated energy deposition, which in turn gives a large number of ionizations. A large number of ionizations gives a large number of damaged tissue molecules. By comparison, γ radiation of the same initial energy travels much further before it is absorbed by the tissue. This means that the energy of the radiation is spread over a longer path. The longer path means lower energy density, fewer ionizations, and fewer damaged molecules.

Average annual radiation exposure mrem/year	
Radiation source	**Dose**
Ground	30
Inhaled source	200
Medical	50
Consumer products	10
Body	35
Space	25
Total	**350**

α radiation is 20 times more damaging than β or γ radiation

Alpha radiation, compared to β and γ radiation, is 20 times more effective at causing biological damage. The rem is obtained by multiplying the dose in rads by a number that is related to effectiveness of each radiation at causing biological damage.

The average annual radiation exposure for a person is about 350 mrem, or 0.35 rem. Most of this radiation comes from natural sources. People are exposed to different amounts of radiation depending on their occupation and where they live. For example, a pilot that flies at 10,000 m for 10 hours is exposed to the same amount of radiation as a person on the ground would be exposed to in 200 days.

People who work around radiation sources carry special monitors that measure their exposure to radiation. These monitors are checked regularly to make certain that the total amount of radiation exposure does not exceed a maximum allowable limit. In general, the limit for all occupations is that the total radiation dose should be below 5 rem/year.

Chemistry terms

dose: refers to the amount of radiation absorbed by the body.

rad: a measure of the energy absorbed by tissue or other biological material.

rem: unit of radiation dose that is weighted for its effect on body tissue.

Nuclear medicine: positron emission tomography

Some of the greatest contributions of nuclear technology are in the area of medical diagnosis and treatment. Nuclear scientists have developed a number of techniques that give medical doctors a way to look inside the human body and diagnose a number of diseases, from cancer tumors to broken bones. Recently, nuclear techniques have also been used in mapping the functions of the brain and other organs as we try to understand conditions such as Alzheimers', Parkinson's, and vascular diseases.

In general, the use of radioactivity in medical diagnosis can be sorted into two categories:

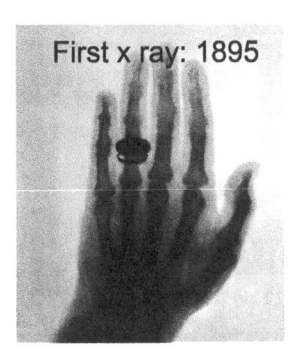

First x ray: 1895

1. *Detect the change in absorption* of radioactivity as it goes through the body.

2. *Map the location* inside the body where radioactivity was released.

The traditional x ray works by detecting the change in the absorption of the radioactivity as it passes through various parts of the body. Dense tissues and bone attenuate x rays more than soft tissues. This is a great technique, and it has been used since its discovery in 1895 by Professor Wilhelm Roentgen.

Modern techniques such as computed tomography (CT) and positron emission tomography (PET) are at the forefront of medical diagnosis. CT is based on the principle of radiation absorption, and it has the ability to create three-dimensional images, which are very useful in detecting structural abnormalities in the body.

PET technology was first demonstrated in 1976, and since then it has become one of the most important tumor diagnostic tools. Early and precise diagnosis of cancerous tumors is the best first step in treating such conditions.

positron-electron annihilation generates two γ-rays

e⁻

γ

e⁺

γ

positron decay

$$^{18}_{9}F \longrightarrow {}^{18}_{8}O + e^{+}$$

γ-ray detectors

PET is based on the decay of certain nuclei by positron emission. As we have learned, a positron is a nuclear particle that has the same mass as an electron but a positive charge. The positron is the antimatter counterpart of the electron.

When a positron and an electron come into contact, they immediately "disappear" or annihilate each other. Since energy and mass are related by Einstein's equation, the mass of the electron and the positron is converted into energy. This energy appears as two γ ray photons traveling in opposite directions.

The PET imaging method is based on the detection of these γ ray photons and their precise mapping in the body.

658

Scientists had to overcome many challenges in order to develop PET technology:

1. They had to understand the details of nuclear decay and position emission.
2. They had to understand the interaction between the positron and the electron.
3. They had to deal with major mathematical and technological challenges such as
   - developing the complicated mathematics required to be able to create an image from the detection of the γ rays,
   - creating the nuclear isotopes that have the appropriate half-lives, and
   - constructing the machine to perform all of these operations.

To achieve these goals many chemists, physicists, and engineers worked for many years.

PET uses the radioisotope fluorine-18 ($^{18}_{9}F$), which has a half-life of 110 minutes. Since the half-life of 110 minutes is relatively short, $^{18}_{9}F$ does not exist naturally, and so it has to be produced in the lab.

The production is done by hitting target oxygen-18 nuclei ($^{18}_{8}O$) with protons obtained in an accelerator. The complete nuclear reaction is:

$$^{1}_{1}H + ^{18}_{8}O \rightarrow ^{18}_{9}F + ^{1}_{0}n$$

The relatively short half-life of the $^{18}_{9}F$ isotope means that it has to be produced close to the hospital where it is used.

Once the $^{18}_{9}F$ isotope is produced, it is then attached to a glucose molecule and injected into the bloodstream. The glucose molecule and the attached $^{18}_{9}F$ isotope are taken up by cells, concentrating in cells with higher activity such as brain and tumor cells.

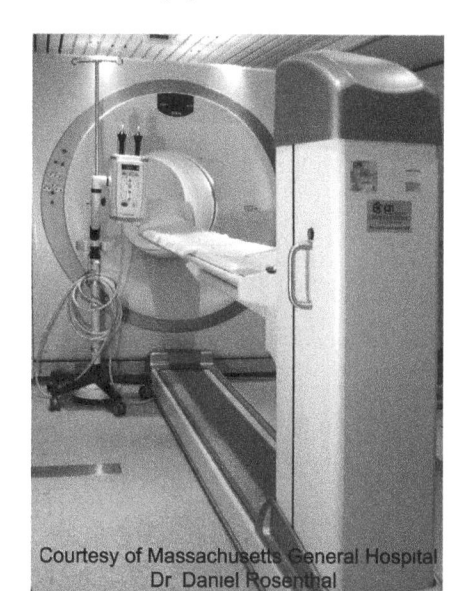

Courtesy of Massachusetts General Hospital
Dr. Daniel Rosenthal

PET   PET-CT

Courtesy of Massachusetts General Hospital
Dr. Daniel Rosenthal

PET images have a very high resolution, and so doctors are able to see details in the range of millimeters.

The combination of PET and CT technologies gives doctors the ability to detect and observe even finer details at every part of the body as shown on the images on the left.

Nuclear technologies such as these help save lives every day.

Chapter 20 Review

Vocabulary

Match each word to the sentence where it best fits.

Section 20.1

atomic number	mass number balance
neutron number	nuclear charge
mass number	

1. The total number of protons and neutrons in a nucleus is called the _____.

2. The number of protons in a nucleus is given by the _____.

3. The _____ gives the number of neutrons in a nucleus.

4. Balanced nuclear equations must conserve _____.

5. There must be _____ in balanced nuclear equations.

Section 20.2

nuclear reactions	daughter nuclide
radioactivity	beta decay
radiation	beta radiation
intensity	gamma decay
inverse square law	positron
alpha decay	positron emission
parent nuclide	

6. The nuclear particle that has the same mass as the electron and a positive charge is called a/an _____.

7. During _____, the nucleus releases a helium nucleus.

8. _____ can change one element into a different element.

9. The transmission of energy through space is called _____.

10. The decrease of radiation intensity with distance is given by the _____.

11. The original nucleus in a nuclear reaction is called the _____.

12. _____ measures how much energy flows per unit area per unit time.

13. The Th-234 nucleus resulting from the alpha decay of U-238 is called the _____.

14. When an unstable nucleus emits an electron, we say that it undergoes _____.

15. _____ is released during beta decay.

16. When a nucleus undergoes _____, it releases electromagnetic radiation.

17. When a nucleus decays by the emission of a positron, it undergoes _____ decay.

18. _____ describes the property of some elements to break up and release energy.

Section 20.3

carbon-14	carbon dating
half-life	rate constant
rate of decay	activity

19. The number of radioactive decays per unit time is called the _____.

20. _____ is an isotope of carbon.

21. The parameter that describes how fast a radio-active nuclide decays is called the _____.

22. The rate of decay of a radioactive element is called the _____ of the element.

23. _____ is a technique used to determine the age of organic materials.

24. The time that it takes for the amount of a pure radioactive substance to decrease by one half is called the _____.

Section 20.4

nuclear energy	fission reaction fission
mass–energy equivalence	products chain reaction
	nuclear power plant
mass change	fusion reaction
binding energy	

25. The by-products of a fission reaction are called _____.

26. Einstein's formula $E = mc^2$ is an expression of _____.

27. The energy of the Sun comes from _____.

28. The energy that is released as a result of the change in mass during a nuclear reaction is called _____.

29. A/An _____ splits up a large nucleus into smaller pieces.

30. The energy that is released during nuclear reactions results from the _____ between the reactants and the products of the reaction.

31. A nuclear _____ occurs when the fission of one nucleus triggers many other fission reactions.

32. The energy generated by a/an _____ comes from fission reactions.

33. Nuclear reactions release _____.

Section 20.5

ionization	dose
ionizing radiation	rad
nonionizing	rem

34. The _____ is a dose unit that measures the effectiveness of radiation in causing biological damage.

35. _____ happens when radiation ejects electrons out of their orbits.

36. Radiation that induces ionization is called _____.

37. The _____ is a unit of measuring radiation, corresponding to 0.01 J of energy absorbed by 1 kg of body mass.

38. The amount of radiation absorbed by our body is called the _____.

39. _____ radiation does not have enough energy to induce ionization.

Conceptual Questions

Section 20.1

40. Describe the differences between chemical and nuclear reactions.

41. Describe the procedure for balancing nuclear equations.

42. How do we describe atomic nuclei? How do we represent the atomic nucleus?

Section 20.2

43. What are the two major types of nuclear reactions?

44. Give four examples of decay reactions.

45. Which nuclear decay reactions release energy in the form of particles?

46. Which nuclear decay reactions release energy in the form of electromagnetic radiation?

47. Why do nuclear reactions release much more energy than chemical reactions?

48. How does the intensity of radiation decrease with distance from the source?

49. Describe the general nuclear equation that represents alpha decay.

50. Describe how the energy released during alpha decay is distributed among the various particles involved in the reaction.

Chapter 20 Review

51. What are the similarities and differences between alpha decay and beta decay?

52. Describe what happens to a nucleus during gamma decay.

53. Compare and contrast beta decay and positron emission.

Section 20.3

54. Describe the concept of half-life. Explain what happens to a radioactive sample after one half-life.

55. Why is carbon-14 useful for dating archeological artifacts?

56. What is the rate of decay, and how is it related to activity?

Section 20.4

57. Give a general explanation for the source of nuclear energy.

58. Explain each symbol in Einstein's equation and describe how it is used in making nuclear energy calculations.

59. What is binding energy, and how is it related to the energy that is released in a nuclear reaction?

60. Why do fission reactions release energy?

61. What is the form of the energy released during fission reactions?

62. Describe the operation of a nuclear power plant.

63. What are the differences and similarities between a fission reaction and a fusion reaction?

64. Why is it difficult to create fusion reactions?

Section 20.5

65. Why is radiation harmful to biological systems?

66. What happens when radiation interacts with the DNA in our cells?

67. How do we protect ourselves when working with radioactive materials?

68. How do we measure the amount of radiation absorbed by our body?

Quantitative Problems

Section 20.1

69. Balance the following nuclear equations:

   a. $^{238}_{92}U \rightarrow ? + ^{4}_{2}He$

   b. $? \rightarrow ^{217}_{85}At + ^{4}_{2}He$

Section 20.2

70. A radiation source releases 1,000 W from one point. What is the intensity of radiation 4 meters from the point and 8 meters from the point?

71. A person stands at a distance of 2 m from a source of radiation that releases 100 J/s. What is the intensity of radiation experienced by the person?

72. Write the complete nuclear equation for the alpha decay of each isotope:

   a. $^{237}_{93}Np$

   b. $^{230}_{90}Th$

   c. $^{210}_{84}Po$

   d. $^{220}_{86}Rn$

73. Complete the following nuclear equations:

   a. $^{241}_{95}Am \rightarrow ^{237}_{93}Np + ?$

   b. $^{19}_{11}Na \rightarrow ^{19}_{10}Ne + ?$

   c. $^{15}_{8}O \rightarrow ? + ^{0}_{+1}e$

Section 20.3

74. Iodine-131 decays with beta decay and has a half life of 8.02 days.

   a. If we start out with a sample that contains 10 g, how many grams are left after 16.04 days?

   b. How many beta decays occur in 8.02 days?

75. Potassium-40 has a rate constant of $k = 5.3 \times 10^{-10}$ years. Calculate its half-life.

76. If we have a sample of potassium-40 that contains 10×10^{10} atoms, how many of these nuclei will decay in one second?

77. What percentage of C-14 ($t_{1/2} = 5{,}730$ years) in a sample remains after 3,000 years? What is the percentage after 20,000 years?

78. The half-life of tritium is 12.3 years. What is the rate constant?

79. Krypton-85 (Kr-85) decays with a half-life of 10.8 years. If we start out with 10 mg of Kr-85, how much would remain after 20 years?

80. A sample that contains Fe-59 is measured with a radiation counter. It is measured to decay at about 11 decays per minute. After 20 days the same sample is measured to decay at about 8 decays per minute. Calculate the half-life of Fe-59 in days.

81. An archeologist finds an ancient bone. After cleaning it, she isolates 5 g and measures the C-14 decay rate to be about 22 disintegrations per minute. What is the age of the bone? (Living organisms have a C-14 decay rate of about 15 disintegrations/minute/g of carbon. You may assume that 80% of the bone is made of carbon.)

82. A paleontologist analyzes a sample of pure carbon by detecting the C-14 decays and finds the data shown on this table:

Time (min)	Counts
0	0
10	125
20	275
30	370
40	529
50	632
60	750

Use your graphing calculator to plot these data and calculate the count rate (counts per minute). If the weight of her sample is 94 g, what is the age of the sample? (Living organisms have a C-14 decay rate of about 15 disintegrations/minute/g of C)

Section 20.4

83. By using Einstein's equation, calculate how much energy would be released if we convert 1 g of mass into energy.

84. How much energy in joules would be released if we convert:
   a. the mass of one electron into energy?
   b. the mass of one proton into energy?

85. Every second the Sun releases about 4×10^{26} joules of energy. How much mass is lost each second?

86. Calculate the nuclear binding energy per nucleon for the following nuclei:

   a. $^{2}_{1}H$ (atomic mass = 2.0135 amu)

   b. $^{7}_{3}Li$ (atomic mass = 7.0160 amu)

   c. $^{16}_{8}O$ (atomic mass = 15.9949 amu)

   d. $^{58}_{28}Ni$ (atomic mass = 57.9353 amu)

   e. $^{129}_{54}Xe$ (atomic mass = 128.9048 amu)

   f. Which of these nuclei is the most stable?

87. Calculate the energy released when 1.0 g of deuterium ($^{2}_{1}H$) reacts with 1.0 g of tritium ($^{3}_{1}H$) according to the reaction:

$$^{3}_{1}H + ^{2}_{1}H \rightarrow ^{4}_{2}He + ^{1}_{0}n$$

The atomic masses of the reactants and products are as follows

$^{2}_{1}H = 2.0134$ amu, $^{3}_{1}H = 3.0149$ amu

$^{4}_{2}He = 4.0015$ amu, $^{1}_{0}n = 1.0073$ amu

88. Calculate the energy released for each $^{4}_{2}He$ nucleon produced in the reaction:

$$^{6}_{3}Li + ^{1}_{0}n \rightarrow ^{4}_{2}He + ^{3}_{1}H$$

The masses of the reactants and products are

$^{6}_{3}Li = 6.0151$ amu, $^{1}_{0}n = 1.0073$ amu

$^{4}_{2}He = 4.0015$ amu, $^{3}_{1}H = 3.0149$ amu

Section 20.5

89. A 1 kg sample exposed to a source emitting beta radiation absorbs 0.2 J of energy. What is the dose in rads?

90. A 70 kg person is exposed to 10 rad of radiation. How much energy in joules is absorbed by the person's body?

91. A laboratory mouse weighing 35 g is exposed to 10 rad of radiation. How much energy in joules is absorbed by the mouse's body?

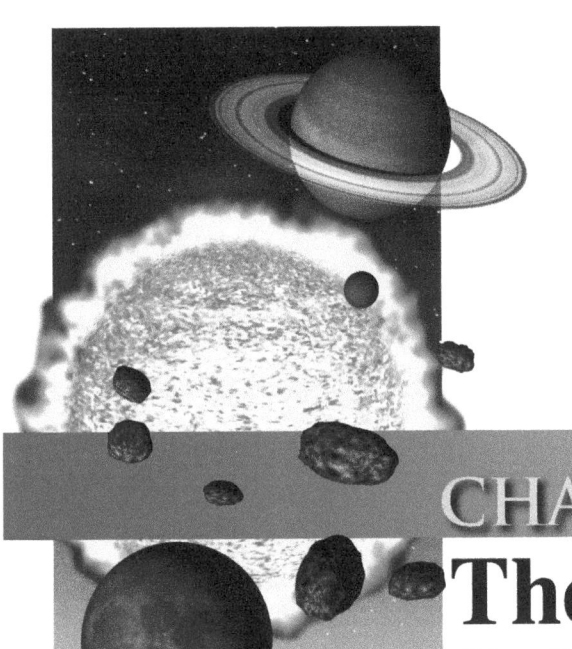

CHAPTER 21

The Chemistry of the Solar System

What kinds of chemistry occur in the Sun and on other planets?

How do we know the universe is similar everywhere?

What can chemistry tell us about the possibility of life outside of Earth?

What is the Sun? Is it literally a ball of fire as believed by many ancient peoples? On Earth, fire is a chemical reaction—combustion in the presence of oxygen. The Sun is something totally different, and flammable compounds such as gasoline or methane do not exist there. However, there are *oceans* of liquid natural gas on Titan, Saturn's largest moon.

The planet Venus is named for the goddess of love because on a clear night, Venus is second only to the Moon as the brightest object in the evening sky. Not long ago, scientists imagined that Venus might be like Earth. On Earth, we breath an atmosphere of 78% nitrogen and 21% oxygen. However, one deep breath of the atmosphere on Venus would be instantly fatal. The atmosphere there is mostly carbon dioxide, with clouds of hydrochloric acid (HCl), hydrofluoric acid (HF), and sulfuric acid (H_2SO_4)!

Earth is just right for living things. People have long wondered if other planets have life. Mars and Europa (a moon of Jupiter) are good candidates for having extraterrestrial life, but they are only just candidates. Space probes have explored only a tiny fraction of Mars so far. The small amount of evidence collected gives no definite answers. The most common type of life on Earth is bacteria. If microscopic life existed on Mars, how would we know? This chapter will pose many such questions, and many of them haven't been answered yet. Our human curiosity about the unknown is part of what makes science so intriguing.

A NATURAL APPROACH TO CHEMISTRY

Eye in the sky

Make a bright image of the Sun using a lens.

Diffraction grating

Black card with a thin slit

Rainbow spectrum

What is the Sun? On a sunny day you can observe the Sun by making an image with a lens on a white surface. You should never look directly at the Sun, but you can look at the image of the Sun! The light appears bright white. Look at sunlight from the image through a diffraction grating. A diffraction grating shows a rainbow spectrum, which tells you that sunlight is made of many colors. However, a diffraction grating or even a classroom spectrometer does not have the ability to show fine detail in a spectrum.

Atoms both emit and absorb light in discrete spectral lines. Absorption lines are dark against the rainbow of the visible spectrum.

NASA's high-resolution solar spectrometer breaks each part of the solar spectrum into a strip of color. The image below shows an actual solar spectrum broken up into 47 bands. The many dark lines are absorption lines from different elements in the surface layers of the Sun.

Emission spectra

Absorption spectra

In fact, one element (helium) was first discovered not on Earth, but in the Sun! In 1868, Sir Norman Lockyer observed yellow lines in the solar spectrum that had not been seen in any laboratories on Earth. Sir Lockyer correctly deduced that the mystery lines must come from an unknown element he named *helium*, from the Greek *helios* (Sun). Helium wasn't proven to exist on Earth until 25 years later.

Telescopes and spectroscopy to-gether allow us to identify elements and compounds that exist outside of our Earth-bound laboratories.

High-resolution solar spectrum

This high-resolution spectrum wraps around approximately every 10 nm of wavelength to spread the individual spectral lines out, making them easier to distinguish

21.1 The Sun and the Stars

What is in the universe?

Scientists learn much from what we can see from telescopes. However, there are vast mysteries regarding what we cannot see. For example, all matter attracts other matter through gravity. When we look out at the universe, we can estimate the amount of matter needed to explain the apparent strength of gravity. However, we can "see" only 15% of the matter! The remaining 85% is "dark matter," which is another way of saying we don't know what it is. There are many theories and little proof, so dark matter remains a mystery.

Visible matter 15%

Dark matter 85%

Hydrogen and helium are the most common elements

Hydrogen comprises 75% of the matter in the known universe that we can see, making it by far the most common element. Helium makes up about 23% and is the second most common element. The third most common element is oxygen at about 1%, followed by carbon at 0.5% and heavier elements. The chart below gives the relative abundances of the first dozen most common elements.

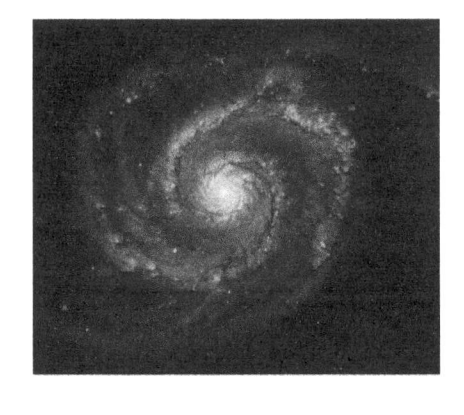

Elemental composition of the visible universe

Atomic #	Element	Parts per million
1	Hydrogen	750,000
2	Helium	230,000
8	Oxygen	10,000
6	Carbon	5,000
10	Neon	1,300
26	Iron	1,100
7	Nitrogen	1,000
14	Silicon	700
12	Magnesium	600
16	Sulfur	500

Planets concentrate the heavier elements

The distribution of elements in the universe outside Earth is very different from our rocky, water covered planet. This is because planets constitute only a tiny fraction of the mass of the Solar System; the Sun has more than a million times the mass of Earth. Hydrogen and helium make up only a tiny fraction of the Earth's total mass.

The Sun

Composition of the Sun

The Solar System is the empire of the Sun. Our Sun contains more than 99.8% of the total mass of the Solar System (with Jupiter containing most of the rest). Today, the mixture of elements in the Sun is 74% hydrogen and 24% helium by mass. Everything else amounts to less than 2%. The chemical makeup of the Sun changes slowly over time as the Sun converts hydrogen to helium in its core. This conversion has been going on for about 4.5 billion years, and it will continue for another 4.5 billion years.

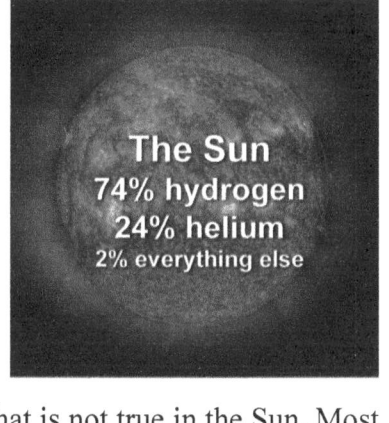

The Sun
74% hydrogen
24% helium
2% everything else

Only pure elements exist in the Sun

Most elements on Earth are combined into compounds. That is not true in the Sun. Most elements in the Sun exist in their pure forms, and *no compounds exist at all*. The reason is that both extremely high temperatures and extraordinary pressure exist in the interior of the Sun. Scientists estimate that the temperature at the Sun's core is 15.6 million K. The thermal energy is so high that chemical bonds cannot exist.

The Sun's internal structure

The Sun's interior

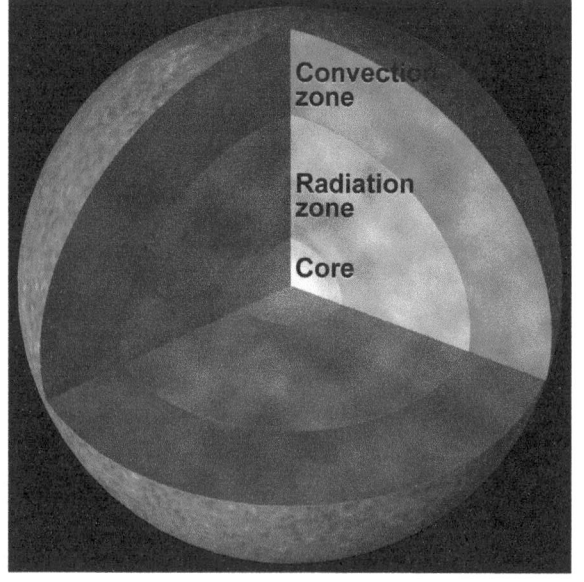

Convection zone

Radiation zone

Core

The photosphere that we see, often called the Sun's "surface," is a hot, low-density gas. The temperature is about 5,800 K, and the density averages about 10 g/m³. This is about 1/10th the density of Earth's atmosphere at sea level.

Just below the photosphere is the convection zone. Here huge circulating currents of gas move heat to the surface. Next in depth is the radiation zone. In this region of the Sun, energy from the core is carried primarily by radiation (light). From the surface to the bottom of the radiation zone, the temperature rises from 5,800 K to more than 10 million K at the edge of the core. The density also rises from less than the density of air to over 150 g/cm³. This is 150 times the density of water. Near the core, a *single cup* of solar matter would have a mass of 34 kg (75 lb)!

Plasma: the fourth state of matter

Ionization and plasmas

Inside the Sun, the thermal energy per atom exceeds the energy it takes to remove one or more electrons. Atoms break apart into positive ions and free electrons. This state of matter is called a *plasma*. A **plasma** is a gas in which the atoms are split apart, or *ionized*, into positive ions and free electrons. **Ionization** is the process of turning a gas into a plasma. Lightning is a plasma ionized by electricity flowing between the clouds and the ground. The Sun is a hot ball of plasma ionized by the energy released by nuclear reactions at the Sun's core. In fact, 99% of the visible matter in the universe is plasma.

Ionization as a function of temperature

At room temperature, a mole of hydrogen gas contains about 3,600 J of thermal energy. Above a few thousand degrees Celsius, molecular hydrogen (H_2) dissociates into atomic hydrogen (H). Above 10,000°C, atomic hydrogen starts to become ionized from gas into plasma. The graph shows that hydrogen is fully ionized above about 20,000°C. Other elements may ionize at lower temperatures because their outer electrons are farther from the nucleus and take less energy to remove. Hydrogen has only one electron that can be ionized, but helium has two and other elements have more. Very hot plasmas may include double, triple, or even more highly ionized atoms.

$$H_2 \rightarrow H + H \qquad H \rightarrow H^+ + e^-$$

Chemical bonds cannot exist in a hot ionized plasma

To understand the reactions that occur in stars, we need to consider interactions between the particles in hot, ionized plasmas. The chemistry of an ionized plasma is hardly chemistry in the normal sense because *chemical bonds cannot form between energetic, ionized atoms*. Since 99% of the visible universe is plasma, you might think that "astronomical" chemistry would be a sparse subject, but you would be quite mistaken! The 1% of visible matter that is not plasma includes all the planets, ourselves, and the matter between the stars that might one day become planets.

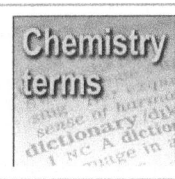

plasma: a hot, energetic phase of matter in which the atoms are broken apart into positive ions and negative electrons that move independently of each other.

ionization: the process of removing one or more electrons from an atom, creating a positive ion and a free electron.

A NATURAL APPROACH TO CHEMISTRY

Energy production in the Sun

Nuclear reactions power the Sun

The core temperature of the Sun is approximately 15 million K. Its matter is a dense plasma, too hot for chemical bonds to exist, so chemical reactions do not occur. However, at this high temperature protons are hot enough to slam together with sufficient force to touch and undergo nuclear reactions. Nuclear reactions *do* occur in the Sun, and they are the source of the Sun's prodigious output of energy.

The proton–proton chain

Like in chemical reactions, the chance of three nuclear particles hitting each other at the exact same instant to have a reaction is negligible. The reactions in the Sun fuse hydrogen to helium in a sequence called the *proton–proton chain*. Each step in the chain involves only two particles. The first step fuses two hydrogen nuclei (protons) into deuterium, releasing a positron and a neutrino as one proton changes into a neutron. The positron immediately annihilates an electron, carrying energy off as gamma rays.

Step 1

$$^1\text{H} + {}^1\text{H} \rightarrow {}^2\text{H} \quad \nu_e \quad e^+$$

The deuterium fuses with another hydrogen to produce helium-3 (^{3}He).

Step 2

$$^2\text{H} + {}^1\text{H} \rightarrow {}^3\text{He}$$

Final steps of the proton–proton chain

Three possible reactions can occur to produce helium-4 (^{4}He). Approximately 86% of the ^{3}He nuclei fuse with another 3He nucleus to make ^{4}He and two protons. About 14% of the ^{3}He nuclei fuse with 4He in a second reaction sequence that results in two ^{4}He nuclei and a single proton. The third reaction (which occurs only 0.11% of the time) also fuses ^{3}He and ^{4}He nuclei together, but with a slightly different outcome. (An extremely rare fourth branch is not shown.) The energy production of each reaction sequence is shown in the diagram.

Step 3

Reaction 3a (86%)
$$^3\text{He} + {}^3\text{He} \rightarrow {}^4\text{He} + {}^1\text{H} + {}^1\text{H}$$

Reaction 3b (14%)
$$^3\text{He} + {}^4\text{He} \rightarrow {}^7\text{Be} + e^- \rightarrow {}^7\text{Li} \quad \nu_e \quad + {}^1\text{H} \rightarrow {}^4\text{He} + {}^4\text{He}$$

Reaction 3c (0.11%)
$$^3\text{He} + {}^4\text{He} \rightarrow {}^7\text{Be} + {}^1\text{H} \rightarrow {}^8\text{B} \quad \nu_e \quad e^+ \rightarrow {}^4\text{He} + {}^4\text{He}$$

The Big Bang theory

The universe is expanding

Our Milky Way galaxy contains some 200 billion stars. Outside the Milky Way are billions more galaxies. Over the past half century, repeated observations show that all the billions of distant galaxies are moving away from each other (and from us). The farther away a distant galaxy is, the faster it is receding. The inescapable conclusion is that *our universe is expanding*. As it expands, the total energy remains constant, so the universe is also cooling down.

The beginning of the universe and the Big Bang

If we think backward, an expanding universe must have been smaller and hotter in the distant past. Taking this idea to its logical beginning, scientists believe that 13.7 billion years ago all of the matter and energy in the universe must have been concentrated in one infinite point. The universe we know exploded from that infinite point in an extraordinary explosion nicknamed the "Big Bang." As strange as it

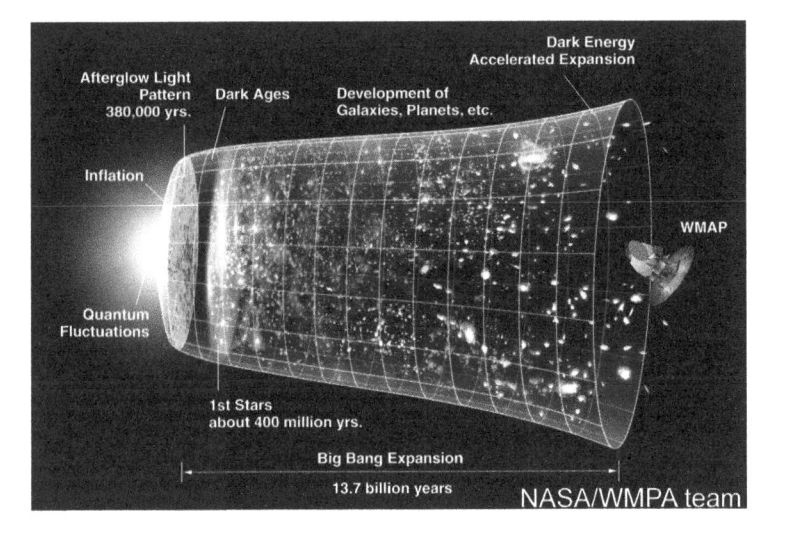

seems, there is a very convincing body of evidence from many areas of physics and astronomy that consistently supports the Big Bang theory.

The first three minutes of the universe

Initially, the universe was so hot that protons and neutrons could not stay bound together to form nuclei. After about one minute, the universe cooled enough for nuclei to begin forming. When the universe was three minutes old, the temperature had dropped far enough that any free neutrons were bound to protons, and any nuclei already formed had insufficient energy to overcome electrostatic Coulomb repulsion and fuse with each other. At the three-minute mark, the elemental composition of the universe was essentially "frozen" in place. Detailed quantum mechanical calculations predict that the "freezing out" of the elements from the hot nuclear plasma should theoretically have produced 75% hydrogen and 25% helium. Only very tiny amounts of lithium and beryllium would theoretically be created. This is almost exactly what we see in the elemental composition of visible matter in the observed universe of today. Hydrogen accounts for 75% of all atoms, and helium accounts for almost all of the remaining 25%. That leaves us with a puzzle. If only four different elements were made in the early universe, where did all of the heavier elements such as oxygen and carbon come from?

Nucleosynthesis

Stars are factories for making elements

The early universe contained essentially just hydrogen and helium. The Sun and other stars convert hydrogen into helium in nuclear reactions. To discover the source of elements heavier than helium, we need to look at the life cycle of stars. In the Sun, gravity tends to pull matter inward. When matter falls inward, energy gained from gravity becomes thermal energy and the temperature goes up. In the Sun today, an equilibrium exists between gravity (inward force) and pressure (outward force). The pressure is sustained by the energy released by nuclear reactions in the Sun's core. As long as the Sun's core contains enough hydrogen, this balance will be maintained.

Helium is fused into carbon and oxygen

Over the next 4.5 billion years the Sun will slowly convert the hydrogen at its core into helium. Energy production will slow down, and the Sun's core will get hotter and denser as gravity compresses it. When the core temperature reaches 100 million K, a new series of nuclear reactions will begin that combine helium into carbon and oxygen.

Synthesis of carbon through nuclear fusion

helium-4 $\qquad$ helium-4 $\qquad$ beryllium-8 $\qquad$ beryllium-8 $\qquad$ helium-4 $\qquad$ carbon-12

$^4_2\text{He} \quad + \quad ^4_2\text{He} \quad \longrightarrow \quad ^8_4\text{Be} \qquad ^8_4\text{Be} \quad + \quad ^4_2\text{He} \quad \longrightarrow \quad ^{12}_6\text{C}$

As the helium in the core is gradually converted to oxygen and carbon, the core is again compressed and heated by gravity. At higher temperatures helium is fused with oxygen and carbon to make even heavier elements such as sodium and magnesium.

Supernovae expel element-enriched matter back into the universe

Eventually the core temperature gets hot enough to fuse iron. Iron is the most tightly bound of all nuclei. That means any nuclear reactions involving iron *use* energy rather than release energy. Once the core fuses to iron, the Sun will become unstable, expanding into a *red giant*. Larger stars can explode as *supernovas*. A supernova is such a powerful explosion that it can outshine the entire galaxy containing it for a short time, releasing as much energy in the initial explosion as our Sun will generate during its entire 9 billion year lifetime. At right is an image of the remnants of a supernova spotted by early astronomers back in the year 1054. It was so bright that it was visible during the day for almost a month.

The Crab Nebula (result of a supernova)

NASA, ESA, Arizona State University

Matter in between the stars and planets

The interstellar medium

In between the stars lies a vast, cold, nearly empty space that astronomers call the *interstellar medium*. We say "nearly empty" because there *is* matter in the interstellar medium, and, in fact, all the matter in our precious Solar System was once part of the interstellar medium. The interstellar medium consists of an extremely dilute mixture of ions, atoms, molecules, and larger dust grains. Astronomers estimate that it is about 99% gas and 1% dust by mass. Densities range from a few thousand to a few hundred million particles per cubic meter. The average mass density in our own Milky Way Galaxy is about a million particles per cubic meter.

Over time, heavy elements are produced

In the 13 billion years since the universe was formed, countless stars have been born, illuminated the emptiness of space with their light, then exploded when their cores reached the iron-burning phase. Each of these explosions has enriched the interstellar medium with heavy elements. Today we have evidence that suggests the interstellar medium is roughly 89% hydrogen, 9% helium, and 2% heavier elements, including oxygen, carbon, and the rest of the periodic table.

Molecular clouds

Stars and galaxies are in constant slow motion, and over millions of years the random gravitational tugs from this motion have swept the interstellar matter into vast, cold molecular clouds. Being hundreds or thousands of light years across—one light year is 9.46×10^{12} km—these clouds typically have temperatures of 10–50 K and contain millions of times as much matter as the Sun. Their composition is mostly molecular hydrogen (H_2) as well as helium and a small percentage of other elements and compounds, including water (H_2O), carbon dioxide (CO_2), ammonia (NH_3), and methane (CH_4). Spectroscopic evidence also suggests that more complex organic compounds such as methanol (CH_3OH) and even amino acids exist in molecular clouds.

New stars and planets condense out of molecular clouds

Astronomers believe molecular clouds are the birthplaces of stars (and planets). This is a natural consequence of their low temperatures and high densities, because gravitational force acting to collapse the cloud can exceed the internal pressures that act outward to expand the cloud. The photograph shows a cluster of hot, young stars that has formed from a molecular cloud in the giant nebula NGC 3603. The stellar wind from the new stars has partially blown a bubble of clear space around the cluster, likely triggering the collapse and formation of more stars at the bubble's edge.

Courtesy NASA / ESA – Hubble Space Telescope

21.2 The Planets

The inner and outer planets

The planets naturally fall into two groups. The inner planets are rocky and include Mercury, Venus, Earth, and Mars. They have relatively high densities, slow rotations, solid surfaces, and few moons. The outer planets are made mostly of hydrogen and helium and include Jupiter, Saturn, Uranus, and Neptune. These planets have relatively low densities, rapid rotations, thick atmospheres, and many moons.

TABLE 21.1. Properties of the planets

Property	Mercury	Venus	Earth	Mars	Jupiter	Saturn	Uranus	Neptune
Diameter (km)	4,878	12,102	12,756	6,794	142,796	120,660	51,200	49,500
Mass (Earth = 1)	0.06	0.82	1.00	0.11	316	94.7	14.5	17.1
Orbit radius ($\times 10^6$ km)	58	108	150	228	778	1,430	2,870	4,500
Major moons (#)	0	0	1	2	39	30	21	8
Gravity (Earth = 1)	3.7	8.9	1	3.7	23.1	9.0	8.7	11.0
Surface temp. (°C)	−170 / +400	430 / 460	−88 / +48	−89 / −31	−108	−139	−197	−201
Atm. press. (Earth = 1)	0	92	1	0.01	Ranges from 0 to >10,000 in interior			

Scale of the Solar System

The orbits of the inner planets are separated by about 50 million km. The outer planets are much more spread out. The distance between Mars's and Jupiter's orbits is 550 million km, almost 10 times the distance between Earth's and Mars's orbits. Notice that the size and mass of the planets are quite different for the inner and outer planets as well. The inner planets range from 6% of Earth's mass to Earth itself. The outer planets are all more than 10 times more massive than Earth. These differences in size, mass, and distance arose from how the Solar System formed some 4.5 billion years ago.

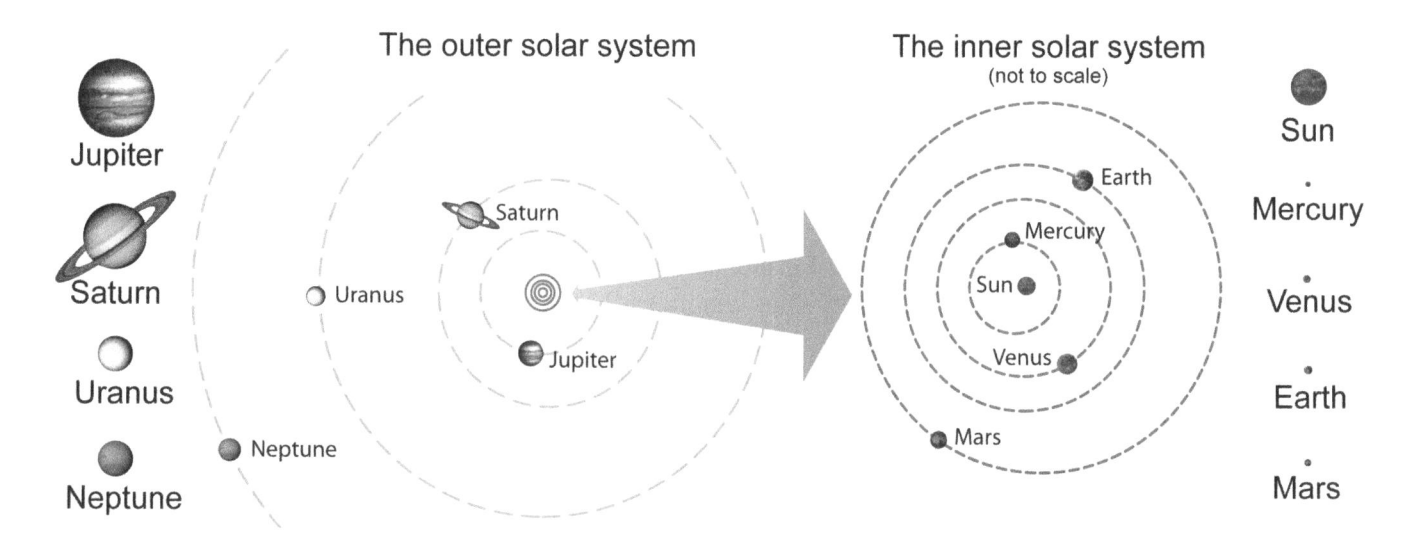

The formation of the Solar System

Birth of the Solar System

The Solar System began as a vast, cold molecular cloud of interstellar material. The cloud pulled in on itself slowly under its own weak gravity. Because it was rotating slowly, the cloud spun faster as it slowly collapsed inward, like a figure skater pulling in her arms to make herself spin faster. Once the center of the cloud had collapsed to stellar density, the Sun ignited. Around the new Sun was a slowly rotating disk of leftover matter that coalesced into the planets.

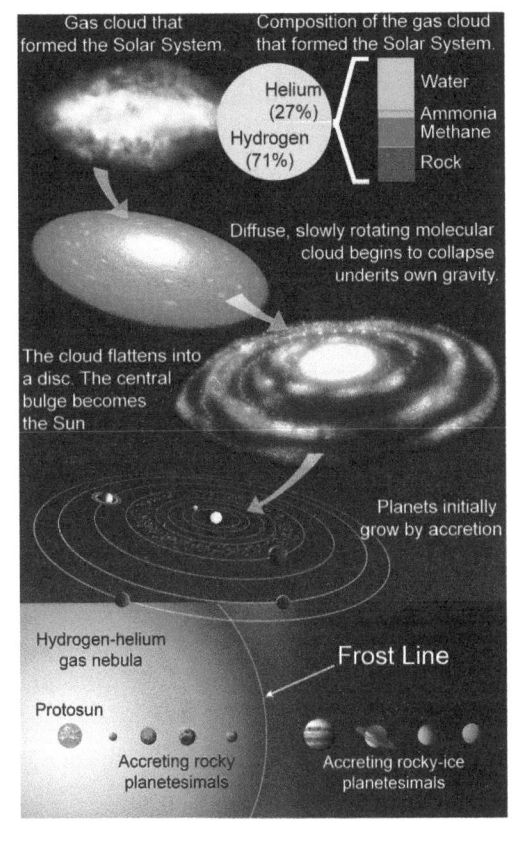

Planets formed initially by accretion

The currently accepted theory is that the planets formed first by *accretion*. Over a few million years, dust particles and molecules formed into clumps between 1 and 10 m in diameter. The clumps collided to form planetesimals of ~5 km in size. These gradually increased through further collisions, growing at the rate of centimeters per year over a few million more years. The differences between the inner and outer planets arose because of differences in melting point, density, and temperature.

Formation of the inner planets

Closer than about 300 million km from the Sun, the temperature was too high for volatile molecules such as water and methane to condense. Planetesimals close to the Sun could only accumulate materials with high melting points, such as metals (for instance, iron, nickel, and aluminum) and rocky silicates. These compounds are relatively rare in the universe, and astronomers believe they made up only 0.6% of matter that formed the Solar System. This is one reason the inner planets are small compared to the outer planets. Scientists believe accretion could build up about 0.05 Earth masses, or five times larger than the Moon. Over the next few million years, collisions and mergers between these planet-sized bodies allowed terrestrial planets to grow to their present sizes.

Formation of the outer planets

The outer gas giant planets formed out beyond the "frost line" approximately between the orbits of Mars and Jupiter. This imaginary boundary is where the temperature was cool enough for volatile icy compounds such as water, methane, and ammonia to remain solid. The outer planets grew large because the ices that formed them were much more abundant than the metals and silicates that formed the terrestrial planets. Once they reached a sufficient mass and gravitational strength, the outer planets were able to capture and retain hydrogen and helium, the lightest and most abundant elements. Today, the four gas giants contain almost 99% of the total mass orbiting the Sun.

Energy from the Sun

Distance from the Sun strongly affects temperature

The chemistry of each planet strongly depends on its temperature. With the exception of Venus, temperature is mostly dependent on distance from the Sun. The Sun radiates 3.8×10^{26} W of power equally in all directions. As you get farther from the Sun, that energy is spread out over a larger and larger area. The diagram below shows how the intensity of sunlight changes with distance from the Sun. The horizontal axis is in *astronomical units* (AU): 1 AU = 1.5×10^8 km, the distance from Earth to the Sun.

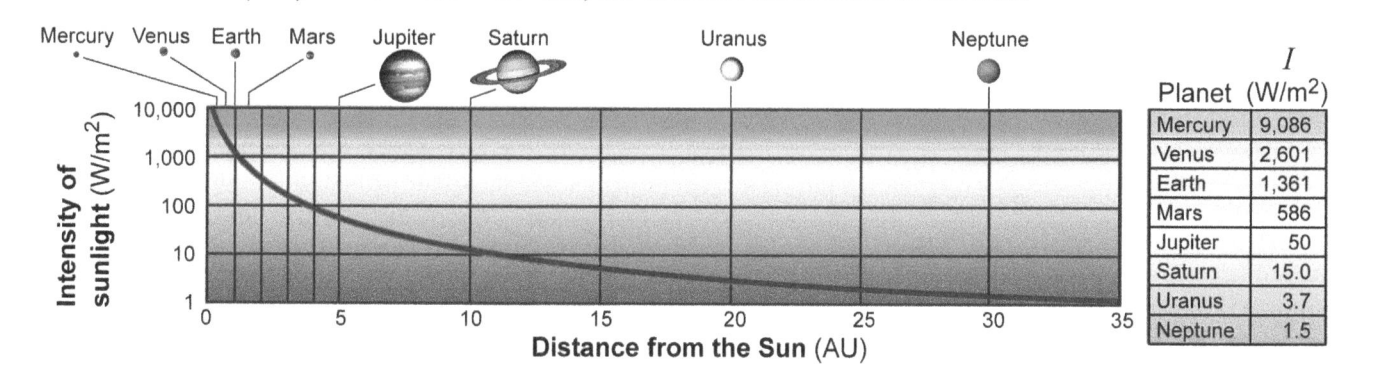

Planet	I (W/m^2)
Mercury	9,086
Venus	2,601
Earth	1,361
Mars	586
Jupiter	50
Saturn	15.0
Uranus	3.7
Neptune	1.5

Intensity is power per unit area

Intensity means how much power falls on each unit area of surface. At the top of Earth's atmosphere, the intensity of sunlight is 1,360 W/m^2. This is sufficient to maintain the average temperature of Earth's surface at a comfortable 15°C. The next graph (below) shows the average surface temperature of each of the planets. For the outer planets that do not have a true surface, the temperature is given just below the cloud tops of the upper atmosphere.

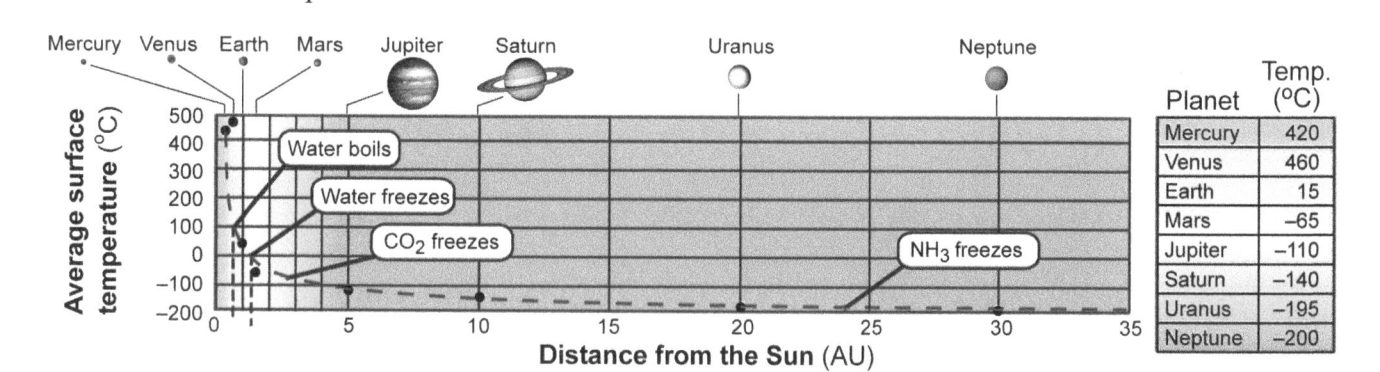

Planet	Temp. (°C)
Mercury	420
Venus	460
Earth	15
Mars	−65
Jupiter	−110
Saturn	−140
Uranus	−195
Neptune	−200

Only a small range of distances allow liquid surface water

The boiling points of several important compounds in planetary atmospheres are shown on the chart. At one atmosphere of pressure, water boils at 100°C and freezes at 0°C. Carbon dioxide freezes at −78°C. Methane freezes at −182°C and nitrogen freezes at −210°C. Water, carbon dioxide, methane, and nitrogen have similar molecular weights (18, 44, 16, and 28). Water has an extraordinarily high melting point, and also a wide range over which it remains liquid. Earth falls within a narrow range of orbits for which water is liquid. Notice that Venus is much too hot for its distance from the Sun. This has to do with the particular chemistry of Venus's atmosphere.

Venus

Why the extreme temperature difference?

	Venus	Earth
Distance from Sun	108 million km	150 million km
Diameter	12,100 km	12,760 km
Composition	rocky, silicates	rocky, silicates
Total CO_2	$9.6 \times 10^{-5}\%$	$16 \times 10^{-5}\%$
Total H_2O	$2 \times 10^{-5}\%$	$28 \times 10^{-5}\%$
Total N_2	$2 \times 10^{-6}\%$	$2.4 \times 10^{-6}\%$

Venus is often thought of as Earth's "sister planet," because Earth and Venus are similar in size, gravity, and composition. They are at comparable distances from the Sun. Like Earth, Venus has a substantial atmosphere; however, Venus is perpetually covered in dense clouds. Only in the past 50 years have space probes revealed the truth about Venus and how its climate and chemistry are very different from those on Earth.

Venus is extraordinarily hot

Today Venus is *hot*! In fact Venus has the highest surface temperature in the Solar System, averaging a blistering 460°C (860°F). Venus is hotter than Mercury, even though Venus is nearly twice as far from the Sun and receives only 25% as much solar energy. The reason for Venus's extreme temperature is the chemistry of its atmosphere, particularly with respect to carbon dioxide and water.

Venus' atmospheric pressure is 92 times greater than Earth's

Venus's atmosphere is 96% carbon dioxide. The atmospheric pressure on Venus's surface is 92 times higher than the pressure at sea level on Earth. On Venus's surface the atmospheric pressure is equivalent to being a kilometer deep under water on Earth. In terms of mass, each cubic meter on Venus contains 65 kg of matter. On Earth, a cubic meter of air contains about 1 kg of matter.

Venus has corrosive, acid weather

Venus's upper atmosphere is perpetually surrounded by dense clouds. However, the clouds on Venus are sulfuric acid, not water! The hot acid fog is a highly corrosive atmosphere. The photograph was taken by the *Venera 13* space probe, which lasted only an hour before being destroyed.

Venera 13 *(Russia)*

Blackbody radiation and planetary energy balance

Absorption and radiation

To understand why Venus is so hot, we need to look at two competing effects that occur on all planets. *Absorption* of energy heats a planet up. *Radiation* of energy cools a planet down. Absorption is something you feel directly on a sunny day. Your skin absorbs energy and heats up.

The blackbody spectrum

Thermal radiation from the Sun, loosely called *light,* is how the energy gets from the Sun to your skin. All objects with a temperature above absolute zero give off thermal radiation, just like the Sun. Most objects are not as hot as the Sun, so the radiation is both lower in intensity and at different wavelengths. The amount of power radiated at different wavelengths (colors) is called the *blackbody spectrum.* The curve for the Sun shows that at 5,500°C the radiation has its highest power in the visible range of wavelengths. Room-temperature objects (20°C) radiate much less power, mostly in the infrared.

Power increases like T⁴

Notice the power scale on the blackbody spectrum. The amount of energy radiated depends on the temperature to the fourth power. If the temperature doubles, then the radiated power is multiplied by 16!

Planetary energy balance

In steady state, a planet must reradiate all the energy it absorbs from the Sun—otherwise the planet will get warmer. If absorbed energy exceeds radiated energy, the planet's temperature slowly increases, also increasing the energy the planet radiates. The temperature stops increasing when radiated energy equals absorbed energy from sunlight.

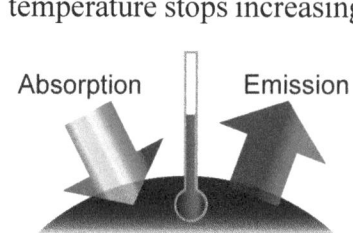

Steady state	Less emission	More emission
temperature constant	*temperature rises*	*temperature drops*

If absorbed energy is *less* than radiated energy, the planet's surface cools down. Cooling down lowers the radiated energy until the two are again in balance and the temperature stabilizes. The average temperature of a planet adjusts itself up or down to keep balance between absorption and radiation.

The greenhouse effect

Carbon on Venus and Earth

Although Venus and Earth have similar amounts of carbon, on Venus most of the carbon is in the form of gas (CO_2) in the atmosphere. On Earth, carbon dissolves into the oceans where it is trapped by organic life and deposited on the ocean floor as solid calcium carbonate and other minerals. The Earth's carbon cycle keeps carbon out of the atmosphere. There is evidence that Venus had surface water in its distant past. However, any water on Venus boiled away long ago as a result of a *runaway greenhouse effect*. Over time Venus's atmospheric water was broken apart by ultraviolet light from the Sun. The light hydrogen escaped so water could not form again, and today Venus is completely dry.

Sunlight and absorption

To explain the greenhouse effect, consider that sunlight contains a spectrum of wavelengths from infrared to visible. Both Venus's and Earth's atmospheres are mostly transparent to sunlight so it passes through and is absorbed by the ground.

The orange-shaded areas show wavelengths of light that are strongly absorbed by CO_2

CO_2 absorbs in the infrared

gas. Notice that CO_2 is transparent to sunlight but absorbs strongly in the infrared. Like Earth, energy from the Sun is absorbed by Venus. However, because of the CO_2, part of the energy radiated by Venus's surface is absorbed by the atmosphere before escaping to space. Because the energy could not escape, Venus slowly became warmer and warmer.

Explanation of Venus's high temperature

As Venus got warmer, its surface water boiled away. That meant there was no way to absorb CO_2 from volcanoes and other sources. The CO_2 concentration in the atmosphere increased. More CO_2 in turn meant even stronger atmospheric absorption of radiated heat. More absorbed heat meant Venus's temperature increased even more in a self-reinforcing cycle until most of Venus's inventory of surface carbon was in the atmosphere. Eventually equilibrium was reached at the very high surface temperature we observe today. Atmospheric CO_2 concentration is strongly correlated to a planet's average temperature because it affects the overall planetary energy balance. Many scientists are concerned because human activities have increased the concentration of CO_2 in Earth's atmosphere by 35% since the industrial revolution.

Mars

Mars

Mars is a cold and relatively small planet, with a mass only 11% the mass of Earth and surface gravity only 38% as strong as Earth's. Like Venus, Mars's atmosphere is mostly carbon dioxide (95%); however, unlike Venus, Mars' atmosphere is very thin. The atmospheric pressure on Mars's surface is 1/100th times that at sea level on Earth. Because of the thin atmosphere and the planet's distance from the Sun, Martian temperatures are below 0°C most of the time.

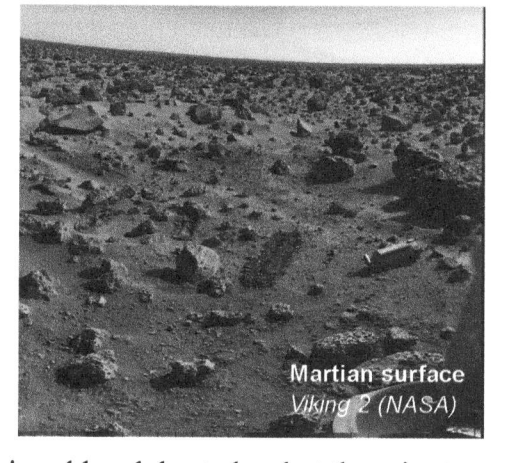

Martian surface
Viking 2 (NASA)

Mars was wetter in the distant past

Fe_2O_3

Grey hematite

Red hematite
(rust)

Mars is cold and dry today, but there is strong evidence that Mars was much wetter and had a thicker atmosphere in the past. Aerial photos of the Martian surface show erosion and patterns of riverbeds similar to those formed by flowing water on Earth. Even today, there is evidence of water beneath the Martian surface. Much of the evidence is chemical in nature, such as the discovery of a gray variety of the iron oxide mineral called hematite (Fe_2O_3). Hematite comes in two forms: red and gray. The red kind is ordinary rust, which forms when iron is in contact with oxygen. Red rust is everywhere on Mars, and it's what gives the planet its reddish color. Gray hematite has a dark gray metallic luster. Unlike red hematite, gray hematite usually precipitates from iron-rich water over long periods of time. The discovery of gray hematite near the Martian equator supports the hypothesis that Mars once had deep liquid water on its surface.

Searching for life on Mars

We know living organisms invariably leave a chemical signature. In 1976, the *Viking* mission landed a robot probe on Mars to search for evidence of life, but the results were ambiguous. A new mission is planned for 2013 to land on the red planet to specifically look for amino acids. Amino acids can form with right-handed or left-handed structures. Nonliving processes produce a 50–50 mix of the two. All life on Earth uses only left-handed amino acids. If amino acids are found with a preference for either right- or left-handed structures, it will be strong evidence for the presence of life.

Mars Rover - 2004 - NASA

The outer planets

The outer planets are much larger

The inner planets are tiny compared to the outer planets both in size and mass. Jupiter is by far the largest object in the Solar System after the Sun. Jupiter contains more than twice the mass of all the other planets combined.

The outer planets compared to Earth

Jupiter's diameter is 11 times the diameter of Earth. The smallest of the outer planets, Neptune is four times as large as Earth. No longer considered a planet, Pluto is half the size of Mercury and is made of ice, not rock. It belongs to neither the inner nor outer planets, but instead it is the closest member of a group of frozen ice balls called Kuiper Belt Objects.

Comparing composition

In composition, all the outer planets are much different from the rocky, inner planets like Earth. Notice that the outer planets have densities between 0.67 and 2.67 g/cm³. The inner planets are much denser, ranging from 3.91 to 5.52 g/cm³. The density difference tells us the outer planets are mostly light gases, liquids, and ices such as frozen ammonia and methane. The inner planets are mostly rock.

Mercury

Venus

Earth

Mars

Jupiter

Relative true sizes of the planets compared to the Sun

Saturn

Uranus

Neptune

TABLE 21.2. Comparing inner and outer planets

Property	Mercury	Venus	Earth	Mars	Jupiter	Saturn	Uranus	Neptune
Diameter (km)	4,878	12,102	12,756	6,794	142,796	120,660	51,200	49,500
Mass (Earth = 1)	0.06	0.82	1.00	0.11	316	94.7	14.5	17.1
Density (g/cm³)	5.44	5.25	5.52	3.91	1.31	0.69	1.21	1.67

The outer planets have multiple moons and rings

The outer planets have many moons and are more like miniature solar systems themselves. This is very different from the inner planets. Earth has one large moon, Mercury and Venus have none, and Mars has two tiny orbiting asteroids that hardly qualify as moons. By comparison, as of the writing of this book, Jupiter has 63 known moons. Four of them are comparable to Earth's moon in size. Saturn has 61 moons, Uranus has 27, and Neptune has 13. Saturn is best known for its rings, but all the outer planets are now known to have rings, even Jupiter.

Jupiter's largest moons

Europa

Size of Earth's moon

Callisto

Io

Ganymede

Composition of the outer planets

Jupiter, Saturn, Uranus and Neptune are gas planets

The word "planet" usually brings to mind a mental picture of a spherical object (like the Moon) with a hard surface on which you could imagine walking. The outer planets of our Solar System don't really fit this description. Instead, the outer planets are giant balls of cold gas and liquid without a definite surface.

Molecular hydrogen
Metallic hydrogen
Frozen H_2O, NH_4, and CH_4 ices
Rock

Atmospheres of the outer planets in percentage by mole

	Sun	Jupiter	Saturn	Uranus	Neptune
H_2	84	86.4	97	83	79
He	16	13.6	3	15	18
H_2O	—	0.1	—	—	—
CH_4	—	0.21	0.2	2	3
NH_3	—	0.07	0.03	—	—

Chemical similarity to the Sun

Chemically, the outer planets are more similar to the Sun than to Earth. All four are predominantly hydrogen and helium with a small percentage of water, ammonia, and methane.

The interiors of the gas planets

The diagram shows that the pressure increases with depth, reaching more than a million atmospheres. At this high pres-sure, molecular hydrogen is literally squeezed apart into separate protons and electrons. Because the temperature is low, this "cold plasma" acts more like a liquid metal than a hot gas and is referred to as *metallic hydrogen*.

Jupiter's atmosphere

Pressure (atm)

Gas   Condensate

0.01
0.1
1
100
1,000
10,000
100,000
1,000,000

H_2O, NH_3, CH_4 NH_3, NH_4SH H_4O

Quenched CO, N_2 Fe, Mg, SiO_2

Molecular H_2

(He-depleted)   He rainout

Metalic H (He-enriched)
(He), O, C, N...,
Core   Fe, Mg, Si

Why Jupiter and Saturn are different from Uranus and Neptune

Jupiter and Saturn have less helium in their atmospheres than the Sun because helium is soluble in metallic hydrogen. Scientists believe a cold, liquid helium "rain" occurs in the transition region between the molecular hydrogen and metallic hydrogen. Over time, this depletes helium from the atmosphere. The effect is strongest on Jupiter, since Jupiter has a larger mass and therefore more metallic hydrogen compared to molecular hydrogen. Saturn has a smaller amount of metallic hydrogen, since it has only a third the mass of Jupiter and therefore lower core pressure. Uranus and Neptune are smaller than Saturn, and pressures are not high enough for metallic hydrogen to form.

Modeling the interior of a planet

Ideal gas laws don't apply at high pressure

How do we know what the inside of Jupiter or Saturn is like? We cannot easily go ourselves to find out, so scientists build models. A model for the interior of a gas planet needs to include (at a minimum) variables of composition, temperature, and pressure. One such model we already know is the ideal gas law. The ideal gas law relates pressure, temperature, and composition for gases that are *weakly interacting*. That means the individual molecules are far apart. At the enormous pressures inside a planet, molecules are squeezed tightly together, so the ideal gas law does not apply.

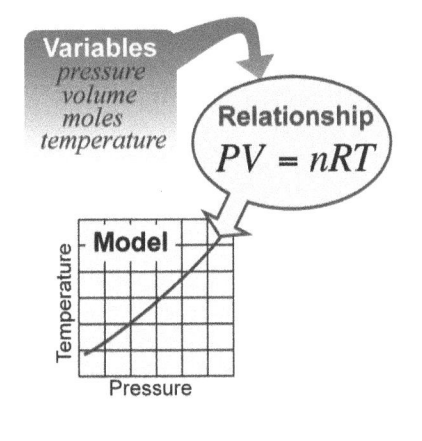

A model for the phases of matter in Jupiter

The diagram below shows the different phases of a hydrogen and helium mixture typical of the outer planets. This model is based on both calculations and on high-pressure experiments on Earth. The ideal gas law describes only the lighter shaded region in the center left of the graph. At pressures above about a million atmospheres, hydrogen is in its metallic phase.

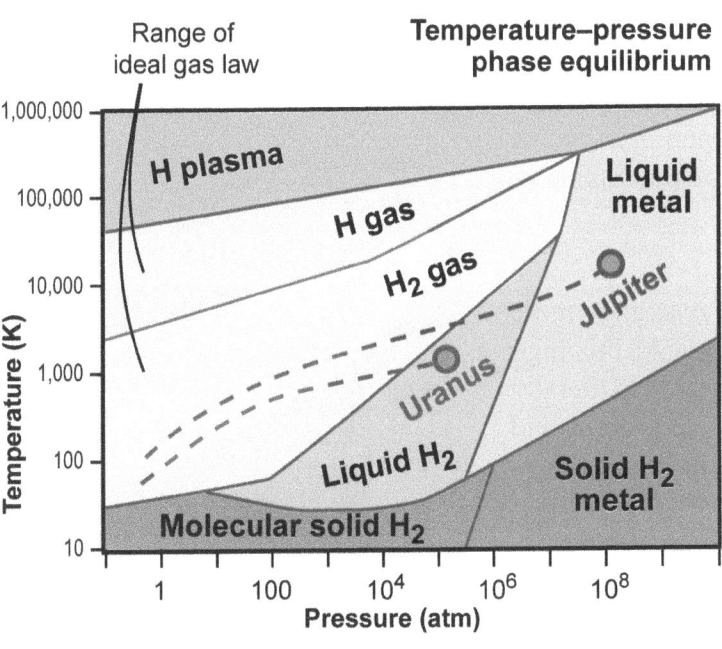

Jupiter's core falls in this region However, the density and temperature at the core of Uranus fall in the liquid H_2 region, so we expect the inner regions of Uranus to be liquid hydrogen.

At high densities, atoms and molecules are squeezed tightly together and their interactions become complex. Hydrogen, like other substances, exhibits distinct phases other than just solid, liquid, and gas. The diagram shows that there are two different liquid phases and two solid phases depending on the temperature and pressure. Molecular solid H_2 is an electrical insulator. At temperatures below 20 K and pressures

Matter can have multiple different liquid and solid phases

above a million atmospheres, solid molecular hydrogen changes into an electrical conductor, its solid metal phase. This phase transition occurs when the intense pressure forces electrons to become dissociated from individual molecules.

A NATURAL APPROACH TO CHEMISTRY

CHAPTER 21
The Chemistry of the Solar System

21.3 The Possibility of Life Elsewhere

What about life on other planets?

Earth is a relatively warm, wet, and lush oasis compared to the rest of the Solar System. At least, we humans think so, along with the rest of the plants and animals evolved to live here. We know that life arose on Earth at least 3 billion years ago when the planet was quite different than it is today. For example, there was very little (or no) oxygen on the primordial Earth.

The universe is vast beyond imagination, and people have always wondered whether there is life on other worlds. As a prerequisite to searching for extraterrestrial life, it seems prudent to ask some basic questions:

- What are the physical and chemical conditions under which life can exist?
- Do those conditions exist outside of Earth? If so, where?
- How would we recognize alien life if we found it?

What are the possible range of conditions where life can exist?

What are the extreme boundaries where life exists here on Earth? Kilometers below the surface, on the sunless floor of the deep ocean, volcanic activity occasionally creates features called *hydrothermal vents*. These vents are jets of acidic, superheated water that exist in absolute darkness, at incredible pressure, and contain concentrations of poison gases and heavy metals. The hot water coming from a hydrothermal vent is rich in dissolved minerals, most notably sulfides. When it comes in contact with cold ocean water, some minerals precipitate, forming a black chimney-like structure around each vent called a *black smoker*.

Depth = 2,400 meters
380°C

Courtesy of Spiess, Macdonald, et al, 1980.

Chemosynthetic life needs no sunlight

Despite the extreme conditions, a variety of *chemosynthetic* life exists at hydrothermal vents. Chemosynthetic bacteria use energy directly from heat and convert toxic minerals such as hydrogen sulfide into carbon compounds. One such reaction creates formaldehyde (CH_2O) from dissolved carbon dioxide, oxygen, and hydrogen sulfide:

Chemosynthesis

$$CO_2 + O_2 + 4H_2S \rightarrow CH_2O + 4S + 3H_2O$$

Chemosynthetic bacteria support a food chain of other animals. Some creatures, such as gastropod snails, eat the bacteria directly. Tubeworms host chemosynthetic bacteria in their tissues in exchange for organic compounds that the bacteria create from the vent chemicals and sea water. This is life at temperatures well over 300°C, at extreme pressures and totally without sunlight or organic matter.

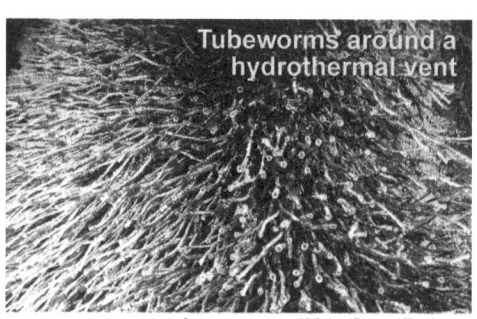

Tubeworms around a hydrothermal vent

Image courtesy NOAA Ocean Explorer

Life deep underground

We once believed life was confined to the surface

Until recently, most scientists believed that life was restricted to the surface of planet Earth. The oceans, the air, the ground, and the soil are alive with animals, plants, and microorganisms. Below the surface, in deep bedrock, there had been little expectation for life. Deep underground the temperature is hot, toxic chemicals are abundant, background radiation is significant, and there is no sunlight.

Recently discovered species of bacteria live deep underground

Geologists and microbiologists have proved that life is plenty tough enough to survive deep underground. In the late 1980s, researchers found microbes living in rock 500 m below the surface in South Carolina. Between 1998 and 2006, researchers discovered active, living colonies of bacteria 2.8 km underground. In some cases, these bacteria have apparently remained prisoners of the deep for millions

Abundant microbial life has been found 2.8 kilometers underground far from sunlight and air

of years, making such colonies actual living fossils. "This is a revolution that's expanding the limits under which we know life to exist," says Princeton professor Dr. Tullis Onstott. "I think we're recognizing that life is a bit more tenacious than we had given it credit for, and there's a much broader realm of possibilities where life can survive." More recently researchers have discovered microorganisms in deep granite formations. These rocks completely lack organic materials. The new discoveries suggest deep subsurface life may be quite common.

Bacillus infernus is an example of thermophilic bacteria

Deep bacteria are classed as _thermophiles_, or heat lovers, because their environment has a temperature of 75°C (167°F). One particular species was recently named _Bacillus infernus_, for its high-temperature survival. Similar thermophilic microbes colonize volcanically heated springs, such as those in Yellowstone National Park, and scalding geysers on the ocean floor.

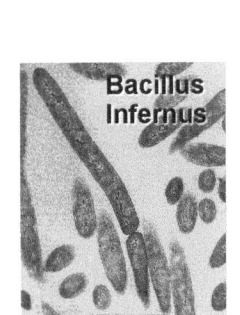

US Department of Energy

Implications for ancient and extraterrestrial life

Biologists say the discovery of deep thermophilic bacteria has broad implications, stretching backward in time and outward into all of space. If bacteria and archaea can survive far below ground without any contact with the surface, then it's possible that life could have even started there. Earth's surface was quite catastrophic when the planet was young. Deep rocks would have provided protection from sterilizing temperatures, meteor impacts, and radiation. Today, many scientists believe life may be hiding beneath the dusty red surface of Mars and other extraterrestrial habitats. The surface of Mars is dry but it is very likely that liquid water exists in the warmer interior of the planet.

A NATURAL APPROACH TO CHEMISTRY

Evidence for life on Mars

The *Viking* mission (1976)

If you had to travel 75 million km and could only look at one tiny spot for evidence of life, how would you do it? In 1976, before there were ATMs or CD-ROMs, NASA launched the *Viking* mission. During one year, a pair *Viking* spacecraft landed on Mars and carried out some basic chemical tests for life.

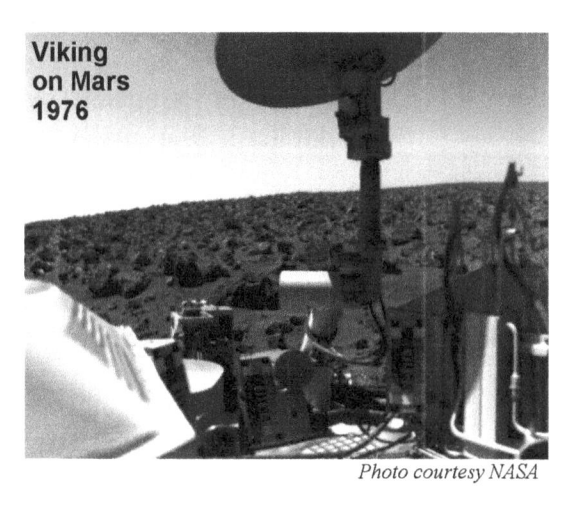

Photo courtesy NASA

Viking carried four chemical experiments to detect the signature of life

A *mass spectrometer* looked for organic compounds, such as alcohols or amino acids in Martian soil. The results were negative and *Viking* found Martian soils to contain less carbon than lifeless lunar soils returned by the *Apollo* program.

The *gas exchange* experiment looked for O_2, CO_2, H_2, CH_4, and N_2 given off by a soil sample that was treated with a liquid complex of organic and inorganic nutrients. The *labeled release* experiment inoculated a sample of Martian soil with a drop of dilute aqueous nutrient solution tagged with radioactive ^{14}C. The *pyrolytic release* experiment exposed Martian soil to light and CO_2 that was tagged with ^{14}C. Any photosynthetic activity would incorporate the tagged carbon and be detected by heating the sample after a few weeks' incubation.

Viking was inconclusive

The results from *Viking* were inconclusive. No life was detected, but life could not be ruled out because the samples were small and the instrumentation of the time was not as sophisticated as it is today.

The Mars Phoenix mission (2008)

In May of 2008, the NASA *Phoenix* mission landed on Mars to continue the search for life. Among *Phoenix's* accomplishments was the definitive observation of water in the Martian soil. One morning there was frost on the sides of a trench the lander had scraped previously. A second chemical

Photos courtesy NASA

finding was the presence of several salts and perchlorate (ClO_4) in Martian soil. Perchlorate is an oxidant but not a powerful one. Perchlorates are found naturally on Earth at such places as Chile's extremely arid Atacama Desert. The presence of percholates is ambiguous as a signature of life, but some microorganisms on Earth are fueled by processes that involve perchlorates, and some plants concentrate the substance.

Europa

Jupiter's sixth moon is unusual

In 1997 the *Galileo* spacecraft flew within 200 km of Europa, the sixth moon of Jupiter. The smallest of Jupiter's four major moons, Europa was an enigma. It is the most reflective object in the Solar System, and its surface is criss-crossed with strange lines. There are almost no craters, yet Ganymede (Jupiter's largest moon) has plenty of craters. Something about Europa provides an active process for erasing craters from its surface.

Europa has a thick crust of water ice

Europa's surface from 200 km altitude

Orbital photographs show a chaotic terrain unlike any other in the Solar System. Scientists believe that the cracks are in a layer of water ice that may be 100 km thick. The observed scarcity of craters is due to periodic cracks in the ice caused by Jupiter's gravity. Upwelling liquid water freezes in the −160°C temperature to make new surface material. Beneath Europa's ice lie the deepest water oceans in the Solar System, estimated at 200 km. For comparison, the deepest oceans on Earth are less than 10 km deep.

Europa may have the deepest oceans in the Solar System

How does water stay liquid so far from the Sun? The answer is that Europa is fairly close to Jupiter for a moon. Jupiter's gravity creates strong tides that pull Europa's inner oceans up and down with each orbit. This repetitive massaging creates frictional heating that keeps the oceans liquid.

The potential for life on Europa

It is very likely that conditions near the base of Europa's oceans are similar to those on the sea floor of Earth. Chemosynthetic or thermophylic bacteria could conceivably thrive there. After Mars, Europa is currently considered by many scientists to be the next most likely candidate for extraterrestrial life.

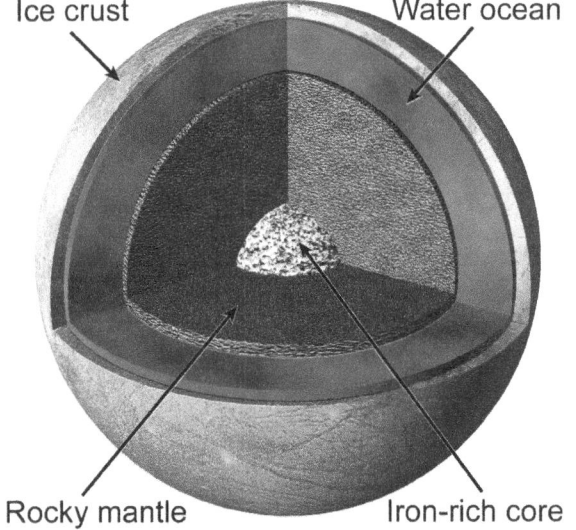

Ice crust   Water ocean

Rocky mantle   Iron-rich core

Titan

Titan is larger than Mercury

Titan is Saturn's sixth moon, and it is larger than the planet Mercury. It is the only moon with a real atmosphere, and the pressure at Titan's surface is one and a half times that on Earth. Titan's atmosphere is 98.4% nitrogen with the remaining 1.6% being methane and trace amounts of many organic compounds, including ethane, diacetylene, methylacetylene, acetylene and propane. The moon itself is composed of water ice and rocky material. Much as with Venus, until the Space Age, the dense, cloudy atmosphere over Titan prevented any glimpse of its surface until the arrival of the *Cassini–Huygens* mission in 2004.

Titan is more like a planet than a moon

In January 2005, after traveling through space for seven years, the *Cassini–Huygens* spacecraft reached Saturn and a probe descended through the clouds to observe the surface for the first time. We now know that Titan is more like a planet, with oceans, rivers, mountains, and even weather! Titan's rivers and oceans are the only large, stable bodies of surface liquid known to exist anywhere other than Earth. Titan even has volcanoes that erupt ammonia ice slush. Based on images from the *Huygens* probe, the artistic rendering below shows shores of a cold ethane ocean on Titan.

The potential for life on Titan

With the exception of the extreme cold (–180°C), Titan's abundant organic liquids and dense nitrogen atmosphere are seen by scientists as similar to the early Earth. Even with the cold, some consider Titan a potential site for finding extraterrestrial life. At a minimum we know Titan contains a prebiotic environment rich in complex organic chemistry. If there are warmer underground features on Titan, the possibility of life there becomes greatly enhanced. Humans will not know until some future space mission when a person might be able to set foot on this distant but intriguing world.

Chapter 21 Review

Conceptual Questions

Section 21.1

1. Consider the element hydrogen.
   a. Is it more abundant than helium in the universe?
   b. Is it less abundant than helium in the universe?
   c. Is it always found combined with carbon as methane in molecular clouds?
   d. Is it always found combined with nitrogen as ammonia in molecular clouds?

2. The Big Bang theory is supported by which of the following observations?
   a. Stars like the Sun are about average in size.
   b. Distant galaxies are all receding from us.
   c. The Sun carries out nuclear fusion reactions in its core.
   d. Stars tend to be grouped into large collections called galaxies.

3. Are chemical reactions likely to occur in the Sun? Why or why not?

4. Research two examples of plasmas you might find on Earth. What gases are involved? What is the average temperature of each one?

5. A person tells you that he believes combustion of flammable gases makes heat in the Sun just as a fireplace makes heat on Earth. Write one paragraph agreeing or disagreeing and state at least two reasons that support your position.

6. Explain why a single nuclear fusion reaction like the one below does not occur, or occurs so rarely that it is completely unimportant, in the Sun.

   $$^1H + {}^1H + {}^1H + {}^1H = {}^4He + 2v_e + 2e^+$$

7. Describe the origin of the element oxygen as it appears on Earth. Where do oxygen atoms come from? Are they made on Earth?

8. Name at least three major substances in the interstellar medium. Identify them as elements or compounds.

9. Which of the following phases of matter is most abundant among the visible matter in our universe? Explain where it is usually found.
   a. solid
   b. liquid
   c. gas
   d. plasma

Section 21.2

10. Suppose there were planets around a star that was larger and hotter than the Sun. Would you expect to find an Earth-like planet closer or farther away form the star? Give the reasoning behind your answer.

11. Explain how the "frost line" affected the formation of the inner and outer planets.

12. List three of the most important differences between the inner and outer planets.

13. Which planet has the highest average surface temperature? Is this planet the closest planet to the Sun?

14. What is the meaning of the term *accretion* in the context of the formation of the Solar System?

15. What happens to all the energy absorbed by a planet from the Sun?

16. What would happen if a planet absorbed *all* the energy it received from the Sun?

17. Explain the difference between thermal radiation and sunlight. Is there a difference?

18. Why does most sunlight pass though Venus's atmosphere but thermal radiation is partly absorbed?

19. What gives Mars its reddish color?

20. Mars's atmosphere is similar in composition to that of Venus (which is mostly CO_2). Why is Mars so cold while Venus is so hot?

Section 21.3

21. Does all life on Earth require sunlight? Give two examples to support your answer.

22. Where do scientists believe the deepest liquid water oceans in the Solar System can be found?

23. If a moon has no craters, what does this tell us about its geology?

24. Research three hydrocarbon compounds that are liquids at −180°C. Are any of these present on Titan?

Quantitative Problems

Section 21.1

25. Write down a possible nuclear reaction that could make magnesium in a star from lighter elements. The rules are as follows:

    a. The total number of protons + neutrons must be the same on both sides of the reaction.
    b. The reaction must involve only two elements.
    c. A neutron can become a proton according to the reaction $n \rightarrow p + \nu_e + e^+$, where ν_e is an electron neutrino and e^+ is a positron (antimatter).

26. The Sun has a mass of 2.0×10^{30} kg. We know from calculated models that the Sun's core, where nuclear reactions occur, is about 50% of its mass, or 1.0×10^{30} kg. From its total energy output, we know that the Sun fuses 3.8×10^{28} protons per second into helium. Calculate how long it will take the Sun to use up 25% of the hydrogen in its core. Express your answer in years. (Hint: The mass of a proton is 1.67×10^{-27} kg).

Section 21.2

27. Make a graph of the surface temperatures of the inner planets versus the distance form the Sun. Fit a smooth curve to Mercury, Earth, and Mars. You may ignore Venus as an anomaly for the purposes of the graph.

    a. Estimate the orbital radius of a planet that would have an average surface temperature of 100°C.

    b. Estimate the orbital radius of a planet that would have an average surface temperature of 0°C.

    c. The region between these two estimates is known as the "life zone" for potential orbits of habitable planets. Where is Earth in the life zone of the Sun? Is our planet in the middle or near an edge of this zone?

28. The inverse square law describes how the intensity (*I*) of solar radiation drops off with distance from the Sun or any other star, where *luminosity (L)* is the total energy output of the star in watts and *R* is the distance from the star to the planet in meters:

$$I = \frac{L}{4\pi R^2}$$

    a. Calculate the intensity (W/m^2) of sunlight at the top of Earth's atmosphere. For the Sun, $L = 3.8 \times 10^{26}$ W and the distance between the Sun and Earth is 150×10^9 m.

    b. Suppose Earth were orbiting Alpha Centauri A, the closest star to Earth. This star has a luminosity of 5.7×10^{26} W. Calculate the intensity of light at Earth's orbit around Alpha Centauri A and discuss whether water would exist on Earth's surface or not. Compare your intensity to that for Venus when arriving at your answer.

29. The power of thermal radiation increases with temperature to the fourth power according to the Stefan–Boltzmann law: $I = R \sigma T^4$, where *I* is the total power emitted (W), *R* is the area of the emitting surface (m^2), *T* is the temperature (K), and σ is the Stefan–Boltzmann constant,

    $\sigma = 5.67 \times 10^{-8}$ J/(s·m²·K⁴.)

    a. The surface area of the Sun is 6.18×10^{18} m^2. The temperature of the Sun's surface is 5,780 K. Calculate the power radiated by the Sun.

    b. Suppose the temperature of the surface of the Sun were to increase by 5%. How does the power radiated by the Sun change? Express your answer as a percent.

Section 21.3

30. Europa has a mass of 4.2×10^{22} kg and a radius of 1,550 km.

    a. Calculate the volume of Europa.

    b. Calculate Europa's average density.

    c. Assume Europa is made of rock (density = 5,500 kg/m^3) and water (density = 1,000 kg/m^3).

    What percentage of Europa is rock and what percentage is water?

GLOSSARY

absolute zero - the lowest possible temperature, at which the energy of molecular motion is essentially zero, or as close to zero as allowed by quantum theory

accuracy - describes how close a measurement is to the true value.

acid - a chemical that dissolves in water to create more H^+ ions than there are in neutral water

activated complex - high energy state where bonds are being broken and reformed. Also referred to as the activated complex

activation energy - the energy necessary to break bonds in the reactants so a chemical reaction can occur. Units are joules per mole (J/mol) or kilojoules per mole (kJ/mol) - The minimum amount of energy required for molecules to react

active site - a small region of an enzyme molecule that is responsible for "binding" or holding on to the substrate molecules

activity - the rate of decay of a radioactive sample

actual yield - the amount obtained in lab by actual experiment

addition polymerization - type of polymer formed by adding monomers together using their double bonds

addition reaction - a chemical reaction that adds atoms to the carbon atoms forming multiple bond(s) in a molecule

adhesion - the property of a liquid that causes it to stick to surfaces

alcohol - a hydrocarbon with a hydroxyl group, -OH, attached

aldehyde - a functional group in which the central carbon makes a double bond with oxygen and then is bonded to hydrogen on one side and to another hydrocarbon

alkane - a hydrocarbon containing only single bonds. A saturated hydrocarbon

alkene - a hydrocarbon containig one or more double bonds

alkyne - a hydrocarbon containing one or more triple bonds

alloy - solid material made up of two or more elements (usually metals) that is evenly mixed on the microscopic level

alloying element - One of the elements that make up a certain alloy

alpha decay - happens when a nucleus decays by releasing a helium nucleus

alpha helix - a common form of the secondary structure of a protein that forms a spiral or twist similar to a slinky or spiral staircase. A single protein chain is held together by hydrogen bonding attractions

alpha radiation - the radiation associated with alpha decay

aluminum - a metallic element, atomic number 13

amide linkage - type of bond formed between an amine group ($-NH_2$) and a carbonyl (C=O) group

amine - an organic molecule containing an amino group, NH_2

amino acid - chiral molecules that have an amino group on one end and a carboxyl group on the other. There are 20 different naturally occurring amino acids

ammonia - NH_3

ammonium - the ion NH_4^+

ammonium nitrate - the compound NH_4NO_3

amorphous - a microstructure that does NOT have any ordered pattern

ampere - SI unit of electrical current

amphoteric - a substance is amphoteric if it can act as either an acid or a base under different circumstances. Water is amphoteric

anode - the electrode at which oxidation occurs

antioxidant - a molecule that reacts easily with free radicals. Some sources of antioxidants include brightly colored fruits and vegetables, vitamin E, and chocolate

aqueous - dissolved in water- indicated by (aq).

aqueous equilibrium - when the amount of dissolved solutes remains constant over time

aqueous solution - An aqueous solution is any solution where the solvent is water. Molecules, atoms, or ions in aqueous solutions are identified by the symbol *(aq)* after a chemical formula.

aromatic hydrocarbon - a hydrocarbon containing one or more cyclic ring structures

Arrhenius theory - definition of acids and baes in which acids form H^+ and bases form OH^- in solution

atmosphere (atm) - a large unit of pressure equal to 101,325 Pa, - the average pressure of air at sea level, also equal to 14.7 pounds per square inch (14.7 psi).

atmospheric pressure - the pressure we feel from the air around us - 101,325 Pa or 14.7 psi (average)

atom economy - the fraction of reactant material that ends up in the final product

atomic mass unit (amu) - a mass unit equal to 1.66×10^{-24} grams or 1.661×10^{-27} kg

atomic number (Z) - the number of protons in a nucleus, unique to each element

atomic radius - the distance from the center of an atom to its "outer edge."

atomic structure - the organization of neutrons, protons, and electrons in an atom

ATP- adenosine triphosphate. A molecule that carries chemical energy from spontaneous chemical reactions to non spontaneous reactions

average - you calculate the average of a set of measurements by adding up all their values and dividing by the total number of measurements.

Avogadro's number - the number of particles contained in one mole. It is 6.02×10^{23}

baking soda - a household variety of the compound sodium bicarbonate $NaHCO_3$

balanced chemical equation - a chemical equation that satisfies the law of conservation of mass, - when the total number of atoms of each element are the same on both the reactant side and the product side of a chemical equation

barometer - an instrument that measures atmospheric pressure

base - a chemical that dissolves in water to create less H^+ ions than there are in pure water (or equivalently, more OH^- ions)

bent - a shape formed when a central atom has two unshared pairs of electrons and is bonded to two other atoms

benzene - an aromatic hydrocarbon C_6H_6, with alternating single and double bonds between the 6 carbon atoms in the ring

beryllium - alkali earth element with atomic number 4

beta decay - when an unstable nucleus releases an electron

beta radiation - the radiation resulting from beta decay

bimolecular- an elementary process involving the collision of two molecules

binary alloy - An alloy made up of only two different elements

binary phase diagram - a graph showing the phase of an alloy at different temperatures and compositions

binding energy - is the process of chemical change

boiling point - the temperature at which a substance changes phase from liquid to gas. For example, the boiling point of water is 100°C

Boltzmann's constant (k) - relates the kinetic energy in molecular motion to temperature. Boltzmann's constant has the value, $k = 1.381 \times 10^{-23}$ J/K

boron - non-mettalic element with atomic number 5

bravais lattices - fourteen groups of crystal structures used to help group the many different types of crystals

British thermal unit (btu) - large unit of heat used in the U.S., 1 btu = 1055 joules

brittle - a property of materials that are hard and require little energy to fracture, materials that break or shatter relatively easily

bromine - element with atomic number 35 - one of the halogens

Bronsted-Lowry definition - a different way to look at what defines acids and bases. Acids are compounds that donate protons (H+). Bases are compounds that accept protons

Brownian motion - the erratic, jerky movement of tiny particles suspended in water, due to the random impacts of individual molecules in thermal motion

buffer - a solution that resists small changes in pH by chemical action

buffer capacity - describes the amount of excess acid or base a buffer can neutralize without changing the pH of the solution

calcium (Ca) - element with atomic number 20

calcium carbonate - the compound $CaCO_3$

calorie - older unit of heat, 1 calorie = 4.184 joules

Calvin cycle - a sequence of chemical reactions that makes energy rich sugars from CO_2 by using the high energy molecules ATP and NADPH formed in the light dependent reactions

capillary action - an effect where liquid is pulled up a thin tube by adhesion

carbohydrate - short and long chain polymers of sugar molecules. All organisms use carbohydrates as a main source of energy

carbon - element with atomic # 6

carbon cycle - the process showing how carbon moves between the atmosphere, the land, and the ocean. Carbon changes it's chemical form as it moves through the cycle. Some of the common chemical forms of carbon are CO_2, $C_6H_{12}O_6$, and H_2CO_3

carbon dioxide - the compound CO_2

carbon-14 - a radioactive isotope of carbon

carbonyl group - formed when a carbon atom is double bonded to an oxygen atom (C=O). Common organic reference

carboxylic acid - an organic molecule containing a carboxyl group, COOH

catalyst - a substance that speeds up the rate of a chemical reaction, by providing a pathway with a lower activation energy

cathode - the electrode at which reduction occurs

cathode ray - a stream of particles produced by high voltage placed across a vacuum tube. Later cathode rays were discoved to be electrons, the first sub-atomic particle to be discovered.

cell-emf - abbreviation for electromotive force of a cell

cellular respiration - a chemical reaction that breaks down glucose molecules in the presence of oxygen and releases energy that is used to carry out life processes

Celsius scale - a temperature scale with 100 degrees between the freezing point and the boiling point of water; water freezes at 0°C and boils at 100°C.

chain reaction - is the process of chemical change

chemical bond - a relatively strong connection between two atoms

chemical change - a change that affects the structure or composition of the molecules that make up a substance, typically turning one substance into another substance with different physical properties - a result of chemical reaction.

chemical energy - energy stored in chemical bonds that can be released during a reaction

chemical engineering - The application of chemistry to solving human problems, such as creating materials, fuels, medicines, or processes

chemical equation - A chemical equation is an expression that describes the changes that happen in a chemical reaction - typically of the form: *reactants → products*.

chemical formula - a combination of element symbols and subscripts that tells you the ratio of elements in a compound. For example, H_2O is the chemical formula for water and tells you there are 2 hydrogen (H) atoms for every one oxygen (O) atom

chemical property - property that can only be observed when one substance changes into a different substance - such as iron's tendency to rust.

chemical reaction - a process that rearranges the atoms in any substance(s) to produce one or more different substances, the process of chemical change

chlorine - element with atomic number 17, a halogen

chlorophyll - pigment molecule that absorbs sunlight and uses it to excite electrons in it's molecular structure, thereby storing energy to aid in photosynthesis

closed system - a system that is not allowed to exchange matter with irs surroundings, often the products and reactants in a chemical reaction, a chemical or a mixture of chemicals in a closed container, a system in which only energy is allowed to be exchanged with the surroundings

coefficient - the number that tells you how many of each molecule participate in the balanced reaction

cohesion - the property of a liquid that causes it to hold together

colligative property - physical property of a solution that depends only on the number of dissolved solute particles not on the type (or nature) of the particle itself

common ion - an ion which is produced by two or more different chemicals in the same solution

compound - a substance containing more than one element in which atoms of different elements are chemically bonded together

concentrated - a solution containing a lot of solute compared to solvent.

concentration - describes the amount of each solute compared to the total solution

conclusion - a stated decision whether the results of experiments or observations confirm an idea or hypothesis, or not.

condensation - a phase change from gas to liquid, a substance in its gas phase may condense at a temperature below its boiling point.

condensation polymerization - type of polymerization reaction that links monomers through the loss of a small molecule such as water

condensed matter - matter in which atoms or molecules are closely packed together and strongly interacting. Both liquids and solids are condensed matter

conduction - the flow of heat energy through the direct contact of matter

conservation of mass - in any chemical reaction, the total mass remains the same: the total mass of reactants equals the total mass of products

control variables - variables that are kept constant.

conversion factor - a ratio of two different units that has a value of 1. For example, 3.785 liters/1 gallon is a conversion factor. The numbers are different but the actual physical quantity is the same because 1 gallon is the same volume as 3.785 liters.

copolymer - a molecule made from repeatedly bonding more than one type of monomer together

core - the center of the earth, sun or other planet, typically where temperature and pressure are very high

coulomb (C) - SI unit of electrical charge

covalent bond - a chemical bond that consists of one shared electron

cracking - a process used to break long chain hydrocarbons down into smaller hydrocarbon fragments. This process requires high temperatures and a catalyst

crystal - a piece of crystalline matter in which the microstructure is uniform and continuous over the entire piece

crystal structure - system which describes the distances and angles between atoms in a crystal

crystalline - a microstructure with a repeating, ordered pattern

cytochrome protein- any iron containing protein with heme groups, these proteins are import as catalysts in oxidation-reduction reactions in the electron transport chain

Dalton's law of partial pressures - the total pressure in a mixture of gasses is the sum of the partial pressures of each individual gas in the mixture

daughter nuclide - the nucleus resulting from a nuclear reaction

decay - the process during which a nucleus undergoes spontaneous change

dehydrogenation reaction - remove hydrogen, H2 from the alkane causing formation of double bonds. This process forms unsaturated alkenes

deionized water - water without ions, purified using filtration methods

density - a property of a substance that describes how much matter the substance contains per unit volume - typical units are grams per cubic centimeter (g/cm3)

dew point - the temperature at which air is saturated with H_2O vapor (Rh = 100%)

diffusion - the spread of molecules through their surroundings through constant collisions with neighboring molecules

dilute - a solution containing relatively little solute compared to solvent

dimensional analysis - using conversion factors to convert between units

dipole-dipole attraction - the attractions between the positive part of one polar molecule and the negative part of another polar molecule

dislocation - a missing half-plane of atoms in a crystal. This is a 1-D defect

dissolved - when molecules of solute are completely separated from each other and dispersed into a solution

distillation - a process of separating, concentrating or purifying liquids by boiling and condensing them again.

distilled water - water purified by heating water to steam and condensing the steam into clean or sterilized container

DNA - long polymer chain of nucleotides that stores and transmits genetic information. Nucleotides - a molecular unit composed of a 5 carbon sugar, a phosphate group, and a nitrogenous base

ductile - Describes materials that require much energy to fracture

electric charge - a fundamental property of matter than comes in positive and negative.

electric current - is the flow of electric charge

electrochemical cell - device in which redox reactions take place

electrode - the part of a cell where oxidation and reduction reactions occur

electrolysis - the result of a chemical reaction in an electrolytic cell

electrolyte - solute capable of conducting electricity when dissolved in an aqueous solution, also - a conductive solution, or the solution in which the electrodes are immersed

electrolytic cell - an electrochemical cell in which chemical reactions result from the application of electrical current

electromagnetic spectrum - the complete range of electromagnetic waves, including visible light

electromotive force (emf) - the difference in the electrical potential between the anode and the cathode of an electrochemical cell

electron - a tiny particle that fills the outer volume of an atom. Electrons have negative charge and are responsible for chemical bonds

electron configuration - a description of which orbitals contain electrons for a particular atom.

electron transport chain - a sequence of biologically important chemical reactions that transfers high-energy electrons from the Krebs cycle to make ATP molecules

electron volt - a unit of energy equal to 1.602×10^{-19} joules

electronegativity - a value between 0 and 4 that describes the relative "pull" of an element for electrons from other atoms. High numbers mean stronger attraction for electrons., the ability for an atom to attract another atom's electrons when bonded to that other atom.

electroneutrality - The property of charges to balance resulting in a charge neutral system

element - a unique type of atom. All atoms of the same element are similar to each other and different from atoms of other elements

element symbol - a one or two letter abbreviation for each element

elementary steps - a series of simple reactions that represent the overall progress of the chemical reaction at the molecular level

empirical formula - the simplest ratio of atoms in a substance

endothermic reaction - a chemical reaction that requires an input of energy to go from reactants to products. Endothermic reactions absorb energy, - a reaction that absorbs energy. $\Delta H > 0$

energy - energy is a measure of a system's ability to change or create change in other systems, measured in joules

energy barrier - The energy needed to initiate a chemical reaction

energy level - for an electron in an atom, an energy level is the set of quantum states that have approximately the same energy

enthalpy - ΔH, the heat energy of a chemical change measured in joules per mole (J/mole) or kilojoules per mole (kJ/mole) at standard temperature and pressure

enthalpy of formation - the change in energy when one mole of a compound is assembled from pure elements

entropy, S - is a measure of the disorder or randomness of a system

enzymes - biological catalysts, responsible for speeding up the chemical reactions inside our bodies

equilibrium - a "balance" in a chemical system. At equilibrium the rate of the forward reaction is equal to the rate of the reverse reaction, and the concentration of reactants and products remain constant over time

equilibrium constant - numeric value of the equilibrium expression

equilibrium expression - is a special ratio of product concentrations to the reactant concentrations. Each concentration is raised to the power of the corresponding coefficient in the balanced equation

equilibrium position - the favored direction of a reversible reaction. Determined by each set of concentrations for the reactant(s) and product(s) at equilibrium

equivalence point - in a titration, the point at which the moles of H^+ from the acid and OH^- from the base are exactly equal

error - the unavoidable difference between a real measurement and the unknown true value of the quantity being measured.

ester - an organic molecule containing a -COOR group, is an ester. Esters are responsible for many smells and tastes in fruits and flowers

ether - a molecule where oxygen is bonded to two carbon groups. The two carbon groups are often hydrocarbon chains

eutectic point - the temperature and composition where an alloy's melting point is the lowest

evaporation - a phase change from liquid to gas at a temperature below the boiling point.

excess reactant - the reactant left over after the reaction is complete. The amount of reactant the did not react to form product

exothermic reaction - a chemical reaction that releases energy in going from reactants to products. Endothermic reactions have negative enthalpy - a reaction that releases energy. $\Delta H < 0$

experiment - a situation specially set up to observe how something happens or to test a hypothesis.

experimental variable - the single variable that is changed to test its effect.

exponent - a number written in scientific notation consists of a value multiplied by a power of ten, such as $500 = 5 \times 10^2$. The exponent is the power of ten. In the example the exponent is 2. Exponents are negative for numbers that are less than 1. For example, 0.05 is the same as 5×10^{-2}, - the power of ten in scientific notation.

extensive property - a physical property that depends on how much matter is present

Fahrenheit scale - a temperature scale with 180 degrees between the freezing point and the boiling point of water; water freezes at 32 °F and boils at 212 °F.

fat - or lipids, are nonpolar molecules made from fatty acids and a glycerol molecule. Fats molecules are an efficient way to store energy for many types of animals. Fats are not soluble in water

first law of thermodynamics - energy can neither be created nor destroyed. The total energy in an isolated system remains constant; all the energy lost by one system must be gained by the surroundings or another system

fission products - is the process of chemical change

fission reaction - is the process of chemical change

flow - The ability of a liquid to move and change shape under a force, like gravity (weight)

fluorine - a reactive element with atomic number 9 - the lightest of the halogens

force - an action such as a push or a pull that has the ability to change the motion of an object, such as to start it moving, stop it, or turn it.

free radical - a molecule or atom that is highly reactive due to its having one or more unpaired valence electrons

frequency - the rate at which an oscillation repeats - one hertz (Hz) is a frequency of 1 oscillation per second

fusion reaction - is the process of chemical change

gallium - a soft metallic element that has a low melting point, atomic number 31

galvanic cell - another name for voltaic cell

gamma decay - when a nucleus decays releasing electromagnetic energy

gene - segment of DNA that contains the code for a specific protein

geologists - scientists that study the matter making up the earth

geometric isomers - are molecules with the same sequence of atoms, but different placement of groups around a double bond

germanium - a mettaloid element with atomic number 32

glass - a solid structure with no long-range order for bond lengths and angles

global warming - the warming of the surface of the earth by gas molecules in the atmosphere which trap heat and reflect it back to the surface of the earth

glycolysis - (gly-KOHL-ih-sis) first step in cellular respiration. During glycolysis one molecule of glucose is broken in half yielding two 3 carbon molecules (of pyruvic acid)

graduated cylinder - a measuring instrument used to measure volume

grain boundary - the interface between two grains in a polycrystalline solid crystal. This is a 2-D defect

gram - SI unit of mass, = 1/1000 kilogram

green chemistry - The practice of chemical science in a manner that is safe, sustainable and produces minimal waste

group - a column of the periodic table - all the elements in a group have similar chemical properties

half-life - the time it takes for half of the atoms in a sample to decay

half-reactions - the oxidation and the reduction parts of a redox reaction

halogens - group 17 elements including chlorine, fluorine, bromine, etc.

hardness - The ease of deforming a material by a small amount

heat - thermal energy, energy due to temperature, the total energy in random molecular motion contained in matter

heat of fusion - the energy required to change the phase of one gram of a material from liquid to solid or solid to liquid at constant temperature, constant pressure, and at the melting point

heat of solution - the energy absorbed or released when a solute dissolves in a particular solvent

heat of vaporization - the energy required to change the phase of one gram of a material from liquid to gas or gas to liquid at constant temperature, constant pressure, and at the boiling point

helium - the second lightest element, atomic number 2, the lightest of the noble gasses

heterogeneous mixture - is a mixture that is not uniform, different samples may have different compositions

homogenous mixture - is a mixture taht is uniform throughout, any sample has the same composition as any other sample

homopolymer - a molecule made from repeatedly bonding the same monomer together

hydration - the process of molecules with any charge separation to collect water molecules around them. While not "chemically bonded" a hydrated molecule does hold fairly tightly to its "private collection" of water molecules

hydrocarbon - a molecule made almost entirely from carbon and hydrogen atoms

hydrogen - the lightest element, atomic number 1

hydrogen bond - an intermolecular bond that forms between a hydrogen atom in one molecule and the negatively charged portion of another molecule (or another part of the same molecule) - in water, the attractions between the partially positive hydrogen from one molecule to the partially negative oxygen on an adjacent molecule

hydrogenation reaction - a type of addition reaction where hydrogen gas, H_2, is added to a double or triple bond in a hydrocarbon, causing the structure to become saturated

hydronium ion - the H_3O^+ ion forms when H^+ bonds to a complete water molecule. Hydronium ions are what give acids their unique properties. Any reference to "H^+" in aqueous solution usually means H_3O^+

hypothesis - a tentative explanation for something, or a tentative answer to a question.

ideal gas - a gas made from molecules that have no volume or interactions with each other. This gas doesn't exist in reality, but is the kind of gas assumed by the various gas laws including the ideal gas law. Gases with temperatures well above their boilng point (such as air) or at low pressures are good approximations of an ideal gas

igneous rock - formed from crystallized magma, covers more than 90%of the earths crust

indicator - a chemical that turns different colors at different values of pH. Indicators may be used to determine pH directly, or in reactions with solutions of known pH

inquiry - the process of learning through asking questions.

insoluble - not dissolvable in a particular solvent

intensity of radiation - the amount of energy that flows per unit area per second

intensive property - a physical property that does not depend on how much matter is present

interatomic forces - bond atoms together into molecules or ions.

intermediate - chemical species that is formed during the elementary steps, but is not present in the overall balanced equation

intermolecular attractions - the attractions between molecules

intermolecular forces - act between molecules, typically much weaker than the forces acting within molecules (interatomic forces)

inverse square law - the intensity of radiaiton emitted from a point source decreases inversely over the square of the distance

iodine - an element, one of the halogens, atomic number 53

ion - an atom or small molecule with an overall positive or negative charge due to an imbalance of protons and electrons

ion product constant - In dilute aqueous solutions, $[H^+] \times [OH^-] = 1.0 \times 10^{-14}$ and the value $K_w = 1.0 \times 10^{-14}$ at 25°C is known as the ion product constant for water

ionic bond - an attraction between oppositely charged ions. This attraction occurs with all nearby ions of opposite charge

ionic compound - a compound in which positive and negative ions attract each other to keep matter together. Salt (NaCl) is a good example.

ionization - the process of removing one or more electrons from an atom, creating a positive ion and a free electron

ionization energy - the energy required to completely remove an electron

ionizing radiation - radiation with high enough energy to remove electrons from their orbits

irreversible change - is a chemical change that rearranges atoms into different substances

isolated system - neither matter nor energy can be exchanged with surroundings

isomer - a specific structure of a molecule. This term is only used when a chemical formula could represent more than one molecule, the same group of atoms bonded into different structures are called isomers

isotopes - atoms or elements that have the same number of protons in the nucleus, but different number of neutrons

joule - the fundamental SI unit of energy (and heat)

Kelvin scale - a temperature scale that starts at absolute zero and has the same size degrees as Celsius degrees. $T_{Kelvin} = T_{Celsius} + 273$

ketone - a functional group in which the central carbon makes a double bond with oxygen and then is bonded to two hydrocarbons one on each side

kilogram - SI unit of mass

kinetic energy - energy of motion

kinetic molecular theory - the theory that explains the observed thermal and physical properties of matter in terms of the average behavior of a collection of atoms and molecules

Krebs cycle - a series of energy extracting chemical reactions that break pyruvic acid down into $CO_2(g)$, during cellular respiration

latent heat - thermal energy that is absorbed or released during a phase change

lava - molten rock or magma released from the vent(s) of a volcano

law of conservation of energy - energy can never be created or destroyed, just converted from one form into another

law of conservation of mass - the total mass of reactants (starting materials) and the total mass of products (materials produced by the reaction) is the same

law of mass action - general description of any equilibrium reaction

Le Chateliers principle - states that when a "change" is placed on a system at equilibrium, the system will shift in a direction that partially offsets the "change". The change can be defined as a change in temperature, concentration, volume or pressure

Lewis dot diagrams - a diagram showing one dot for each valence electron an atom has. These dots surround the element symbol for the atom

limiting reactant - the reactant present in the least amount. The reactant that "runs out" first

lipid - a molecule that typically falls into the category of fat or steroid

liter - an SI unit of volume equal to a cube 10 centimeters on a side, or 1,000 cm^3

lithium - the lightest metal in the alkali metals group, atomic number 3

logarithm - the logarithm of a number (A) is another number (B) such that $10^B = A$. For example, the logarithm of 1,000 = 3 since $10^3 = 1,000$. Logarithms are positive for numbers greater than one and negative for numbers less than one. For example, the logarithm of 0.01 is -2 since $10^{-2} = 0.01$. Logarithms are often abbreviated "log" so the expression 2 = log(100) means "2 equals the logarithm of 100"

London dispersion attraction - the attraction that occurs between non-polar molecules due to temporary slight polarizations that occur when the normally equal distribution of electrons is shifted

lone pairs - electrons that are paired up in a Lewis dot diagram, but are not shared between atoms in a covalent bond

macronutrients - elements needed in large quantity by your body. Note: Often only Na, Mg, P, S, Cl, K, and Ca are listed here because they come from mineral sources.The other elements (C,H,N, and O) are found in organic matter

macroscopic - on the scale that can be directly seen and measured, from a bacteria up to the size of a planet.

magma - molten rock found below the surface of the upper mantle

malleable - means a substance can be hammered into thin sheets without cracking.

mantissa - a decimal number that multiplies the power of ten in scientific notation

mass - measures how much matter there is, units of grams or kilograms (SI)

mass number (A) - the number of protons plus neutrons in the nucleus

matter - material, has mass and takes up space.

measurement - information that describes a physical quantity with both a number and a unit

melting point - the temperature at which a substance changes phase from solid to liquid. For example, the melting point of water is 0°C

meniscus - the curved top of a column of liquid

metallic bond - an attraction between metal atoms that loosely involves many electrons

metallic glass - a special form of glass made by cooling metal extremely quickly

metamorphic rock - rock created when existing rock layers are subjected to different conditions of heat and pressure

micelle - a collection of phospholipid molecules that form a small sphere which allows the nonpolar tails to be away from the aqueous solvent in the center of the sphere

microscopic - to a chemist, on the scale of atoms, 10^{-9} meters and smaller.

microstructure - the spatial arrangement of atoms and molecules in matter

milliliter - an SI unit of volume equal to a cube 1 cm on a side, or 1 cm^3

minerals - a natural non-organic solid with an organized internal structure, where the atoms have a definite pattern

mixture - matter that contains more than one substance.

Mohs hardness scale - A hardness scale describing how easy it is to scratch one material with another

molality, m - unit of concentration used when temperature varies, moles of solute per kilogram of solvent

molar mass - the mass of one mole of a compound with a given chemical formula

molar volume - 22.7 liters per mole at 0°C and 1 atmosphere of pressure, - the amount of space occupied by a mole of gas at standard temperature and pressure

molarity - the number of moles of solute per liter of solution

mole - the number 6.02×10^{23}, the average atomic mass in grams is the mass of one mole of atoms

mole ratio - A ratio comparison between substances in a balanced equation. The ratio is obtained from the coefficients in the balanced equation. The ratio allows for the conversion of one substance to another substance by using molar equivalent amounts

molecular formula - the exact number and types of atoms in a molecule

molecule - a neutral group of atoms that are covalently bonded together

monomer - a small molecule which is a building block of larger molecules called polymers

monosaccharide - a single sugar unit. Mono - meaning one and saccharide meaning sugar molecule

NADH - nicotinamide adenine dinucleotide; is a molecule capable of carrying high-energy electrons and transferring them to another pathway

NADPH- molecule that carries two high energy electrons and stores sunlight as chemical energy

nanometer (nm) - is 10^{-9} meters

natural laws - the unwritten rules that govern everything in the universe.

neon - a noble gas with atomic number 10

Nernst equation - the mathematical equation that relates the electrical potential of a cell to the standard reduction potential and the state of the reaction as given by the concentration of reactants and products

network covalent - a type of large molecule, usually made from hundreds to billions of atoms, in which each atom is covalently bonded to multiple neighboring atoms, forming a web of connections

neutral - an atom or molecule is neutral when it has zero total electric charge - in the context of acids and bases, neutral means the pH = 7.0 which also means the concentrations of H^+ and OH^- ions are equal

neutralization - a reaction in which the pH of an acid is raised by combining with a base, or the pH of a base is lowered by combining with an acid. Complete neutralization results in a pH of 7, the same as neutral water

neutron number (N) - the number of neutrons in a nucleus

nitrogen - an element that makes up 78% of earth's atmosphere, atomic number 7

nitrogen cycle - the process that shows how nitrogen moves from the atmosphere to the ocean, land and living systems

nitrogen fixation - the ability to use nitrogen gas from the atmosphere and convert it into a nitrogen compound such as ammonia or nitrate

nitrogenous base - nitrogen containing bases, one component of nucleotides

non-spontaneous - a reaction that does not occur in the indicated direction

non-ionizing radiation - radiation that cannot cause ionization of atoms

non-polar covalent bond - a bond formed between two atoms in which electrons are shared equally or almost equally between the two atoms

non-viscous - having a low viscosity

nuclear energy - the energy released during nuclear reactions

nuclear power plant - a facility that harnesses nuclear reactions to produce commercial electricity

nuclear reactions - involve the nuclei and may change one element into another

nucleotides - a molecular unit composed of a 5 carbon sugar, a phosphate group, and a nitrogenous base

nucleus - the tiny core of an atom that contains all the protons and neutrons. The nucleus is extraordinarily small - about 1/10,000 the diameter of the atom

objective - describing only what actually occured without opinion or bias

octet rule - elements transfer or share electrons in chemical bonds to reach a stable configuration of 8 valence electrons. The light elements H, Li, Be, and B have helium as the closest noble gas so the preferred state is 2 valence electrons instead of 8

ohm (Ω) - the unit of electrical resistance

Ohm's law - the relationship between voltage, current and electrical resistance

oligosaccharides - two to ten monosaccharides linked together in a chain

open system - matter and energy can be exchanged with the surroundings

optical isomers - are formed when the carbon atom has four different groups attached to it. These isomers form "mirror images" of one another

orbit - the imaginary path on an electron around the nucleus of an atom. The electron orbit representation was an early model of electrons in an atom

orbital - group of quantum states that have similar spatial shapes. The orbitals are labeled s, p, d and f

organic molecule - a molecule primarily made from carbon and hydrogen, but often with some oxygen, nitrogen, one of the halides, or some other non-metal atoms

oxidation - a chemical reaction that increases the charge of an atom or ion by giving up electrons - loss of electrons - element charge increases

oxidation number - gives the number of electrons that an element has lost or gained in forming a chemical bond with another element

oxidized - loss of electrons resulting in increase of oxidation number

oxidizing agent - the element that oxidizes another element

oxygen - an element with atomic number 8

parent compound - the longest continuous chain of carbons in an organic compound. The parent compound tells us the base alkane name

parent nuclide - the original nucleus involved in a nuclear reaction

partial hydrogenation - a chemical reaction where only some of the unsaturated fat is hydrogenated. In this case some double bonds remain in the structure, causing the formation of transfats in place of the naturally occurring cis configuration

Pascal (Pa) - the SI unit of pressure, a very small unit of pressure equal to one newton of force per square meter of area ($1 N/m^2$).

Pauli exclusion principle - two electrons in the same atom may never be in the same quantum state

peptide bond - a bond formed between the amino group and the carboxyl group of two amino acids. The peptide bond is formed through condensation polymerization or the loss of water molecules

percent yield - the ratio of the amount of product actually obtained by experiment (actual yield) as compared to the amount of product calculated theoretically (theoretical yield) multiplied by 100

period - a row of the periodic table

periodic - repeating at regular intervals. The periodic table is named for this because the rows are organized by repeated patterns found in both the atomic structure and the properties of the elements

periodic table - a graphical chart of information on the elements that groups the elements in rows and columns according to their chemical properties

petroleum - a blend of hydrocarbons, formed from prehistoric organic matter, containing mainly straight and branched chain alkanes

pH scale - a measurement of the H^+ ion concentration that tells whether a solution is acid or base. Pure water has a pH of 7. Solutions with pH <7 are acidic. Solutions with pH >7 are basic

phase change - occurs when a substance changes how its molecules are organized without changing the individual molecules themselves. Examples are changing from solid to liquid or liquid to gas

phase equilibrium diagram - shows the relationship between the phases of matter, temperature and pressure

phases - the physical forms of matter: solid, liquid, and gas (and plasma)

phospholipid - a lipid that has a phosphate group attached, giving it a polar head and a nonpolar tail. The phosphate group is the polar region of the molecule and the hydrocarbon chain is the nonpolar region

phosphorous cycle - the process that shows how phosphorous moves between the land, the ocean, and living systems

photodissociation - the breaking of a chemical bond in a molecule caused by the absorption of a photon

photoionization - when a molecule absorbs a photon and ejects an electron causing it to become an ion

photon - the smallest possible quantity (or quanta) of light. Light exists in discrete bundles of energy called photons

photosynthesis - the chemical reaction that occurs almost exclusively in plants and algae and combines CO_2 and H_2O to form glucose $C_6H_{12}O_6$ and oxygen. The reaction is endothermic and it driven by sunlight

physical change - a change in physical properties, such as shape, phase or temperature; for example, grinding, melting, boiling, dissolving, heating or cooling.

physical property - property such as mass, density or color that you can measure or see through direct observation.

Planck's constant - defines the scale of energy at which quantum effects must be considered. It is equal to $h = 6.626 \times 10^{-34}$ joule-seconds (J·s)

plasma - a hot, energetic phase of matter in which the atoms are broken apart into positive ions and negative electrons that move independent of each othe

pleated sheet - a secondary structure of protein that forms a folded or pleated pattern similar to an old fashioned fan. Formed by two or more side by side protein chains held together by hydrogen bonding

point defects - single atom defects in a crystal. These are 0-D defects

polar - a molecule is polar when there is a charge separation that makes one side (or end) of the molecule more positive or negative than the other side (or end)

polar covalent bond - a bond formed between two atoms in which electrons are unequally shared

polarization - uneven distribution of positive and negative charge

polyatomic ion - a small molecule with an overall positive or negative charge

polymer - from "poly" many and "meros" parts. A long chain molecule formed by connecting small repeating units with covalent bonds - a molecule built up from many repeating units of a smaller molecular fragment

polymerization - a reaction that assembles a polymer through repeated additions of smaller molecular fragments, - chemical reaction that joins monomers to produce a polymer

polysaccharide - a long chain, greater than ten, monosaccharides connected together. Poly- means many and saccharide means sugar units. Examples are starch, cellulose and glycogen molecules

positive, negative - the charge on a proton is defined to be positive and the charge on an electron is defined to be negative

positron - a particle that has the same mass as the electron and positive charge

positron emission - when a nucleus decays by releasing a positron

potential energy - stored energy due to the position of an object

precipitate - an insoluble compound that forms in a chemical reaction in aqueous solution

precision - describes how close measured values are to each other.

pressure - force per unit area, units of Pa (N/m^2) or psi (lbs/in^2) or atm, a expansive force per unit area that acts equally in all directions within a liquid or a gas.

primary structure - sequence of amino acids in a protein chain

principal quantum number - a number that specifies the quantum state and is related to the energy level of the electron

procedure - detailed instructions on how to do an experiment or make an observation

product - a substance that is created or released in a chemical reaction

protein - biologically functional polymers of amino acids, typically very large molecules with 100 or more amino acids

proton - a tiny particle in the nucleus that has a positive charge

pure substance - a kind of matter that can't be separated into other substances by physical means such as heating, cooling, filtering, drying, sorting, or dissolving

quantum state - a specific combination of values of variables such as energy and position that is allowed by quantum theory

quantum theory - a theory of physics and chemistry that accurately describes the universe on very small scales, such as the inside of an atom

rad - radiation with high enough energy to remove electrons from their orbits

radiation - the transmission of energy through space

radioactivity - a process by which the nucleus of an atom spontaneously changes itself by emitting particles or energy, - property of some element to break up and release energy

random - scattered equally among all possible choices with no organized pattern

rate constant - a number that descrubes how fast a radioactive nuclide decays

rate determining step - The "slow" elementary step in the reaction mechanism determines the overall rate (or speed) of the chemical reaction

rate of decay - the number of decays per unit time

reactant - a substance that is used or changed in a chemical reaction, - the starting materials or substances in a chemical reaction

reaction mechanism- a proposed sequence of elementary steps that leads to product formation. Must be determined using experimental evidence

reaction profile : a graph showing the progress of a reaction with respect to the energy changes that occur during a collision

reaction rate - the speed at which a chemical reaction occurs, the change in concentration, of a reactant or product, per unit time

reactivity - the tendency of elements to form chemical bonds. A reactive element forms bonds easily therefore tends to have many reactions

redox - abbreviation for oxidation reduction

reducing agent - the element that reduces another element

reduced - gain of electrons resulting in decrease of oxidation number

reduction - a chemical reaction that decreases the charge of an atom or ion by accepting electrons, - gain of electrons. Element charge decreases

region of electron density - an area represented by shared or unshared electrons around an atom

relative humidity - the actual partial pressure of water vapor in air divided by the saturation vapor pressure at the same temperature

rem - unit of radiation dose that is weighted for its effect on body tissue, stande for Radiation Equivalent Man

repeatable - others who do the experiment or make the observation the same way obtain the same results or observations.

R-group - in an organic formula the R- group can stand for an H, hydrogen atom, or a hydrocarbon side chain, of any length. It can also refer to any group of atoms

RNA - a polymer composed of nucleotides that contain a 5 carbon sugar called ribose, a phosphate group, and a nitrogenous base. This molecule transmits the information stored in DNA to cell "machinery."

salinity - is a measure of how salty water is. The concentration of salt in ocean water is a measure of it's salinity

salt - an ionic compound in which the positive ion comes from a base and the negative ion comes from an acid - an ionic compound that dissolves in water to produce ions

salt bridge - an electrical connection between the oxidation and the reduction half-cells of an electrochemical cell

saturated - when a solution has dissolved all the solute it can possibly hold. Saturation occurs when the amount of dissolved solute gets high enough that the rate of "undissolving" matches the rate of dissolving

saturated hydrocarbon - a hydrocarbon containing only single carbon to carbon bonds

scale - a typical size that shows a certain level of detail.

science - the process of using evidence to create predictions that can be tested, as well as the knowledge resulting from this process

scientific method - a process of learning that constantly poses questions and tentative answers that can be evaluated by comparison with objective evidence

scientific notation - a method of writing numbers as a base times a power of ten

second law of thermodynamics - energy (heat) spontaneously flows from higher temperature to lower temperature (basic interpretation of 2nd law)

sedimentary rock -rock formed from the compression and cementation of eroded pieces of other rocks

significant - a difference between two results is only significant when it is substantially greater than the error in either result.

silicates - the most abundant class of minerals in the Earth's crust consisting primarily of $(SiO4)2-$ combined with various metal ions.

significant figures - a way of writing data that tells the reader how precise a measurement is.

solar nebula - disk shaped region of dust and gases around a forming star. The sun's solar nebula is where the earth formed

solubility - the amount of a solute that will dissolve in a particular solvent at a particular temperature and pressure

solute - any substance in a solution other than the solvent

solution - a mixture that is homogeneous on the molecular level

solvent - the substance that makes up the biggest percentage of the mixture and is usually a liquid

specific heat - the quantity of heat energy, measured in J/g°C, it takes per gram to raise the temperature one degree Celsius

spectrometer - a device that measures the spectrum of light

spectroscopy - the science of analyzing matter using electromagnetic emission or absorption spectra

spectrum - a representation that analyzes a sample of light into its component energies or colors, can be a picture, graph or table of data

speed of light, c - a constant speed at which all electromagnetic radiation travels through vacuum, including visible light. The speed of light in vacuum is 3×10^8 m/s

spontaneous - a reaction that occurs in the indicated direction without any energy input

spontaneous reaction - A chemical reaction that happens without the need for external energy input

standard reduction potential - the potential of a cell measured under standard conditions of temperature, pressure and concentration

standard temperature and pressure - (STP) - conditions of one atmosphere of pressure and 0°C

steroid - a molecule with four carbon rings that is biologically active as either a hormone, vitamin, drug or poison

stoichiometric equivalent - the mole amounts of each substance in a balanced chemical equation are proportionate

stoichiometry - STOY-KEE-AHM-EH-TREE - is the study of the amounts of substances involved in a chemical reaction. The amounts can be studied in moles or in mass relationships

stratosphere - the second layer of gases after the troposphere. This region of gases extends from 10 to 50 km above the earth

strong acid/base - dissociates completely (or almost completely) usually yielding 1 mole of H+ or OH- ions for every mole of acid or base dissolved

structural isomer - molecule with the same number and type of atoms as another molecule but a different bonding pattern

substitution reaction - a reaction in which one or more hydrogen atoms on an alkane are removed and replaced by different atoms. The name substitution reaction comes from the fact that a different atom is "substituted" for one or more of the hydrogen atoms

substrate - a reactant molecule that is able to be bound by a particular enzyme

supersaturation - when a solution contains more dissolved solute than it can hold. Supersaturated solutions are always unstable and the excess solute becomes "undissolved", often rapidly

surface tension - a force created by intermolecular attraction in liquids, such as hydrogen bonding in water. Surface tension acts to pull a liquid surface into the smallest possible area, for example, pulling a droplet of water into a sphere - a property of liquids to resist having their surface broken. The energy needed to remove a certain amount of area on a liquid surface, measured in J/m^2

surfactant - a substance that reduces the surface tension of a liquid

surroundings - everything outside the "system"

system - an interrelated group of matter and energy that we choose to investigate

tap water - drinking water from the sink or "tap."

temperature - a measure of the average kinetic energy of atoms or molecules, units of degrees Fahrenheit (°F) degrees Celsius (°C) or Kelvins (K)

tensile strength - A measure of the energy needed to break a material in two

tertiary structure - protein structure that forms from the bending or folding of the secondary alpha helix. Tertiary structures form specific globular proteins. The structures are held together by intermolecular attractions, hydrophobicity of nonpolar regions, and ion-dipole interactions

tetrahedral - a shape formed when a central atom is bonded to four other atoms that all point into the corners of a tetrahedron

theoretical yield - the calculated amount produced if everything reacts perfectly

theory - an explanation that is supported by evidence.

thermal conductor - a material that conducts heat easily

thermal equilibrium - a condition in which two systems have the same temperature and no net heat flows from one system to the other.

thermal insulator - a material that resists the flow of heat

thermistor - electronic sensor for measuring temperature by changes in resistance

thermochemical equation - the equation that gives the chemical reaction and the energy information of the reaction

thermocouple - electronic sensor for measuring temperature that produces a temperature dependent voltage

thermometer - an instrument that measures temperature

titration - a laboratory process to determine the precise volume of acid or base of known concentration which exactly neutralizes a solution of unknown pH

trace amount - refers to a very small quantity

trace elements - elements which are needed in very small quantities to maintain optimum health. Too much can be toxic. Not enough can be fatal or cause disease

transition state: high energy state where bonds are being broken and reformed, also referred to as the activated complex

transpiration - is the release of water from the leaves of plants as they carry out photosynthesis

triglyceride - is a fat or lipid molecule used for energy storage. It is made of a glycerol molecule and three long chain fatty acids

trigonal planar - a flat, triangular geometry typical of molecules with three regions of electron density surrounding a central atom

trigonal pyramidal - a 3-D shape formed when a central atom has one unshared pair of electrons and is bonded to three other atoms, the central atom is not in the same plane as the surrounding three

triple point - the temperature and pressure at which the solid, liquid, and gas phases of a substance can all exist in equilibrium together

troposphere - the layer of gases closest to the earth, extending up to approximately 10 km above the earths surface

A NATURAL APPROACH TO CHEMISTRY

unbalanced chemical equation - a chemical equation that does not satisfy the law of conservation of mass. The number of each type of atom on the reactant side of the equation does not equal the same number for each atom on the product side

unimolecular - an elementary step where only one reactant is involved

unsaturated - situation in which more of a solute can be dissolved in a solvent at a certain temperature; solute concentration is lower than the solubility

unsaturated hydrocarbon - a hydrocarbon containing multiple bonds between the carbon atoms

valence electrons - electrons in highest unfilled energy level. These are the electrons that make chemical bonds

van der Waals attractions - another term used to describe the attractions between molecules. Most sources consider these identical to the broad term "intermolecular attractions". However, some people only associate the term van der Waals attractions with the London dispersion type of intermolecular attraction

variable - a quantity that is measured or changed in an experiment or observation.

viscosity -the resistance of a liquid to flow under an applied force

viscous - having a high viscosity

volcano - opening in the earth were magma, gases and other materials can escape from inside the earth

volt - the unit of voltage

voltage -the electrical potential difference

voltaic cell - electrochemical cell in which chemical reactions generate electricity

volume - an amount of space having length, width and height

VSEPR - an acronym that stands for Valence Shell Electron Pair Repulsion, a theory that states the shapes of molecules are dictated, in part, by the repulsion of the shared electrons and the unshared pairs of electrons

water - the compound H_2O

water cycle - the process showing how water molecules move between the atmosphere, the land, and the ocean

wavelength - the distance (separation) between any two successive peaks (or valleys) of a wave

weak acid/base - only partially dissociates in solution, typically only a few percent (or less) of molecules dissociate to yield H^+ or OH^- ions

weak base - a chemical that only partially dissociates in solution, typically only a few percent (or less) to produce OH- ions

weight - a force (push or a pull) that results from gravity acting on mass, measured in newtons in the SI system of units and pounds or ounces in the English system of units

INDEX

G

H

Table 1: SI Base Units

Quantity	Unit	Symbol
length	meter	m
mass	kilogram	kg
time	second	s
electric current	ampere	A
thermodynamic temperature	kelvin	K
amount of substance	mole	mol
luminous intensity	candela	cd

Table 2: SI Derived Units

Derived quantity	Name	Symbol
area	square meter	m^2
volume	cubic meter	m^3
speed, velocity	meter per second	m/s
acceleration	meter per second squared	m/s^2
mass density	kilogram per cubic meter	kg/m^3
specific volume	cubic meter per kilogram	m^3/kg
current density	ampere per square meter	A/m^2
magnetic field strength	ampere per meter	A/m
amount-of-substance concentration	mole per cubic meter	mol/m^3

Table 3: Fundamental constants and useful parameters of nature

Quantity	Symbol	Value	Units
Absolute zero	0 K	–273.15	°C
Strength of gravity at Earth's surface	g	9.8	N/kg or m/s^2
Avogadro's number	N_A	6.02×10^{23}	atoms/mol
Boltzmann's constant	k	1.381×10^{-23}	J/K
Electron mass	m_e	9.109×10^{-31}	kg
Proton mass	m_p	1.673×10^{-27}	kg
Neutron mass	m_n	1.675×10^{-27}	kg
Planck's constant	h	6.626×10^{-34}	J · s
Stefan–Boltzmann constant	s	5.670×10^{-8}	$W/m^2/kg^4$
Speed of light in vacuum	c	2.998×10^8	m/s
Universal gravitational constant	G	6.670×10^{-11}	N · m^2/kg^2
Elementary charge	e	1.602×10^{-19}	coulombs (C)
Gas constant for air	R	287.1	J/kg · K
Speed of sound at 20°C	v_s	343	m/s
Coulomb's law constant	K	9×10^9	N · m^2/C^2
Earth: mass	m_{earth}	5.98×10^{24}	kg
Earth: radius	r_{earth}	6.38×10^6	m
Moon: mass	m_{moon}	7.36×10^{22}	kg
Moon: radius	r_{moon}	1.74×10^6	m
Sun: mass	m_{sun}	1.99×10^{30}	kg
Sun: radius	r_{sun}	6.96×10^8	m

Table 4: Conversions

Time
1 hour = 60 minutes = 3,600 seconds
1 day = 1,440 minutes = 8.64×10^4 seconds
1 year = 365.25 days = 3.156×10^7 seconds

Length
1 meter (m) = 100 centimeters (cm) = 39.37 inches
1 kilometer (km) = 1,000 meters = 0.6214 miles (mi)
1 foot (ft) = 12 inches (in.) = 2.54 centimeters (cm)
1 miles (mi) = 5,280 feet (ft) = 1.609 kilometers (km)

Speed
1 m/sec = 2.237 mi/hr = 3.600 km/hr
1 mi/hr = 0.4470 m/sec = 1.609 km/hr

Area
1 m^2 = 10,000 cm^2 = 10.76 ft^2 = 1,5550 in^2
1 in^2 = 6.452 cm^2 = 0.000645 m^2
1 acre = 43,560 ft^2 = 4,047 m^2

Volume
1m^3 = 1,000 liters = 10^6 cm^3 = 35.32 ft^3
= 264.2 gallons
1 gallon = 3.785 liters = 0.003785 m^3

Angles and angular speed
1 radian = 57.3 degrees
1 degree = 0.01745 radians
1 rad/sec = 9.549 rev/min (rpm)

Mass
1 kilogram (kg) = 1,000 grams (g)
1 atomic mass unit (amu) = 1.660×10^{-27} kg

Force
1 newton (N) = 0.2248 pounds (lbs)
1 pound (lb) = 4.448 newtons (N)

Pressure
1 pascal (Pa) = $1N/m^2$
= 1.450×10^{-4} lbs/in^2 (psi)
1 lb/in^2 (psi) = 6,895 N/m^2 (Pa)
1 atmosphere (atm) = 14.70 lb/in^2 (psi)
= 101,300 N/m^2 (Pa)

Energy
1 kilowatt · hour (kWh) = 3.6x106 joules (J)
1 British thermal unit (Btu) = 1,054 joules (J)
1 electron volt (eV) = 1.60×10^{-19} joule (J)
1 J = 1 N · m = $9,484 \times 10^{-4}$ Btu
= 2.778×10^{-7} kwh

Power
1 watt (w) = 1 J/sec
= 0.001341 horsepower (hp)
1 horsepower (hp) = 745.7 watts (W)

Table of the Elements

Element Name	Symbol	Atomic Number	Atomic Mass	Element Name	Symbol	Atomic Number	Atomic Mass
Actinium	Ac	89	[227]	Mendelevium	Md	101	[258]
Aluminum	Al	13	26.98	Mercury	Hg	80	200.59
Americium	Am	95	[243]	Molybdenum	Mo	42	95.96
Antimony	Sb	51	121.76	Neodymium	Nd	60	144.24
Argon	Ar	18	39.95	Neon	Ne	10	20.18
Arsenic	As	33	74.92	Neptunium	Np	93	[237]
Astatine	At	85	[210]	Nickel	Ni	28	58.69
Barium	Ba	56	137.33	Niobium	Nb	41	92.91
Berkelium	Bk	97	[247]	Nitrogen	N	7	14.01
Beryllium	Be	4	9.01	Nobelium	No	102	[259]
Bismuth	Bi	83	208.98	Osmium	Os	76	190.23
Bohrium	Bh	107	[264]	Oxygen	O	8	16.00
Boron	B	5	10.81	Palladium	Pd	46	106.42
Bromine	Br	35	79.90	Phosphorus	P	15	30.97
Cadmium	Cd	48	112.41	Platinum	Pt	78	195.08
Calcium	Ca	20	40.08	Plutonium	Pu	94	[244]
Californium	Cf	98	[251]	Polonium	Po	84	[209]
Carbon	C	6	12.01	Potassium	K	19	39.10
Cerium	Ce	58	140.12	Praseodymium	Pr	59	140.91
Cesium	Cs	55	132.91	Promethium	Pm	61	[145]
Chlorine	Cl	17	35.45	Protactinium	Pa	91	231.04
Chromium	Cr	24	52.00	Radium	Ra	88	[226]
Cobalt	Co	27	58.93	Radon	Rn	86	[222]
Copernicium	Cn	112	[285]	Rhenium	Re	75	186.21
Copper	Cu	29	63.55	Rhodium	Rh	45	102.91
Curium	Cm	96	[247]	Roentgenium	Rg	111	[280]
Darmstadtium	Ds	110	[281]	Rubidium	Rb	37	85.47
Dubnium	Db	105	[262]	Ruthenium	Ru	44	101.07
Dysprosium	Dy	66	162.5	Rutherfordium	Rf	104	[261]
Einsteinium	Es	99	[252]	Samarium	Sm	62	150.36
Erbium	Er	68	167.26	Scandium	Sc	21	44.96
Europium	Eu	63	151.96	Seaborgium	Sg	106	[266]
Fermium	Fm	100	[257]	Selenium	Se	34	78.96
Flerovium	Fl	114	[289]	Silicon	Si	14	28.09
Fluorine	F	9	19.00	Silver	Ag	47	107.87
Francium	Fr	87	[223]	Sodium	Na	11	22.99
Gadolinium	Gd	64	157.25	Strontium	Sr	38	87.62
Gallium	Ga	31	69.72	Sulfur	S	16	32.07
Germanium	Ge	32	72.61	Tantalum	Ta	73	180.95
Gold	Au	79	196.97	Technetium	Tc	43	[98]
Hafnium	Hf	72	178.49	Tellurium	Te	52	127.6
Hassium	Hs	108	[277]	Terbium	Tb	65	158.93
Helium	He	2	4.00	Thallium	Tl	81	204.38
Holmium	Ho	67	164.93	Thorium	Th	90	232.04
Hydrogen	H	1	1.01	Thulium	Tm	69	168.93
Indium	In	49	114.82	Tin	Sn	50	118.71
Iodine	I	53	126.90	Titanium	Ti	22	47.87
Iridium	Ir	77	192.22	Tungsten	W	74	183.84
Iron	Fe	26	55.85	Ununoctium	Uuo	118	[294]
Krypton	Kr	36	83.79	Ununpentium	Uup	115	[288]
Lanthanum	La	57	138.91	Ununseptium	Uus	117	[293]
Lawrencium	Lr	103	[262]	Ununtrium	Uut	113	[284]
Lead	Pb	82	207.2	Uranium	U	92	238.03
Lithium	Li	3	6.94	Vanadium	V	23	50.94
Livermorium	Lv	116	[293]	Xenon	Xe	54	131.29
Lutetium	Lu	71	174.97	Ytterbium	Yb	70	173.0
Magnesium	Mg	12	24.31	Yttrium	Y	39	88.91
Manganese	Mn	25	54.94	Zinc	Zn	30	65.38
Meitnerium	Mt	109	[276]	Zirconium	Zr	40	91.22

Atomic mass values as reported by Los Alamos National Laboratory in June 2016.
Atomic mass values in brackets indicate the mass of the most stable isotope.

Common Words with Multiple Meanings

Word	Common meaning	Scientific meaning
atmosphere	a general mood or social environment	a mixture of gases that surrounds a planet or moon
channel	a band of frequencies of sufficient width for a single radio or television communication	the path that a stream follows
crust	the hard, crisp outer part of bread	the thin and solid outermost layer of Earth above the mantle
current	at the present time	a horizontal movement of water in a well-defined pattern, such as a river or stream; the movement of air in a certain direction
date	an engagement to go out socially	to measure the age of an event or object
divide	to separate into parts	the boundary between drainage areas that have streams that flow in opposite directions
fault	responsibility for a mistake	a break in a body of rock along which one block slides relative to another
focus	a center of activity or attention	the location within Earth along a fault at which the first motion of an earthquake occurs
front	the part of something that faces forward	the boundary between air masses of different densities and usually different temperatures
gas	short for gasoline; a liquid fuel used by vehicles, such as cars and buses	a form of matter that does not have a definite volume or shape
kettle	a metal container for boiling or cooking things	a bowl-shaped depression in a glacial drift deposit
law	a rule of conduct established by the government	a descriptive statement or equation that reliably predicts events under certain conditions
legend	a romanticized story or myth	a list of map symbols and their meanings
mass	a quantity of matter that has an unspecified shape	a measure of the amount of matter in an object
period	a punctuation mark used to indicate the end of a sentence	a unit of geologic time that is longer than an epoch but shorter than an era
plate	a shallow dish from which food is eaten	a large piece of the lithosphere (tectonic plate)
relief	any aid given in times of need	the difference between the highest and lowest elevations in a given area; the variations in elevation of a land surface
scale	a machine used to measure weight	the relationship between the measurements on a model, map, or diagram and the actual measurement or distance
tension	mental or nervous strain	stress that occurs when forces act to stretch an object
theory	an assumption based on limited knowledge	a system of ideas that explains many related observations and is supported by a large body of evidence acquired through scientific investigation
vent	to give expression to feelings	an opening at the surface of Earth through which volcanic material passes
weather	to pass through safely or to survive	the short-term state of the atmosphere, including temperature, humidity, precipitation, wind, and visibility

Lab Safety

Safety symbol	What it means	What to do in the event of an accident
Eye protection	Wear safety goggles anytime there is the slightest chance that your eyes could be harmed.	If anything gets into your eyes, notify your teacher immediately and flush your eyes with running water for 15 minutes.
Hand safety	Wear appropriate protective gloves when working with an open flame, chemicals, or plants. Your teacher will provide the type of gloves necessary for a given activity.	If any chemical gets on your hands, rinse it off immediately with water for at least 5 minutes while calling to your teacher. Report any burn of the hands to your teacher no matter how minor it seems. Wash your hands with soap and hot water at the end of every lab.
Clothing protection	Wear your apron whenever you are working with chemicals or whenever you are instructed to do so.	If you spill a corrosive chemical onto your clothing, rinse it off immediately by using a faucet or the safety shower and remove the affected clothing while calling to your teacher.
Sharp/pointed object safety	Use knives and other sharp objects with extreme care. Place objects on a suitable work surface for cutting.	Notify your teacher immediately in the event of a cut or puncture no matter how minor it seems.
Heating safety	Wear safety goggles when using a heating device or flame. Wear heat-resistant gloves whenever instructed to do so. When heating materials in a test tube, angle the test tube away from yourself and others.	Notify your teacher immediately in the event of a burn or fire no matter how minor it seems.
Electrical safety	Do not place electrical cords where they could trip someone or cause equipment to fall. Do not use equipment with damaged cords. Do not use electrical equipment near water or when your clothing or hands are wet. Make sure that electrical equipment is in the "off" position before plugging it in. Turn off and unplug electrical equipment when you have finished using it.	Notify your teacher immediately if you notice any abnormal or potentially dangerous equipment. In the event of an electric shock, notify your teacher no matter how minor it seems.
Chemical safety	Wear safety goggles, an apron, and gloves whenever working with chemicals.	If a chemical spills onto your skin, rinse it off immediately by using the faucet or safety shower for at least 5 minutes while calling to your teacher.
Animal safety	Handle animals only as your teacher directs. Treat animals carefully and respectfully. Wash your hands thoroughly after handling any animal.	Notify your teacher immediately if you injure yourself or any live specimen no matter how minor the injury seems.
Plant safety	Do not eat any part of a plant or plant seed used in the laboratory. When in nature, do not pick any wild plants unless your teacher instructs you to do so. Wash your hands thoroughly after handling any part of a plant.	Notify your teacher immediately if any potentially dangerous plant material comes into contact with your skin or if any plant matter is inhaled or ingested no matter how minor the event seems.